Christ Church

KT-385-572

T014494

Fundamentals of Classical Thermodynamics

SERIES IN THERMAL AND TRANSPORT SCIENCES
Gordon J. Van Wylen, Coordinator

FUNDAMENTALS OF CLASSICAL THERMODYNAMICS
Gordon J. Van Wylen and Richard E. Sonntag

FUNDAMENTALS OF STATISTICAL THERMODYNAMICS
Richard E. Sonntag and Gordon J. Van Wylen

FLUID MECHANICS
Arthur G. Hansen

THE TRANSPORT OF HEAT AND MASS
John A. Clark

Fundamentals of
Classical Thermodynamics

GORDON J. VAN WYLEN & RICHARD E. SONNTAG

Department of Mechanical Engineering
University of Michigan, Ann Arbor, Michigan

JOHN WILEY AND SONS, INC.   NEW YORK · LONDON · SYDNEY

COPYRIGHT © 1965 BY JOHN WILEY & SONS, INC.

All Rights Reserved. This book or any part thereof must not be reproduced in any form without the written permission of the publisher.

LIBRARY OF CONGRESS CATALOG CARD NUMBER: 65-19470
PRINTED IN THE UNITED STATES OF AMERICA

CHRIST CHURCH
LIBRARY
OXFORD

Preface to the Series
in Thermal and Transport Sciences

This Series in Thermal and Transport Sciences had its origin in a number of discussions regarding curriculum among engineering faculty members of the University of Michigan. We believed that by integrating the teaching of thermodynamics, fluid mechanics, and heat and mass transfer at the undergraduate level, we could present this material more effectively and efficiently. There was, however, a need for carefully integrated textbooks; and my colleagues Professors John A. Clark, Arthur G. Hansen, Richard E. Sonntag, and I have undertaken to write a series of basic undergraduate textbooks in these fields.

We decided at the outset that each book should be complete in itself so that it could be used quite independently of the series. At the same time, however, it was our goal to provide such correlation between the books that their use in a series of courses would provide an integrated coverage of thermodynamics, fluid mechanics, and heat transfer. Thus, it would be possible to achieve the educational advantages inherent in such an approach.

It was also evident that a series such as this would provide an excellent foundation for the preparation of a number of applied or specialized books which might involve all three of these areas. With a uniform approach and definitions in these basic books, the transition from the basic courses to these applied and specialized topics would be accomplished smoothly and efficiently. We also anticipate that a number of advanced textbooks in related areas will be included in the series. Thus this series will contain the basic books in thermodynamics, fluid mechanics, and heat transfer, as well as applied and advanced books in these areas.

The first decision we faced in writing the basic books concerned classical and statistical thermodynamics. It was our conviction that the series should cover both these topics, and that the classical thermodynamics should precede the statistical thermodynamics. Professor Sonntag and I are co-authors of *Fundamentals of Classical Thermodynamics* and

Fundamentals of Statistical Thermodynamics, with Professor Sonntag as principal author of the latter book and myself of the former.

The second decision we faced concerned the sequence of the series as a whole. We decided the order of topical presentation would be classical thermodynamics, fluid mechanics, and heat and mass transfer, and that each book would be written on the assumption that the student has covered the material in the prerequisite courses. Statistical thermodynamics would follow classical thermodynamics in this order of presentation and parallel the subject matter in fluid mechanics and heat transfer. Schematically this is as follows.

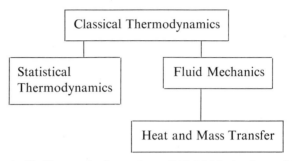

Professor A. G. Hansen is the author of *Fluid Mechanics* and Professor J. A. Clark is the author of *The Transport of Heat and Mass*.

Our original goal was to use the same symbols throughout the four books. However, we have realized that each of these fields does have a certain body of widely accepted symbols, and therefore in a limited number of cases we deemed it best to follow the conventions of each of the three fields and use different symbols for the same quantities in the books. In any case, uniformity of concepts and definitions is of much more importance and of greater benefit to the student than uniformity of symbols. We have attempted, therefore, to establish this uniformity in fundamental principles throughout the series. The concepts of system and control volume have been used throughout. Every effort has been made to maintain a consistent set of definitions and use of terms in each of the four basic texts.

As authors we extend our appreciation to our colleagues and to Mr. A. R. Beckett and his associates at John Wiley and Sons; and as editor, I thank each of the authors for the stimulating experience of working with them.

G. J. Van Wylen
March, 1965

Preface

This book is the first volume in the Series in Thermal and Transport Sciences. As such it has had a twofold objective, namely, to effectively present a comprehensive and rigorous treatment of classical thermodynamics while retaining an engineering perspective, and second, to lay the groundwork for the presentation of fluid mechanics, heat and mass transfer, and statistical thermodynamics in succeeding books in the series. This same groundwork must also prepare students for more specialized study in the various fields of application of thermodynamics or for further study in classical thermodynamics.

The first objective has dictated a number of considerations. If the presentation is to be effective as a textbook, it must be directed toward students. Thus new concepts and definitions are presented in the context where they are first relevant. The first thermodynamic properties to be defined (Chapter 2) are those which can be measured, namely, pressure, specific volume, and temperature. In the following chapter, tables of thermodynamic properties are introduced, but only as regards these measurable properties. Internal energy is introduced in connection with the first law for a system, enthalpy with the first law for a control volume, entropy with the second law, and the Helmholtz and Gibbs functions in the chapter on availability. A number of examples have been included to assist the student in gaining an understanding of thermodynamics, and the problems at the end of each chapter have been carefully sequenced to correlate with the subject matter and provide some progression in difficulty.

We have attempted to cover fairly comprehensively the basic subject matter of classical thermodynamics, and believe that the book provides adequate preparation for study of the application of thermodynamics to the various professional fields as well as for study of more advanced topics in thermodynamics, such as those related to materials, surface phenomena, plasmas, and cryogenics. We also recognize that a number of colleges now offer a single introductory course in thermodynamics for all departments, and we have attempted to include everything the various departments might wish to have included in such a course. However, since specific courses vary considerably in prerequisites, specific objectives, duration, and background of the students, we have so arranged the material, particularly in the later chapters, that there is considerable flexibility in the amount of material that may be covered.

Throughout this book we have attempted to maintain an engineering perspective, primarily through the choice of the examples and problems. In addition, the first chapter introduces a number of applications to thermodynamics that are of current interest. Our initial intention had been to omit any additional chapters that deal primarily with applications. However, on further reflection we recognized that many students enjoy at least a brief coverage of cycles and that a well-taught study of cycles serves to strengthen the student's understanding of the first and second laws of thermodynamics. For this reason Chapter 9, which is relatively brief, has been included. It can be omitted without loss of continuity.

Our objective of providing in this book a foundation for the study of fluid mechanics, heat and mass transfer, and statistical thermodynamics has influenced our writing in at least two ways. First, we have included a fairly detailed coverage of the control volume, since the presentation of fluid mechanics and heat transfer in the subsequent books in this series is developed from this concept. Second, our choices of terminology, definitions, and specific topics covered were influenced by our earlier decisions as to the preparation a student should have in thermodynamics for his subsequent studies in the thermal and transport sciences.

The matter of symbols presented a number of difficult decisions for us. In order to emphasize the distinctions between force and mass, the symbols lbf and lbm have been used for force and mass in the English system. Such symbols as $lbf/in.^2$ have been used for pressure (rather than psi) and ft^3/lbm for specific volume (rather than cu ft/lb) in order to emphasize the fundamental units involved in the various parameters. As regards the extensive properties, a lower-case letter (u, h, s) designates the property per unit mass, an upper-case one (U, H, S) the property for the entire system; the lower-case with a bar $(\bar{u}, \bar{h}, \bar{s})$ the property per unit mole and the upper case with a bar $(\bar{U}, \bar{H}, \bar{S})$ the partial molal property. Following this pattern, we have found it convenient to designate the total heat transfer as Q, the heat transfer per unit mass of the system as q, the total work as W, and the work per unit mass of the system as w.

We further decided to represent the rate of flow across a system boundary or control surface by a dot over a given quantity. Thus $\dot{Q}$ represents a rate of heat transfer across the system boundary, $\dot{W}$ the rate at which work crosses the system boundary (i.e., the power), and $\dot{m}$ the mass rate of flow across a control surface ($\dot{n}$ is used when the mass rate of flow is expressed in moles per unit time). The rate of heat transfer across a control surface is designated $\dot{Q}_{c.v.}$, and the rate of work (other than flow work) crossing a control surface is designated $\dot{W}_{c.v.}$. We realize that we have departed from the usual mathematical use of a dotted symbol, for in mathematics the dotted symbol usually refers to a derivative with respect to time. However, we have used the dotted symbol only to indicate a flow of heat and work across a system boundary, and heat, work, and mass across a control surface, and believe that it has contributed to a simple and consistent use of symbols for this book.

A brief survey of the contents of the book may be of assistance to the reader. Chapter 1, which serves as an introduction to thermodynamics, includes a brief description of the fuel cell and the thermoelectric refrigerator and power generator as well as a number of more conventional systems. A brief description of an air separation plant is included as an example of both a chemical process and cryogenics; a number of problems in various chapters are based on this system. Chapters 2, 3, and 4 cover a number of basic definitions such as property, cycle, pressure, specific volume, temperature, heat, and work. The discussion of work includes a description of the magnetic cooling process. The first law of thermodynamics for both the system and control volume and the conservation of mass are covered in Chapter 5. The steady-state, steady-flow, and uniform-state, uniform-flow processes; the definitions of the constant-pressure and constant-volume specific heats and Joule-Thomson coefficient; and the enthalpy and internal energy of ideal gases are also presented in this chapter.

Chapters 6, 7, and 8 involve a progressive development of the second law of thermodynamics. The Kelvin-Planck and Clausius statements of the second law, the Carnot cycle, and the thermodynamic temperature scale are introduced in Chapter 6. The inequality of Clausius, the definition of entropy, the second law of thermodynamics for a control volume, and the principle of the increase of entropy are covered in Chapter 7. Chapter 8, which extends the development of both the first and second laws to the concepts of availability and irreversibility, may be omitted without loss in continuity. As already noted, Chapter 9 deals with various thermodynamic cycles.

General thermodynamic relations, generalized charts, fugacity, and equations of state are treated in Chapter 10. Chapter 11 deals with mixtures, from mixtures of ideal gases to a simplified model which applies to ordinary air-vapor mixtures, and finally to a more general treatment of mixtures, including a discussion of partial molal properties, ideal solutions, and activity and activity coefficients. The thermodynamics of chemical reaction is the subject of Chapter 12, and involves a consideration of the enthalpy of formation and the third law of thermodynamics. Chapter 13 deals with equilibrium, with particular emphasis on the equilibrium of systems undergoing chemical reaction, including simultaneous reactions. Phase equilibrium and the equilibrium of systems involving ionization are also considered.

In view of the role this book plays in the Series on Thermal and Transport Sciences, we originally did not intend to include any fluid flow topics. However, on the recommendation of one of the reviewers we have included an introduction to compressible flow and flow through nozzles and blade passages in Chapter 14, in order to provide a more comprehensive coverage for those students who would not otherwise undertake extensive studies in fluid flow. We recognize that in many cases the material in this chapter will be covered in other courses.

The Appendix includes tables of thermodynamic properties for a number of substances, critical properties, specific heat equations, equilibrium constants, and various generalized charts.

Much of the introductory material and the sections involving the application of thermodynamics to cycles and fluid flow have been adapted from the principal author's earlier textbook, *Thermodynamics*, which was published in 1959.

We find it very difficult, in fact quite impossible, to acknowledge all those who in one way or another have contributed to this book. The number to whom acknowledgment is due is very large, because many have contributed to our knowledge of thermodynamics, either in person or through their writing. Moreover, in many cases we have long since forgotten the source of a given idea or approach, a problem having a particular educational value, or a sketch illustrating a process or device. We have attempted to give references at a number of points in the text, but we do recognize that these are incomplete, and take this occasion to note with appreciation the contribution of many to our writing of this book.

We do wish to acknowledge the counsel of and valuable discussions with our colleagues, Professors A. G. Hansen and J. A. Clark, with whom we have worked closely in this Series on the Thermal and Transport Sciences. The presentation of the control volume given in this book follows very closely the development which Professor Clark has prepared for his subsequent book in this series, *The Transport of Heat and Mass*. We also acknowledge the help of many of our other colleagues. Professors G. E. Smith and E. R. Lady have been of particular value to us at many points. We believe that Professor W. C. Reynolds of Stanford University was the first to introduce the term "simple compressible substance" and we have adopted this term with his approval. Our students also have always been very helpful, particularly in their critical evaluation of lecture notes and their probing questions, which have forced us to rethink various points and problems. Our department secretary, Mrs. Bernice Ogilvy, and her associates have contributed immeasurably to the preparation of the manuscript.

Our hope is that this book will contribute to our educational programs in thermodynamics. Your comments, criticisms, and suggestions will be appreciated.

Ann Arbor, Michigan   GORDON J. VAN WYLEN
March, 1965   RICHARD E. SONNTAG

Contents

Symbols

a	acceleration
a	activity
a, A	specific Helmholtz function and total Helmholtz function
A	area
AF	air-fuel ratio
c	velocity of sound
C_D	coefficient of discharge
C_p	constant-pressure specific heat
C_v	constant-volume specific heat
C_{po}	zero-pressure constant-pressure specific heat
C_{vo}	zero-pressure constant-volume specific heat
e, E	specific energy and total energy
f	fugacity
f_i	fugacity of component i in a mixture
F	force
FA	fuel-air ratio
g	acceleration due to gravity
g, G	specific Gibbs function and total Gibbs function
g_c	a constant that relates force, mass, length, and time
h, H	specific enthalpy and total enthalpy
i	electrical current
I	irreversibility
J	proportionality factor to relate units of work to units of heat
k	specific heat ratio: C_p/C_v
K	equilibrium constant
KE	kinetic energy
L	length
lbf	pound force
lbm	pound mass
lb mole	pound mole
lw, LW	lost work per unit mass and total lost work

m	mass
$\dot{m}$	mass rate of flow
M	molecular weight
M	Mach number
mf	mass fraction
n	number of moles
n	polytropic exponent
P	pressure
P_i	partial pressure of component i in a mixture
PE	potential energy
P_r	relative pressure as used in gas tables
q, Q	heat transfer per unit mass and total heat transfer
$\dot{Q}$	rate of heat transfer
Q_H, Q_L	heat transfer with high-temperature body and heat transfer with low-temperature body; sign determined from context
R	gas constant
$\bar{R}$	universal gas constant
s, S	specific entropy and total entropy
t	time
T	temperature
u, U	specific internal energy and total internal energy
v, V	specific volume and total volume
v_r	relative specific volume as used in gas tables
vf	volume fraction
V	velocity
V_r	relative velocity
w, W	work per unit mass and total work
$\dot{W}$	rate of work, or power
w_{rev}	reversible work between two states assuming heat transfer with surroundings
x	quality
x	liquid-phase or solid-phase mole fraction
y	vapor-phase mole fraction
Z	elevation
Z	compressibility factor
Z	electrical charge

Script Letters

$\mathscr{C}$	number of components
$\mathscr{E}$	electrical potential
$\mathscr{H}$	magnetic field intensity
$\mathscr{M}$	magnetization
$\mathscr{P}$	number of phases
$\mathscr{S}$	surface tension
$\mathscr{T}$	tension
$\mathscr{V}$	variance

Greek Letters

α	residual volume
α	volume expansivity
β	coefficient of performance for a refrigerator
β'	coefficient of performance for a heat pump
β_S	adiabatic compressibility
β_T	isothermal compressibility
γ	activity coefficient
η	efficiency
μ	chemical potential
μ_J	Joule-Thomson coefficient
ν	stoichiometric coefficient
ρ	density
ϕ	a property associated with entropy as used in the gas tables
ϕ	relative humidity
ϕ	availability for a system
ψ	availability associated with a steady-state, steady-flow process
ω	humidity ratio or specific humidity

Subscripts

c	property at the critical point
c.v.	control volume
e	state of a substance leaving a control volume
f	formation
f	property of saturated liquid
fg	difference in property for saturated vapor and saturated liquid
g	property of saturated vapor
i	state of a substance entering a control volume
i	property of saturated solid
ig	difference in property for saturated vapor and saturated solid
r	reduced property
s	isentropic process
0	property of the surroundings
0	stagnation property

Superscripts

—	bar over symbol denotes property on a molal basis (over $V, H, S, U,$ $A, G,$ the bar denotes partial molal property)
$\circ$	property at standard-state condition
$*$	ideal gas
$*$	property at the throat of a nozzle
L	liquid-phase
S	solid-phase
V	vapor-phase

1 Some Introductory Comments

In the course of our study of thermodynamics, a number of the examples and problems presented refer to processes that occur in such equipment as a steam power plant, a fuel cell, a vapor compression refrigerator, a thermoelectric cooler, a rocket engine, and an air separation plant. In this introductory chapter a brief description of this equipment is given. There are at least two reasons for including such a chapter. First, many students have had limited contact with such equipment, and the solution of problems will be more significant and relevant when they have some familiarity with the actual processes and the equipment involved. Second, this chapter will provide an introduction to thermodynamics, including the use of certain terms (which will be more formally defined in later chapters), some of the problems for which thermodynamics is relevant, and some accomplishments that have resulted, at least in part, from the application of thermodynamics.

It should be emphasized that thermodynamics is relevant to many other processes than those cited in this chapter. It is basic to the study of materials, chemical reactions, and plasmas. The student should bear in mind that this chapter is only a brief and necessarily very incomplete introduction to the subject of thermodynamics.

1.1 The Simple Steam Power Plant

A schematic diagram of a simple steam power plant is shown in Fig. 1.1. High-pressure superheated steam leaves the boiler, which is also referred to as a steam generator, and enters the turbine. The steam expands in the turbine and in doing so, does work, which enables the turbine to drive the electric generator. The low-pressure steam leaves the turbine and enters the condenser, where heat is transferred from the steam (causing it to condense) to the cooling water. Since large quantities of cooling water are required, power plants are frequently located near rivers or lakes.

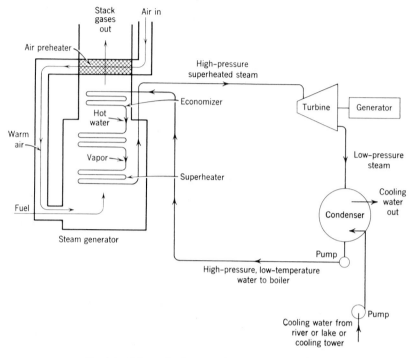

Fig. 1.1   Schematic diagram of a steam power plant.

When the supply of cooling water is limited, a cooling tower may be used. In the cooling tower some of the cooling water evaporates in such a way as to lower the temperature of the water that remains as a liquid.

The pressure of the condensate leaving the condenser is increased in the pump, thus enabling the condensate to flow into the steam generator. In many steam generators an economizer is used. An economizer is simply a heat exchanger in which heat is transferred from the products of combustion (just before they leave the steam generator) to the condensate, with the result that the temperature of the condensate is increased, but no evaporation takes place. In other sections of the steam generator, heat is transferred from the products of combustion to the water, causing it to evaporate. The temperature at which evaporation occurs is called the saturation temperature. The steam then flows through another heat exchanger known as a superheater, where the temperature of the steam is increased well above the saturation temperature.

In many power plants the air that is used for combustion is preheated in the air preheater by transferring heat from the stack gases as they are leaving the furnace. This air is then mixed with fuel—which might be coal,

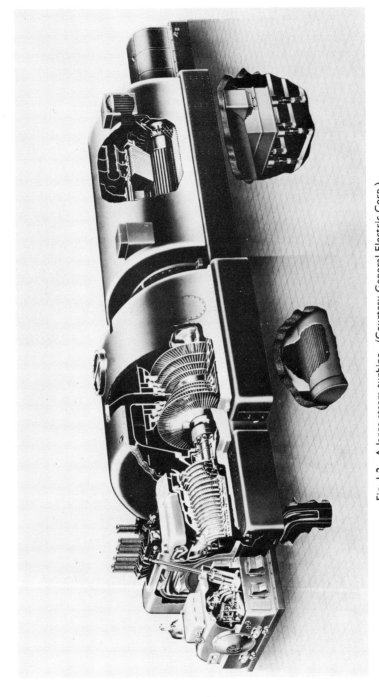

Fig. 1.2 A large steam turbine. (Courtesy General Electric Corp.)

fuel oil, natural gas, or other combustible material—and combustion takes place in the furnace. As the products of combustion pass through the furnace, heat is transferred to the water in the superheater, the boiler, the economizer, and to the air in the air preheater.

A large power plant will have many other pieces of equipment, some of which will be considered in later chapters.

Figure 1.2 shows a steam turbine and the generator that it drives. Steam turbines vary in capacity from less than 10 kilowatts to 1,000,000 kilowatts.

Figure 1.3 shows a cutaway view of a condenser. The steam enters at the top and the condensate is collected in the hot well at the bottom while the cooling water flows through the tubes. A large condenser has a tremendous number of tubes, as shown in Fig. 1.3.

Figure 1.4 shows a large steam generator. The flow of air and products of combustion are indicated. The condensate, also called the boiler feedwater, enters at the economizer inlet, and the superheated steam leaves at the superheater outlet.

The number of nuclear power plants in operation is rapidly increasing. In these power plants the reactor replaces the steam generator of the conventional power plant, and the radioactive fuel elements replace the coal, oil, or natural gas.

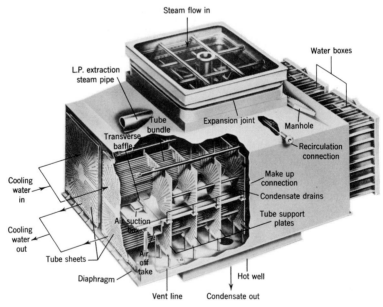

Fig. 1.3   A condenser used in a large power plant. (Courtesy Westinghouse Corp.)

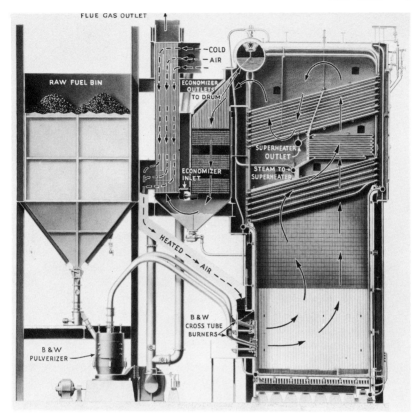

Fig. 1.4   A large steam generator. (Courtesy Babcock and Wilcox Corp.)

There are several different reactor designs in current use. One of these is the boiling water reactor, such as the system shown in Fig. 1.5. In other nuclear power plants a secondary fluid circulates from the reactor to the steam generator, where heat is transferred from the secondary fluid to the water which in turn goes through a conventional steam cycle. Safety considerations and the necessity to keep the turbine, condenser, and related equipment from becoming radioactive are always major considerations in the design of a nuclear power plant.

1.2   Fuel Cells

When a conventional power plant is viewed as a whole, as shown in Fig. 1.6, we see that fuel and air enter the power plant and products of combustion leave the unit. There is also a transfer of heat to the cooling water,

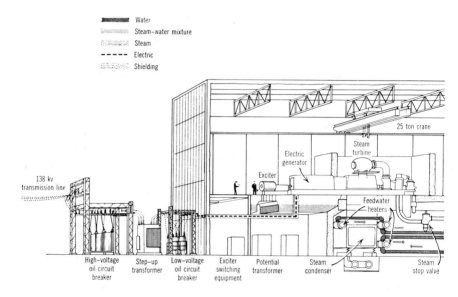

Fig. I.5   Schematic diagram of the Big Rock Point nuclear plant of Consumers Power

and work is done in the form of the electrical energy leaving the power plant. The overall objective of a power plant is to convert the availability (to do work) of the fuel into work (in the form of electrical energy) in the most efficient manner, consistent with such considerations as cost, space, and safety.

We might well ask if all of the equipment in the power plant, such as the steam generator, the turbine, the condenser, and the pump, is necessary. Is it not possible to produce electrical energy from the fuel in a more direct manner?

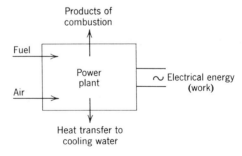

Fig. I.6   Schematic diagram of a power plant.

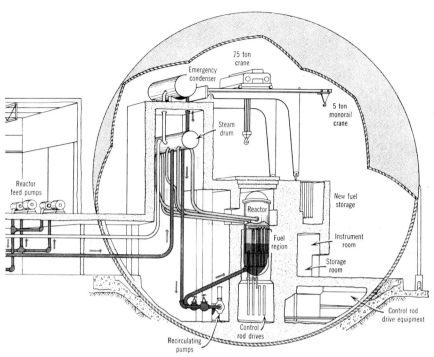

Company at Charlevoix, Michigan. (Courtesy Consumers Power Company.)

The fuel cell is a device in which this objective is accomplished. Figure 1.7 shows a schematic arrangement of a fuel cell of the ion-exchange membrane type. In this fuel cell hydrogen and oxygen react to form water. Let us consider the general features of the operation of this type of fuel cell.

The flow of electrons in the external circuit is from anode to cathode. Hydrogen enters at the anode side and oxygen enters at the cathode side. At the surface of the ion-exchange membrane the hydrogen is ionized according to the reaction

$$2H_2 \rightarrow 4H^+ + 4e^-$$

The electrons flow through the external circuit and the hydrogen ions flow through the membrane to the cathode, where the following reaction takes place.

$$4H^+ + 4e^- + O_2 \rightarrow 2H_2O$$

There is a potential difference between the anode and cathode, and thus there is a flow of electricity through a potential difference which, in thermodynamic terms, is called work. There may also be a transfer of heat between the fuel cell and the surroundings.

At the present time the fuel used in fuel cells is usually either hydrogen or a mixture of gaseous hydrocarbons and hydrogen. The oxidizer is

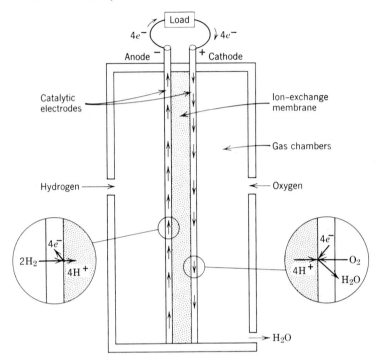

Fig. 1.7 Schematic arrangement of an ion-exchange membrane type of fuel cell.

usually oxygen. However, current research is directed toward the development of fuel cells that use hydrocarbon fuels and air. Although the conventional (or nuclear) steam power plant is still used in large-scale power generating systems, and conventional piston engines and gas turbines are still used in most transportation power systems, the fuel cell may eventually become a serious competitor. The fuel cell is already being used to produce power for certain space applications.

Thermodynamics plays a vital role in the analysis, development, and design of all power-producing systems, including reciprocating internal combustion engines and gas turbines. Such considerations as the increase of efficiency, improved design, optimum operating conditions, and alternate methods of power generation involve, among other factors, the careful application of the fundamentals of thermodynamics.

1.3 The Vapor-Compression Refrigeration Cycle

A simple vapor-compression refrigeration cycle is shown schematically in Fig. 1.8. The refrigerant enters the compressor as a slightly superheated

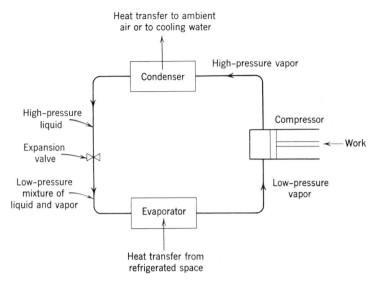

Fig. 1.8   Schematic diagram of a simple refrigeration cycle.

vapor at a low pressure. It then leaves the compressor and enters the condenser as a vapor at some elevated pressure, where the refrigerant is condensed as a result of heat transfer to cooling water or to the surroundings. The refrigerant then leaves the condenser as a high-pressure liquid. The pressure of the liquid is decreased as it flows through the expansion valve and, as a result, some of the liquid flashes into vapor. The remaining liquid, now at a low pressure, is vaporized in the evaporator as a result of heat transfer from the refrigerated space. This vapor then enters the compressor.

In a typical home refrigerator the compressor is located in the rear near the bottom of the unit. The compressors are usually hermetically sealed; that is, the motor and compressor are mounted in a sealed housing, and the electric leads for the motor pass through this housing. This is done to prevent leakage of the refrigerant. The condenser is also located at the back of the refrigerator and is so arranged that the air in the room flows past the condenser by natural convection. The expansion valve takes the form of a long capillary tube and the evaporator is located around the outside of the freezing compartment inside the refrigerator.

Figure 1.9 shows a large centrifugal unit that is used to provide refrigeration for an air-conditioning unit. In this unit, brine is cooled and then circulated to provide cooling where needed. The expansion valve is not shown; it is hidden from view by the compressor.

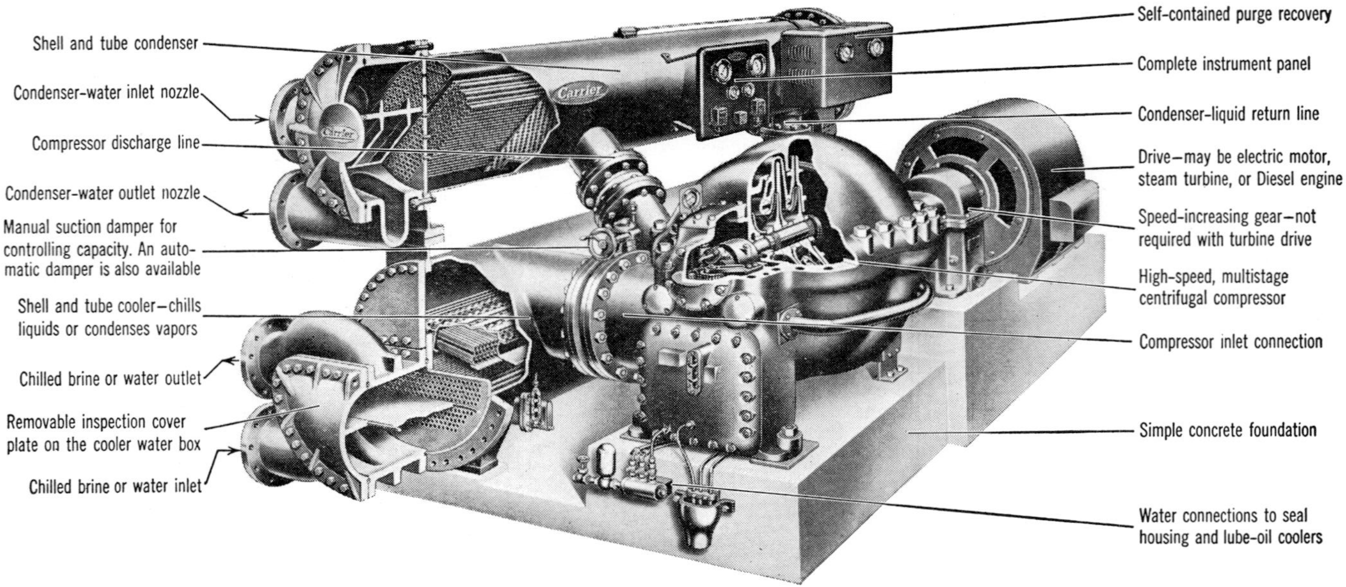

Fig. 1.9 A refrigeration unit for an air-conditioning system. (Courtesy Carrier Corp.)

Self-contained purge recovery

Complete instrument panel

Condenser-liquid return line

Drive—may be electric motor, steam turbine, or Diesel engine

Speed-increasing gear—not required with turbine drive

High-speed, multistage centrifugal compressor

Compressor inlet connection

Simple concrete foundation

Water connections to seal housing and lube-oil coolers

Shell and tube condenser

Condenser-water inlet nozzle

Compressor discharge line

Condenser-water outlet nozzle

Manual suction damper for controlling capacity. An auto-matic damper is also available

Shell and tube cooler—chills liquids or condenses vapors

Chilled brine or water outlet

Removable inspection cover plate on the cooler water box

Chilled brine or water inlet

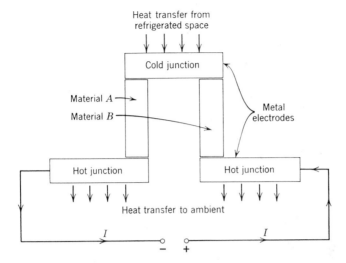

Fig. 1.10   A thermoelectric refrigerator.

1.4 The Thermoelectric Refrigerator

We may well ask the same question about the vapor compression refrigerator that we asked about the steam power plant, namely, isn't it possible to accomplish our objective in a more direct manner? Isn't it possible, in the case of a refrigerator, to use the electrical energy, (which goes to the electric motor that drives the compressor) to produce cooling in a more direct manner, and avoid the cost of the compressor, condenser, evaporator, and all the related piping.

The thermoelectric refrigerator is such a device. This is shown schematically in Fig. 1.10. The thermoelectric device, like the conventional thermocouple, utilizes two dissimilar materials. There are two junctions between these two materials in a thermoelectric refrigerator. One is located in the refrigerated space, and the other in ambient surroundings. When a potential difference is applied, as indicated, the temperature of the junction located in the refrigerated space will decrease and the temperature of the other junction will increase. Under steady-state operating conditions heat will be transferred from the refrigerated space to the cold junction. The other junction will be at a temperature above the ambient, and heat will be transferred from the junction to the surroundings.

It should be emphasized that a thermoelectric device can also be used to generate power by replacing the refrigerated space with a body which is at a temperature above the ambient. Such a system is shown in Fig. 1.11.

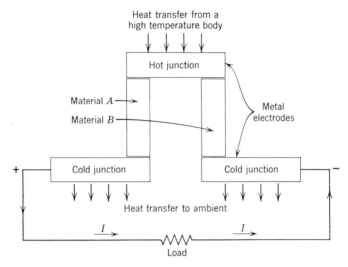

Fig. 1.11   A thermoelectric power generation device.

The thermoelectric refrigerator cannot yet compete economically with the conventional vapor-compression units. However, in certain special applications the thermoelectric refrigerator is already in use, and in view of the major research and development efforts underway in this field, it is quite possible that the use of thermoelectric refrigerators will be much more extensive in the future.

1.5   The Air Separation Plant

One process of great industrial significance is the air separation plant, in which air is separated into its various components. The oxygen, nitrogen, argon, and rare gases so produced are used extensively in various industrial, research, space, and consumer goods applications. The air separation plant may be considered as an example from two major fields, the chemical process industry and the field of cryogenics. Cryogenics is a term that refers to technology, processes, and research at very low temperatures (in general, below 150 K). In both chemical processing and cryogenics, thermodynamics is basic to an understanding of many phenomena that occur and to the design and development of processes and equipment.

A number of different designs of air separation plants have been developed. Consider Fig. 1.12, which shows a somewhat simplified sketch of a type of plant that is frequently used. Air from the atmosphere is compressed to a pressure of several hundred pounds per square inch. It is then purified, particularly to remove carbon dioxide (which would

plug the flow passages as it solidifies when the air is cooled to its liquefaction temperature). The air is then compressed to a pressure of 2500
to 3000 pounds per square inch, cooled to the ambient temperature in
the aftercooler, and dried to remove the water vapor (which would also
plug the flow passages as it freezes).

The basic refrigeration in the liquefaction process is provided by two
different processes. One involves expansion of the air in the expansion
engine. During this process the air does work and as a result the temperature of the air is reduced. The other refrigeration process involves
passing the air through a throttle valve that is so designed and so located
that there is a substantial drop in the pressure of the air and, associated
with this, a substantial drop in the temperature of the air.

As shown in Fig. 1.12, the dry, high pressure air enters a heat exchanger.
The air temperature drops as it flows through the heat exchanger. At some
intermediate point in the heat exchanger, part of the air is bled off and
flows through the expansion engine. The remaining air flows through the
rest of the heat exchanger and through the throttle valve. The two streams

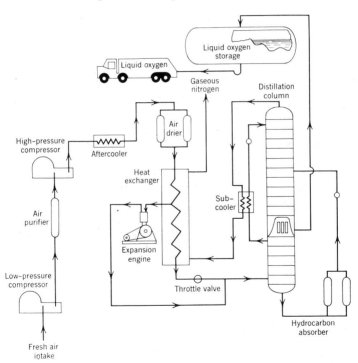

Fig. 1.12 A simplified diagram of a liquid oxygen plant. (Courtesy Air Products and
Chemicals, Inc.)

join, both being at a pressure of 5–10 atmospheres, and enter the bottom of the distillation column, which is referred to as the high pressure column. The function of the distillation column is to separate the air into its various components, principally oxygen and nitrogen. Two streams of different composition flow from the high pressure column through throttle valves to the upper column (also called the low-pressure column). One of these is an oxygen-rich liquid that flows from the bottom of the lower column, and the other is a nitrogen-rich stream that flows through the subcooler. The separation is completed in the upper column, with liquid oxygen leaving from the bottom of the upper column and gaseous nitrogen from the top of the column. The nitrogen gas flows through the subcooler and the main heat exchanger. It is the heat transfer to this cold nitrogen gas that causes the cooling of the high pressure air entering the heat exchanger.

Not only is a thermodynamic analysis essential to the design of the system as a whole, but essentially every component of such a system, including the compressors, the expansion engine, the purifiers and driers, and the distillation column, involves thermodynamics. In this separation process we are also concerned with the thermodynamic properties of mixtures and the principles and procedures by which these mixtures can be separated. This is the type of problem encountered in the refining of petroleum and many other chemical processes. It should also be noted that cryogenics is particularly relevant to many aspects of the space program, and a thorough knowledge of thermodynamics is essential for creative and effective work in cryogenics.

1.6   The Chemical Rocket Engine

The advent of missiles and satellites has brought to prominence the use of the rocket engine as a propulsion power plant. Chemical rocket engines may be classified as either liquid propellant or solid propellant, according to the fuel used.

Figure 1.13 shows a simplified schematic diagram of a liquid-propellant rocket. The oxidizer and fuel are pumped through the injector plate into the combustion chamber where combustion takes place at high pressure. The high-pressure, high-temperature products of combustion expand as they flow through the nozzle, and as a result they leave the nozzle with a high velocity. The momentum change associated with this increase in velocity gives rise to the forward thrust on the vehicle.

The oxidizer and fuel must be pumped into the combustion chamber, and some auxiliary power plant is necessary to drive the pumps. In a large rocket this auxiliary power plant must be very reliable and have a relatively high power output, yet it must be light in weight. The oxidizer and fuel

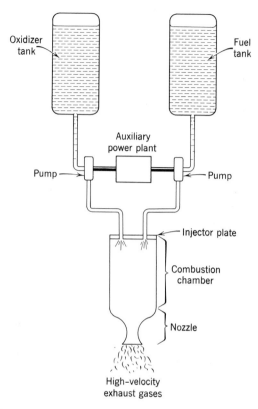

Fig. 1.13 Simplified schematic diagram of a liquid-propellant rocket engine.

tanks occupy the largest part of the volume of an actual rocket, and the range of a rocket is determined largely by the amount of oxidizer and fuel that can be carried. Many different fuels and oxidizers have been considered and tested, and much effort has gone into the development of fuels and oxidizers that will give a higher thrust per unit mass rate of flow of reactants. Liquid oxygen is frequently used as the oxidizer in liquid-propellant rockets.

Much work has also been done on solid-propellant rockets. They have been very successfully used for jet-assisted take-offs of airplanes, military missiles, and space vehicles. They are much simpler in both the basic equipment required for operation and the logistic problems involved in their use by the military.

2 *Some Concepts and Definitions*

One very excellent definition of thermodynamics is that it is the science of energy and entropy. However, since we have not yet defined those terms, an alternate definition in terms with which we are already familiar is: thermodynamics is the science that deals with heat and work and those properties of substances that bear a relation to heat and work. Like all sciences, the basis of thermodynamics is experimental observation. In thermodynamics these findings have been formalized into certain basic laws, which are known as the first, second, and third laws of thermodynamics. In addition to these, the zeroth law of thermodynamics, which in the logical development of thermodynamics precedes the first law, has been set forth.

In the chapters that follow, we shall present these laws and the thermodynamic properties related to these laws, and apply them to a number of representative examples. The objective of the student should be to gain a thorough understanding of the fundamentals and an ability to apply these fundamentals to thermodynamic problems. The purpose of the examples and problems is to further this two-fold objective. It should be emphasized that it is not necessary for the student to memorize numerous equations, for problems are best solved by the application of the definitions and laws of thermodynamics. In this chapter some concepts and definitions basic to thermodynamics are presented.

2.1 The Thermodynamic System and the Control Volume

A thermodynamic system is defined as a quantity of matter of fixed mass and identity upon which attention is focused for study. Everything external to the system is the surroundings, and the system is separated from the surroundings by the system boundaries. These boundaries may be either movable or fixed.

In Fig. 2.1 the gas in the cylinder is considered the system. If a Bunsen

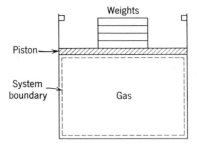

Fig. 2.1   Example of a system.

burner is placed under the cylinder, the temperature of the gas will increase and the piston will rise. As the piston rises, the boundary of the system moves. As we shall see later, heat and work cross the boundary of the system during this process, but the matter that comprises the system can always be identified.

An isolated system is one that is not influenced in any way by the surroundings. This means that no heat or work cross the boundary of the system.

In many cases a thermodynamic analysis must be made of a device, such as an air compressor, that involves a flow of mass into and/or out of the device, as shown schematically in Fig. 2.2. The procedure that is followed in such an analysis is to specify a control volume that surrounds the device under consideration. The surface of this control volume is referred to as a control surface. Mass, as well as heat and work (and momentum) can flow across the control surface.

Thus, a system is defined when dealing with a fixed quantity of mass, and a control volume is specified when an analysis is to be made that involves a flow of mass. The difference in these two approaches is considered in detail in Chapter 5. It should be noted that the terms closed system and

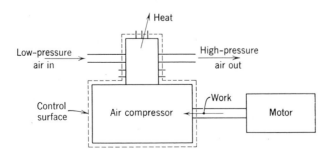

Fig. 2.2   Example of a control volume.

open system are sometimes used as the equivalent of the terms system (fixed mass) and control volume (involving a flow of mass). The procedure that will be followed in the presentation of the first and second laws of thermodynamics is first to present these laws for a system, and then to make the necessary transformations to apply them to a control volume.

2.2 Macroscopic vs. Microscopic Point of View

An investigation into the behavior of a system may be undertaken from either a microscopic or macroscopic point of view. Let us briefly consider the problem we would have if we describe a system from a microscopic point of view. Consider a system consisting of a one cubic inch volume of a monatomic gas at atmospheric pressure and temperature. This volume contains approximately 10^{20} atoms. To describe the position of each atom, three coordinates must be specified; to describe the velocity of each atom, three velocity components must be specified.

Thus, to completely describe the behavior of this system from a microscopic point of view, it would be necessary to deal with at least 6×10^{20} equations. Even with a large digital computer, this is a quite hopeless computational task. However, there are two approaches to this problem that reduce the number of equations and variables to a few that can be handled relatively easily in performing computations. One of these approaches is the statistical approach in which, on the basis of statistical considerations and probability theory, we deal with "average" values for all particles under consideration. This is usually done in connection with a model of the atom under consideration. This is the approach used in the disciplines known as kinetic theory and statistical mechanics.

The other approach that reduces the number of variables to a few that can be handled is the macroscopic point of view of classical thermodynamics. As the word macroscopic implies, we are concerned with the gross or average effects of many molecules. Furthermore, these effects can be perceived by our senses and measured by instruments. In so doing, however, what we really perceive and measure is the time-averaged influence of many molecules. For example, consider the pressure a gas exerts on the walls of its container. This pressure results from the change in momentum of the molecules as they collide with the wall. However, from a macroscopic point of view, we are not concerned with the action of the individual molecules but with the time-averaged force on a given area, which can be measured by a pressure gage. In fact, these macroscopic observations are completely independent of our assumptions regarding the nature of matter.

Although the theory and development in this book will be presented from a macroscopic point of view, a few supplementary remarks regarding the significance of the microscopic perspective, are included as an aid to the understanding of the physical processes involved. Another book in this series on Thermal and Transport Sciences, namely, *Fundamentals of Statistical Thermodynamics*, by R. E. Sonntag and G. J. Van Wylen deals with thermodynamics from the microscopic and statistical point of view.

A few remarks should be made regarding the continuum. From the macroscopic point of view, we are always concerned with volumes that are very large compared to molecular dimensions, and, therefore, with systems that contain many molecules. Since we are not concerned with the behavior of individual molecules, we can treat the substance as being continuous, disregarding the action of individual molecules, and this is called a continuum. The concept of a continuum, of course, is only a convenient assumption that loses validity when the mean free path of the molecules approaches the order of magnitude of the dimensions of the vessel, as, for example, in high-vacuum technology. In much engineering work the assumption of a continuum is valid and convenient, and goes hand in hand with the macroscopic point of view.

2.3 Properties and State of a Substance

If we consider a given mass of water, we recognize that this water can exist in various forms. If it is a liquid initially, it may become a vapor when it is heated, or a solid when it is cooled. Thus we speak of the different phases of a substance. A phase is defined as a quantity of matter that is homogeneous throughout. When more than one phase is present the phases are separated from each other by the phase boundaries. In each phase the substance may exist at various pressures and temperatures or, to use the thermodynamic term, in various states. The state may be identified or described by certain observable, macroscopic properties; some familiar ones are temperature, pressure, and density. In later chapters other properties will be introduced. Each of the properties of a substance in a given state has only one definite value, and these properties always have the same value for a given state, regardless of how the substance arrived at that state. In fact, a property can be defined as any quantity that depends on the state of the system and is independent of the path (i.e., the prior history) by which the system arrived at the given state. Conversely, the state is specified or described by the properties, and later we shall consider the number of independent properties a substance can have, i.e., the minimum number of properties that must be specified in order to fix the state of the substance.

Thermodynamic properties can be divided into two general classes, intensive and extensive properties. An intensive property is independent of the mass; the value of an extensive property varies directly with the mass. Thus, if a quantity of matter in a given state is divided into two equal parts, each part will have the same value of intensive properties as the original, and half the value of the extensive properties. Pressure, temperature, and density are examples of intensive properties. Mass and total volume are examples of extensive properties. Extensive properties per unit mass, such as specific volume, are intensive properties.

Frequently we will refer not only to the properties of a substance but to the properties of a system. When we do so we necessarily imply that the value of the property has significance for the entire system, and this implies what is called equilibrium. For example, if the gas that comprises the system in Fig. 2.1 is in thermal equilibrium, the temperature will be the same thoughout the entire system, and we may speak of the temperature as a property of the system. We may also consider mechanical equilibrium and this is related to pressure. If a system is in mechanical equilibrium, there is no tendency for the pressure at any point to change with time as long as the system is isolated from the surroundings. There will be a variation in pressure with elevation, due to the influence of gravitational forces, although under equilibrium conditions there will be no tendency for the pressure at any location to change. However, in many thermo-dynamic problems this variation in pressure with elevation is so small that it can be neglected. Chemical equilibrium is also important and will be considered in Chapter 13.

When a system is in equilibrium as regards all possible changes of state, we say that the system is in thermodynamic equilibrium.

2.4 Processes and Cycles

Whenever one or more of the properties of a system change we say that a change in state has occurred. For example, when one of the weights on the piston in Fig. 2.3 is removed, the piston rises and a change in state occurs, for the pressure decreases and the specific volume increases. The path of the succession of states through which the system passes is called the process.

Let us consider the equilibrium of a system as it undergoes a change in state. The moment the weight is removed from the piston in Fig. 2.3, mechanical equilibrium does not exist and as a result the piston is moved upward until mechanical equilibrium is again restored. The question that arises is this: since the properties describe the state of a system only when it is equilibrium, how can we describe the states of a system during a process if the actual process occurs only when equilibrium does not exist.

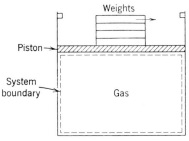

Fig. 2.3   Example of a system that may undergo a quasiequilibrium process.

One step in the answer to this question concerns the definition of an ideal process, which we call a quasiequilibrium process. A quasiequilibrium process is one in which the deviation from thermodynamic equilibrium is infinitesimal, and all the states the system passes through during a quasiequilibrium process may be considered as equilibrium states. Many actual processes closely approach a quasiequilibrium process, and may be so treated with essentially no error. If the weights on the piston in Fig. 2.3 are small and are taken off one by one, the process could be considered quasiequilibrium. On the other hand, if all the weights were removed at once, the piston would rise rapidly until it hit the stops. This would be a nonequilibrium process, and the system would not be in equilibrium at any time during this change of state.

For nonequilibrium processes, we are limited to a description of the system before the process occurs and after the process is completed and equilibrium is restored. We are not able to specify each state through which the system passes, nor the rate at which the process occurs. However, as we shall see later, we are able to describe certain over-all effects which occur during the process.

Several processes are described by the fact that one property remains constant. The prefix iso- is used to describe this. An isothermal process is a constant-temperature process, an isobaric (sometimes called isopiestic) process is a constant-pressure process, and an isometric process is a constant-volume process.

When a system in a given initial state goes through a number of different changes of state or processes and finally returns to its initial state, the system has undergone a cycle. Therefore, at the conclusion of a cycle all the properties have the same value they had at the beginning. Steam (water) that circulates through a steam power plant undergoes a cycle.

A distinction should be made between a thermodynamic cycle, which has just been described, and a mechanical cycle. A four-stroke cycle internal-combustion engine goes through a mechanical cycle once every two revolutions. However, the working fluid does not go through a thermodynamic cycle in the engine, since air and fuel are burned and changed to products of combustion which are exhausted to the atmosphere. In this text the term cycle will refer to a thermodynamic 'cycle' unless otherwise designated.

2.5   Units for Mass, Length, Time, and Force

Since we are considering thermodynamic properties from a macroscopic perspective, we are dealing with quantities which can either directly or indirectly be measured and counted. Therefore, the matter of units becomes an important consideration. In the remaining sections of this chapter we will define certain thermodynamic properties and the basic units involved. The relation between force and mass is often a difficult matter for students, and is considered in this section in some detail.

Force, mass, length, and time are related by Newton's second law of motion, which states that the force acting on a body is proportional to the product of the mass and the acceleration in the direction of the force.

$$F \propto ma$$

The concept of time is well established. The basic unit of time is the solar day, the time interval for one complete revolution of the earth relative to the sun. Since this period will vary with the season of the year, an average value over a one-year period is used and is called the mean solar day. The legal standard time unit is the mean solar second and is $1/86{,}400$ of the mean solar day. (The measurement of the earth's rotation is sometimes made relative to a fixed star, in which case the period is called a sidereal day.)

For periods less than one second the terms millisecond (10^{-3} second), microsecond (10^{-6} seconds), and nanosecond (10^{-9} seconds) are frequently used.

It has been proposed that the unit of time be fixed in terms of a resonator using a beam of cesium atoms. The time required for $9{,}192{,}631{,}770 \pm 20$ cycles of the cesium resonator has provisionally been adopted as equivalent to 1 second.

The concept of length is also well established. The basic unit of length is the meter, and for many years the accepted standard was the International Prototype Meter, the distance between two marks on a platinum-iridium bar under certain prescribed conditions. This bar is maintained at the International Bureau of Weights and Measures, Sevres, France. In 1960, the International Conference of Weights and Measures adopted a definition of the meter in terms of the wavelength of the orange-red line of krypton 86. The definition of the length of the meter is

1 meter $= 1{,}650{,}763.73$ wavelengths of the orange-red line of Kr-86

The inch is defined in terms of the meter.

$$1 \text{ in.} = 2.540 \text{ cm}$$

The concept of mass is also well understood. It involves the quantity or amount of material under consideration. In the various English systems the unit for mass is the pound mass, designated lbm, which was originally specified as the mass of a certain platinum cylinder in the Tower of London. It has now been defined in terms of the standard kilogram mass as

$$1 \text{ kilogram} = 2.2046 \text{ lbm.}$$

In the English Engineering system of units the concept of force is established as an independent quantity and the unit for force is defined in terms of an experimental procedure as follows. Let the standard pound mass be suspended in the earth's gravitational field at a location where the acceleration due to gravity is 32.1740 ft/sec². The force with which the standard pound mass is attracted to the earth (the buoyant effects of the atmosphere on the standard pound mass must also be standardized) is defined as the unit for force and is termed a pound force. Note that we now have arbitrary and independent definitions for force, mass, length, and time. Since these are related by Newton's second law we can write

$$F = \frac{ma}{g_c}$$

where g_c is a constant that relates the units of force, mass, length, and time. For the system of units defined above, namely, the English Engineering System we have

$$1 \text{ lbf} = \frac{1 \text{ lbm} \times 32.174 \text{ ft/sec}^2}{g_c}$$

or

$$g_c = 32.174 \frac{\text{lbm-ft}}{\text{lbf-sec}^2}$$

Note that g_c has both a numerical value and dimensions in this system.

To illustrate the use of this equation, let us calculate the force due to gravity on a pound mass at a location where the acceleration due to gravity is 30.0 ft/sec².

$$F = \frac{ma}{g_c}$$

$$F = \frac{1 \text{ lbm} \times 30.0 \text{ ft/sec}^2}{32.174 \text{ lbm-ft/lbf-sec}^2} = 0.933 \text{ lbf}$$

Note that the answer is dimensionally correct when the units of g_c as well as the magnitude are used. This is the system of units and the approach that will be used in this text.

We should briefly discuss three other systems of units. These three systems, namely the Absolute Metric, the Absolute English and the British Gravitational systems, involve a different concept, that of arbitrarily defining three of the four parameters mass, force, length, and time, and defining the fourth in terms of Newton's second law. In the Absolute Metric system (CGS system) the gram is the unit of mass, the second is the unit of time, and the centimeter is the unit of length, and each is arbitrarily and independently defined. The unit of force, the dyne, is defined in terms of Newton's second law.

$$1 \text{ dyne} \equiv 1 \frac{\text{gm-cm}}{\text{sec}^2}$$

Similarly, in the Absolute English system, which is used very little today, the units of mass, length, and time are defined, as in the English Engineering system, as pound mass, the foot, and the second. The unit for force in this system, the poundal, is defined as

$$1 \text{ poundal} \equiv \frac{1 \text{ lbm-ft}}{\text{sec}^2}$$

Note that in these two systems we could have taken the same perspective as in the English Engineering system, and defined force as an independent quantity. For example, we could have defined a dyne as the force acting on a mass of one gram at the location where the acceleration due to gravity is 1 cm/sec^2 (It might be difficult to locate this exact spot in space and remain there long enough to do the experiment.) We would then introduce g_c as a dimensional constant in Newton's second law.

$$F = \frac{ma}{g_c}$$

$$1 \text{ dyne} = \frac{1 \text{ gm} \times 1 \text{ cm/sec}^2}{g_c}$$

$$g_c = \frac{1 \text{ gm-cm}}{\text{dyne-sec}^2}$$

Similarly, we could have defined the poundal as the force acting on a mass of one pound at a location where the acceleration due to gravity is

1 ft/sec². Then

$$F = \frac{ma}{g_c}$$

$$1 \text{ poundal} = \frac{1 \text{ lbm} \times 1 \text{ ft/sec}^2}{g_c}$$

$$g_c = \frac{1 \text{ lbm-ft}}{\text{poundal-sec}^2}$$

Or, to return to the English Engineering system, we could have defined a pound force (lbf) as

$$1 \text{ lbf} = 32.174 \text{ lbm-ft/sec}^2$$

and have a definition of force parallel to that for the Absolute Metric and Absolute English systems.

There is a fourth system in common use, the British Gravitational system. In this system the independently defined units are force, length, and time. The unit for length is the foot; for time, the second; and for force, the pound force. Although this unit for force is exactly equal to the unit for force in the English Engineering system, we can think of it as an independent quantity in terms of a force required to compress a standard spring a fixed distance. The unit for the mass in this system is the slug and is defined from Newton's second law as

$$1 \text{ slug} \equiv \frac{1 \text{ lbf}}{1 \text{ ft/sec}^2} = \frac{1 \text{ lbf-sec}^2}{\text{ft}}$$

Had we adopted the slug as a fourth independently defined unit of mass as

$$1 \text{ slug} = 32.174 \text{ lbm}$$

we could have written

$$F = \frac{ma}{g_c}$$

$$1 \text{ lbf} = \frac{1 \text{ slug} \times 1 \text{ ft/sec}^2}{g_c}$$

$$g_c = \frac{1 \text{ slug-ft}}{\text{lbf-sec}^2}$$

This matter can be summarized in the tables as follows: If we arbitrarily define mass, length, time, and force as independent quantities, the constant g_c must be introduced into Newton's second law, and for the four systems considered we have

Name of System	Mass	Length	Time	Force	g_c
English Engineering	lbm	ft	sec	lbf	$g_c = 32.174 \dfrac{\text{lbm-ft}}{\text{lbf-sec}^2}$
not named	slug	ft	sec	lbf	$g_c = \dfrac{1 \text{ slug-ft}}{\text{lbf-sec}^2}$
not named	lbm	ft	sec	poundal	$g_c = \dfrac{1 \text{ lbm-ft}}{\text{poundal-sec}^2}$
not named	gm	cm	sec	dyne	$g_c = \dfrac{1 \text{ gm-cm}}{\text{dyne-sec}^2}$

If we arbitrarily define mass, length, and time as independent quantities we have

Name of System	Mass	Length	Time	Definition of Force
not named	lbm	ft	sec	$1 \text{ lbf} \equiv 32.174 \dfrac{\text{lbm-ft}}{\text{sec}^2}$
Absolute Metric	gm	cm	sec	$1 \text{ dyne} \equiv \dfrac{1 \text{ gm-cm}}{\text{sec}^2}$
Absolute English	lbm	ft	sec	$1 \text{ poundal} \equiv \dfrac{1 \text{ lbm-ft}}{\text{sec}^2}$

If we define force, length, and time as independent quantities we have

Name of System	Force	Length	Time	Definition of Mass
British Gravitational	lbf	ft	sec	$1 \text{ slug} \equiv \dfrac{1 \text{ lbf-sec}^2}{\text{ft}}$

In dealing with the matter of units in equations it is helpful to recall that since

$$1 \text{ lbf} \equiv 32.174 \frac{\text{lbm-ft}}{\text{sec}^2}$$

it follows that

$$1 = 32.174 \frac{\text{lbm-ft}}{\text{lbf-sec}^2}$$

Comparing this with g_c for this system we note that

$$g_c = 32.174 \frac{\text{lbm-ft}}{\text{lbf-sec}^2} = 1$$

Since a pure number can be inserted into an equation at any point, we can, in effect, substitute

$$1 = 32.174 \frac{\text{lbm-ft}}{\text{lbf-sec}^2} = g_c$$

into an equation at any point where it is advantageous to do so from the point of view of units. For example, the viscosity of water (the exact definition of viscosity is not important at this point) at atmospheric pressure and 80 F is given as 1.80×10^{-6} lbf-sec/ft². Suppose we wish to know this viscosity in terms of units involving lbm, sec, and ft.

$$\text{Viscosity} = 1.80 \times 10^{-6} \frac{\text{lbf-sec}}{\text{ft}^2} \times 1$$

$$= 1.80 \times 10^{-6} \frac{\text{lbf-sec}}{\text{ft}^2} \times 32.17 \frac{\text{lbm-ft}}{\text{lbf-sec}^2}$$

$$= 57.8 \frac{\text{lbm}}{\text{ft-sec}}$$

The English Engineering system has been adopted in this text and therefore Newton's second law will be written

$$F = \frac{ma}{g_c}$$

and the g_c will be included in equations involving Newton's second law. It should be emphasized that the term pound, the symbol lb (or $\#$) should never be used by itself, since it would not be evident whether pound mass or pound force is being referred to.

It should also be noted that weight always refers to a force. When we say a body weighs so much we mean that this is the force with which it is attracted to the earth (or any other body). The mass of a substance remains constant with elevation, but its weight varies with elevation.

Two other units for mass, namely the pound mole and gram mole are frequently used in thermodynamics. The pound mole, designated lb mole, is the quantity of a substance whose mass in pounds mass is equal to the molecular weight of the substance. Similarly the gram mole, designated gm mole, is the quantity of a substance whose mass in grams is equal to the molecular weight of the substance.

2.6 Specific Volume

The specific volume of a substance is defined as the volume per unit mass, and is given the symbol v. The density of a substance is defined as the mass per unit volume, and is therefore the reciprocal of the specific volume. Density is designated by the symbol ρ. Specific volume and density are intensive properties.

The specific volume of a system in a gravitational field may vary from point to point. For example, considering the atmosphere as a system, the specific volume increases as the elevation increases. Therefore the definition of specific volume involves the specific volume of a substance at a point in a system.

Consider a small volume δV of a system, and let the mass be designated δm. The specific volume is defined by the relation

$$v = \lim_{\delta V \to \delta V'} \frac{\delta V}{\delta m}$$

where $\delta V'$ is the smallest volume for which the system can be considered a continuum.

Thus in a given system we should speak of the specific volume or density at a point in the system, and recognize that this may vary with elevation. However, most of the systems that we consider are relatively small, and the change in specific volume with elevation is not significant. In this case, we can speak of one value of specific volume or density for the entire system.

In this text the specific volume and density will usually be given either on a pound-mass or a pound-mole basis. A bar over the symbol (lower case) will be used to designate the property on a mole basis. Thus, $\bar{v}$ will designate the molal specific volume and $\bar{\rho}$ will designate the molal density. The most common units used in this text for specific volume are ft³/lbm and ft³/lb mole; for density the corresponding units are lbm/ft³ and lb mole/ft³.

2.7 Pressure

When dealing with liquids and gases we ordinarily speak of pressure; in solids we speak of stresses. The pressure in a fluid at rest at a given point is the same in all directions, and we define pressure as the normal component of force per unit area. More specifically, if δA is a small area, and $\delta A'$ is the smallest area over which we can consider the fluid a continuum, and δF_n is the component of force normal to δA, we define pressure, P, as

$$P = \lim_{\delta A \to \delta A'} \frac{\delta F_n}{\delta A}$$

The pressure P at a point in a fluid in equilibrium is the same in all directions. In a viscous fluid in motion the variation in the state of stress with orientation becomes an important consideration. These considerations are beyond the scope of this book, and we will consider pressure only in terms of a fluid in equilibrium.*

In general, the unit for pressure that is consistent with the other units used in this text is pounds force per square foot (lbf/ft²). On the other hand, in common parlance and general experimental work, pressures are often measured in pounds force per square inch (lbf/in.²). Therefore, the student should be careful in numerical calculations to introduce the conversion 144 in.² = 1 ft², as necessary.

In most thermodynamic investigations we are concerned with absolute pressure. Most pressure and vacuum gages, however, read the difference between the absolute pressure and the atmospheric pressure existing at the gage, and this is referred to as gage pressure. This is shown graphically in Fig. 2.4, and the following examples illustrate the principles involved. Pressures below atmospheric and slightly above atmospheric, and pressure differences (for example, across an orifice in a pipe) are frequently

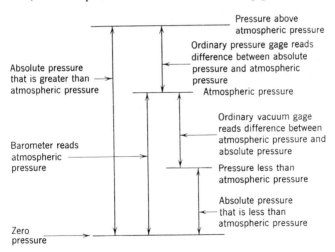

Fig. 2.4   Illustration of terms used in pressure measurement.

* The state of stress of a viscous fluid in motion is considered in two subsequent books in this series, *Fluid Mechanics*, by A. G. Hansen and *Heat and Mass Transfer* by J. A. Clark.

measured with a manometer, which contains water, mercury, alcohol, oil, or other fluids. From the principles of hydrostatics one concludes that for a difference in level of L ft, the pressure difference in pounds per square foot is calculated by the relation

$$\Delta P = \rho \frac{Lg}{g_c} \qquad (2.5)$$

where ρ = density of the fluid in lbm/ft^3. Figure 2.5 illustrates such a manometer.

From this relation the student should verify the fact that at ordinary room temperatures

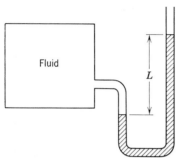

Fig. 2.5 Example of pressure measurement using a column of fluid.

1 in. Hg = 0.490 $lbf/in.^2$

Standard atmospheric pressure is defined as the pressure produced by a column of mercury exactly 760 mm in length, the mercury density being 13.5951 gm/cm^3 and the acceleration due to gravity being standard. Therefore,

1 std atm = 14.6959 $lbf/in.^2$

= 1.01325 × 10^6 dynes/cm²

Another common unit of pressure is the atmosphere, which implies a standard atmosphere. Thus, a pressure of 1000 atmospheres is a pressure of 14,696 $lbf/in.^2$

Extremely low pressures (i.e., a high vacuum) are often measured in microns of mercury (usually only the word micron is used). A micron is one millionth of a meter or 10^{-3} mm. Thus,

1 micron = 1 × 10^{-6} meters = 1 × 10^{-3} mm

1 micron Hg = 1 × 10^{-3} mm Hg = 1.933 × 10^{-5} $lbf/in.^2$

The term torr (after Evangelista Torricelli, 1608–1647, the pioneer worker in vacuum technology) has been introduced for a pressure of 1 mm Hg.

In order to distinguish between absolute and gage pressures in this text, the term $lbf/in.^2$ or lbf/ft^2 will refer to absolute pressure. The gage pressure will be indicated by $lbf/in.^2$ gage or lbf/ft^2 gage. It should also be noted that the symbols psia and psig are often used in technical literature to designate absolute and gage pressures, respectively. However, since the matter of units is emphasized in this book, the symbols $lbf/in.^2$ and $lbf/in.^2$ gage are used.

2.8 Equality of Temperature

Although temperature is a property with which we are all familiar, an exact definition of it is difficult. We are aware of "temperature" first of all as a sense of hotness or coldness when we touch an object. We also learn early in our experience that when a hot body and a cold body are brought into contact, the hot body becomes cooler and the cold body becomes warmer. If these bodies remain in contact for some time, they usually appear to have the same hotness or coldness. However, we also realize that our sense of hotness or coldness is very unreliable. Sometimes very cold bodies may seem hot, and bodies of different materials that are at the same temperature appear to be at different temperatures.

Because of these difficulties in defining temperature, we define equality of temperature. Consider two blocks of copper, one hot and the other cold, each of which is in contact with a mercury-in-glass thermometer. If these two blocks of copper are brought into thermal communication, we then observe that the electrical resistance of the hot block decreases with time and for the cold block it increases with time. After a period of time has elapsed, however, no further changes in resistance are observed. Similarly, when the blocks are first brought in thermal communication, the length of a side of the hot block decreases with time, whereas for the cold block it increases with time. After a period of time, no further change in length of either of the blocks is perceived. Also, the mercury column of the thermometer in the hot block drops at first and in the cold block it rises, but after a period of time no further changes in height are observed. We may say, therefore, that two bodies have equality of temperature when no change in any observable property occurs when they are in thermal communication.

2.9 The Zeroth Law of Thermodynamics

Now consider the same two blocks of copper, and also another thermometer. Let one block of copper be brought into contact with the thermometer until equality of temperature is established, and then removed. Then let the second block of copper be brought into contact with the thermometer, and suppose that no change in the mercury level of the thermometer occurs during this operation with the second block. Then we can say that both blocks are in thermal equilibrium with the given thermometer.

The zeroth law of thermodynamics states that when two bodies have equality of temperature with a third body, they in turn have equality of temperature with each other. This seems very obvious to us because we are so familiar with this experiment. However, since this fact is not derivable from other laws, and since in the logical presentation of thermodynamics it precedes the first and second laws of thermodynamics, it has been called the zeroth law of thermodynamics. This law is really the basis of temperature measurement, for numbers can be placed on the mercury thermometer, and every time a body has equality of temperature with the thermometer, we can say that the body has the temperature we read on the thermometer. The problem remains, however, of relating temperatures that we might read on different mercury thermometers, or that we obtain when using different temperature-measuring devices, such as thermocouples and resistance thermometers. This suggests the need for a standard scale for temperature measurements.

2.10 Temperature Scales

There are two commonly used scales for measuring temperature, namely the Fahrenheit (after Gabriel Fahrenheit, 1686–1736) and Celsius scales. The Celsius scale was formerly called the Centigrade scale, but is now designated the Celsius scale, after Anders Celsius (1701–1744) the Swedish astronomer who devised this scale.

Until 1954 each of these scales was based on two fixed, easily duplicated points, the ice point and the steam point. The temperature of the ice point is defined as the temperature of a mixture of ice and water which is in equilibrium with saturated air at a pressure of 1 atm. The temperature of the steam point is the temperature of water and steam which are in equilibrium at a pressure of 1 atm. On the Fahrenheit scale these two points are assigned the numbers 32 and 212, respectively, and on the Celsius scale the respective points are numbered 0 and 100. The basis for numbers on the Fahrenheit scale has an interesting background. In searching for an easily reproducible point, Fahrenheit selected the temperature of the human body and assigned it the number 96. He assigned the number 0 to the temperature of a certain mixture of salt, ice, and salt solution. On this scale the ice point was approximately 32. When this scale was slightly revised and fixed in terms of the ice point and steam point, the normal temperature of the human body was found to be 98.6 F.

In this text the letters F and C will denote the Fahrenheit and Celsius scales, respectively. The usual symbol (°) for degree will not be used, but will rather be implied with the symbol F or C. The symbol T will refer to temperature on all temperature scales.

At the Tenth Conference on Weights and Measures in 1954, the Celsius scale was redefined in terms of a single fixed point and the ideal-gas temperature scale. The single fixed point is the triple point of water (the state in which the solid, liquid, and vapor phases of water exist together in equilibrium). The magnitude of the degree is defined in terms of the ideal-gas temperature scale, which is discussed in Chapter 6. The essential features of this new scale are a single fixed point and a definition of the magnitude of the degree. The triple point of water is assigned the value 0.01 C. On this scale the steam point is experimentally found to be 100.00 C. Thus, there is essential agreement between the old and new temperature scales.

It should be noted that we have not yet considered an absolute scale of temperature. The possibility of such a scale arises from the second law of thermodynamics and is discussed in Chapter 6. On the basis of the second law of thermodynamics a temperature scale which is independent of any thermometric substance can be defined. This absolute scale is usually referred to as the thermodynamic scale of temperature. However, it is very complicated to use this scale directly, and therefore a more practical scale, the International Temperature Scale, which closely represents the thermodynamic scale, has been adopted.

The absolute scale related to the Celsius scale is referred to as the Kelvin scale (after William Thomson, 1824–1907, who is also known as Lord Kelvin), and is designated K. The relation between these scales is

$$^\circ K = {}^\circ C + 273.15$$

The absolute scale related to the Fahrenheit scale is referred to as the Rankine scale and is designated R. The relation between these scales is

$$^\circ R = {}^\circ F + 459.67$$

2.11   The International Temperature Scale

In 1948 the Ninth General Conference of Weights and Measures adopted the International Temperature Scale, which is described below. This scale is very similar to an earlier one adopted in 1927. It is based on a number of fixed and easily reproducible points that are assigned definite numerical values of temperature, and on specified formulas which relate temperature to the readings on certain temperature-measuring instruments. This scale was so defined that it conforms closely to the thermodynamic temperature scale. The entire scale is given here for the sake of completeness, even though the student will have limited need for it at this point.

The fixed points, for each of which the pressure is 1 atm, are as follows;

$^\circ$C

1. Temperature of equilibrium between liquid and vapor oxygen (oxygen point) -182.970

2. Temperature of equilibrium between ice and air-saturated water (ice point) 0.000

3. Temperature of equilibrium between liquid water and its vapor (steam point)   100.000

4. Temperature of equilibrium between liquid sulfur and its vapor (sulfur point)   444.600

5. Temperature of equilibrium between solid silver and liquid silver (silver point)   960.800

6. Temperature of equilibrium between solid gold and liquid gold (gold point)   1063.000

The means available for interpolation lead to a division of the scale into four parts:

1. From the ice point to the freezing point of antimony the temperature is determined from measurements on a platinum resistance thermometer using the formula

$$R_t = R_0(1 + AT + BT^2)$$

R_0 is the resistance at the ice point, and the constants A and B are determined by calibration at the steam and sulfur points. The purity and physical condition of the platinum must be such that R_t/R_0 at 100 C is greater than 1.3910.

2. From the oxygen point to the ice point the temperature is determined from measurements on a platinum resistance thermometer by means of the formula

$$R_t = R_0[1 + AT + BT^2 + C(T - 100)T^3]$$

The constants are determined in the same manner as in 1, and the constant C is determined by calibration at the oxygen point.

3. From the freezing point of antimony to the gold point the temperature is determined from measurements on a platinum vs. platinum-rhodium thermocouple using the relation

$$E = a + bT + cT^2$$

The constants a, b, and c are determined by calibration at the freezing point of antimony, and at the silver and gold points.

4. Above the gold point the temperature is determined by measuring the intensity of radiation, J, and comparing this to the intensity of radiation of the same wave length at the gold point. The formula to determine the temperature is

$$\frac{J_t}{J_{Au}} = \frac{\exp[c_2/\lambda(T_{Au} + T_0)] - 1}{\exp[c_2/\lambda(T + T_0)] - 1}$$

The radiation must be in the visible spectrum, and must be emitted by a black body. The constant c_2 equals 1.4388 cm-K, T_0 is the temperature of the ice point in degrees Kelvin (273.15), and λ is the wave length in centimeters.

PROBLEMS

2.1 A 1-kg mass is accelerated with a force of 10 lbf. Calculate the acceleration in ft/sec² and cm/sec².

2.2 With what force is a mass of 10 slugs attracted to the earth at a point where the gravitational acceleration is 30.6 ft/sec²? What is its weight in lbf? What is its mass in lbm?

2.3 A piston has an area of 1 ft². What mass must the piston have if it exerts a pressure of 10 lbf/in.² above atmospheric pressure on the gas enclosed in the cylinder? Assume standard gravitational acceleration.

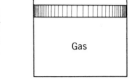

Fig. 2.6   Sketch for Problem 2.3.

2.4 A pound mass is "weighed" with a beam balance at a point where $g = 31.0$ ft/sec². What reading would be expected? If it is weighed with a spring scale that reads correctly for standard gravity, what reading would be obtained?

2.5 Verify the fact that 1 lbf = 4.448 × 10⁵ dynes.

2.6 A pressure gage reads 30.7 lbf/in.², and the barometer reads 29.7 in. Hg. Calculate the absolute pressure in lbf/in.² and atm.

2.7 A manometer contains a fluid with a density of 56.0 lbm/ft³. The difference in level of the two columns is 15 in. What pressure difference is indicated in lbf/in.²?

2.8 A mercury manometer which is used to measure a vacuum reads 29.3 in., and the barometer reads 29.7 in. Hg. Determine the pressure in lbf/in.² and in microns.

2.9 A body of fixed mass is "weighed" at an elevation of 20,000 ft ($g = 32.11$ ft/sec²) by a spring balance which was calibrated at sea level. The reading on the spring balance is 9.3 pounds. What is the mass of the body?

2.10 In an experimental bomber flying at 40,000 ft ($g = 32.05$ ft/sec²), the air flow in a piece of apparatus is measured by using a mercury manometer. The difference in the level is 30 in. At sea level and the same temperature, mercury has a density of 13.60 gm/cm³. Determine the pressure drop across the orifice in lbf/in.²

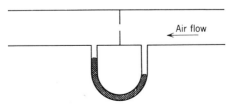

Fig. 2.7   Sketch for Problem 2.10.

2.11 A cylinder containing a gas is fitted with a piston having a mass of 150 lbm. The cross-sectional area of the piston is 60 in.^{2} The atmospheric pressure is 14.2 lbf/in.^{2}, and the acceleration due to gravity at this location is 30.9 ft/sec^2. What is the absolute pressure of the gas?

2.12 A mercury column is used to measure the pressure difference of 30 lbf/in.^{2} in a piece of apparatus which is located out of doors. The minimum temperature in the winter is 0 F and the maximum temperature in the summer is 100 F. What will be the difference in the height of the mercury column in the summer as compared to the winter when measuring this pressure difference of 30 lbf/in.^{2}? Assume standard gravitational acceleration. The following data are given for the density of mercury:

T °C	Density
−10	13.6198 gm/cm^3
0	13.5951
10	13.5704
20	13.5458
30	13.5213

2.13 In space simulation chambers very low pressures are achieved by cryopumping. This involves maintaining certain surfaces at very low temperatures (as low as 5 K). Essentially all of the gas present (except helium) will freeze on these surfaces. Pressures of 1×10^{-8} torr and lower are achieved in space chambers by this technique. What is this pressure of 10^{-8} torr in atmospheres, lbf/in.^{2}, and dynes/cm^2?

2.14 Figure 3.6 shows various phases of ice at pressures as high as 30,000 atm. What is this pressure of 30,000 atm in lbf/in.^{2}, lbf/ft^2, and dynes/cm^2?

2.15 The level of the water in an enclosed water tank is 100 feet above the ground. The pressure in the air space above the water is 16 lbf/in^2. The average density of the water is 62.4 lbm/ft^3. What is the pressure of the water at the ground level?

3 *Properties of a Pure Substance*

In the previous chapter we considered three familiar properties of a substance, namely, specific volume, pressure, and temperature. We now turn our attention to pure substances and consider some of the phases in which a pure substance may exist, the number of independent properties a pure substance may have, and methods of presenting thermodynamic properties.

3.1 The Pure Substance

A pure substance is one that has a homogeneous and invariable chemical composition. It may exist in more than one phase, but the chemical composition is the same in all phases. Thus, liquid water, a mixture of liquid water and water vapor (steam), or a mixture of ice and liquid water are all pure substances, for every phase has the same chemical composition. On the other hand, a mixture of liquid air and gaseous air is not a pure substance, since the composition of the liquid phase is different from that of the vapor phase.

Sometimes a mixture of gases, such as air, is considered a pure substance as long as there is no change of phase. Strictly speaking, this is not true, but rather, as we shall see later, we should say that a mixture of gases such as air exhibits some of the characteristics of a pure substance as long as there is no change of phase.

In this text the emphasis will be on those substances which may be called simple compressible substances. By this we understand that surface effects, magnetic effects, and electrical effects are not significant when dealing with these substances. On the other hand changes in volume, such as those associated with the expansion of a gas in a cylinder, are most important. However, reference will be made to other substances in which surface, magnetic, or electrical effects are important. We will refer to a system consisting of a simple compressible substance as a simple compressible system.

3.2 Vapor-Liquid-Solid Phase Equilibrium in a Pure Substance

Consider as a system 1 lbm of water contained in the piston-cylinder arrangement of Fig. 3.1a. Suppose that the piston and weight maintain a pressure of 14.7 lbf/in.^{2} in the cylinder, and that the initial temperature is 60 F. As heat is transferred to the water the temperature increases appreciably, the specific volume increases slightly, and the pressure remains constant. When the temperature reaches 212 F, additional heat transfer results in a change of phase, as indicated in Fig. 3.1b. That is, some of the liquid becomes vapor, and during this process both the temperature and pressure remain constant, but the specific volume increases considerably. When the last drop of liquid has vaporized, further transfer of heat results in an increase in both temperature and specific volume of the vapor, Fig. 3.1c.

The term saturation temperature designates the temperature at which vaporization takes place at a given pressure, and this pressure is called the saturation pressure for the given temperature. Thus for water at 212 F the saturation pressure is 14.7 lbf/in.^{2}, and for water at 14.7 lbf/in.^{2} the saturation temperature is 212 F. For a pure substance there is a definite relation between saturation pressure and saturation temperature, a typical curve being shown in Fig. 3.2. This is called the vapor-pressure curve.

If a substance exists as liquid at the saturation temperature and pressure, it is called saturated liquid. If the temperature of the liquid is lower than the saturation temperature for the existing pressure, it is called either a subcooled liquid (implying that the temperature is lower than the saturation temperature for the given pressure) or a compressed liquid (implying that the pressure is greater than the saturation pressure for the given temperature). Either term may be used, but the latter term will be used in this text.

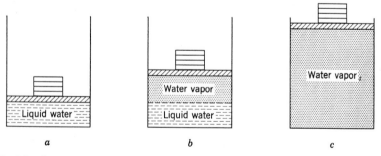

Fig. 3.1   Constant-pressure change from liquid to vapor phase for a pure substance.

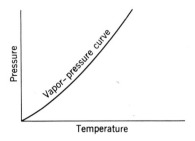

Fig. 3.2   Vapor-pressure curve of a pure substance.

When a substance exists as part liquid and part vapor at the saturation temperature, its quality is defined as the ratio of the mass of vapor to the total mass. Thus, in Fig. 3.1b, if the mass of the vapor is 0.2 lbm and the mass of the liquid is 0.8 lbm, the quality is 0.2 or 20 per cent. The quality may be considered as an intensive property, and it has the symbol x. Quality has meaning only when the substance is in a saturated state, i.e., at saturation pressure and temperature.

If a substance exists as vapor at the saturation temperature, it is called saturated vapor. (Sometimes the term dry saturated vapor is used to emphasize that the quality is 100 per cent.) When the vapor is at a temperature greater than the saturation temperature, it is said to exist as superheated vapor. The pressure and temperature of superheated vapor are independent properties, since the temperature may increase while the pressure remains constant. Actually, the substances we call gases are highly superheated vapors.

Consider Fig. 3.1 again, and let us plot on the temperature-volume diagram of Fig. 3.3 the constant-pressure line that represents the states through which the water passes as it is heated from the initial state of 14.7 lbf/in.² and 60 F. Let state A represent the initial state, B the saturated-liquid state (212 F), and line AB the process in which the liquid is heated from the initial temperature to the saturation temperature. Point C is the saturated vapor state, and line BC is the constant-temperature process in which the change of phase from liquid to vapor occurs. Line CD represents the process in which the steam is superheated at constant pressure. Temperature and volume both increase during this process.

Now let the process take place at a constant pressure of 100 lbf/in.², beginning from an initial temperature of 60 F. Point E represents the initial state, the specific volume being slightly less than at 14.7 lbf/in.² and 60 F. Vaporization now begins at point F, where the temperature is 327.8 F. Point G is the saturated-vapor state, and line GH the constant-pressure process in which the steam is superheated.

In a similar manner, a constant pressure of 1000 lbf/in.^{2} is represented by line *IJKL*, the saturation temperature being 544.6 F.

At a pressure of 3206.2 lbf/in.^{2}, represented by line *MNO*, we find, however, that there is no constant-temperature vaporization process. Rather, point *N* is a point of inflection with a zero slope. This point is called the critical point, and at the critical point the saturated-liquid and saturated-vapor states are identical. The temperature, pressure, and specific volume at the critical point are called the critical temperature, critical pressure, and critical volume. The critical-point data for some substances are given in Table 3.1, and more extensive data are given in Table A.7 in the Appendix.

TABLE 3.1

Some Critical Point Data

	Critical Temperature °F	Critical Pressure lbf/in.^{2}	Critical Volume ft^3/lbm
Water	705	3206.2	0.0503
Carbon Dioxide	88	1071	0.0348
Oxygen	−203	735	0.0364
Hydrogen	−400	188	0.534

A constant-pressure process at a pressure greater than the critical pressure is represented by line *PQ*. If water at 5500 lbf/in.^{2}, 60 F is heated in a constant-pressure process in a cylinder such as shown in Fig. 3.1, there will never be two phases present, and the state shown in Fig. 3.1*b* will never exist. Rather, there will be a continuous change in density and at all times there will be only one phase present. The question then arises as to when do we have a liquid and when do we have a vapor? The answer is that this is not a valid question at supercritical pressures. Instead, we simply term the substance a fluid. However, rather arbitrarily at temperatures below the critical temperature we usually refer to it as a compressed liquid and at temperatures above the critical temperature as a superheated vapor. It should be emphasized, however, that at pressures above the critical pressure we never have a liquid and vapor phase of a pure substance existing in equilibrium.

In Fig. 3.3 line *NJFB* represents the saturated-liquid line and line *NKGC* represents the saturated-vapor line.

Let us consider another experiment with the piston-cylinder arrangement. Suppose that the cylinder contains 1 lbm of ice at 0 F, 14.7 lbf/in.^{2} When heat is transferred to the ice, the pressure remains constant, the

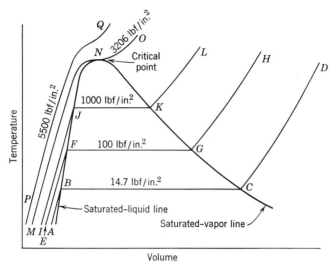

Fig. 3.3 Temperature-volume diagram for water showing liquid and vapor phases. (Not to scale.)

specific volume increases slightly, and the temperature increases until it reaches 32 F, at which point the ice melts while the temperature remains constant. In this state the ice is called saturated solid. For most substances the specific volume increases during this melting process, but for water the specific volume of the liquid is less than the specific volume of the solid. When all of the ice has melted, a further heat transfer causes an increase in temperature of the liquid.

If the initial pressure of the ice at 0 F is 0.0505 lbf/in.², heat transfer to the ice first results in an increase in temperature to 20 F. At this point, however, the ice would pass directly from the solid phase to the vapor phase in the process known as sublimation. Further heat transfer would result in superheating of the vapor.

Finally consider an initial pressure of the ice of 0.08854 lbf/in.² and a temperature of 0 F. As a result of heat transfer let the temperature increase until it reaches 32.02 F (0.01 C). At this point, however, further heat transfer may result in some of the ice becoming vapor and some becoming liquid, for at this point it is possible to have the three phases in equilibrium. This is called the triple point, which is defined as the state in which three phases may all be present in equilibrium. The pressure and temperature at the triple point for a number of substances is given in Table 3.2.

This whole matter is best summarized by the diagram of Fig. 3.4, which shows how the solid, liquid, and vapor phases may exist together in

TABLE 3.2

Some Solid-Liquid-Vapor Triple Point Data

	Temperature °F	Pressure atm
Hydrogen (normal)	−435	0.071
Nitrogen	−346	0.1237
Oxygen	−362	0.00150
Mercury	−38	0.0000000013
Water	32	0.00602
Zinc	786	0.05
Silver	1760	0.0001
Copper	1981	0.00000078

equilibrium. Along the sublimation line the solid and vapor phases are in equilibrium, along the fusion line the solid and liquid phases are in equilibrium, and along the vaporization line the liquid and vapor phases are in equilibrium. The only point at which all three phases may exist in equilibrium is the triple point. The vaporization line ends at the critical point because there is no distinct change from the liquid phase to the vapor phase above the critical point.

Thus, when the temperature increases at constant pressure, the pressure being below the triple-point pressure (such as represented by line AB), the substance passes directly from the solid to the vapor phase. Along the

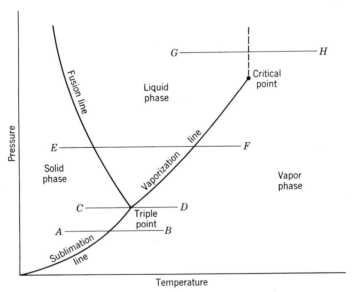

Fig. 3.4   Pressure-temperature diagram for a substance such as water.

constant-pressure line *EF*, the substance first passes from the solid to the liquid phase at one temperature, and then from the liquid to the vapor phase at a higher temperature. Constant-pressure line *CD* passes through the triple point, and it is only at the triple point that the three phases may exist together in equilibrium. At a pressure above the critical pressure, such as *GH*, there is no sharp distinction between the liquid and vapor phases.

Although we have made these comments with rather specific reference to water (only because of our familiarity with water) all pure substances exhibit the same general behavior. However, the triple point temperature and critical temperature vary greatly from one substance to another. For example, the critical temperature of helium, as given in Table A.7, is 9.5 R. Therefore, the absolute temperature of helium at ambient conditions is over 50 times greater than the critical temperature. On the other hand, water has a critical temperature of 705.4 F (1165 R) and at ambient conditions the temperature of water is less than half the critical temperature. Most metals have a much higher critical temperature than water. In considering the behavior of a substance in a given state, it is often helpful to think of this state in relation to the critical state or triple point. For example, if the pressure is greater than the critical pressure, it is impossible to have a liquid and a vapor phase in equilibrium. Or, to consider another example, the states at which vacuum melting a given metal is possible can

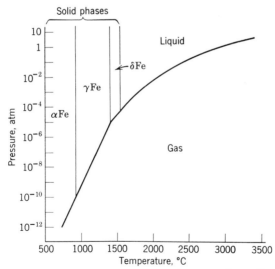

Fig. 3.5 Estimated pressure-temperature diagram for iron. From *Phase Diagrams in Metallurgy*, by F. N. Rhines, copyright 1956, McGraw-Hill Book Company. Used by permission.

be ascertained by a consideration of the properties at the triple point. In the case of iron at a pressure just above 0.0005 atm (the triple point pressure), iron would melt at a temperature of about 1535 C (the triple point temperature).

It should also be pointed out that a pure substance can exist in a number of different solid phases. A transition from one solid phase to another is called an allotropic transformation. Figure 3.5 is a pressure-temperature diagram for iron that shows three solid phases, the liquid phase, and the vapor phase. Figure 3.6 shows a number of solid phases for water. It is evident that a pure substance can have a number of triple points, but only

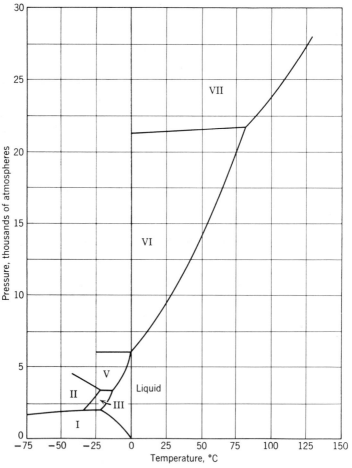

Fig. 3.6   Phase diagram of water. Adapted from the *American Institute of Physics Handbook*, 2nd Ed., 1963, McGraw-Hill.

one triple point involves solid, liquid, and vapor equilibrium. Other triple points for a pure substance can involve two solid phases and a liquid phase, two solid phases and a vapor phase, or three solid phases.

3.3 Independent Properties of a Pure Substance

One important reason for introducing the concept of a pure substance is that the state of a simple compressible pure substance (i.e., a pure substance in the absence of motion, gravity, and surface, magnetic or electrical effects) is defined by two independent properties. This means, for example, that if the specific volume and temperature of superheated steam are specified, the state of the steam is determined.

To understand the significance of the term independent property, consider the saturated-liquid and saturated-vapor states of a pure substance. These two states have the same pressure and same temperature, but are definitely not the same state. In a saturation state, therefore, pressure and temperature are not independent properties. Two independent properties such as pressure and specific volume, or pressure and quality, are required to specify a saturation state of a pure substance.

The reason for mentioning previously that a mixture of gases, such as air, has the same characteristics as a pure substance as long as only one phase is present, concerns precisely this point. The state of air, which is a mixture of gases of definite composition, is determined by specifying two properties as long as it remains in the gaseous phase, and in this regard air can be treated as a pure substance.

3.4 Equations of State for the Vapor Phase of a Simple Compressible Substance

We consider for the moment only the vapor phase, which includes everything we call gas as well as vapor, of a simple compressible substance. In this case the relation between pressure, specific volume, and temperature of the vapor phase may be expressed by an equation that is called an equation of state. This is, of course, based on the fact that a simple compressible pure substance has only two independent properties. The equation of state is usually explicit in either P or v. That is

$$P = f(v, T)$$
or
$$v = f(P, T)$$

There are several different forms of the equation of state. The simplest is that for an ideal gas.

$$P\bar{v} = \bar{R}T \tag{3.1}$$

where $\bar{R}$ is the universal gas constant. The value for $\bar{R}$ depends on the units chosen for P, $\bar{v}$, and T. For the most frequently used units in this text the value of $\bar{R}$ is as follows:

$$\bar{R} = 1545 \text{ ft-lbf/lb mole R}$$
$$\bar{R} = 1.986 \text{ Btu/lb mole R}$$
$$\bar{R} = 1.986 \text{ cal/gm mole K}$$
$$\bar{R} = 0.08206 \text{ atm-liters/gm mole K}$$

Dividing Eq. 3.1 by M, the molecular weight, we have the equation of state on a unit mass basis.

$$\frac{P\bar{v}}{M} = \frac{\bar{R}T}{M}$$

or

$$Pv = RT \tag{3.2}$$

where

$$R = \frac{\bar{R}}{M} \tag{3.3}$$

R is a constant for a particular gas. The value of R for a number of substances is given in Table A.8 of the Appendix.

It also follows from Eqs. 3.1 and 3.2 that the equation of state for an ideal gas can be written in terms of the total volume.

$$PV = n\bar{R}T \tag{3.4}$$

$$PV = mRT \tag{3.5}$$

We also note that for an ideal gas the initial and final states are related by the equation.

$$\frac{P_1 V_1}{T_1} = \frac{P_2 V_2}{T_2} \tag{3.6}$$

Thus an ideal gas is a gas that follows Boyle's and Charles' laws.

Example 3.1

What is the mass of air contained in a room 20 ft $\times$ 30 ft $\times$ 12 ft if the pressure is 14.7 lbf/in.^{2}, and the temperature is 80 F? Assume air to be an ideal gas.

By using Eq. 3.5, and the value of R from Table A.8,

$$m = \frac{PV}{RT} = \frac{14.7 \times 144 \text{ lbf/ft}^2 \times 7200 \text{ ft}^3}{53.34 \text{ ft-lbf/lbm R} \times 540 \text{ R}} = 529 \text{ lbm}$$

Example 3.2

A tank has a volume of 15 ft^3 and contains 20 lbm of an ideal gas having a molecular weight of 24. The temperature is 80 F. What is the pressure?

The gas constant is first determined:

$$R = \frac{\bar{R}}{M} = \frac{1545 \text{ ft-lbf/lb mole R}}{24 \text{ lbm/lb mole}} = 64.4 \text{ ft-lbf/lbm R}$$

We now solve for P.

$$P = \frac{mRT}{V} = \frac{20 \text{ lbm} \times 64.4 \text{ ft-lbf/lbm R} \times 540 \text{ R}}{144 \text{ in.}^2/\text{ft}^2 \times 15 \text{ ft}^3} = 321 \text{ lbf/in.}^2$$

At relevant points in subsequent chapters other properties of ideal gases will be introduced. In addition the matter of ideal gases will be considered further in Chapter 10. It should be noted here, however, that the equation of state for an ideal gas holds exactly for a real gas only as the pressure approaches zero. It also holds with a fair degree of accuracy for highly superheated vapor (air at room temperature is a highly superheated vapor) at somewhat higher pressures. In the region of the critical point the deviation from ideal gas behavior is very great.

In order to have an equation of state that is fairly accurate throughout the entire superheated vapor region, more complicated expressions have been developed. One of the best known such equations is the Beattie-Bridgeman equation of state. This equation is

$$P = \frac{\bar{R}T(1 - \epsilon)}{\bar{v}^2}(\bar{v} + B) - \frac{A}{\bar{v}^2} \tag{3.7}$$

where $A = A_0(1 - a/\bar{v})$, $B = B_0(1 - b/\bar{v})$, $\epsilon = c/\bar{v}T^3$, and A_0, a, B_0, b, and c are constants for different gases. The values of these constants for various substances are given in Table 3.3.

TABLE 3.3

Constants of the Beattie-Bridgeman Equation of State

Pressure in Atmospheres; specific volume in liters per gram mole; temperature in degrees Kelvin:
$\bar{R} = 0.08206$ atm-liters/gm mole K

Gas	A_0	a	B_0	b	$10^{-4} c$
Helium	0.0216	0.05984	0.01400	0.0	0.0040
Argon	1.2907	0.02328	0.03931	0.0	5.99
Hydrogen	0.1975	−0.00506	0.02096	−0.04359	0.0504
Nitrogen	1.3445	0.02617	0.05046	−0.00691	4.20
Oxygen	1.4911	0.02562	0.04624	0.004208	4.80
Air	1.3012	0.01931	0.04611	−0.001101	4.34
Carbon Dioxide	5.0065	0.07132	0.10476	0.07235	66.00

The matter of equations of state will be discussed further in Chapter 10. The observation to be made here in particular is that an equation of state that accurately describes the relation between pressure, temperature, and specific volume is rather cumbersome and the solution requires considerable time. Therefore, it is much more convenient to tabulate values of pressure, temperature, specific volume, and other thermodynamic properties for various substances. The Appendix includes summary tables of the thermodynamic properties of water, ammonia, Freon-12, nitrogen, oxygen, and mercury. The tables of the properties of water are usually referred to as the "steam tables" and are extracted from *Thermodynamic Properties of Steam* by Keenan and Keyes. The method for compiling the *P-v-T* data for such a table is to find an equation of state that accurately fits the experimental data, and then to solve the equation of state for the values listed in the table.

3.5 Tables of Thermodynamic Properties

Tables of thermodynamic properties of many substances are available, and in general all these have the same form. In this section we will refer to the steam tables, primarily in order to present the nature of thermodynamic tables. Once the steam tables are understood, other thermodynamic tables can readily be used.

Tables 1 and 2 of Keenan and Keyes' steam tables, which are summarized in Tables A.1.1 and A.1.2 of the Appendix, give the properties of saturated liquid and saturated vapor. In Table A.1.1 these properties are given as a function of saturation temperature, and Table A.1.2 lists the properties as a function of saturation pressure. Since the information contained in these two tables is the same, it is simply a matter of convenience as to which table one uses.

Considering Table A.1.1 the first column after the temperature gives the corresponding saturation pressure in pounds force per square inch. The next columns give specific volume in cubic feet per pound mass. The first of these gives the specific volume of the saturated liquid, v_f; the second column gives the increase in specific volume when the state changes from saturated liquid to saturated vapor, v_{fg}; the third column gives the specific volume of saturated vapor, v_g. It follows that

$$v_f + v_{fg} = v_g$$

The specific volume of a substance having a given quality can be found by introducing the definition of quality. Quality has already been defined as the ratio of the mass of vapor to total mass of liquid plus vapor when a substance is in a saturation state. Let us consider a mass of 1 lbm having a quality x. The specific volume is the sum of the volume of the liquid and the volume of the vapor. The volume of the liquid is $(1 - x)v_f$, and the volume of the vapor is xv_g. Therefore the specific volume v is

$$v = xv_g + (1 - x)v_f \tag{3.8}$$

Since $v_f + v_{fg} = v_g$, Eq. 3.8 can also be written in the following forms

$$v = v_f + xv_{fg} \tag{3.9}$$

$$v = v_g - (1 - x)v_{fg} \tag{3.10}$$

As an example, let us calculate the specific volume of saturated steam at 500 F having a quality of 70 per cent. Using Eq. 3.9

$$v = 0.0204 + 0.7(0.6545) = 0.4785 \text{ ft}^3/\text{lbm}$$

Using Eq. 3.10

$$v = 0.6749 - 0.3(0.6545) = 0.4785 \text{ ft}^3/\text{lbm}$$

When using a slide rule, Eq. 3.10 is more accurate for high quality and Eq. 3.9 is more accurate for low quality.

In Table A.1.2, the first column after the pressure lists the saturation temperature for each pressure. The next columns list specific volume in a manner similar to Table A.1.1, except that v_{fg} is not listed. When necessary, v_{fg} can readily be found by subtracting v_f from v_g.

Table 3 of Keenan and Keyes' steam tables, which is summarized in Table A.1.3 in the Appendix, gives the properties of superheated vapor. In the superheat region, pressure and temperature are independent properties, and therefore, for each pressure a large number of temperatures is given, and for each temperature three thermodynamic properties are listed, the first one being specific volume. Thus, the specific volume of steam at a pressure of 100 lbf/in.^{2} and 500 F is 5.589 ft^3/lbm.

Table 4 of Keenan and Keyes' steam tables, summarized in Table A.1.4 in the Appendix, gives data that enables us to determine the specific volume of a compressed liquid. To demonstrate the use of this table, consider a piston and a cylinder (as shown in Fig. 3.7) that contains 1 lbm of saturated liquid at 200 F. Its properties are given in Table A.1.1, and we note that the pressure is 11.53 lbf/in.^{2}. Suppose the pressure is increased to 1000 lbf/in.^{2} while the temperature is held constant at 200 F by the necessary transfer of heat, Q. Since water is slightly compressible, we would expect a slight decrease in specific volume during this process. The difference in specific volume between a saturated liquid at a given temperature and a compressed liquid at the same temperature is given in Table A.1.4 of the steam tables. Thus, for the example cited above, at 1000 lbf/in.^{2} and 200 F.

$$(v - v_f)10^5 = -5.4 \text{ ft}^3/\text{lbm} \qquad \text{and} \qquad v_f = 0.016634 \text{ ft}^3/\text{lbm}$$

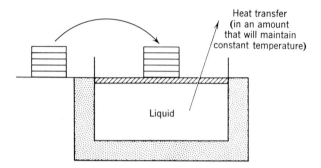

Fig. 3.7   Illustration of compressed liquid state.

Therefore
$$v = 0.016634 - 0.000054 = 0.016580 \text{ ft}^3/\text{lbm}$$

One observes that the magnitude of the correction in this case is about 0.3 per cent. For many engineering calculations the accuracy of the data is such that a correction of this order of magnitude is not justified. This is especially true for a liquid that is only slightly compressed, i.e., if the pressure is only 100 or 200 lbf/in.² higher than the saturation pressure. In such a case one can use the specific volume of saturated liquid at the same temperature with only a very small error. Thus, the specific volume of liquid at 100 lbf/in.², 200 F would be found by using the specific volume of saturated liquid at 200 F. Whether or not to use the correction from Table A.1.4 depends on the accuracy one is interested in.

Table 5 of Keenan and Keyes, which is summarized in Table A.1.5, gives the properties of saturated solid and saturated vapor that are in equilibrium. The first column gives the temperature, and the second column gives the corresponding saturation pressure. As would be expected, all these pressures are less than the triple-point pressure. The next two columns give the specific volume of the saturated solid and saturated vapor (note that the tabulated value is $v_g \times 10^{-3}$).

3.6   Thermodynamic Surfaces

The matter discussed in this chapter can be well summarized by a consideration of a pressure-specific volume-temperature surface. Two such surfaces are shown in Figs. 3.8 and 3.9. Figure 3.8 shows a substance such as water in which the specific volume increases during freezing, and Fig. 3.9 shows a substance in which the specific volume decreases during freezing.

In these diagrams the pressure, specific volume, and temperature are

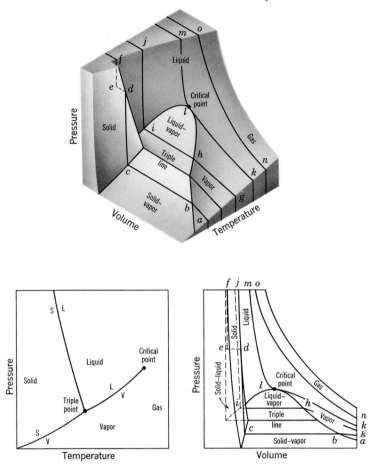

Fig. 3.8   Pressure-volume-temperature surface for a substance that expands on freezing.

plotted on mutually perpendicular coordinates, and each possible equilibrium state is thus represented by a point on the surface. This follows directly from the fact that a pure substance has only two independent intensive properties. All points along a quasiequilibrium process lie on the $P\text{-}v\text{-}T$ surface, since such a process always passes through equilibrium states.

The regions of the surface that represent a single phase, namely, the solid, liquid, and vapor phases, are indicated, these surfaces being curved. The two-phase regions, namely, the solid-liquid, solid-vapor, and liquid-vapor regions, are ruled surfaces. By this we understand that they are made up of straight lines parallel to the specific volume axis. This, of

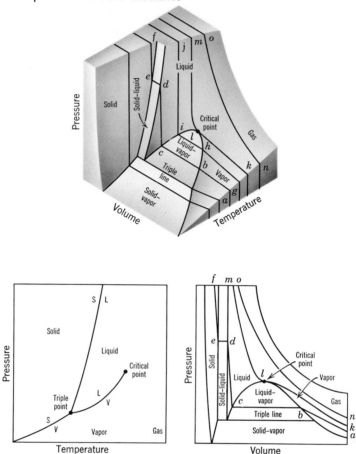

Fig. 3.9   Pressure-volume-temperature surface for a substance that contracts on freezing.

course, follows from the fact that in the two-phase region, lines of constant pressure are also lines of constant temperature, though the specific volume may change. The triple point actually appears as the triple line on the P-v-T surface, since the pressure and temperature of the triple point are fixed, but the specific volume may vary, depending on the proportion of each phase.

It is also of interest to note the pressure-temperature and pressure-volume projections of these surfaces. We have already considered the pressure-temperature diagram for a substance such as water. It is on this diagram that we observe the triple point. Various lines of constant temperature are shown on the pressure-volume diagram, and the corresponding constant-temperature sections are lettered identically on the

P-v-T surface. The critical isotherm has a point of inflection at the critical point. Various lines of constant temperature are shown on both the *P-v-T* surface and the *P-v* diagram, and the corresponding lines are lettered alike.

One notices that with a substance such as water, which expands on freezing, the freezing temperature decreases with an increase in pressure. With a substance that contracts on freezing, the freezing temperature increases as the pressure increases. Thus, as the pressure of vapor is increased along the constant-temperature line *abcdef* in Fig. 3.8, a substance that expands on freezing first becomes solid and then liquid. For the substance that contracts on freezing, the corresponding constant-temperature line, Fig. 3.9, indicates that as the pressure on the vapor is increased, it first becomes liquid and then solid.

Example 3.3

A vessel having a volume of 10 ft³ contains 3.0 lbm of a liquid water and water vapor mixture in equilibrium at a pressure of 100 lbf/in.². Calculate

(*a*) The volume and mass of liquid.

(*b*) The volume and mass of vapor.

The specific volume is calculated first:

$$v = \frac{10.0}{3.0} = 3.333 \text{ ft}^3/\text{lbm}$$

The quality can now be calculated, using Eq. 3.10

$$3.333 = 4.432 - (1 - x)4.414$$

$$(1 - x) = \frac{1.099}{4.414} = 0.249$$

$$x = 0.751$$

Therefore the mass of liquid is

$$3(0.249) = 0.747 \text{ lbm}$$

The mass of vapor is

$$3(0.751) = 2.253 \text{ lbm}$$

The volume of liquid is

$$V_{\text{liq}} = m_{\text{liq}}v_f = 0.747(0.01774) = 0.0133 \text{ ft}^3$$

The volume of the vapor is

$$V_{\text{vap}} = m_{\text{vap}}v_g = 2.253(4.432) = 9.99 \text{ ft}^3$$

Example 3.4

A pressure vessel contains saturated ammonia vapor at 60 F. Heat is transferred to the ammonia until the temperature reaches 200 F. What is the final pressure?

Since the volume does not change during this process, the specific volume also remains constant.

$$v_1 = v_2 = 2.751 \text{ ft}^3/\text{lbm}$$

We know one other property in the final state, namely the temperature, $T_2 = 200$ F, and therefore the final state is determined.

From the superheat tables, by interpolation

$$P_2 = 142.4 \text{ lbf/in.}^2$$

PROBLEMS

3.1 A spherical balloon has a radius of 20 ft. The atmospheric pressure is 14.7 lbf/in.² and the temperature is 60 F.

(a) Calculate the mass and the number of moles of air this balloon displaces.

(b) If the balloon is filled with helium at 14.7 lbf/in.², 60 F, what is the mass and the number of moles of helium?

3.2 The mass of a certain ideal gas in a given container is 0.13 lbm. The pressure is 0.5 atm, the temperature is 60 F, and the volume of the gas is 3 ft³. Determine the molecular weight of the gas.

3.3 Air is contained in a "stepped" cylinder which is fitted with a frictionless piston as shown in Fig. 3.10. The cross-sectional area of the larger section of

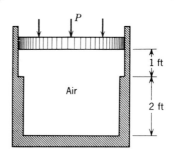

Fig. 3.10   Sketch for Problem 3.3.

the cylinder is 0.1 ft², while that of the smaller section is 0.075 ft.² With the piston at the position indicated, the air is at 50 lbf/in.², 800 F. The air is then cooled as the result of heat transfer to the surroundings.

(a) What is the temperature of the air when the piston reaches the step?

(b) If the air is further cooled until it reaches 70 F, what is the pressure of the air at this state?

3.4 A vacuum pump is used to pump a vacuum over a bath of liquid helium. The volume rate of flow into the vacuum pump is 3000 cubic feet per minute. The pressure at the vacuum pump inlet is 0.1 torr and the temperature is −10 F. What mass of helium enters the pump per minute?

3.5 Plot the following vapor-pressure curves (saturation pressure vs. saturation temperature):
(a) Water on Cartesian coordinates, −40 F to 60 F.
(b) Water on Cartesian coordinates, 0 to 3500 lbf/in.^{2}
(c) Water, Freon-12, and ammonia, on semilog paper (pressure on log scale), 1.0 to 1000 lbf/in.^{2}, −50 F to 300 F.

3.6 Calculate the following specific volumes:
(a) Ammonia, 50 F, 80% quality.
(b) Freon-12, 20 F, 15% quality.
(c) Water, 1000 lbf/in.^{2}, 98% quality.
(d) Nitrogen, −300 F, 40% quality.

3.7 Determine the quality (if saturated) or temperature (if superheated) of the following substances in the given states:
(a) Ammonia, 80 F, 1.43 ft^3/lbm; 80 lbf/in.^{2}, 4.75 ft^3/lbm.
(b) Freon-12, 50 lbf/in.^{2}, 0.6 ft^3/lbm; 50 lbf/in.^{2}, 0.960 ft^3/lbm.
(c) Water, 80 F, 20 ft^3/lbm; 1000 lbf/in.^{2}, 0.4 ft^3/lbm.
(d) Nitrogen, 100 lbf/in.^{2}, 0.9 ft^3/lbm; 1 atm., 3 ft^3/lbm.

3.8 Plot a pressure-specific volume diagram on log log paper (3 × 5 cycles) for water showing the following lines:
(a) Saturated liquid.
(b) Saturated vapor.
(c) The following constant-temperature lines (including the compressed-liquid region): 300 F, 500 F, 700 F, 800 F, 1000 F.
(d) The following lines of constant quality: 10%, 50%, 90%.

3.9 Plot a pressure-specific volume diagram on log log paper (2 × 3 cycles) for Freon-12, showing the following lines:
(a) Saturated liquid.
(b) Saturated vapor.
(c) The following constant-temperature lines: 0 F, 100 F, 230 F, 300 F.
(d) The following constant-quality lines: 10%, 50%, 90%.

3.10 The radiator of a heating system has a volume of 2 ft^3 and contains saturated vapor at 20 lbf/in.^{2} The valves are then closed on the radiator, and as a result of heat transfer to the room the pressure drops to 15 lbf/in.^{2} Calculate:
(a) The total mass of steam in the radiator.
(b) The volume and mass of liquid in the final state.
(c) The volume and mass of vapor in the final state.

3.11 Steam at the critical state is contained in a rigid vessel. Heat is transferred from the steam until the pressure is 300 lbf/in.^{2} Calculate the final quality.

3.12 The rigid vessel shown in Fig. 3.11 contains saturated water at 14.7 lbf/in.^{2} Determine the proportions by volume of liquid and vapor at 14.7 lbf/in.^{2} necessary to make the water pass through the critical state when heated.

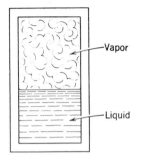

Fig. 3.11   Sketch for Problem 3.12.

3.13 Same as Problem 3.12, but let the contents initially be saturated Freon-12 at 60 F.

3.14 A vessel fitted with a sight glass contains Freon-12 at 80 F. Liquid is withdrawn from the bottom at a slow rate, and the temperature remains constant during the process. If the area of the vessel is 50 in.² and the level drops 6 in., determine the mass of Freon-12 withdrawn.

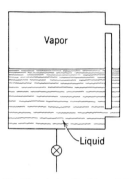

Fig. 3.12   Sketch for Problem 3.14.

3.15 There is a tendency for students to write down automatically that there are 62.4 lbm of liquid water per ft³. Using the steam tables determine the actual density of water in lbm/ft³ at the following states:
  (a) Saturated liquid at 60 F.
  (b) Liquid at 60 F, 100 lbf/in.²
  (c) Saturated liquid at 100 lbf/in.²
  (d) Saturated liquid at 500 F.

3.16 A boiler feed pump delivers 500,000 lbm of water per hr at 2000 lbf/in.², 560 F. What is the volume rate of flow in ft³/min? What would be the per cent error if the correction from Table A.1.4 of the steam tables were neglected?

3.17 Liquid nitrogen at a temperature of −240 F exists in a container, and both the liquid and vapor phases are present. The volume of the container is 3 ft³, and it is determined that the mass of nitrogen in the container is 44.5 lbm. What is the mass of liquid and the mass of vapor present in the container?

3.18 A refrigeration system is to be charged with Freon-12. The system, which has a volume of 0.85 ft³, is first evacuated, and then slowly charged with Freon-12. The temperature of the Freon-12 remains constant at the ambient temperature of 80 F.

(a) What will be the mass of Freon-12 in the system when the pressure reaches 35 lbf/in.²?

(b) What will be the mass of Freon-12 in the system when the system is filled with saturated vapor?

(c) What fraction of the Freon-12 will exist as a liquid when 3 lbm of Freon-12 have been placed in the system?

3.19 One lbm of H_2O exists at the triple point. The volume of the liquid phase is equal to the volume of the solid phase, and the volume of the vapor phase is equal to 10^4 times the volume of the liquid phase. What is the mass of H_2O in each phase?

3.20 Compare the specific volume of nitrogen at 1000 lbf/in.², −210 F as reported in the nitrogen tables with the value calculated from the Beattie-Bridgeman equation of state.

3.21 A closed pressure vessel contains saturated liquid water at 30 lbf/in.² The liquid is heated until the temperature is 300 F. During this process the volume of the pressure vessel increases 1%. What is the final pressure in the tank?

3.22 A tank contains Freon-12 at 100 F. The volume of the tank is 2 ft³, and initially the volume of the liquid in the tank is equal to the volume of the vapor. Additional Freon-12 is forced into the tank until the mass of Freon-12 in the tank reaches 100 lbm. What is the final volume of liquid in the tank, assuming that the temperature is maintained at 100 F? How much mass enters the tank?

3.23 A closed tank contains vapor and liquid H_2O in equilibrium at 400 F.

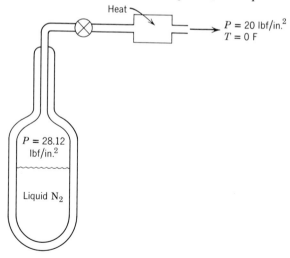

Fig. 3.13   Sketch for Problem 3.24.

The distance from the bottom of the tank to the liquid level is 10 ft. What is the pressure reading at the bottom of the tank as compared to the pressure reading at the top of the tank?

3.24 A container of liquid nitrogen at 28.12 lbf/in.^{2} pressure has a cross-sectional area of 40 in.^{2} As the result of heat transfer to the liquid nitrogen, some of the nitrogen evaporates and in one hour, the level drops one inch. The vapor that leaves the insulated container passes through a heater and leaves at 20 lbf/in.^{2}, 0 F. Calculate the volume rate of flow out of the heater in ft^3/hr, assuming ideal gas behavior, and compare this with the result obtained when using the nitrogen tables, Table A.5.

4 Work and Heat

In this chapter we shall consider work and heat. It is essential for the student of thermodynamics to understand clearly the definitions of both work and heat, because the correct analysis of many thermodynamic problems depends upon distinguishing between them.

4.1 Definition of Work

Work is usually defined as a force F acting through a displacement x, the displacement being in the direction of the force. That is,

$$W = \int_1^2 F \cdot dx \tag{4.1}$$

This is a very useful relationship because it enables us to find the work required to raise a weight, to stretch a wire, or to move a charged particle through a magnetic field.

However, in view of the fact that we are treating thermodynamics from a macroscopic point of view, it is advantageous to tie in our definition of work with our concepts of systems, properties, and processes. We therefore define work as follows: work is done by a system if the sole effect on the surroundings (everything external to the system) could be the raising of a weight. Notice that the raising of a weight is in effect a force acting through a distance. Notice, also, that our definition does not state that a weight was actually raised, or that a force actually acted through a given distance but that the sole effect external to the system could be the raising of a weight. Work done *by* a system is considered positive and work done *on* a system is considered negative. The symbol W designates the work done by a system.

In general, we will speak of work as a form of energy. No attempt will be made to give a rigorous definition of energy. Rather, since the concept is familiar, the term energy will be used as appropriate, and various forms

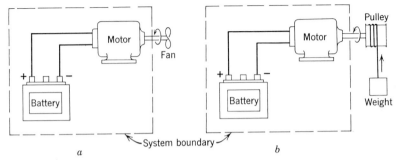

Fig. 4.1   Example of work done at the boundary of a system.

of energy will be identified. Work is the form of energy that fulfills the definition given above.

Let us illustrate this definition of work with a few examples. Consider as a system the battery and motor of Fig. 4.1*a* and let the motor drive a fan. Does work cross the boundary of the system? To answer this question using the definition of work given above, let the fan be replaced with a pulley and weight arrangement shown in Fig. 4.1*b*. As the motor turns, the weight is raised, and the sole effect external to the system is the raising of a weight. Thus, for our original system of Fig. 4.1*a*, we conclude that work is crossing the boundary of the system since the sole effect external to the system could be the raising of a weight.

Let the boundaries of the system be changed now to include only the battery shown in Fig. 4.2. Again we ask the question, does work cross the boundary of the system? In answering this question, we will be answering a more general question; namely, does the flow of electrical energy across the boundary of a system constitute work?

The only limiting factor in having the sole external effect the raising of a weight is the inefficiency of the motor. However, as we design a more efficient motor, with lower bearing and electrical losses, we recognize that

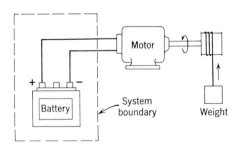

Fig. 4.2   Example of work crossing the boundary of a system because of a flow of an electric current across the system boundary.

we can approach a certain limit, which does meet the requirement of having the only external effect the raising of a weight. Therefore, we can conclude that when there is a flow of electricity across the boundary of a system, as in Fig. 4.2, it is work with which we are concerned.

4.2 Units for Work

As already noted, we consider work done *by* a system, such as that done by a gas expanding against a piston as positive, and work done *on* a system, such as that done by a piston compressing a gas, as negative. Thus, positive work means that energy leaves the system and negative work means that energy is added to the system.

Our definition of work involves the raising of a weight. The unit of work should therefore be defined in terms of raising a unit weight a given distance at a given location. Let us define our unit of work as the work required to raise a mass of 1 lbm a distance of 1 ft at a location where the acceleration due to gravity is the standard value, 32.174 ft/sec². This is exactly equivalent to saying that our unit of work is a force of 1 lbf acting through a distance of 1 ft. This unit for work is called the foot-pound force.

Similarly, in the metric system the unit of work is the erg. An erg is the work done by a force of 1 dyne acting through a distance of 1 cm. This is a very small unit, and for engineering use, a joule is the common unit of work in the metric system. One joule is 10^7 ergs.

Another unit for work that has come into common use as a result of developments in nuclear physics is the electron volt, abbreviated ev. An electron volt is the work required to move an electron through a potential difference of 1 volt. The relation between the electron volt and other units for work is:

$$1 \text{ ev} = 1.608 \times 10^{-12} \text{ erg} = 1.18 \times 10^{-19} \text{ ft-lbf}$$

One million electron volts, abbreviated mev, is also commonly used.

$$1 \text{ mev} = 1.608 \times 10^{-6} \text{ erg} = 1.18 \times 10^{-13} \text{ ft-lbf}$$

Power is the time rate of doing work, and is designated by the symbol $\dot{W}$.

$$\dot{W} \equiv \frac{\delta W}{dt}$$

One familiar unit of power is the horsepower (hp).

$$1 \text{ hp} = 33{,}000 \text{ ft-lbf/min.}$$

Another familiar unit is the kilowatt (kw). Actually the kilowatt is defined in terms of electrical units, but for our purposes we can define the kilowatt as follows:

$$1 \text{ kw} = 44{,}240 \text{ ft-lbf/min.}$$

It follows that

$$1 \text{ hp} = 0.746 \text{ kw}$$

It is often convenient to speak of the work per unit mass of the system. This quantity is designated w and is defined

$$w \equiv \frac{W}{m}$$

These definitions of power lead to two other units of work, the horse-power-hour (hp-hr) and kilowatt-hour (kw-hr). The horsepower-hour is the work done in 1 hr when the power is 1 hp. Similarly, one kilowatt-hour is the work done in 1 hr when the rate of work is 1 kw.

$$1 \text{ hp-hr} = 33{,}000 \times 60 = 1.98 \times 10^6 \text{ ft-lbf} = 2545 \text{ Btu}$$

$$1 \text{ kw-hr} = 44{,}240 \times 60 = 2.654 \times 10^6 \text{ ft-lbf} = 3412 \text{ Btu}$$

4.3 Work Done at the Moving Boundary of a Simple Compressible System in a Quasiequilibrium Process

We have already noted that there are a variety of ways in which work can be done on or by a system. These include work done by a rotating shaft, electrical work, and the work done by the movement of the system boundary, such as the work done in moving the piston in a cylinder. In this section we will consider in some detail the work done at the moving boundary of a simple com-pressible system during a quasiequilib-rium process.

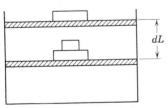

Fig. 4.3 Example of work done at the moving boundary of a system in a quasiequilibrium process.

Consider as a system the gas contained in a cylinder and piston, as in Fig. 4.3. Let one of the small weights be removed from the piston, causing the piston to move upward a distance dL. We can consider this a quasiequilibrium process and calculate the amount of work W done by the system during this process. The total force on the piston is PA, where P is the pressure of the gas and A is the area of the piston. Therefore, the work δW is

$$\delta W = PA \, dL$$

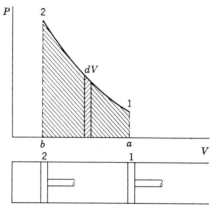

Fig. 4.4 Use of pressure-volume diagram to show work done at the moving boundary of a system in a quasiequilibrium process.

But $A\,dL = dV$, the change in volume of the gas. Therefore,

$$\delta W = P\,dV \qquad (4.2)$$

The work done at the moving boundary during a given quasiequilibrium process can be found by integrating Eq. 4.2. However, this integration can be performed only if we know the relationship between P and V during this process. This relationship might be expressed in the form of an equation, or it might be shown in the form of a graph.

Let us consider a graphical solution first, using as an example a compression process such as that which occurs during the compression of air in a cylinder, Fig. 4.4. At the beginning of the process the piston is at position 1, the pressure being relatively low. This state is represented on a pressure-volume diagram (usually referred to as a P-V diagram) as shown. At the conclusion of the process the piston is in position 2, and the corresponding state of the gas is shown at point 2 on the P-V diagram. Let us assume that this compression was a quasiequilibrium process, and that during the process the system passed through the states shown by the line connecting states 1 and 2 on the P-V diagram. The assumption of a quasiequilibrium process is essential here because each point on line 1-2 represents a definite state, and these states will correspond to the actual state of the system only if the deviation from equilibrium is infinitesimal. The work done on the air during this compression process can be found by integrating Eq. 4.2.

$$_1W_2 = \int_1^2 \delta W = \int_1^2 P\,dV \qquad (4.3)$$

The symbol $_1W_2$ is to be interpreted as the work done during the process from state 1 to state 2. It is clear from examining the P-V diagram that the work done during this process, namely, $\int_1^2 P\,dV$ is represented by the area under the curve 1–2, area a–1–2–b–a. In this example the volume decreased, and the area a–1–2–b–a represents work done on the system. If the process had proceeded from state 2 to state 1 along the same path, the same area would represent work done by the system.

Further consideration of a P-V diagram, Fig. 4.5, leads to another important conclusion. It is possible to go from state 1 to state 2 along many different quasiequilibrium paths, such as A, B, or C. Since the area underneath each curve represents the work for each process, it is evident that the amount of work involved in each case is a function not only of the end states of the process, but in addition is dependent on the path that is followed in going from one state to another. For this reason work is called a path function, or in mathematical parlance, δW is an inexact differential.

This leads to a brief consideration of point and path functions or, to use another term, exact and inexact differentials. Thermodynamic properties are point functions, a name that arises from the fact that for a given point on a diagram (such as Fig. 4.5) or surface (such as Fig. 3.8), the state is fixed, and thus there is a definite value of each property corresponding to this point. The differentials of point functions are exact differentials, and the integration is simply

$$\int_1^2 dV = V_2 - V_1$$

Thus, we can speak of the volume in state 2 and the volume in state 1, and the change in volume depends only on the initial and final states.

Work, on the other hand, is a path function, for, as has been indicated, the work done in a quasiequilibrium process between two given states

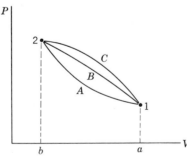

Fig. 4.5 Various quasiequilibrium processes between two given states, indicating that work is a path function.

depends on the path followed. The differentials of path functions are inexact differentials, and the symbol δ will be used in this text to designate inexact differentials (in contrast to d for exact differentials). Thus, for work we would write

$$\int_1^2 \delta W = {}_1W_2$$

It would be more precise to use the notation $({}_1W_{2,A})$ which would indicate the work done during the change from state 1 to 2 along path A. However, implied in the notation ${}_1W_2$ is that the process between states 1 and 2 has been specified. It should be noted, we never speak about the work in the system in state 1 or state 2, and thus we would never write $W_2 - W_1$.

Example 4.1

Consider as a system the gas contained in the cylinder shown in Fig. 4.6, which is fitted with a piston on which a number of small weights are placed. The initial pressure is 20 lbf/in.² and the initial volume of the gas is 1 ft³.

(a) Let a Bunsen burner be placed under the cylinder, and let the volume of the gas increase to 3 ft³ while the pressure remains constant. Calculate the work done by the system during this process.

$$_1W_2 = \int_1^2 P \, dV$$

Since the pressure is constant, we conclude from Eq. 4.3,

$$_1W_2 = P\int_1^2 dV = P(V_2 - V_1)$$
$$_1W_2 = 20 \text{ lbf/in.}^2 \times 144 \text{ in.}^2/\text{ft}^2 \times (3-1)\text{ft}^3 = 5760 \text{ ft-lbf}$$

(b) Consider the same system and initial conditions, but at the same time that the Bunsen burner is under the cylinder and the piston is rising, let weights be removed from the piston at such a rate that, during the process, the relation between pressure and volume is given by the expression $PV = \text{constant} = P_1V_1 = P_2V_2$. Let the final volume again be 3 ft³. Calculate the work done during this process.

We first determine the final pressure.

$$P_2 = \frac{P_1V_1}{V_2} = 20 \times \frac{1}{3} = 6.67 \text{ lbf/in.}^2$$

Again we use Eq. 4.3 to calculate the work.

$$_1W_2 = \int_1^2 P \, dV$$

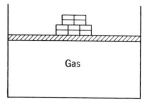

Fig. 4.6 Sketch for Example 4.1.

We can substitute $P = \text{constant}/V = P_1V_1/V$ into this equation.

$$_1W_2 = \text{constant} \int_1^2 \frac{dV}{V} = P_1V_1 \ln \frac{V_2}{V_1}$$

$$_1W_2 = 20 \text{ lbf/in.}^2 \times 144 \text{ in.}^2/\text{ft}^2 \times 1 \text{ ft}^3 \times \ln 3 = 3164 \text{ ft-lbf}$$

(c) Consider the same system, but during the heat transfer let the weights be removed at such a rate that the expression $PV^{1.3} = \text{constant}$ describes the relation between pressure and volume during the process. Again the final volume is 3 ft³. Calculate the work.

Let us first solve this problem for the general case of $PV^n = \text{constant}$:

$$PV^n = \text{constant} = P_1V_1^n = P_2V_2^n$$

$$P = \frac{\text{constant}}{V^n} = \frac{P_1V_1^n}{V^n} = \frac{P_2V_2^n}{V^n}$$

$$_1W_2 = \int_1^2 P\,dV = \text{constant} \int_1^2 \frac{dV}{V^n} = \text{constant} \left[\frac{V^{-n+1}}{-n+1}\right]_1^2$$

$$= \frac{\text{constant}}{1-n}(V_2^{1-n} - V_1^{1-n}) = \frac{P_2V_2^nV_2^{1-n} - P_1V_1^nV_1^{1-n}}{1-n}$$

$$_1W_2 = \frac{P_2V_2 - P_1V_1}{1-n}$$

For our problem

$$_1W_2 = \frac{P_2V_2 - P_1V_1}{1-1.3} = \frac{(4.80 \times 144 \times 3) - (20 \times 144 \times 1)}{1-1.3}$$

$$= 2688 \text{ ft-lbf}$$

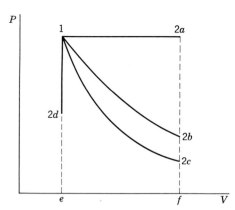

Fig. 4.7 Pressure-volume diagram showing work done in the various processes of Example 4.1.

(*d*) Consider the system and initial state given in the first three examples, but let the piston be held by a pin so that the volume remains constant. In addition, let heat be transferred from the system until the pressure drops to 10 lbf/in.^{2}. Calculate the work.

Since $\delta W = P\,dV$ for a quasiequilibrium process, the work is zero, because in this case there is no change in volume.

The process for each of four examples is shown on the $P\text{-}V$ diagram of Fig. 4.7. Process 1–2*a* is a constant-pressure process, and area 1–2*a*–*f*–*e*–1 represents the work. Similarly, line 1–2*b* represents the process in which $PV = $ constant, line 1–2*c* the process in which $PV^{1.3} = $ constant, and line 1–2*d* represents the constant-volume process. The student should compare the relative areas under each curve with the numerical results obtained above.

4.4 Some Other Systems Involving Work at a Moving Boundary

In the preceding section we considered the work done at the moving boundary of a simple compressible system during a quasiequilibrium process. There are other types of systems that involve work at a moving boundary, and in this section we shall briefly consider two such systems, a stretched wire and a surface film.

Consider as a system a stretched wire that is under a given tension $\mathscr{T}$. When the length of the wire changes by the amount dL, the work done by the system is

$$\delta W = -\mathscr{T}\,dL \tag{4.4}$$

The minus sign is necessary because work is done by the system when dL is negative. This can be integrated to give

$$_1W_2 = -\int_1^2 \mathscr{T}\,dL \tag{4.5}$$

The integration can be performed either graphically or analytically if the relation between $\mathscr{T}$ and L is known. The stretched wire is a simple example of the type of problem in solid body mechanics that involves the calculation of work.

Example 4.2

A metallic wire of initial length L_0 is stretched. Assuming elastic behavior, determine the work done in terms of the modulus of elasticity and the strain.

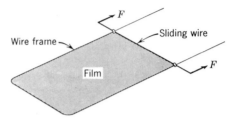

Fig. 4.8   Schematic arrangement showing work done on a surface film.

Let σ = stress, e = strain, and E = modulus of elasticity.

$$\sigma = \frac{\mathscr{T}}{A} = Ee$$

Therefore

$$\mathscr{T} = AEe$$

From the definition of strain,

$$de = \frac{dL}{L_0}$$

Therefore,

$$\delta W = -\mathscr{T}\, dL = -AEeL_0\, de$$

$$W = -AEL_0 \int_{e=0}^{e} e\, de = \frac{AEL_0}{2}\,(e)^2$$

Now consider a system that consists of a liquid film having a surface tension $\mathscr{S}$. A schematic arrangement of such a film is shown in Fig. 4.8, where a film is maintained on a wire frame, one side of which can be moved. When the area of the film is changed, for example by sliding the movable wire along the frame, work is done on or by the film. When the area changes by an amount dA, the work done by the system is

$$\delta W = -\mathscr{S}\, dA \qquad\qquad (4.6)$$

For finite changes

$$_1W_2 = -\int_1^2 \mathscr{S}\, dA \qquad\qquad (4.7)$$

4.5   Systems That Involve Other Modes of Work

There are systems that involve other modes of work, and in this section we shall consider two of these, namely, systems involving magnetic and systems involving electrical modes of work. We shall consider a quasi-equilibrium process for these systems, and present expressions for the work done during such a process.

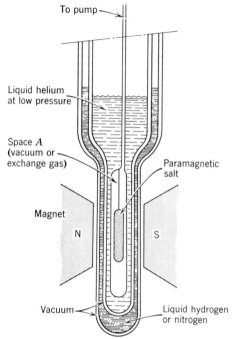

To pump

Liquid helium
at low pressure

Space A
(vacuum or
exchange gas)

Paramagnetic
salt

Magnet

N   S

Vacuum

Liquid hydrogen
or nitrogen

Fig. 4.9   Schematic arrangement for magnetic cooling.

In order to visualize how work can be accomplished by magnetic effects, let us briefly describe magnetic cooling, or adiabatic demagnetization, which is a process used to produce temperatures well below 1 K. A temperature of 1.0 K can be produced by pumping a vacuum over a bath of liquid helium (helium has the lowest normal boiling point of any substance, namely 4.2 K at one atmosphere pressure). An apparatus in which the magnetic cooling is accomplished is shown schematically in Fig. 4.9. The paramagnetic salt is the magnetic substance in which temperatures well below 1 K are achieved. When the magnetic field is slowly increased, work is done on the paramagnetic salt. From a microscopic point of view this work is associated with the fact that in the presence of the magnetic field the ions in the salt tend to align themselves with their magnetic axes in the direction of the field. As a result of this work done on the salt, the temperature of the salt tends to increase. However, at this point in the experiment space A is filled with low pressure helium gas, and heat is transferred from the paramagnetic salt to the liquid helium, which is maintained at about 1 K. When the magnetic field is at full strength, and the paramagnetic salt is at the temperature of the liquid helium, space A is evacuated, thus insulating the paramagnetic salt. The magnetic field is now reduced to zero, and in this process work is done by the paramagnetic salt, and its temperature drops sharply. This entire process may be compared to the compression of a gas that is initially at ambient pressure and temperature. As the result of the compression, the temperature of the gas tends to increase. However, the high pressure gas can be cooled to the ambient temperature. If this gas is now isolated from the surroundings and allowed to expand and do work (against a piston for example) the temperature of the gas will decrease below the ambient temperature during the expansion process.

The basic parameters in this process are the intensity of the magnetic field (an intensive property like pressure) and the magnetization (an extensive property like volume). It may be shown that in a reversible quasiequilibrium process, the work done on a simple magnetic substance is

$$\delta W = -\mu_0 \, V \mathcal{H} \, d\mathcal{M} \tag{4.8}$$

where: μ_0 = permeability of free space

V = volume

$\mathcal{H}$ = intensity of the magnetic field

$\mathcal{M}$ = magnetization

The minus sign indicates that as the magnetization $d\mathcal{M}$ increases, work is done on the simple magnetic substance.

We have already noted that electrical energy flowing across the boundary of a system is work. However, we can gain further insight into such a process by considering a system in which the only work mode is electrical. As an example of such a system we can think of a charged condenser, an electrolytic cell, or the type of fuel cell described in Chapter 1. Consider a quasiequilibrium process for such a system, and during this process let the potential difference be $\mathcal{E}$ and the amount of electrical energy that flows into the system be dZ. For this quasiequilibrium process the work is given by the relation

$$\delta W = -\mathcal{E} \, dZ \tag{4.9}$$

Since the current, i, equals dZ/dt (where t = time) we can also write

$$\delta W = -\mathcal{E} i \, dt$$

$$_1W_2 = -\int_1^2 \mathcal{E} i \, dt \tag{4.10}$$

Eq. 4.10 may also be written as a rate equation for work (the power).

$$\frac{\delta W}{dt} = -\mathcal{E} i \tag{4.11}$$

This leads to the definition of a unit of power, the watt. A watt is the power developed by a current of 1 ampere flowing through a potential of 1 volt. This is consistent with our earlier observation that electrical energy is work.

4.6   Some Concluding Remarks Regarding Work

The similarity between the expressions for work in the two processes mentioned in Section 4.5 and the three processes involving a moving boundary should be noted. In each of these quasiequilibrium processes the work is given by the integral of the product of an intensive property and the change of an extensive property. These are summarized below:

Simple compressible system $_1W_2 = \int_1^2 P\,dV$

Stretched wire $_1W_2 = -\int_1^2 \mathcal{T}\,dL$

Surface film $_1W_2 = -\int_1^2 \mathcal{S}\,dA$ (4.12)

System involving magnetic work only $_1W_2 = -\int_1^2 \mu_0 V \mathcal{H}\,d\mathcal{M}$

System involving electrical work only $_1W_2 = -\int_1^2 \mathcal{E}\,dZ$

Although we will deal primarily with systems involving one mode of work, it is quite possible to have more than one work mode involved in a given process. Thus we could write

$$\delta W = P\,dV - \mathcal{T}\,dL - \mathcal{S}\,dA - \mu_0 V \mathcal{H}\,d\mathcal{M} - \mathcal{E}\,dZ + \cdots \quad (4.13)$$

where the dotted lines represent other products of an intensive property and the derivative of a related extensive property.

It should also be noted that there are many other forms of work which can be identified in processes that are not quasiequilibrium processes. An example of these is the work done by shearing forces in a process involving friction in a viscous fluid or the work done by a rotating shaft that crosses the system boundary.

The identification of work is an important aspect of many thermo-dynamic problems. We have already noted that work can be identified only at the boundaries of the system. For example, consider Fig. 4.10, which shows a gas separated from the vacuum by a membrane. Let the membrane rupture and the gas fill the entire volume. Neglecting any work

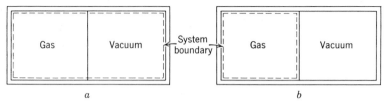

Fig. 4.10   Example of a process involving a change of volume for which the work is zero.

associated with the rupturing of the membrane, we can ask if there is work involved in the process. If we take as our system the gas and the vacuum space, we readily conclude that there is no work involved, since no work can be identified at the system boundary. It we take the gas as a system we do have a change of volume, and we might be tempted to calculate the work from the integral $\int_1^2 P\,dV$. However, this is not a quasiequilibrium process, and therefore the work cannot be calculated from this relation. Rather, since there is no resistance at the system boundary as the volume increases we conclude that for this system there is no work involved in this process.

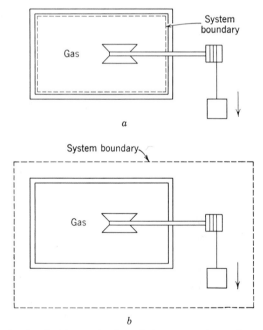

Fig. 4.11   Example showing how selection of the system determines whether or not work is involved in a process.

Another example can be cited with the aid of Fig. 4.11. In Fig. 4.11*a* the system consists of the container plus the gas. Work crosses the boundary of the system at the point where the system boundary intersects the shaft, and can be associated with the shearing forces in the rotating shaft. In Fig. 4.11*b* the system includes shaft and weight as well as the gas and the container. In this case there is no work crossing the system boundary as the weight moves downward. As we will see in the next chapter, we can identify a change of potential energy within the system, but this should not be confused with work crossing the system boundary.

4.7 Definition of Heat

The thermodynamic definition of heat is somewhat different from the everyday understanding of the word. Therefore, it is essential to understand clearly the definition of heat given here, because it is involved in so many thermodynamic problems.

If a block of hot copper is placed in a beaker of cold water, we know from experience that the block of copper cools down and the water warms up until the copper and water reach the same temperature. What causes this decrease in the temperature of the copper and the increase in the temperature of the water? We say that it is the result of the transfer of energy from the copper block to the water. It is out of such a transfer of energy that we arrive at a definition of heat.

Heat is defined as the form of energy that is transferred across the boundary of a system at a given temperature to another system (or the surroundings) at a lower temperature by virtue of the temperature difference between the two systems. That is, heat is transferred from the system at the higher to the system at the lower temperature, and the heat transfer occurs solely because of the temperature difference between the two systems. Another aspect of this definition of heat is that a body never contains heat. Rather heat can be identified only as it crosses the boundary. Thus, heat is a transient phenomenon. If we consider the hot block of copper as one system and the cold water in the beaker as another system, we recognize that originally neither system contains any heat (they do contain energy, of course). When the copper is placed in the water and the two are in thermal communication, heat is transferred from the copper to the water, until equilibrium of temperature is established. At that point we no longer have heat transfer, since there is no temperature difference. Neither of the systems contains heat at the conclusion of the process. It also follows that heat is identified at the boundary of the system, for heat is defined as energy being transferred across the system boundary.

4.8   Units of Heat

We must have units for heat, as for all other quantities in thermodynamics. Consider as a system 1 lbm water at 59.5 F, and let a block of hot copper be placed in the water. Let the block of copper have such a mass and such a temperature that when thermal equilibrium is established the temperature of the water is 60.5 F. We define as our unit of heat the quantity of heat transferred from the copper to the water, and call the unit of heat the British thermal unit, which is abbreviated Btu. More specifically, this is called the 60-degree Btu, which may be defined as the quantity of heat required to raise 1 lbm of water from 59.5 F to 60.5 F.*

Similarly, a calorie can be identified as the amount of heat required to raise the temperature of 1 gram of water from 14.5 C to 15.5 C.

Further, heat transferred *to* a system is considered to be positive, and heat transferred *from* a system, negative. Thus, positive heat represents energy transferred to a system, and negative heat represents energy transferred from a system. The symbol Q is used to represent heat.

A process in which there is no heat transfer ($Q = 0$) is called an adiabatic process.

From a mathematical perspective, heat, like work, is a path function and is recognized as an inexact differential. That is, the amount of heat transferred when a system undergoes a change of state from state 1 to state 2 depends on the path that the system follows during the change of state. Since heat is an inexact differential, the differential is written δQ. On integrating we write

$$\int_1^2 \delta Q = {}_1Q_2$$

In words, ${}_1Q_2$ is the heat transferred during the given process between state 1 and state 2.

The rate at which heat is transferred to a system is designated by the symbol $\dot{Q}$.

$$\dot{Q} \equiv \frac{\delta Q}{dt}$$

It is also convenient to speak of the heat transfer per unit mass of the system, q, which is defined as

$$q \equiv \frac{Q}{m}$$

---

* Actually the Btu as used today is defined in terms of electrical units. This point is explained in the next chapter.

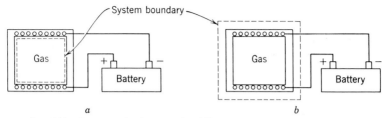

Fig. 4.12   An example showing the difference between heat and work.

4.9   Comparison of Heat and Work

At this point it is evident that there are many similarities between heat and work, and these are summarized here.

(*a*) Heat and work are both transient phenomena. Systems never possess heat or work, but either or both cross the system boundary when a system undergoes a change of state.

(*b*) Both heat and work are boundary phenomena. Both are observed only at the boundaries of the system, and both represent energy crossing the boundary of the system.

(*c*) Both heat and work are path functions and inexact differentials.

It should also be noted that in our sign convention, $+Q$ represents heat transferred *to* the system, and thus is energy added to the system, and $+W$ represents work done *by* the system and thus represents energy leaving the system.

A final illustration may be helpful to indicate the difference between heat and work. Figure 4.12 shows a gas contained in a rigid vessel. Resistance coils are wound around the outside of the vessel. When current flows through the resistance coils, the temperature of the gas increases. Which crosses the boundary of the system, heat or work?

In Fig. 4.12*a* we consider only the gas as the system. In this case the energy crosses the boundary of the system because the temperature of the walls is higher than the temperature of the gas. Therefore, we recognize that heat crosses the boundary of the system.

In Fig. 4.12*b* the system includes the vessel and the resistance heater. Electricity crosses the boundary of the system, and as indicated earlier, this is work.

PROBLEMS

4.1 A cylinder fitted with a piston contains 4 lbm of saturated water vapor at a pressure of 100 lbf/in.^{2} The steam is heated until the temperature is 500 F. During this process the pressure remains constant. Calculate the work done by the steam during the process.

4.2 The vertical cylinder shown in Fig. 4.13 contains 0.185 lbm of H_2O at 100 F. The initial volume enclosed beneath the piston is 0.65 ft.^{3} The piston has an area of 60 in.^{2} and a mass of 125 lbm. Initially the piston rests on the

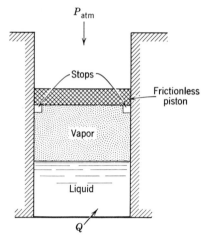

Fig. 4.13   Sketch for Problem 4.2.

stops as shown. The atmospheric pressure is 14.0 lbf/in.^{2} and the gravitational acceleration is 30.9 ft/sec^2. Heat is then transferred to the steam until the cylinder contains saturated vapor.

(*a*) What is the temperature of the H_2O when the piston first rises from the stops?

(*b*) How much work is done by the steam during the entire process?

(*c*) Show the process on a T-V diagram.

4.3 A cylinder in which the piston is restrained by a spring contains 1 ft^3 of air at a pressure of 15 lbf/in.^{2}, which just balances the atmospheric pressure of

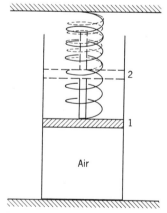

Fig. 4.14   Sketch for Problem 4.3.

15 lbf/in.^{2} Assume that the weight of the piston is negligible. In this initial state, the spring exerts no force on the piston. The gas is then heated until the volume is doubled. The final pressure of the gas is 50 lbf/in.^{2}, and during the process the spring exerts a force which is proportional to the displacement of the piston from the initial position.

(a) Show this process on a P-V diagram.

(b) Considering the gas as the system, calculate the total work done by the system.

(c) Of the total work, how much is done against the atmosphere? How much against the spring?

4.4 A balloon which is initially flat is inflated by filling it with air from a tank of compressed air. The final volume of the balloon is 50 ft^3. The barometer reads 29.7 in. Hg. Consider the tank, the balloon, and the connecting pipe as a system. Determine the work for this process.

4.5 A spherical balloon has a diameter of 10 in., and contains air at a pressure of 20 lbf/in.^{2} The diameter of the balloon increases to 12 in. due to heating, and during this process the pressure is proportional to the diameter. Calculate the work done by the air during this process.

4.6 Ammonia is compressed in a cylinder by a piston. The initial temperature is 100 F, the initial pressure is 60 lbf/in.^{2}, and the final pressure is 180 lbf/in.^{2} The following data are available for this process:

Pressure, lbf/in.^{2}	Volume, in.^{3}
60	80.0
80	67.5
100	60.0
120	52.5
140	45.0
160	37.5
180	32.5

(a) Determine the work for the process considering the ammonia as the system.

(b) What is the final temperature of the ammonia?

4.7 Saturated water vapor at 400 F is contained in a cylinder fitted with a piston. The initial volume of the steam is 0.3 ft.^{3} The steam then expands in a quasiequilibrium, isothermal process until the final pressure is 20 lbf/in^2., and in so doing does work against the piston.

Determine the work done during this process.

4.8 During static tests of rocket motors a compressed gas is often used to force the propellants into the combustion chamber. Consider the arrangement shown in Fig. 4.15. Compressed air is used to expel the liquid propellant from the propellant tank. The initial pressure of the air is 3000 lbf/in.^{2} and the initial temperature is 100 F. The propellant has a density of 70 lbm/ft^3 and the propellant tank is filled to capacity and contains 2000 lbm of propellant. The propellant leaves at constant pressure of 300 lbf/in.^{2} Considering the air as the system, determine the work done by the air in forcing the propellant from the propellant tank.

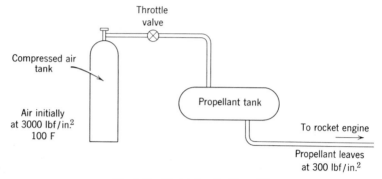

Fig. 4.15   Sketch for Problem 4.8.

4.9 A sealed vessel having the shape of a rectangular prism with the area of the base A and height L_2, and of negligible mass, is initially floating on a liquid of density ρ, Fig. 4.16.   Derive an expression in terms of the given variables for

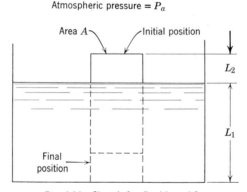

Fig. 4.16   Sketch for Problem 4.9.

the work required to move the vessel to the bottom of a very large tank in which depth of the liquid is L_1.

4.10 Repeat Problem 4.9 assuming that the sealed tank has a mass m.

4.11 A metallic wire of initial length L_0 is stretched in the elastic region. Determine the work done in terms of the modulus of elasticity and the strain.

4.12 At 20 C methanol has a surface tension of 22.6 dynes/cm.   Suppose that a film of methanol is maintained on the wire frame as shown in Fig. 4.17, one side of which can be moved.   The original dimensions of the wire frame are as shown.   Determine the work done (consider the film to be the system), when the wire is moved 1 cm in the direction indicated.

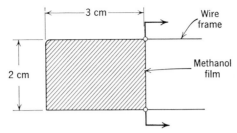

Fig. 4.17   Sketch for Problem 4.12.

4.13 A spherical balloon having a radius of 30 feet is to be filled with helium from a bank of high pressure gas cylinders that contain helium at 2000 lbf/in.^{2}, 80 F. The balloon is initially flat, and the atmospheric pressure is 30.06 in. Hg.

(*a*) How much work is done against the atmosphere as the balloon is inflated? Assume no stretching of the material from which the balloon is made and that the pressure in the balloon is essentially equal to the atmospheric pressure.

(*b*) What is the required volume of the high pressure cylinders, if the final pressure in the cylinders is the same as that in the balloon?

4.14 The cylinder-piston arrangement shown in Fig. 4.18 contains two lb moles of air at 100 lbf/in.^{2} and 500 F. Heat is transferred to the air and the small weights on the piston are removed at such a rate that during the expansion the

Fig. 4.18   Sketch for Problem 4.14.

relation between pressure and volume is $PV^{1.3}$ = constant. Determine the work done by the gas during this process.

4.15 A storage battery is well insulated (thermally) while it is being charged. The charging voltage is 12.3 v and the current is 24.0 amp. Considering the storage battery as the system, what are the heat transfer and work in a 15 min period?

4.16 A room is heated with steam radiators on a winter day. Examine the following systems regarding heat transfer (including sign):

(*a*) The radiator.

(*b*) The room.

(*c*) The radiator and the room.

4.17 Consider a hot-air heating system for a home and examine the following systems for heat transfer:

(*a*) The combustion chamber and combustion gas side of the heat transfer area.

(*b*) The furnace as a whole including the hot and cold air ducts and chimney.

5 The First Law of Thermodynamics

Having completed our consideration of basic definitions and concepts we are ready to proceed to a discussion of the first law of thermodynamics. Often this law is called the law of the conservation of energy, and as we shall see later, this is essentially true. Our procedure will be to state this law first for a system undergoing a cycle, and then for a change of state of a system. Finally the first law of thermodynamics will be applied to a control volume. The law of the conservation of matter will also be considered in this chapter.

5.1 The First Law of Thermodynamics for a System Undergoing a Cycle

The first law of thermodynamics states that during any cycle a system undergoes, the cyclic integral of the heat is proportional to the cyclic integral of the work.

To illustrate this law, consider as a system the gas in the container shown in Fig. 5.1. Let this system go through a cycle that is comprised of two processes. In the first process work is done on the system by the paddle that turns as the weight is lowered. Let the system then be returned to its initial state by transferring heat from the system until the cycle has been completed.

We have already noted that we can measure the work in foot-pounds force and the heat in Btu. Let measurements of work and heat be made during such a cycle for a wide variety of systems and for various amounts of work and heat. When the amount of work and heat are compared, we find that these two are always proportional. Observations such as this have led to the formulation of the first law of thermodynamics, which in equation form is written

$$J \oint \delta Q = \oint \delta W \qquad (5.1)$$

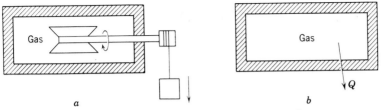

Fig. 5.1 Example of a system undergoing a cycle.

The symbol $\oint \delta Q$, which is called the cyclic integral of the heat transfer, represents the net heat transfer during the cycle, and $\oint \delta W$, the cyclic integral of the work, represents the net work during the cycle. J is a proportionality factor. Equation 5.1 states that the cyclic integral of the work is proportional to the cyclic integral of the heat transfer.

The basis of every law of nature is experimental evidence, and this is true also of the first law of thermodynamics. Every experiment that has been conducted thus far has verified the first law either directly or indirectly. The basis of this law is, therefore, experimental evidence; it has never been disproved, and has been verified by many experiments.

Thus far we have used the unit foot-pounds for work and Btu for heat. We might also use other units, such as joules for work and calories for heat. The first law states that there is a proportionality between the units for heat and work. The magnitude of the proportionality constant J will depend, of course, on the units used for heat and work. James P. Joule (1818–1889) did the first accurate work in the 1840's on measurement of the proportionality factor J. The generally accepted value for J, based on the 60-degree Btu and the foot-pound force, is that $J = 778.2$ ft-lbf/Btu.

However, at the International Steam Table Conference in 1929, the Btu was, in effect, defined in terms of the foot-pound force by the following relation:

$$1 \text{ Btu} = 778.26 \text{ ft-lbf}$$

This definition fixes the magnitude of the Btu in terms of previously defined units, and is called the International British thermal unit. Throughout the rest of the text this will be the British thermal unit with which we are concerned whenever the term is used. Thus, when using the international Btu, the question is not to accurately determine the value of J for the 60 F Btu, but rather how many International Btu's are required to raise 1 lbm of water from 59.5 F to 60.5 F.

For much engineering work, however, the accuracy of other data does not warrant more accuracy than the relation 778 ft-lbf = 1 Btu, and, in general, this relation will be used in the examples given in this text.

It is also evident from this discussion that heat and work can be expressed in the same units. Thus, it is perfectly correct to speak of Btu of work and ft-lbf of heat, or calories of work and joules of heat. Therefore we can write Eq. 5.1 without the proportionality factor J.

$$\oint \delta Q = \oint \delta W \qquad (5.2)$$

The implication of the equation thus written is that heat and work are expressed in the same units, and in fact can be expressed in any of the units that are used for energy. In this text, therefore, the proportionality factor J will not be written into equations, but the student should realize that each equation must have consistent units throughout.

We also note that

$$1 \text{ hp} = 33,000 \text{ ft-lbf/min} = 42.4 \text{ Btu/min} = 2545 \text{ Btu/hr}$$
$$1 \text{ kw} = 44,240 \text{ ft-lbf/min} = 56.9 \text{ Btu/min} = 3412 \text{ Btu/hr}$$

5.2 The First Law of Thermodynamics for a Change in State of a System

Equation 5.2 states the first law of thermodynamics for a system during a cycle. Many times, however, we are concerned with a process rather than a cycle, and we now consider the first law of thermodynamics for a system that undergoes a change of state. This can be done by introducing a new property, the energy, which is given the symbol E. Consider a system that undergoes a cycle, changing from state 1 to state 2 by process A, and returning from state 2 to state 1 by process B. This cycle is shown in Fig. 5.2 on a pressure (or other intensive property)-volume (or other extensive property) diagram. From the first law of thermodynamics, Eq. 5.2,

$$\oint \delta Q = \oint \delta W$$

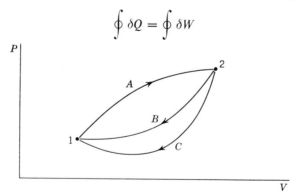

Fig. 5.2   Demonstration of the existence of the thermodynamic property E.

Considering the two separate processes we have

$$\int_{1A}^{2A} \delta Q + \int_{2B}^{1B} \delta Q = \int_{1A}^{2A} \delta W + \int_{2B}^{1B} \delta W$$

Now consider another cycle, the system changing from state 1 to state 2 by process A, as before, and returning to state 1 by process C. For this cycle we can write

$$\int_{1A}^{2A} \delta Q + \int_{2C}^{1C} \delta Q = \int_{1A}^{2A} \delta W + \int_{2C}^{1C} \delta W$$

Subtracting the second of these equations from the first, we have

$$\int_{2B}^{1B} \delta Q - \int_{2C}^{1C} \delta Q = \int_{2B}^{1B} \delta W - \int_{2C}^{1C} \delta W$$

or, by rearranging

$$\int_{2B}^{1B} (\delta Q - \delta W) = \int_{2C}^{1C} (\delta Q - \delta W) \tag{5.3}$$

Since B and C represent arbitrary processes between states 1 and 2, we conclude that the quantity $(\delta Q - \delta W)$ is the same for all processes between state 1 and state 2. Therefore, $(\delta Q - \delta W)$ depends only on the initial and final states and not on the path followed between the two states. We conclude that this is a point function, and therefore is the differential of a property of the system. This property is the energy of the system and is given the symbol E. Thus, we can write

$$\delta Q - \delta W = dE$$

$$\delta Q = dE + \delta W \tag{5.4}$$

Note that since E is a property, its derivative is written dE. When Eq. 5.4 is integrated from an initial state 1 to the final state 2, we have

$${}_1Q_2 = E_2 - E_1 + {}_1W_2 \tag{5.5}$$

where ${}_1Q_2$ is the heat transferred to the system during the process from state 1 to state 2, E_1 and E_2 are the initial and final values of the energy E of the system, and ${}_1W_2$ is the work done by the system during the process.

The physical significance of the property E is that it represents all the energy of the system in the given state. This energy might be present in a variety of forms, such as the kinetic or potential energy of the system as a whole, energy associated with the motion and position of the molecules, energy associated with the structure of the atom, chemical energy such as is present in a storage battery, energy present in a charged condenser, or in any of a number of other forms.

In the study of thermodynamics it is convenient to consider the kinetic and potential energy separately and then to consider all the other energy of the system in a single property which we call the internal energy, and to which we give the symbol U. Thus, we would write

$$E = \text{Internal energy} + \text{Kinetic energy} + \text{Potential energy}$$

or

$$E = U + \text{KE} + \text{PE}$$

The reason for doing this is that the kinetic and potential energy are associated with the coordinate frame that we select and can be specified by the macroscopic parameters of mass, velocity, and elevation. The internal energy U includes all other forms of energy of the system and is associated with the thermodynamic state of the system. Since each of these are thermodynamic properties we can write

$$dE = dU + d(\text{KE}) + d(\text{PE}) \tag{5.6}$$

The first law of thermodynamics for a change of state of a system may therefore be written

$$\delta Q = dU + d(\text{KE}) + d(\text{PE}) + \delta W \tag{5.7}$$

In words this equation states that as a system undergoes a change of state, energy may cross the boundary as either heat or work, and each may be positive or negative. The net change in the energy of the system will be exactly equal to the net energy that crosses the boundary of the system. The energy of the system may change in any of three ways, namely, by a change in internal energy, kinetic energy, or potential energy. Since the mass of a system is fixed, we can also say that a quantity of matter may have energy in three forms, internal energy, kinetic energy, or potential energy.

This section will be concluded by deriving an expression for the kinetic and potential energy of a system. Consider first a system that is initially at rest relative to the earth, which is taken as the coordinate frame, and let this system be acted upon by an external horizontal force F which moves the system a distance dx in the direction of the force. Thus there is no change in potential energy. Let there be no heat transfer and no change in internal energy. Then, from the first law, Eq. 5.7,

$$\delta W = -F\,dx = -d\text{KE}$$

But

$$F = \frac{ma}{g_c} = \frac{m}{g_c}\frac{d\text{V}}{dt} = \frac{m}{g_c}\frac{dx}{dt}\frac{d\text{V}}{dx} = \frac{m}{g_c}\text{V}\frac{d\text{V}}{dx}$$

Then

$$d\text{KE} = F\,dx = \frac{m}{g_c}\text{V}\,d\text{V}$$

Integrating, we obtain

$$\int_{V=0}^{V} \frac{m}{g_c} \, V \, dV = \int_{KE=0}^{KE} dKE$$

$$KE = \frac{1}{2} \frac{mV^2}{g_c}$$

An expression for potential energy can be found in a similar manner. Consider a system that is initially at rest and at the elevation of some reference level. Let this system be acted upon by a vertical force F which is of such magnitude that it raises (in elevation) the system with constant velocity an amount dZ. Let the acceleration due to gravity at this point be g. From the first law, Eq. 5.7

$$\delta W = -F \, dZ = -d\text{PE}$$

$$F = \frac{ma}{g_c} = \frac{mg}{g_c}$$

Then

$$d\text{PE} = F \, dZ = \frac{mg}{g_c} \, dZ$$

Integrating

$$\int_{\text{PE}_1}^{\text{PE}_2} d\text{PE} = m \int_{Z_1}^{Z_2} \frac{g}{g_c} \, dZ \tag{5.8}$$

Assuming that g does not vary with Z (which is a very reasonable assumption for moderate changes in elevation)

$$\text{PE}_2 - \text{PE}_1 = \frac{mg}{g_c} (Z_2 - Z_1) \tag{5.9}$$

Substituting these expressions for kinetic and potential energy into Eq. 5.6 we have

$$dE = dU + \frac{m}{g_c} \, V \, dV + \frac{mg}{g_c} \, dZ$$

Integrating for a change of state from state 1 to state 2 with constant g we have

$$E_2 - E_1 = U_2 - U_1 + \frac{mV_2^2}{2g_c} - \frac{mV_1^2}{2g_c} + \frac{mg}{g_c} Z_2 - \frac{mg}{g_c} Z_1$$

Similarly, substituting these expressions for kinetic and potential energy into Eq. 5.7 we have

$$\delta Q = dU + \frac{d(mV^2)}{2g_c} + d\left(\frac{mgZ}{g_c}\right) + \delta W \tag{5.10}$$

In the integrated form this equation is, assuming g is a constant,

$$_1Q_2 = U_2 - U_1 + \frac{m(V_2{}^2 - V_1{}^2)}{2g_c} + \frac{mg}{g_c}(Z_2 - Z_1) + {_1}W_2 \quad (5.11)$$

Three observations should be made regarding this equation. The first is that the property E, the energy of the system, was found to exist, and we were able to write the first law for a change of state using Eq. 5.5. However, rather than deal with this property E, we find it more convenient to consider internal energy, kinetic energy, and potential energy. In general, this will be the procedure followed in the rest of this book.

The second observation is that Eqs. 5.10 and 5.11 are in effect a statement of the conservation of energy. The net change of the energy of the system is always equal to the net transfer of energy across the system boundary as heat and work. This is somewhat analogous to a joint checking account which a man might have with his wife. There are two ways in which deposits and withdrawals can be made, either by the man or by his wife, and the balance will always reflect the net amount of the transaction. Similarly, there are two ways in which energy can cross the boundary of a system, either as heat or work, and the energy of the system will change by the exact amount of the net energy crossing the system boundary. The concept of energy and the law of the conservation of energy are basic to thermodynamics.

The third observation is that Eqs. 5.10 and 5.11 can give only changes in internal energy, kinetic energy, and potential energy. We can learn nothing about absolute values of these quantities from these equations. If we wish to assign values to internal energy, kinetic energy, and potential energy we must assume reference states and assign a value to the quantity in this reference state. The kinetic energy of a body with zero velocity relative to the earth is assumed to be zero. Similarly, the value of the potential energy is assumed to be zero when the body is at some reference elevation. With internal energy, therefore, we must also have a reference state if we wish to assign values of this property. This matter is considered in the following section.

5.3 Internal Energy—A Thermodynamic Property

Internal energy is an extensive property, since it depends upon the mass of the system. Similarly, the kinetic and potential energies are extensive properties.

The symbol U designates the internal energy of a given mass of a substance. Following the convention used with other extensive properties the symbol u designates the internal energy per unit mass. We could speak of u as the specific internal energy, as we do in the case of specific volume. However, since the context will usually make it clear whether u or U is referred to, we will simply use the term internal energy to refer to both internal energy per unit mass and the total internal energy.

In Chapter 3 it was noted that in the absence of the effects of motion, gravity, surface effects, electricity, and magnetism, the state of a pure substance is specified by two independent properties. It is very significant that with these restrictions, the internal energy may be one of the independent properties of a pure substance. This means, for example, that if we specify the pressure and internal energy (with reference to an arbitrary base) of superheated steam, the temperature is also specified.

Thus, in a table of thermodynamic properties such as the steam tables, the value of internal energy can be tabulated along with other thermodynamic properties. Table 2 of the steam tables by Keenan and Keyes (Appendix Table A.1.2) lists the internal energy for saturated states. Included is the internal energy of saturated liquid u_f, the internal energy of saturated vapor u_g, and the difference between the internal energy of saturated liquid and saturated vapor u_{fg}. The values are given in relation to an arbitrarily assumed reference state. This reference state will be discussed later. The internal energy of saturated steam of a given quality is calculated in the same way specific volume is calculated. The relations are

$$u = (1 - x)u_f + xu_g$$

$$u = u_f + xu_{fg}$$

$$u = u_g - (1 - x)u_{fg}$$

The same value is obtained from each equation, but, as pointed out in the discussion of specific volume, when using a slide rule, for high quality the last equation gives more accuracy, and for low quality the second equation gives more accuracy. For example, the specific internal energy of saturated steam having a pressure of 80 lbf/in.^{2} and a quality of 95 per cent can be calculated as follows:

$$u = u_g - (1 - x)u_{fg}$$

$$u = 1102.1 - 0.05(820.3) = 1061.1 \text{ Btu/lbm}$$

Example 5.1

A tank containing a fluid is stirred by a paddle wheel. The work input to the paddle wheel is 5090 Btu. The heat transfer from the tank is 1500 Btu. Considering the tank and the fluid as the system, determine the change in the internal energy of the system. The first law of thermodynamics is (Eq. 5.11)

$$_1Q_2 = U_2 - U_1 + m\frac{(V_2{}^2 - V_1{}^2)}{2g_c} + \frac{mg}{g_c}(Z_2 - Z_1) + {}_1W_2$$

Since there is no change in kinetic and potential energy, this reduces to

$$_1Q_2 = U_2 - U_1 + {}_1W_2$$
$$-1500 = U_2 - U_1 - 5090$$
$$U_2 - U_1 = 3590 \text{ Btu}$$

Example 5.2

Consider a system composed of a stone having a mass of 10 lbm and a bucket containing 100 lbm of water. Initially the stone is 77.8 ft above the water and the stone and water are at the same temperature. The stone then falls into the water.

Determine ΔU, ΔKE, ΔPE, Q, and W for the following changes of state.

(a) The stone is about to enter the water.

(b) The stone has just come to rest in the bucket.

(c) Heat has been transferred to the surroundings in such an amount that the stone and water are at the same temperature they were initially.

The first law of thermodynamics is

$$_1Q_2 = U_2 - U_1 + m\frac{(V_2{}^2 - V_1{}^2)}{2g_c} + \frac{mg}{g_c}(Z_2 - Z_1) + {}_1W_2$$

(a) The stone is about to enter the water: assuming no heat transfer to or from the stone as it falls, we conclude that during the change from the initial state to the state that exists at the moment the stone enters the water,

$$_1Q_2 = 0 \qquad {}_1W_2 = 0 \qquad \Delta U = 0$$

Therefore the first law reduces to

$$-\Delta KE = \Delta PE = \frac{mg}{g_c}(Z_2 - Z_1)$$

$$= \frac{10 \text{ lbm} \times 32.17 \text{ ft/sec}^2}{32.17 \text{ lbm-ft/lbf-sec}^2} \times (-77.8) \text{ ft} = -778 \text{ ft-lbf}$$

$$= -1 \text{ Btu}$$

That is, $\Delta KE = 1$ Btu and $\Delta PE = -1$ Btu.

(b) Just after the stone comes to rest in the bucket:

$$_1Q_2 = 0 \qquad _1W_2 = 0 \qquad \Delta KE = 0$$

Then

$$\Delta PE = -\Delta U = \frac{mg}{g_c}(Z_2 - Z_1) = -1 \text{ Btu}$$

$$\Delta U = 1 \text{ Btu} \qquad \Delta PE = -1 \text{ Btu}$$

(c) After enough heat has been transferred so that the stone and water are at the same temperature they were initially, we conclude that $\Delta U = 0$. Therefore in this case

$$\Delta U = 0 \qquad \Delta KE = 0 \qquad _1W_2 = 0$$

$$_1Q_2 = \Delta PE = \frac{mg}{g_c}(Z_2 - Z_1) = 1 \text{ Btu}$$

Example 5.3

A vessel having a volume of 100 ft³ contains 1 ft³ of saturated liquid water and 99 ft³ of saturated water vapor at 14.7 lbf/in.². Heat is transferred until the vessel is filled with saturated vapor. Determine the heat transfer for this process.

Consider the total mass within the vessel as our system. Therefore the first law for this process is

$$Q = U_2 - U_1 + m\frac{(V_2^2 - V_1^2)}{2g_c} + \frac{mg}{g_c}(Z_2 - Z_1) + _1W_2$$

Since changes in kinetic and potential energy are not involved, this reduces to

$$_1Q_2 = U_2 - U_1 + _1W_2$$

Further, the work for this process is zero, and therefore

$$_1Q_2 = U_2 - U_1$$

The thermodynamic properties can be found in Table 2 of the steam tables. The initial internal energy U_1 is the sum of the initial internal energy of the liquid and the vapor.

$$U_1 = m_{1\text{liq}}u_{1\text{liq}} + m_{1\text{vap}}u_{1\text{vap}}$$

$$m_{1\text{liq}} = \frac{V_{\text{liq}}}{v_f} = \frac{1}{0.01672} = 59.81 \text{ lbm}$$

$$m_{1\text{vap}} = \frac{V_{\text{vap}}}{v_g} = \frac{99}{26.80} = 3.69 \text{ lbm}$$

$$U_1 = 59.8(180.0) + 3.69(1077.5) = 14{,}740 \text{ Btu}$$

To determine u_2 we need to know two thermodynamic properties, since this determines the final state. The properties we know are the quality, $x = 100\%$, and v_2, the final specific volume, which can readily be determined.

$$m = m_{1\text{liq}} + m_{1\text{vap}} = 59.81 + 3.69 = 63.50 \text{ lbm}$$

$$v_2 = \frac{V}{m} = \frac{100}{63.50} = 1.575 \text{ ft}^3/\text{lbm}$$

In Table 2 of the steam tables we find that at a pressure of 294 lbf/in.² $v_g = 1.575$. The final pressure of the steam is therefore 294 lbf/in.². Then,

$$u_2 = 1117.0 \text{ Btu/lbm}$$

$$U_2 = mu_2 = 63.50(1117.0) = 70,930 \text{ Btu}$$

$$_1Q_2 = U_2 - U_1 = 70,930 - 14,740 = 56,190 \text{ Btu}$$

5.4   The First Law as a Rate Equation

We frequently find it desirable to use the first law as a rate equation that expresses either the instantaneous or average rate at which energy crosses the system boundary as heat and work and the rate at which the energy of the system changes. In so doing we are departing from a strictly classical point of view, because basically classical thermodynamics deals with systems that are in equilibrium, and time is not a relevant parameter for systems that are in equilibrium. However, since these rate equations are developed from the concepts of classical thermodynamics, and are used in many applications of thermodynamics, they are included in this book. This rate form of the first law will be used in the development of the first law for the control volume in a subsequent section of this chapter, and in this form the first law finds extensive applications in thermodynamics, fluid mechanics and heat transfer.

Consider a time interval δt during which an amount of heat δQ crosses the system boundary, an amount of work δW is done by the system, the internal energy changes by the amount ΔU, the kinetic energy change is ΔKE, and the potential energy change is ΔPE. From the first law we can write

$$\delta Q = \Delta U + \Delta \text{KE} + \Delta \text{PE} + \delta W$$

Dividing by δt we have the average rate of energy transfer as heat and work and increase of the energy of the system.

$$\frac{\delta Q}{\delta t} = \frac{\Delta U}{\delta t} + \frac{\Delta \text{KE}}{\delta t} + \frac{\Delta \text{PE}}{\delta t} + \frac{\delta W}{\delta t}$$

Taking the limit for each of these quantities as δt approaches zero we have

$$\lim_{\delta t \to 0} \frac{\delta Q}{\delta t} = \dot{Q}, \quad \text{the heat transfer rate}$$

$$\lim_{\delta t \to 0} \frac{\delta W}{\delta t} = \dot{W}, \quad \text{the power} \tag{5.12}$$

$$\lim_{\delta t \to 0} \frac{\Delta U}{\delta t} = \frac{dU}{dt} \; ; \quad \lim_{\delta t \to 0} \frac{\Delta(KE)}{\delta t} = \frac{d(KE)}{dt} \; ; \quad \lim_{\delta t \to 0} \frac{\Delta(PE)}{\delta t} = \frac{d(PE)}{dt}$$

Therefore, the rate equation form of the first law is

$$\dot{Q} = \frac{dU}{dt} + \frac{d(KE)}{dt} + \frac{d(PE)}{dt} + \dot{W} \tag{5.13}$$

We could also write this in the form

$$\dot{Q} = \frac{dE}{dt} + \dot{W} \tag{5.14}$$

Example 5.4

During the charging of a storage battery the current is 20 amp, and the voltage is 12.8 v. The rate of heat transfer from the battery is 25 Btu/hr. At what rate is the internal energy increasing?

Since changes in kinetic and potential energy are not significant, the first law can be written as a rate equation in the form, Eq. 5.13,

$$\dot{Q} = \frac{dU}{dt} + \dot{W}$$

$$\dot{W} = -\mathscr{E}i = -20 \times 12.8 = -256 \text{ watts}$$

$$1 \text{ watt} = 3.412 \text{ Btu/hr}$$

Therefore,

$$\dot{W} = -256 \text{ watts} \times 3.412 \frac{\text{Btu}}{\text{watt hr}} = -873 \text{ Btu/hr}$$

$$\frac{dU}{dt} = \dot{Q} - \dot{W} = -25 \frac{\text{Btu}}{\text{hr}} - (-873) \frac{\text{Btu}}{\text{hr}}$$

$$= 848 \text{ Btu/hr}$$

5.5 Conservation of Mass

In the previous section we have considered the first law of thermodynamics for a system undergoing a change of state. A system is defined as a fixed quantity of mass. The question now arises, does the mass of the system change when the energy of a system changes? If it does, then our definition of a system as a fixed quantity of mass is no longer valid when the energy of the system changes.

We know from relativistic considerations that mass and energy are related by the well-known equation

$$E = mc^2 \qquad (5.15)$$

where c = velocity of light, and E = energy.

We conclude from this equation that the mass of a system does change when its energy changes. Let us calculate the magnitude of this change of mass for a typical problem, and determine whether this change in mass is significant.

Consider as a system a rigid vessel that contains a 1-lbm stoichiometric mixture of a hydrocarbon fuel (such as gasoline) and air. From our knowledge of combustion, we know that after combustion takes place it will be necessary to transfer about 1250 Btu from the system in order to restore the system to its initial temperature. From the first law

$$_1Q_2 = U_2 - U_1 + {}_1W_2$$

we conclude, since $_1W_2 = 0$ and $_1Q_2 = -1250$ Btu, that the internal energy of the system decreases by 1250 Btu during the heat transfer process. Let us now calculate the decrease in mass during this process using Eq. 5.15.

The velocity of light, c, is 9.83×10^8 ft/sec. Therefore

$$1250 \, (\text{Btu}) = \frac{m \, (\text{lbm}) \times 9.83^2 \times 10^8 \times 10^8 \, \text{ft}^2/\text{sec}^2 \times \tfrac{1}{778} \, \text{Btu/ft-lbf}}{32.17 \, \text{lbm-ft/lbf-sec}^2}$$

$$m = 3.24 \times 10^{-11} \, \text{lbm}$$

Therefore, when the energy of the system decreases by 1250 Btu, the decrease in mass is 3.24×10^{-11} lbm.

A change in mass of this magnitude cannot be detected by even our most accurate chemical balance. And, certainly, a fractional change in mass of this magnitude is beyond the accuracy required in essentially all engineering calculations. Therefore, if we use the laws of conservation of mass and conservation of energy as separate laws, we will not introduce significant error into most thermodynamic problems, and our definition of a system as having a fixed mass can be used even though the energy of the system changes.

5.6 Conservation of Mass and the Control Volume

A control volume is a volume in space in which one has interest for a particular study or analysis. The surface of this control volume is referred

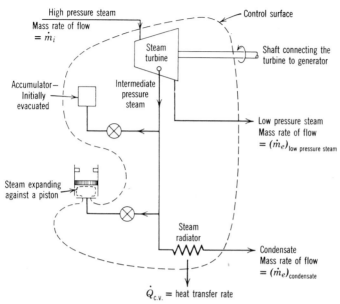

Fig. 5.3   Schematic diagram of a control volume showing mass and energy transfers and accumulation.

to as a control surface and always consists of a closed surface. The size and shape of the control volume are completely arbitrary, and are so defined as to best suit the analysis which is to be made. The surface may be fixed, or it may move or expand. However, the surface must be defined relative to some coordinate system. In some analyses it may be desirable to consider a rotating or moving coordinate system, and to describe the position of the control surface relative to such a coordinate system.

Mass as well as heat and work can cross the control surface and the mass in the control volume, as well as the properties of this mass, can change with time. Figure 5.3 shows a schematic diagram of a control volume, with heat transfer, shaft work, accumulation of mass within the control volume and a moving boundary.

Let us first consider the law of the conservation of mass as it relates to the control volume. In doing so we consider the mass flow into and out of the control volume and the net increase of mass within the control volume. During a time interval δt let the mass δm_i, as shown in Fig. 5.4, enter the control volume, and the mass δm_e leave the control volume. Further, let us designate the mass within the control volume at the beginning of this time interval as m_t and the mass within the control volume after this interval as $m_{t+\delta t}$. Then, from the law of the conservation

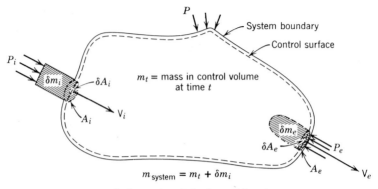

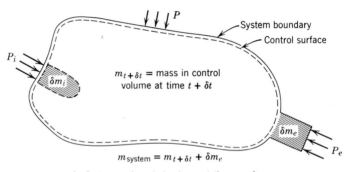

Fig. 5.4   Schematic diagram of a control volume for analysis of the continuity equation as applied to a control volume.

of mass we can write

$$m_t + \delta m_i = m_{t+\delta t} + \delta m_e$$

We can also look at this from the point of view of the net flow across the control surface and the change of mass within the control volume.

Net flow into the control volume during δt = increase of mass within the control volume during δt

$$(\delta m_i - \delta m_e) = m_{t+\delta t} - m_t$$

or $\qquad\qquad (m_{t+\delta t} - m_t) + (\delta m_e - \delta m_i) = 0 \qquad\qquad (5.16)$

As written, this equation simply states that the change of mass within the control volume during δt, namely, $(m_{t+\delta t} - m_t)$, and the net mass flow into the control volume during δt, namely, $(\delta m_i - \delta m_e)$ are equal. However, in many problems requiring a thermodynamic analysis we find it very convenient to have the law of the conservation of mass (as well as the first and second laws of thermodynamics and the momentum equation) expressed as a rate equation for the control volume. This involves the instantaneous rate of mass flow across the control surface and the instantaneous rate of change of mass within the control volume.

Let us now proceed to write the law of the conservation of mass as a rate equation for a control volume.

First, considering Eq. 5.16, we can write an expression for the average rate of change of mass within the control volume during δt, and the average mass rate of flow across the control surface during δt by dividing Eq. 5.16 by δt.

$$\frac{(m_{t+\delta t} - m_t)}{\delta t} + \frac{(\delta m_e - \delta m_i)}{\delta t} = 0. \tag{5.17}$$

We now proceed to develop an equation giving the instantaneous rates of change for each of the terms of Eq. 5.17.

Consider first the second term of this equation. An element of the control surface, δA_e, is shown in Fig. 5.5, and across this area there is a flow outward. The rate of flow outward across this area element is $\delta \dot{m}_e$. The symbol $\dot{m}$ will be used to designate mass rate of flow across a control surface. The δ signifies that this is the flow rate across only an element of area, δA_e, on the control surface. The outward rate of flow across the

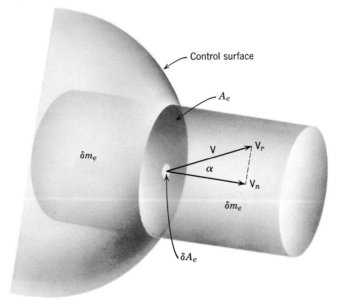

Fig. 5.5   Area on a control surface across which there is an outward flow of mass.

entire control surface can be found by integrating over the entire area, namely

$$\dot{m}_e = \int_A \delta \dot{m}_e \qquad (5.18)$$

A similar expression can be written for the inward rate of flow.

The rate of flow can also be expressed in terms of velocity and density in accordance with the relation

$$\delta \dot{m}_e = \rho V_n \, \delta A_e$$

where V_n is the component of velocity normal to and relative to the area δA_e, as shown in Fig. 5.5, and ρ is the density of the mass crossing the control surface at this point. We note also that

$$V_n = V_r \cos \alpha$$

where V_r is the velocity relative to δA_e and in the direction α relative to the outward normal to δA_e. If the flow is inward, the same expression applies, but $\cos \alpha$ is then negative. Thus the net rate of flow outward across the entire volume can be written as a surface integral by the equation

$$(\delta \dot{m}_e)_{net} = \rho V_r \cos \alpha \, dA$$

Integrating over the entire control surface, we have the net outward rate of flow.

$$(\dot{m}_e)_{net} = \int_A \rho V_r \cos \alpha \, dA \qquad (5.19)$$

Consider the time interval δt. Let us designate $[\int \rho V_r \cos \alpha \, dA]_{av}$ as the average rate of flow across the control surface during this time interval. Then the net mass flow across the control surface during δt, namely $(\delta m_e - \delta m_i)$, is given by

$$(\delta m_e - \delta m_i) = \left[\int_A \rho V_r \cos \alpha \, dA \right]_{av} \delta t \qquad (5.20)$$

Rearranging this we can write

$$\frac{(\delta m_e - \delta m_i)}{\delta t} = \left[\int_A \rho V_r \cos \alpha \, dA \right]_{av} \qquad (5.21)$$

The first term of Eq. 5.17 $(m_{t+\delta t} - m_t)$, which represents the change of mass within the control volume during δt, can be written as a volume integral by considering an element of volume, dV, within the control volume, where the density is ρ, and integrating over the entire control volume. Thus at an instant of time the mass in the control volume is $\int_V \rho \, dV$. Therefore

$$(m_{t+\delta t} - m_t) = \delta \int_V \rho \, dV \qquad (5.22)$$

Considering the time interval δt, we can write an expression for the average rate of change in the mass within the control volume during δt.

$$\frac{(m_{t+\delta t} - m_t)}{\delta t} = \frac{\delta}{\delta t} \int_V \rho \, dV \qquad (5.23)$$

Substituting Eqs. 5.21 and 5.23 into Eq. 5.17 we have

$$\frac{\delta}{\delta t} \int_V \rho \, dV + \left[\int_A \rho V_r \cos \alpha \, dA \right]_{av} = 0 \qquad (5.24)$$

As δt approaches zero we have, in the limit, the instantaneous rate of change of mass within the control volume and the instantaneous rate of mass flow across the control surface.

$$\lim_{\delta t \to 0} \frac{m_{t+\delta t} - m_t}{\delta t} = \lim_{\delta t \to 0} \frac{\delta}{\delta t} \int_V \rho \, dV = \frac{d}{dt} \int_V \rho \, dV$$

$$\lim_{\delta t \to 0} \frac{\delta m_e - \delta m_i}{\delta t} = \lim_{\delta t \to 0} \left[\int_A \rho V_r \cos \alpha \, dA \right]_{av} = \int_A \rho V_r \cos \alpha \, dA$$

Substituting these expressions into Eq. 5.24 we have, as $\delta t \to 0$, the rate equation of the law of the conservation of mass for a control volume, namely,

$$\frac{d}{dt} \int_V \rho \, dV + \int_A \rho V_r \cos \alpha \, dA = 0 \qquad (5.25)$$

Equation 5.25 is frequently referred to as the continuity equation. We note that V_r is relative to the control surface at area dA. If the control surface is not moving relative to the coordinate system, $V_r = V$, where V is the velocity of the fluid relative to the coordinate system. If the control surface is moving with a velocity V_s relative to the coordinate system, $\vec{V}_r = \vec{V} - \vec{V}_s$, where $\vec{V} - \vec{V}_s$ represents the vectorial difference of these velocities. In this text we will always assume that the control volume is fixed relative to the coordinate frame.

5.7 The First Law of Thermodynamics for a Control Volume

We have already considered the first law of thermodynamics for a system, which consists of a fixed quantity of mass, and noted, Eq. 5.5, that it may be written

$$_1Q_2 = E_2 - E_1 + _1W_2$$

We have also noted that this may be written as an average rate equation, over the time interval δt by dividing by δt

$$\frac{\delta Q}{\delta t} = \frac{\Delta E}{\delta t} + \frac{\delta W}{\delta t} \qquad (5.26)$$

In order to write the first law as a rate equation for a control volume we proceed in a manner analogous to that used in developing a rate

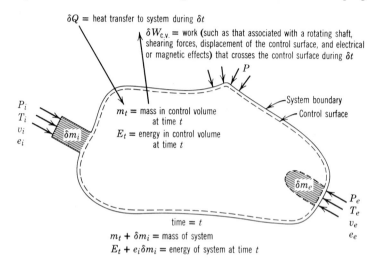

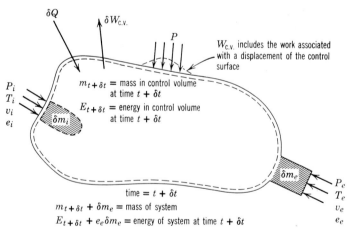

Fig. 5.6   Schematic diagram for a first law analysis of a control volume, showing heat and work as well as mass crossing the control surface.

equation for the law of the conservation of mass. A system and control volume are shown in Fig. 5.6. The system consists of all the mass initially in the control volume plus the mass δm_i.

Consider the changes that take place in the system and control volume during the time interval δt. During this time δt the mass δm_i enters the control volume through area δA_i, and the mass δm_e leaves the control volume through area δA_e. The total work done by the system during this process is that associated with the masses δm_i and δm_e crossing the control surface, which is usually referred to as flow work, and the work $\delta W_{\text{c.v.}}$ which includes all other forms of work, such as work associated with a rotating shaft that crosses the system boundary, shear forces, electrical, magnetic or surface effects, or expansion or contraction of the control volume. An amount of heat δQ crosses the boundary during δt.

Let us now consider each of the terms of the first law as it is written for the system, and transform each term into an equivalent form that applies to the control volume. Consider first the term $E_2 - E_1$.

Let E_t = the energy in the control volume at time t

$E_{t+\delta t}$ = the energy in the control volume at time $t + \delta t$.

Then

$$E_1 = E_t + e_i \, \delta m_i = \text{energy of the system at time } t$$

$$E_2 = E_{t+\delta t} + e_e \delta m_e = \text{energy of the system at time } t + \delta t.$$

Therefore

$$E_2 - E_1 = E_{t+\delta t} + e_e \, \delta m_e - E_t - e_i \, \delta m_i$$

$$= (E_{t+\delta t} - E_t) + (e_e \, \delta m_e - e_i \, \delta m_i) \qquad (5.27)$$

The term $(e_e \, \delta m_e - e_i \, \delta m_i)$ represents the net flow of energy that crosses the control surface during δt as the result of the masses δm_e and δm_i crossing the control surface.

We have already noted, Eq. 5.20, that the mass flow across the control surface during δt can be written

$$\delta m_e - \delta m_i = \left[\int_A \rho V_r \cos \alpha \, dA \right]_{\text{av}} \delta t$$

In a similar manner we can write an expression for the flow of energy across the control surface during δt as

$$e_e \, \delta m_e - e_i \, \delta m_i = \left[\int_A e\rho V_r \cos \alpha \, dA \right]_{\text{av}} \delta t \qquad (5.28)$$

Rearranging, we have the average rate at which energy crosses the control surface during δt

$$\frac{e_e \, \delta m_e - e_i \, \delta m_i}{\delta t} = \left[\int_A e\rho V_r \cos \alpha \, dA \right]_{\text{av}} \qquad (5.29)$$

The second term of Eq. 5.27, $E_{t+\delta t} - E_t$, which represents the change of energy within the control volume during δt, can be written in terms of a volume integral. We note that at any instant of time, the energy in the control volume can be written

$$E_{\text{c.v.}} = \int_m e \, dm = \int_V e\rho \, dV$$

where dV represents an element of volume in the control volume, and the integration is over the entire control volume. Therefore, we can write

$$E_{t+\delta t} - E_t = \delta \int_m e \, dm = \delta \int_V e\rho \, dV \qquad (5.30)$$

Considering the time interval δt, the average rate of change of energy in the control volume during δt is

$$\frac{E_{t+\delta t} - E_t}{\delta t} = \frac{\delta}{\delta t} \int_m e \, dm = \frac{\delta}{\delta t} \int_V e\rho \, dV \qquad (5.31)$$

Substituting Eqs. 5.28 and 5.30 in Eq. 5.27 we have

$$E_2 - E_1 = \Delta E = \delta \int_V e\rho \, dV + \left[\int_A e\rho V_r \cos \alpha \, dA \right]_{\text{av}} \delta t \qquad (5.32)$$

Dividing by δt we have the average rate of change of the energy of the system during δt

$$\frac{\Delta E}{\delta t} = \frac{\delta}{\delta t} \int_V e\rho \, dV + \left[\int_A e\rho V_r \cos \alpha \, dA \right]_{\text{av}} \qquad (5.33)$$

In connection with the work δW done by the system, it is convenient to distinguish between the work done on the masses δm_i and δm_e as they enter and leave the control volume, and $W_{\text{c.v.}}$, which represents all other work done by the system during time δt. The latter work, $W_{\text{c.v.}}$, includes such work as electrical or magnetic work crossing the control surface, and work associated with the expansion or contraction of the control volume, work done by shear forces at the system boundary, and work done by a rotating shaft (which is really a form of shear work at that point where the control surface intersects the rotating shaft).

Let us consider in more detail the work associated with the masses δm_i and δm_e crossing the control surface. Work is done by the normal force (normal to area δA) acting on δm_i and δm_e as these masses cross the control surface. This normal force is equal to the product of the normal tensile stress, $-\sigma_n$, and the area, δA. The work done is

$$-\sigma_n \, \delta A \, dl = \sigma_n \, \delta V = -\sigma_n v \, \delta m \tag{5.34}$$

A complete analysis of the nature of the normal stress, σ_n, for an actual fluid involves both static pressure and viscous effects, and is beyond the scope of this book.* We will assume in this book that the normal stress, σ_n, at a point is equal to the static pressure at this point, P, and simply note that in many applications this is a very reasonable assumption and yields results of good accuracy.

With this assumption the work done on mass δm_i as it enters the control volume is $P_i v_i \, \delta m_i$, and the work done by mass δm_e as it leaves the control volume is $P_e v_e \, \delta m_e$. We will refer to these terms as the flow work. Various other terms are encountered in the literature such as flow energy and work of introduction and work of expulsion.

Thus the total work done by the system during time δt is

$$\delta W = \delta W_{\text{c.v.}} + [P_e v_e \, \delta m_e - P_i v_i \, \delta m_i] \tag{5.35}$$

In a manner analogous to that used for mass and energy crossing the control surface we can write the last term in this equation as a surface integral.

$$\delta W = \delta W_{\text{c.v.}} + \left[\int_A P v \rho V_r \cos \alpha \, dA \right]_{\text{av}} \delta t \tag{5.36}$$

This can also be written as an average rate equation for the interval δt.

$$\frac{\delta W}{\delta t} = \frac{\delta W_{\text{c.v.}}}{\delta t} + \left[\int_A P v \rho V_r \cos \alpha \, dA \right]_{\text{av}} \tag{5.37}$$

Substituting Eqs. 5.33 and 5.37 into Eq. 5.26 we have

$$\frac{\delta Q}{\delta t} = \frac{\delta}{\delta t} \int_V e\rho \, dV + \left[\int_A e\rho V_r \cos \alpha \, dA \right]_{\text{av}}$$
$$+ \frac{\delta W_{\text{c.v.}}}{\delta t} + \left[\int_A P v \rho V_r \cos \alpha \, dA \right]_{\text{av}} \tag{5.38}$$

We can combine the two terms that involve a surface integral.

$$\frac{\delta Q}{\delta t} = \frac{\delta}{\delta t} \int_V e\rho \, dV + \left[\int_A (e + Pv)\rho V_r \cos \alpha \, dA \right]_{\text{av}} + \frac{\delta W_{\text{c.v.}}}{\delta t} \tag{5.39}$$

* It is, however, included in a subsequent book in this series, *Fluid Mechanics*, by A. G. Hansen.

Let us now examine each of these terms and establish the limit as δt approaches zero.

As regards the heat transfer, as δt approaches zero, the system and the control volume coincide, and the heat transfer rate to the system is also the heat transfer rate to the control volume. Therefore,

$$\lim_{\delta t \to 0} \frac{\delta Q}{\delta t} = \dot{Q}_{\text{c.v.}},$$

the rate of heat transfer to the control volume. Further,

$$\lim_{\delta t \to 0} \frac{\delta}{\delta t} \int_V e\rho \, dV = \frac{d}{dt} \int_V e\rho \, dV$$

$$\lim_{\delta t \to 0} \left[\int_A (e + Pv)\rho V_r \cos \alpha \, dA \right]_{\text{av}} = \int_A (e + Pv)\rho V_r \cos \alpha \, dA$$

$$\lim_{\delta t \to 0} \frac{\delta W_{\text{c.v.}}}{\delta t} = \dot{W}_{\text{c.v.}}$$

Therefore, as δt approaches zero we can write the first law for the control volume as a rate equation.

$$\dot{Q}_{\text{c.v.}} = \frac{d}{dt} \int_V e\rho \, dV + \int_A (e + Pv)\rho V_r \cos \alpha \, dA + \dot{W}_{\text{c.v.}} \qquad (5.40)$$

This equation is the basic rate equation for the first law of thermodynamics for a control volume. The first term represents the rate of heat transfer, the second term the rate at which the energy within the control volume increases, the third term represents the net rate of flow of energy out of the control volume that results from the mass flow across the control surface, and the last term represents the power output that is associated with the shear forces, electrical effects and other factors that have already been mentioned.

Equation 5.40 can be integrated over time t to give the total energy changes that occur during this period.

$$\int_0^t \dot{Q}_{\text{c.v.}} \, dt = \int_0^t \left(\frac{d}{dt} \int_V e\rho \, dV \right) dt$$

$$+ \int_0^t \left[\int_A (e + Pv)\rho V_r \cos \alpha \, dA \right] dt + \int_0^t \dot{W}_{\text{c.v.}} \, dt \qquad (5.41)$$

The actual integration can of course be performed only if we know each of these rates as a function of time.

It should be noted that if there is no mass flow across the control surface, the control volume analysis reduces to a system analysis. This is evident from a consideration of Eq. 5.40, for when there is no mass flow across the control surface we can write,

$$\frac{d}{dt} \int_V e\rho \, dV = \frac{dE}{dt}$$

and

$$\int_A (e + Pv)\rho V_r \cos \alpha \, dA = 0$$

Also, since there is no flow work (see Eq. 5.37)

$$\dot{W}_{\text{c.v.}} = \dot{W}$$

Under these conditions Eq. 5.40 reduces to the rate equation form of the first law statement for a system,

$$\dot{Q} = \frac{dE}{dt} + \dot{W}$$

which is Eq. 5.14.

Since the control volume approach is more general, and reduces to the usual statement of the first law for a system when there is no mass flow across the control surface we will, when making a general statement of the first law, utilize Eq. 5.40, the rate form of the first law for a control volume.

The term flux should also be introduced at this point. Flux is defined as a rate of flow of any quantity per unit area across a control surface. Thus the mass flux is the rate of mass flow per unit area and heat flux is the heat flow rate per unit area across the control surface.

5.8 The Thermodynamic Property Enthalpy

It will be observed in writing the first law for a control volume that the term $(e + Pv)$, which is equivalent to $\left(u + \dfrac{V^2}{2g_c} + Z\dfrac{g}{g_c} + Pv \right)$, occurs in the term associated with flow of mass across the control surface. We also note that u, P, and v are all thermodynamic properties of the mass that flows across the control surface. Therefore, for convenience, a new thermodynamic property is defined.

$$h = u + Pv$$
or,
$$H = U + PV \tag{5.42}$$

This property, which is called enthalpy, is an extensive property. As in the case of internal energy, we could speak of specific enthalpy, h, and total enthalpy, H. However, we will simply refer to both as enthalpy, since the context will make it clear which is referred to.

In order to add the internal energy and pressure volume product, the units for both must be the same. In this text the usual unit for enthalpy and internal energy is Btu/lbm. When pressure is in lbf/ft^2 and specific volume in ft^3/lbm, the factor $J = 778$ ft-lbf/Btu must be introduced in the denominator (i.e., Pv/J) in order to express the Pv term in Btu/lbm. However, the factor J will not be carried along in the equations because the only essential consideration is that consistent units be used, and many other units than Btu/lbm can be used.

Tables of thermodynamic properties, such as those included in Appendix Tables A.1 to A.6, give values of enthalpy in both the saturated and superheated regions. The values given are all relative to some arbitrarily selected base. In the steam tables, the enthalpy of saturated liquid at 32 F is the reference state and is given a value of zero. For refrigerants, such as ammonia and Freon-12, the reference state is saturated liquid at -40 F, the enthalpy in this reference state being assigned the value of zero. Thus, it is possible to have negative values of enthalpy, as is the case for saturated solid in Table 5 of Keenan and Keyes' steam tables (Table A.1.5 of the Appendix). It should be pointed out that when enthalpy and internal energy are given values relative to the same reference state, as is the case in essentially all thermodynamic tables, the internal energy u is equal to $-Pv$ at the reference state. For example, at 32 F the enthalpy of saturated liquid water is zero. Therefore, in this state the internal energy u is found as follows:

$$u = h - Pv$$

$$u = 0 - \frac{0.08854 \times 144 \times 0.01602}{778} = -0.000263 \text{ Btu/lbm}$$

This is negligible as far as the significant figures of the tables are concerned, but the principle should be kept in mind, as in certain cases it is significant.

In the superheat region of most thermodynamic tables, values of the specific internal energy u are not given. However, these can be readily calculated from the relation $u = h - Pv$, though it is important to keep the units in mind. As an example, let us calculate the internal energy u of superheated steam at 100 $lbf/in.^2$, 500 F.

$$u = h - Pv$$

$$u = 1279.1 - \frac{100 \times 144 \times 5.589}{778} = 1175.6 \text{ Btu/lbm}$$

The enthalpy of a substance in a saturation state and having a given quality is found in the same way that the specific volume and internal energy were found. The enthalpy of saturated liquid has the symbol h_f, saturated vapor h_g, and the increase in enthalpy during vaporization, h_{fg}.

For a saturation state, the enthalpy can be calculated by one of the following relations:

$$h = (1 - x)h_f + xh_g$$
$$h = h_f + xh_{fg}$$
$$h = h_g - (1 - x)h_{fg}$$

The enthalpy of compressed water may be found by using the corrections from Table 4 of the steam tables (Table A.1.4 of the Appendix) in the same manner that the specific volume was found in Chapter 3.

Introducing the definition of enthalpy, the first law for a control volume, Eq. 5.40, can be written

$$\dot{Q}_{\text{c.v.}} = \frac{d}{dt} \int_V e\rho \, dV + \int_A \left(h + \frac{\mathsf{V}^2}{2g_c} + Z\frac{g}{g_c}\right)\rho \mathsf{V}_r \cos \alpha \, dA + \dot{W}_{\text{c.v.}} \quad (5.43)$$

5.9 The Steady-State, Steady-Flow Process

We have digressed from our consideration of the first law to introduce the thermodynamic property enthalpy. We shall now return to our discussion of the first law for a control volume and consider certain assumptions that lead to the definition of a process that we shall refer to as the steady-state, steady-flow process. These are very reasonable assumptions in many cases and lead to a simplified and more readily usable form of the first law for a control volume.

The assumptions for the steady-state, steady-flow process are as follows.

1. The control volume does not move relative to the coordinate frame.

2. As for the mass that flows across the control surface, the mass flux and the state of this mass at each element of area on the control surface do not vary with time. Furthermore, the total mass rate of flow into the control volume is equal to the total mass rate of flow out of the control volume.

3. As for the mass in the control volume, the state of the mass at each point in the control volume does not vary with time, and, as a consequence of assumption 2, the total mass within the control volume remains constant with time.

4. The rates at which heat and work cross the control surface remain constant.

As an example of a steady-state, steady-flow process consider a centrifugal air compressor that operates with constant mass rate of flow into and out of the compressor, constant properties at each point across the inlet and exit ducts, a constant rate of heat transfer to the surroundings, and a constant power input. At each point in the compressor the properties are constant with time, even though the properties of a given elemental mass of air vary as it flows through the compressor. Usually such a process is referred to simply as a steady flow process, since we are concerned primarily with the properties of the fluid entering and leaving the control volume. On the other hand, in the analysis of certain heat transfer problems in which the same assumptions apply, we are primarily interested in the spatial distribution of properties, particularly temperature, and such a process is often referred to as a steady state process. Since this is an introductory book we will use the term steady-state, steady-flow process in order to emphasize the basic assumptions involved. The student should realize that the terms steady-state process and steady-flow process are both used extensively in the literature.

Let us now consider the significance of each of these assumptions for the steady-state, steady-flow process.

1. The assumption that the control volume does not move relative to the coordinate frame means that all velocities measured relative to the coordinate frame are also velocities relative to the control surface, and there is no work associated with the acceleration of the control volume.

2. From the assumption that the mass flux (flow rate per unit area) is constant at each point on the control surface, and the mass rates of flow into and out of the control volume are equal, we conclude that

$$\frac{d}{dt} \int_V \rho \, dV = 0$$

and therefore, from the continuity equation, Eq. 5.25,

$$\frac{d}{dt} \int_V \rho \, dV + \int_A \rho V_r \cos \alpha \, dA = 0$$

we conclude that for the steady-state, steady-flow process

$$\int_A \rho V_r \cos \alpha \, dA = 0$$

3. The assumption that the state of the mass at each point in the control volume does not vary with time can be considered in relation to the first law for the control volume, Eq. 5.43.

$$\dot{Q}_{c.v.} = \frac{d}{dt} \int_V e\rho \, dV + \int_A \left(h + \frac{V^2}{2g_c} + Z\frac{g}{g_c} \right) \rho V_r \cos \alpha \, dA + \dot{W}_{c.v.}$$

It follows that for the steady-state, steady-flow process

$$\frac{d}{dt} \int_V e\rho \, dV = 0$$

Therefore, for the steady-state, steady-flow process we can write:
Continuity Equation:

$$\int_A \rho V_r \cos \alpha \, dA = 0 \tag{5.44}$$

First Law:

$$\dot{Q}_{c.v.} = \int_A \left(h + \frac{V^2}{2g_c} + Z \frac{g}{g_c} \right) \rho V_r \cos \alpha \, dA + \dot{W}_{c.v.} \tag{5.45}$$

Let us now make one additional assumption, namely, that there are a number of areas on the control surface over which the mass flux and the state of the mass crossing the control surface are uniform as well as constant with respect to time. With this assumption we can write:
Continuity Equation:

$$\int_A \rho V_r \cos \alpha \, dA = \sum \dot{m}_e - \sum \dot{m}_i = 0$$

or

$$\sum \dot{m}_e = \sum \dot{m}_i$$

where the summation is over all the areas where flow occurs.
Consider also the term from Eq. 5.45,

$$\int_A \left(h + \frac{V^2}{2g_c} + Z \frac{g}{g_c} \right) \rho V_r \cos \alpha \, dA$$

in the light of this same assumption of uniform mass flux and thermodynamic state over various areas on the control surface. With these assumptions this term can be written

$$\int_A \left(h + \frac{V^2}{2g_c} + Z \frac{g}{g_c} \right) \rho V_r \cos \alpha \, dA = \sum \dot{m}_e \left(h_e + \frac{V_e^2}{2g_c} + Z_e \frac{g}{g_c} \right)$$

$$- \sum \dot{m}_i \left(h_i + \frac{V_i^2}{2g_c} + Z_i \frac{g}{g_c} \right)$$

where the summation is over all the areas where flow occurs.
Therefore, for the steady-state, steady-flow process with uniform mass

flux and uniform thermodynamic state over various areas on the control surface we can write:

Continuity Equation:

$$\sum \dot{m}_i = \sum \dot{m}_e \qquad (5.46)$$

First Law:

$$\dot{Q}_{c.v.} + \sum \dot{m}_i\left(h_i + \frac{V_i^2}{2g_c} + Z_i\frac{g}{g_c}\right) = \dot{W}_{c.v.} + \sum \dot{m}_e\left(h_e + \frac{V_e^2}{2g_c} + Z_e\frac{g}{g_c}\right)$$

$$(5.47)$$

If there is only one area over which mass flows into the control volume, and one area over which mass flows out of the control volume, both at a uniform rate and with uniform properties, we can write:

Continuity Equation:

$$\dot{m}_i = \dot{m}_e = \dot{m} \qquad (5.48)$$

First Law:

$$\dot{Q}_{c.v.} + \dot{m}\left(h_i + \frac{V_i^2}{2g_c} + Z_i\frac{g}{g_c}\right) = \dot{W}_{c.v.} + \dot{m}\left(h_e + \frac{V_e^2}{2g_c} + Z_e\frac{g}{g_c}\right) \quad (5.49)$$

Rearranging this equation we have:

$$q + h_i + \frac{V_i^2}{2g_c} + Z_i\frac{g}{g_c} = w + h_e + \frac{V_e^2}{2g_c} + Z_e\frac{g}{g_c} \qquad (5.50)$$

where, by definition,

$$q = \frac{\dot{Q}_{c.v.}}{\dot{m}} \quad \text{and} \quad w = \frac{\dot{W}_{c.v.}}{\dot{m}}$$

Note that the units for q and w are Btu/lbm. From their definition q and w can be thought of as the heat transfer and work (other than flow work) per unit mass flowing into and out of the control volume for this particular steady-state, steady-flow process.

The symbols q and w are also used for the heat transfer and work per unit mass of a system. However, since it is always evident from the context whether it is a system (fixed mass) or control volume (involving a flow of mass) with which we are concerned, the significance of the symbols q and w will also be readily evident in each situation.

The steady-state, steady-flow process is often used in the analysis of reciprocating machines, such as reciprocating compressors or engines. In this case the rate of flow, which may actually be pulsating, is considered to be the average rate of flow for an integral number of cycles. A similar assumption is made as regards the properties of the fluid flowing across the control surface, and the heat transfer and work crossing the control surface. It is also assumed that for an integral number of cycles the reciprocating device undergoes, the energy and mass within the control volume do not change.

A number of examples are now given to illustrate the analysis of steady-state steady-flow processes.

Example 5.5

The mass rate of flow into a steam turbine is 10,000 lbm/hr, and the heat transfer from the turbine is 30,000 Btu/hr. The following data are known for the steam entering and leaving the turbine.

	Inlet Conditions	Exit Conditions
Pressure	300 lbf/in.²	15 lbf/in.²
Temperature	700 F	
Quality		100%
Velocity	200 ft/sec	600 ft/sec
Elevation above reference plane	16 feet	10 feet

$g = 32.17$ ft/sec²

Determine the power output of the turbine.

Consider a control surface around the turbine, as shown in Fig. 5.7. From the data available it is evident that we can assume a steady-state steady-flow process. Since flow enters at only one point and leaves at only one point the equation for the first law is given by Eq. 5.49.

$$\dot{Q}_{\text{c.v.}} + \dot{m}\left(h_i + \frac{V_i^2}{2g_c} + Z_i\frac{g}{g_c}\right) = \dot{m}\left(h_e + \frac{V_e^2}{2g_c} + Z_e\frac{g}{g_c}\right) + \dot{W}_{\text{c.v.}}$$

$\dot{Q}_{\text{c.v.}} = -30,000$ Btu/hr

$h_i = 1368.3$ Btu/lbm (From the steam tables)

$$\frac{V_i^2}{2g_c} = \frac{200 \times 200 \text{ ft}^2/\text{sec}^2}{2 \times 32.17 \text{ lbm-ft/lbf-sec}^2 \times 778 \text{ ft-lbf/Btu}} = 0.799 \text{ Btu/lbm}$$

$$Z_i\frac{g}{g_c} = \frac{16 \text{ ft} \times 32.17 \text{ ft/sec}^2}{32.17 \text{ lbm-ft/lbf-sec}^2 \times 778 \text{ ft-lbf/Btu}} = 0.0206 \text{ Btu/lbm}$$

Similarly

$h_e = 1150.8$ Btu/lbm

$$\frac{V_e^2}{2g_c} = \frac{(600)^2}{2 \times 32.17 \times 778} = 7.2 \text{ Btu/lbm}$$

$$Z_e\frac{g}{g_c} = \frac{10}{778} = 0.0128 \text{ Btu/lbm}$$

Therefore, substituting into Eq. 5.49,

$$-30,000 + 10,000(1368.3 + 0.799 + 0.0206)$$
$$= 10,000(1150.8 + 7.2 + 0.0128) + \dot{W}_{\text{c.v.}}$$

$$\dot{W}_{\text{c.v.}} = -30,000 + 13,691,000 - 11,580,000 = 2,081,000 \text{ Btu/hr}$$

$$= \frac{2,081,000 \text{ Btu/hr}}{2545 \text{ Btu/hp-hr}} = 816 \text{ hp}$$

If Eq. 5.50 is used, the work per pound mass of fluid flowing is found first.

$$q + h_i + \frac{V_i^2}{2g_c} + Z_i \frac{g}{g_c} = h_e + \frac{V_e^2}{2g_c} + Z_e \frac{g}{g_c} + w$$

$$q = \frac{-30,000}{10,000} = -3 \text{ Btu/lbm}$$

Therefore, substituting into Eq. 5.50,

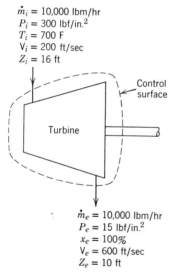

$\dot{m}_i = 10,000$ lbm/hr
$P_i = 300$ lbf/in.²
$T_i = 700$ F
$V_i = 200$ ft/sec
$Z_i = 16$ ft

Control surface

Turbine

$\dot{m}_e = 10,000$ lbm/hr
$P_e = 15$ lbf/in.²
$x_e = 100\%$
$V_e = 600$ ft/sec
$Z_e = 10$ ft

Fig. 5.7 Illustration for Example 5.5.

$$-3 + 1368.3 + \frac{(200)^2}{2 \times 32.17 \times 778} + \frac{16}{778}$$

$$= 1152.0 + \frac{(600)^2}{2 \times 32.17 \times 778} + \frac{10}{778} + w$$

$$-3 + 1368.3 + 0.799 + 0.0206$$
$$= 1150.8 + 7.2 + 0.0128 + w$$

$$w = 208.1 \text{ Btu/lbm}$$

$$\dot{W}_{\text{c.v.}} = \frac{208.1 \text{ Btu/lbm} \times 10,000 \text{ lbm/hr}}{2545 \text{ Btu/hp-hr}}$$

$$= 816 \text{ hp}$$

Two further observations can be made by referring to this example. First, in many engineering problems potential energy changes are insignificant when compared with the other energy quantities. In the above example the potential energy change did not affect any of the significant figures. In most problems where the change in elevation is small the potential energy terms may be neglected.

Second, if velocities are small, say under 100 ft/sec, in many cases the kinetic energy is insignificant compared with other energy quantities. Further, when the velocities entering and leaving the system are essentially the same, the change in kinetic energy is small. Since it is the change in kinetic energy that is important in the steady-state, steady-flow energy equation, the kinetic energy terms can usually be neglected when there is no significant difference between the velocity of the fluid entering and leaving the control volume. Thus in many thermodynamic problems one must make judgments as to which quantities may be negligible for a given analysis.

Example 5.6

Steam at 100 lbf/in.², 400 F, enters an insulated nozzle with a velocity of 200 ft/sec. It leaves at a pressure of 20 lbf/in.² and a velocity of 2000 ft/sec. Determine the final temperature if the steam is superheated in the final state, and the quality if it is saturated.

Considering a control surface around the nozzle (Fig. 5.8) it is evident that a steady-state, steady-flow process is a reasonable assumption. Further, $\dot{Q}_{c.v.}$ and $\dot{W}_{c.v.}$ are zero in this problem. Also, since there is no significant change in elevation between the inlet and exit of the nozzle, the change in potential energy is negligible. Therefore, for this process the first law, Eq. 5.50, reduces to

$$h_i + \frac{V_i^2}{2g_c} = h_e + \frac{V_e^2}{2g_c}$$

$$h_e = 1227.6 + \frac{(200)^2}{2 \times 32.17 \times 778} - \frac{(2000)^2}{2 \times 32.17 \times 778}$$

$$h_e = 1227.6 - 79.2 = 1148.4 \text{ Btu/lbm}$$

The two properties of the fluid leaving which we now know are pressure and enthalpy, and therefore the state of this fluid is determined. Since h_e

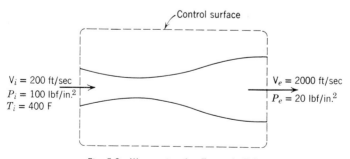

Control surface

V_i = 200 ft/sec
P_i = 100 lbf/in.²
T_i = 400 F

V_e = 2000 ft/sec
P_e = 20 lbf/in.²

Fig. 5.8   Illustration for Example 5.6.

is less than h_g at 20 lbf/in.², the quality is calculated.

$$h = h_g - (1 - x)h_{fg}$$

$$1148.4 = 1156.3 - (1 - x)960.1$$

$$(1 - x) = \frac{7.9}{960.1} = 0.8\%$$

$$x = 99.2\%$$

Example 5.7

In a refrigeration system, in which Freon-12 is the refrigerant, the Freon-12 enters the compressor at 30 lbf/in.², 20 F. The mass rate of flow is 125 lbm/hr, and the power input to the compressor is 1 kw.

On leaving the compressor the Freon-12 enters a water-cooled condenser at 160 lbf/in.², 180 F, and leaves as a liquid at 150 lbf/in.², 100 F. Water enters the condenser at 55 F and leaves at 75 F. Determine:

(a) The heat transfer from the compressor per hour.
(b) The rate at which cooling water flows through the condenser.

Consider first a control volume analysis of the compressor. A steady-state, steady-flow process is a reasonable assumption.

$$w = -\frac{3412}{125} = -27.3 \text{ Btu/lbm}$$

From the Freon-12 tables

$$h_i = 79.76 \text{ Btu/lbm} \qquad h_e = 103.91 \text{ Btu/lbm}$$

Since the velocity of the vapor entering a refrigeration compressor is low and not greatly different from the velocity leaving, kinetic energy changes, as well as potential energy changes, can be neglected. Therefore, the first law for this process, Eq. 5.50 reduces to

$$q + h_i = w + h_e$$

$$q = -27.30 + 103.91 - 79.76 = -3.15 \text{ Btu/lbm}$$

$$\dot{Q}_{c.v.} = 125 \text{ lbm/hr} \times (-3.15) \text{ Btu/lbm} = -394 \text{ Btu/hr}$$

Next consider a control volume analysis of the condenser and a steady-state, steady-flow process. The schematic diagram for this condenser is shown in Fig. 5.9.

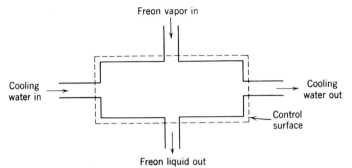

Fig. 5.9   Schematic diagram of a Freon condenser.

With this control volume we have two fluid streams, the Freon and the water, entering and leaving the control volume. It is reasonable to assume that the kinetic and potential energy changes are negligible. We note that the work is zero, and we make the other reasonable assumption that there is no heat transfer across the control surface. Therefore, the first law, Eq. 5.47, reduces to

$$\sum \dot{m}_i h_i = \sum \dot{m}_e h_e$$

In this case we have two streams entering and two streams leaving. Using the subscript r for refrigerant and w for water

$$\dot{m}_r(h_i)_r + \dot{m}_w(h_i)_w = \dot{m}_r(h_e)_r + \dot{m}_w(h_e)_w$$

From the Freon-12 and steam tables we have

$$(h_i)_r = 100.34 \text{ Btu/lbm} \qquad (h_i)_w = 23.07 \text{ Btu/lbm}$$
$$(h_e)_r = 31.10 \qquad\qquad (h_e)_w = 43.03$$

Solving the above equation for $\dot{m}_w$, the rate of flow of water, we have

$$\dot{m}_w = \dot{m}_r \frac{(h_i - h_e)_r}{(h_e - h_i)_w} = 125 \text{ lbm/hr} \frac{(100.34 - 31.10) \text{ Btu/lbm}}{(43.03 - 23.07) \text{ Btu/lbm}} = 433 \text{ lbm/hr}$$

This problem can also be solved by considering two separate control volumes, one of which has the flow of Freon-12 across its control surface, and the other having the flow of water across its control surface. Further there is heat transfer from one control volume to the other. This is shown schematically in Fig. 5.10.

The heat transfer for the control volume involving Freon is calculated first. In this case the steady-state, steady-flow energy equation, Eq. 5.49, reduces to

$$\dot{Q}_{c.v.} = \dot{m}_r(h_e - h_i)_r$$
$$\dot{Q}_{c.v.} = 125 \text{ lbm/hr} \, (31.10 - 100.34) \text{ Btu/lbm} = -8655 \text{ Btu/hr}$$

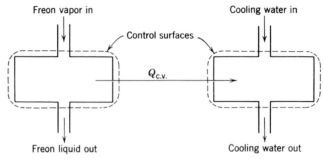

Freon vapor in

Cooling water in

Control surfaces

$Q_{c.v.}$

Freon liquid out

Cooling water out

Fig. 5.10   Schematic diagram of Freon condenser considering two control surfaces.

This is also the heat transfer to the other control volume, for which $\dot{Q}_{c.v.} = +8655$ Btu/hr.

$$\dot{Q}_{c.v.} = \dot{m}_w (h_e - h_i)_w$$

$$\dot{m}_w = \frac{8655 \text{ Btu/hr}}{(43.03 - 23.07) \text{ Btu/lbm}} = 433 \text{ lbm/hr}$$

Example 5.8

Consider the simple steam power plant, as shown in Fig. 5.11. The following data are for such a power plant.

Location	Pressure	Temperature or quality
Leaving boiler	300 lbf/in.²	600 F
Entering turbine	280 lbf/in.²	550 F
Leaving turbine, entering condenser	2 lbf/in.²	93%
Leaving condenser, entering pump	1.9 lbf/in.²	110 F
Pump work = 3 Btu/lbm		

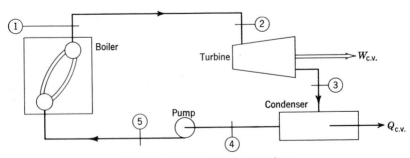

Fig. 5.11   Simple steam power plant.

Determine the following quantities per pound mass flowing through the unit.

(a) Heat transfer in line between boiler and turbine.
(b) Turbine work.
(c) Heat transfer in condenser.
(d) Heat transfer in boiler.

There is a certain advantage in assigning a number to various points in the cycle. For this reason the subscripts i and e in the steady-state, steady-flow energy equation are often replaced by appropriate numbers. Thus, for a steady-state, steady-flow process for a control volume around the turbine one can write

$$q_{turb} + h_2 + \frac{V_2^2}{2g_c} + Z_2 \frac{g}{g_c} = w_{turb} + h_3 + \frac{V_3^2}{2g_c} + Z_3 \frac{g}{g_c}$$

Similarly, for a control volume around the boiler

$$q_{boiler} + h_5 + \frac{V_5^2}{2g_c} + Z_5 \frac{g}{g_c} = h_1 + \frac{V_1^2}{2g_c} + Z_1 \frac{g}{g_c}$$

We might also use the alternate but equally acceptable notation

$$q_{turb} = {}_2q_3; \qquad q_{boiler} = {}_5q_1$$

In this problem we will neglect changes in kinetic energy and potential energy.

The following property values are obtained from the steam tables, where the subscripts refer to Fig. 5.11

$$h_1 = 1314.7 \text{ Btu/lbm}$$
$$h_2 = 1288.7 \text{ Btu/lbm}$$
$$h_3 = 1116.2 - 0.07(1022.2) = 1044.7 \text{ Btu/lbm}$$
$$h_4 = 77.9 \text{ Btu/lbm}$$

(a) Considering a control volume that includes the pipe line between boiler and turbine,

$$_1q_2 + h_1 = h_2$$
$$_1q_2 = h_2 - h_1 = 1288.7 - 1314.7 = -26.0 \text{ Btu/lbm}$$

(b) A turbine is essentially an adiabatic machine, and therefore, considering a control volume around the turbine we can write

$$h_2 = h_3 + {}_2w_3$$
$$_2w_3 = 1288.7 - 1044.7 = 244.0 \text{ Btu/lbm}$$

(c) For the condenser the work is zero, and therefore

$$_3q_4 + h_3 = h_4$$

$$_3q_4 = 77.9 - 1044.7 = -966.8 \text{ Btu/lbm}$$

(d) The enthalpy at point 5 may be found by considering a control volume around the pump

$$h_4 = h_5 + {_4}w_5$$

$$h_5 = 3.0 + 77.9 = 80.9 \text{ Btu/lbm}$$

(e) For the boiler we can write

$$_5q_1 + h_5 = h_1$$

$$_5q_1 = 1314.7 - 80.9 = 1233.8 \text{ Btu/lbm}$$

5.10 The Uniform-State, Uniform-Flow Process

In the last section we considered the steady-state, steady-flow process with the added assumption that the mass flux and the state of the mass crossing the control surface are uniform over the various areas on the control surface where flow occurs. Let us now consider another set of assumptions which leads to another simplified but very reasonable and very useful form of the first law. We will call the process that results from these assumptions the uniform-state, uniform-flow process. These assumptions are:

1. The control volume remains constant relative to the coordinate frame.

2. The state of the mass crossing the control surface is constant with time and uniform over the various areas of the control surface where flow occurs.

3. The state of the mass within the control volume may change with time, but at any instant of time the state is uniform over the entire control volume (or over several identifiable regions that make up the entire control volume).

Let us examine the consequence of these assumptions and derive an expression for the first law that applies to this process. The assumption that the control volume remains stationary relative to the coordinate frame has already been discussed in Section 5.9. The remaining assumptions lead to the following simplifications for the continuity equations and the first law.

With these assumptions, the continuity equation, Eq. 5.25,

$$\frac{d}{dt} \int_V \rho \, dV + \int_A \rho V_r \cos \alpha \, dA = 0$$

can be written

$$\frac{dm_{\text{c.v.}}}{dt} + \Sigma \dot{m}_e - \Sigma \dot{m}_i = 0 \qquad (5.51)$$

where the summation is over all areas on the control surface through which flow occurs. Integrating Eq. 5.51 over time t gives the change of mass in the control volume during time t,

$$\int_0^t \left(\frac{dm_{\text{c.v.}}}{dt} \right) dt = (m_2 - m_1)_{\text{c.v.}}$$

the mass leaving the control volume during time t,

$$\int_0^t (\Sigma \dot{m}_e) \, dt = \Sigma m_e$$

and the mass entering the control volume during time t.

$$\int_0^t (\Sigma \dot{m}_i) \, dt = \Sigma m_i \qquad (5.52)$$

Therefore, for this period of time t we can write the continuity equation for the uniform-state, uniform-flow process as

$$(m_2 - m_1)_{\text{c.v.}} + \Sigma m_e - \Sigma m_i = 0 \qquad (5.53)$$

In writing the first law for the uniform-state, uniform-flow process we consider Eq. 5.43.

$$\dot{Q}_{\text{c.v.}} = \frac{d}{dt} \int_V e\rho \, dV + \int_A \left(h + \frac{V^2}{2g_c} + Z \frac{g}{g_c} \right) \rho V_r \cos \alpha \, dA + \dot{W}_{\text{c.v.}}$$

With the assumptions cited above we can write

$$\frac{d}{dt} \int_V e\rho \, dV = \frac{d}{dt}(me)_{\text{c.v.}} = \frac{d}{dt} \left[(m) \left(u + \frac{V^2}{2g_c} + Z \frac{g}{g_c} \right) \right]_{\text{c.v.}}$$

and

$$\int_A \left(h + \frac{V^2}{2g_c} + Z \frac{g}{g_c} \right) \rho V_r \cos \alpha \, dA = \Sigma \dot{m}_e \left(h_e + \frac{V_e^2}{2g_c} + Z_e \frac{g}{g_c} \right)$$
$$- \Sigma \dot{m}_i \left(h_i + \frac{V_i^2}{2g_c} + Z_i \frac{g}{g_c} \right)$$

Therefore the first law for the uniform-state, uniform-flow process becomes

$$\dot{Q}_{\text{c.v.}} + \sum \dot{m}_i\left(h_i + \frac{V_i^2}{2g_c} + Z_i\frac{g}{g_c}\right) = \dot{W}_{\text{c.v.}} + \sum \dot{m}_e\left(h_e + \frac{V_e^2}{2g_c} + Z_e\frac{g}{g_c}\right)$$
$$+ \frac{d}{dt}\left[(m)\left(u + \frac{V^2}{2g_c} + Z\frac{g}{g_c}\right)\right]_{\text{c.v.}} \quad (5.54)$$

Let us now integrate this equation over time t, during which time we have

$$\int_0^t \dot{Q}_{\text{c.v.}}\, dt = Q_{\text{c.v.}}$$

$$\int_0^t\left[\sum \dot{m}_i\left(h_i + \frac{V_i^2}{2g_c} + Z_i\frac{g}{g_c}\right)\right] dt = \sum m_i\left(h_i + \frac{V_i^2}{2g_c} + Z_i\frac{g}{g_c}\right)$$

$$\int_0^t\left[\sum \dot{m}_e\left(h_e + \frac{V_e^2}{2g_c} + Z_e\frac{g}{g_c}\right)\right] dt = \sum m_e\left(h_e + \frac{V_e^2}{2g_c} + Z_e\frac{g}{g_c}\right)$$

$$\int_0^t \dot{W}_{\text{c.v.}}\, dt = W_{\text{c.v.}} \quad (5.55)$$

$$\int_0^t \frac{d}{dt}\left[(m)\left(u + \frac{V^2}{2g_c} + Z\frac{g}{g_c}\right)\right]_{\text{c.v.}} dt$$
$$= \left[m_2\left(u_2 + \frac{V_2^2}{2g_c} + Z_2\frac{g}{g_c}\right) - m_1\left(u_1 + \frac{V_1^2}{2g_c} + Z_1\frac{g}{g_c}\right)\right]_{\text{c.v.}}$$

Therefore, for this period of time t we can write the first law for the uniform-state, uniform-flow process as

$$Q_{\text{c.v.}} + \sum m_i\left(h_i + \frac{V_i^2}{2g_c} + Z_i\frac{g}{g_c}\right) = W_{\text{c.v.}} + \sum m_e\left(h_e + \frac{V_e^2}{2g_c} + Z_e\frac{g}{g_c}\right)$$
$$+ \left[m_2\left(u_2 + \frac{V_2^2}{2g_c} + Z_2\frac{g}{g_c}\right) - m_1\left(u_1 + \frac{V_1^2}{2g_c} + Z_1\frac{g}{g_c}\right)\right]_{\text{c.v.}} \quad (5.56)$$

As an example of the type of problem for which these assumptions are valid and Eq. 5.56 is appropriate, let us consider the classic problem of flow into an evacuated vessel. This is the subject of Example 5.9.

Example 5.9

Steam at a pressure of 200 lbf/in.², 600 F, is flowing in a pipe, Fig. 5.12. Connected to this pipe through a valve is an evacuated tank. The valve is opened and the tank fills with steam until the pressure is 200 lbf/in.², and then the valve is closed. The process takes place adiabatically and kinetic energies and potential energies are negligible. Determine the final temperature of the steam.

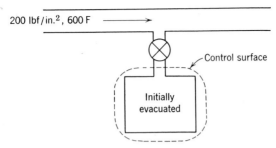

Fig. 5.12   Flow into an evacuated vessel—control volume analysis.

Consider first the control volume shown in Fig. 5.12. The assumptions of uniform state in the control volume and across the pipe are both reasonable, and therefore the first law can be written as stated in Eq. 5.56.

$$Q_{\text{c.v.}} + \sum m_i\left(h_i + \frac{V_i^2}{2g_c} + Z_i\frac{g}{g_c}\right) = W_{\text{c.v.}} + \sum m_e\left(h_e + \frac{V_e^2}{2g_c} + Z_e\frac{g}{g_c}\right)$$
$$+ \left[m_2\left(u_2 + \frac{V_2^2}{2g_c} + Z_2\frac{g}{g_c}\right) - m_1\left(u_1 + \frac{V_1^2}{2g_c} + Z_1\frac{g}{g_c}\right)\right]_{\text{c.v.}}$$

We note that $Q_{\text{c.v.}} = 0$, $W_{\text{c.v.}} = 0$, $m_e = 0$, $(m_1)_{\text{c.v.}} = 0$. We further assume that changes in kinetic and potential energy are negligible. Therefore, the statement of the first law for this process reduces to

$$m_i h_i = m_2 u_2$$

From the continuity equation for this process, Eq. 5.53, we conclude that

$$m_2 = m_i$$

Therefore, combining the continuity equation with the first law we have

$$h_i = u_2$$

That is, the final internal energy of the steam in the tank is equal to the enthalpy of the steam entering the tank.

From the steam tables

$$h_i = u_2 = 1322.1 \text{ Btu/lbm}$$

Since the final pressure is given as 200 lbf/in.², we know two properties of the final state and therefore the final state is determined. However, the internal energies of superheated steam are not listed in the steam tables, and therefore one must calculate a few internal energies before an interpolation can be made for the final temperature. The temperature corresponding to a pressure of 200 lbf/in.² and an internal energy of 1322.1 Btu/lbm is found to be 885 F.

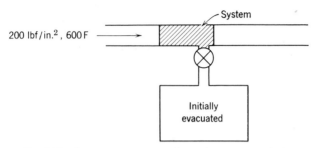

Fig. 5.13   Flow into an evacuated vessel—system analysis.

This problem can also be solved by considering the steam that enters the tank and the evacuated space as a system, as indicated in Fig. 5.13.

The process is adiabatic, but we must examine the boundaries for work. If we visualize a piston between the steam that is included in the system and the steam that flows behind, we readily recognize that the boundaries of the system move and that the steam in the pipe does work on the steam that comprises the system. The amount of this work is

$$-W = P_1 V_1 = m P_1 v_1$$

Writing the first law for the system, Eq. 5.11, and noting that kinetic and potential energies can be neglected, we have

$$_1Q_2 = U_2 - U_1 + {_1}W_2$$
$$0 = U_2 - U_1 - P_1 V_1$$
$$0 = m u_2 - m u_1 - m P_1 v_1 = m u_2 - m h_1$$

Therefore,

$$u_2 = h_1$$

which is the same conclusion which was reached using a control volume analysis.

The two other examples that follow illustrate further the uniform-state, uniform-flow process.

Example 5.10

Let the tank of the previous example have a volume of 10 ft³ and initially contain saturated vapor at 50 lbf/in.². The valve is then opened and steam from the line at 200 lbf/in.², 600 F, flows into the tank until the pressure is 200 lbf/in.²

Calculate the mass of steam that flows into the tank.

Let us again consider a control surface around the tank as indicated in Fig. 5.12. In this case, however, the control volume initially contains the mass m_1 and the internal energy $m_1 u_1$.

Again we note that $Q_{c.v.} = 0$, $W_{c.v.} = 0$, $m_e = 0$, and we assume that changes in kinetic energy and potential energy are zero. The statement of the first law for this process, Eq. 5.56 reduces to

$$m_i h_i = m_2 u_2 - m_1 u_1$$

The continuity equation, Eq. 5.53 reduces to

$$m_2 - m_1 = m_i$$

Therefore, combining the continuity equation and the first law we have

$$(m_2 - m_1)h_i = m_2 u_2 - m_1 u_1$$
$$m_2(h_i - u_2) = m_i(h_i - u_1) \qquad (a)$$

There are two unknowns in this equation; namely, m_2 and u_2. However, we have one additional equation,

$$m_2 v_2 = V = 10 \text{ ft}^3 \qquad (b)$$

These two equations, a and b, can be solved simultaneously by trial and error. The correct solution is shown below:

$$v_1 = 8.515 \text{ ft}^3/\text{lbm} \qquad m_1 = \frac{10}{8.515} = 1.173 \text{ lbm}$$

$$h_i = 1322.1 \text{ Btu/lbm} \qquad u_1 = 1095.3 \text{ Btu/lbm}$$

Assume

$$m_2 = 3.05 \text{ lbm}$$

Then, from Eq. b

$$v_2 = \frac{10}{3.05} = 3.28 \text{ ft}^3/\text{lbm}$$

For this specific volume and $P_2 = 200 \text{ lbf/in.}^2$, $u_2 = h_2 - P_2 v_2 = 1234.8$ Btu/lbm. We can now solve for m_2 from Eq. a and check on the accuracy of our assumption

$$m_2 = m_1 \frac{(h_i - u_1)}{(h_i - u_2)} = \frac{1.173(1322.1 - 1095.3)}{1322.1 - 1234.8} = \frac{265}{87.3} = 3.05 \text{ lbm}$$

This checks our original assumption.

The mass of steam that flows into the tank is

$$m_2 - m_1 = 3.05 - 1.17 = 1.88 \text{ lbm}$$

A plot of the assumed m_2 vs. calculated m_2 is of help in arriving quickly at a solution to such a problem.

Example 5.11

A tank of 50 ft³ volume contains saturated ammonia at a pressure of 200 lbf/in.². Initially the tank contains 50 per cent liquid and 50 per cent vapor by volume. Vapor is withdrawn from the top of the tank until the pressure is 100 lbf/in.². Assuming that only vapor (i.e., no liquid) leaves and that the process is adiabatic, calculate the mass of ammonia that is withdrawn.

We consider a control volume around the tank and note that $Q_{c.v.} = 0$, $W_{c.v.} = 0$, $m_i = 0$, and we assume that changes in kinetic and potential energy are negligible. However, the enthalpy of saturated vapor varies with temperature, and therefore we cannot simply assume that the enthalpy of the vapor leaving the tank remains constant. However we note that at 200 lbf/in.², $h_g = 632.7$ Btu/lbm and at 100 lbf/in.², $h_g = 626.5$ Btu/lbm. Since the change in h_g during this process is small, we may accurately assume that h_e is the average of the two values given above. Therefore

$$(h_e)_{av} = 629.6 \text{ Btu/lbm}$$

With this assumption we can assume a uniform-state, uniform-flow process, and write:
First law (from Eq. 5.56):

$$m_e h_e + m_2 u_2 - m_1 u_1 = 0$$

Continuity equation (from Eq. 5.53):

$$(m_2 - m_1)_{c.v.} + m_e = 0$$

Combining these two equations we have

$$m_2(h_e - u_2) = m_1 h_e - m_1 u_1$$

The following values are from the ammonia tables:

$$v_{f1} = 0.02732 \text{ ft}^3/\text{lbm} \qquad v_{g1} = 1.502 \text{ ft}^3/\text{lbm}$$
$$v_{f2} = 0.02584 \qquad\qquad v_{g2} = 2.952$$

$$u_{f1} = 150.9 - \frac{200 \times 144 \times 0.0273}{778} = 149.9 \text{ Btu/lbm}$$

$$u_{f2} = 104.7 - \frac{100 \times 144 \times 0.0258}{778} = 104.2$$

$$u_{g1} = 632.7 - \frac{200 \times 144 \times 1.502}{778} = 577.1$$

$$u_{g2} = 626.5 - \frac{100 \times 144 \times 2.952}{778} = 571.9$$

$$u_{fg2} = 571.9 - 104.2 = 467.7$$

Calculating first the initial mass, m_1, in the tank: the mass of the liquid initially present, m_{f1}, is

$$m_{f1} = \frac{25}{0.02732} = 915 \text{ lbm}$$

Similarly, the initial mass of vapor, m_{g1}, is

$$m_{g1} = \frac{25}{1.502} = 16.6 \text{ lbm}$$

$$m_1 = m_{f1} + m_{g1} = 915 + 17 = 932 \text{ lbm}$$

$$m_1 h_e = 932 \times 629.6 = 586,800 \text{ Btu}$$

$$m_1 u_1 = (mu)_{f1} + (mu)_{g1} = 915 \times 149.9 + 16.6 \times 577.0 = 146,700 \text{ Btu}$$

Substituting these into the first law,

$$m_2(h_e - u_2) = m_1 h_e - m_1 u_1 = 586,800 - 146,700 = 440,100 \text{ Btu}$$

Again we have a trial-and-error solution.
Assume $m_2 = 850$ lbm. Then

$$v_2 = \frac{50}{850} = 0.0588 \text{ ft}^3/\text{lbm}$$

The final quality and internal energy can now be calculated.

$$v_2 = 0.0588 = 0.0258 + x_2(2.952 - 0.0258)$$

$$x_2 = \frac{0.0334}{2.926} = 0.01127$$

$$u_2 = 104.2 + 0.01127(467.7) = 109.5 \text{ Btu/lbm}$$

This assumed value of m_2 is now checked by the first law equation

$$m_2 = \frac{m_1 h_e - m_1 u_1}{h_e - u_2} = \frac{442,100}{629.6 - 109.5} = 850 \text{ lbm}$$

This checks the assumed value. Therefore the mass of ammonia that was withdrawn, m_e, is

$$m_e = m_1 - m_2 = 932 - 850 = 82 \text{ lbm}$$

5.11 The Constant-Volume and Constant-Pressure Specific Heats and the Joule-Thomson Coefficient

The constant-volume specific heat, the constant-pressure specific heat, and the Joule-Thomson coefficient are each defined in terms of properties that have already been considered, and therefore the definitions are given here. The full significance of these quantities will be evident in later chapters.

The constant-volume specific heat C_v is defined by the relation

$$C_v \equiv \left(\frac{\partial u}{\partial T}\right)_v \tag{5.57}$$

The constant-pressure specific heat C_p is defined by the relation

$$C_p \equiv \left(\frac{\partial h}{\partial T}\right)_P \tag{5.58}$$

The Joule-Thomson coefficient μ_J is defined by the relation

$$\mu_J \equiv \left(\frac{\partial T}{\partial P}\right)_h \tag{5.59}$$

Note that each of these quantities is defined in terms of properties, and therefore the constant-volume and constant-pressure specific heats and the Joule-Thomson coefficient are thermodynamic properties of a substance. These definitions assume constant composition, and also that there are no surface, electrical, or magnetic effects.

The term heat capacity is often used instead of specific heat. However, neither term adequately conveys the nature of the thermodynamic property involved. For example, consider the two identical systems of Fig. 5.14. In the first, 100 Btu of heat is transferred to the system, and in the second, 100 Btu of work is done on the system. Thus, the change of internal energy is the same in each, and therefore the final state and the final temperature are the same in each. In accordance with Eq. 5.57, therefore, exactly the same value for the average constant-volume specific heat would be found for the substance for the two processes. However, if the specific heat is defined in terms of the heat transfer, different values will be obtained for the specific heat, since in the first case the heat transfer

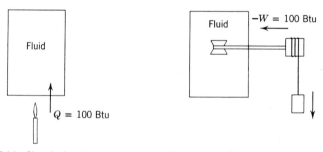

Fig. 5.14   Sketch showing two ways in which a given ΔU may be achieved.

is finite and in the second case it is zero. Thus, although the terms "specific heat" and "heat capacity" are not the most appropriate, it is always important to keep in mind that these are thermodynamic properties, and are defined by Eqs. 5.57 and 5.58. When other effects are involved, additional specific heats can be defined, such as specific heat at constant magnetization for a system involving magnetic effects.

Example 5.12

Estimate the constant-pressure specific heat of steam at 100 lbf/in.², 500 F.

If we consider a change of state at constant pressure, Eq. 5.58 may be written

$$C_p \approx \left(\frac{\Delta h}{\Delta T}\right)_P$$

From the steam tables

$$\text{at } 100 \text{ lbf/in.}^2, 480 \text{ F}, h = 1269.0$$
$$\text{at } 100 \text{ lbf/in.}^2, 520 \text{ F}, h = 1289.2$$

Since we are interested in C_p at 100 lbf/in.², 500 F,

$$C_p \approx \frac{20.2}{40} = 0.505 \text{ Btu/lbm F}$$

The significance of the Joule-Thomson coefficient may be demonstrated by considering a throttling process that is a steady-state, steady-flow process across a restriction, with a resulting drop in pressure. A typical example is the flow through a partially opened valve or a restriction in the line. In most cases this occurs so rapidly and in such a small space, that there is neither sufficient time nor a large enough area for much heat transfer. Therefore, we usually may assume such processes to be adiabatic.

If we consider the control surface shown in Fig. 5.15, we can write the steady-state, steady-flow energy equation for this process. There is no work, no change in potential energy, and we make the reasonable assumption that there is no heat transfer. The steady-state, steady-flow energy equation, Eq. 5.50, reduces to

$$h_i + \frac{V_i^2}{2g_c} = h_e + \frac{V_e^2}{2g_c}$$

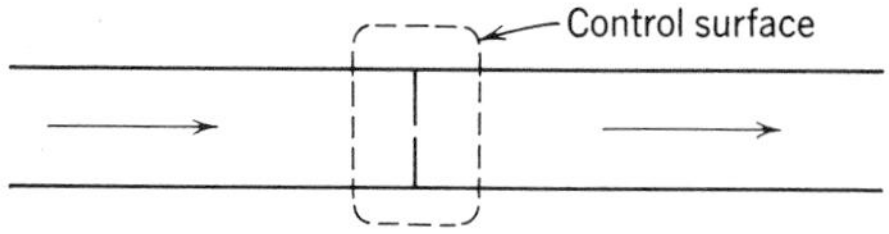

Fig. 5.15   The throttling process.

If the fluid is a gas, the specific volume always increases in such a process, and, therefore, if the pipe is of constant diameter, the kinetic energy of the fluid increases. In many cases, however, this increase in kinetic energy is small (or perhaps the diameter of the exit pipe is larger than that of the inlet pipe) and we can say with a high degree of accuracy that in this process the final and initial enthalpies are equal.

It is for such a process that the Joule-Thomson coefficient, μ_J, is significant. It was defined previously as

$$\mu_J = \left(\frac{\partial T}{\partial P}\right)_h$$

A positive Joule-Thomson coefficient means that the temperature drops during throttling, and when the Joule-Thomson coefficient is negative the temperature rises during throttling.

Example 5.13

Steam at 100 lbf/in.^{2}, 500 F is throttled to 20 lbf/in.^{2} Changes in kinetic energy are negligible for this process. Determine the final temperature and specific volume of the steam, and the average Joule-Thomson coefficient.

For this process,

$$h_i = h_e = 1279.1 \text{ Btu/lbm}$$

$$P_e = 20 \text{ lbf/in.}^2$$

These two properties determine the final state. From the superheat table for steam

$$T_e = 484.2 \text{ F}$$

$$\mu_{J(av)} = \left(\frac{\Delta T}{\Delta P}\right)_h = \frac{-15.8 \text{ F}}{-80 \text{ lbf/in.}^2} = 0.198 \text{ in.}^2\text{-F/lbf}$$

Frequently a throttling process involves a change in the phase of the fluid. A typical example is the flow through the expansion valve of a vapor compression refrigeration system. The following example deals with this problem.

Example 5.14

Consider the throttling process across the expansion valve or through the capillary tube in a vapor compression refrigeration cycle. In this process the pressure of the refrigerant drops from the high pressure in the condenser to the low pressure in the evaporator, and during this process some of the liquid flashes into vapor. If we consider this process to be adiabatic, the quality of the refrigerant entering the evaporator can be calculated.

Consider the following process, in which ammonia is the refrigerant. The ammonia enters the expansion valve at a pressure of 225 lbf/in.^{2} and a temperature of 90 F. Its pressure on leaving the expansion valve is 38.5 lbf/in.^{2} Calculate the quality of the ammonia leaving the expansion valve.

Considering a steady-state, steady-flow process for a control surface around the expansion valve or capillary tube, we conclude that $\dot{Q}_{c.v.} = 0$, $\dot{W}_{c.v.} = 0$, $\Delta KE = 0$, $\Delta PE = 0$, and therefore the statement of the first law reduces to

$$h_i = h_e$$

From the ammonia tables

$$h_i = 143.6 \text{ Btu/lbm}$$

(The enthalpy of a slightly compressed liquid is essentially equal to the enthalpy of saturated liquid at the same temperature.)

$$h_e = h_i = 143.6 = 53.8 + x_e(561.1)$$

$$x_e = \frac{89.7}{561.1} = 0.160 = 16.0\%$$

5.12 The Constant-Pressure, Quasiequilibrium Process for a System

The constant-pressure process for a system undergoing a change of volume is of particular interest if it is quasiequilibrium. Consider Fig. 5.16 in which heat is transferred to the gas which comprises the system, while the pressure remains constant. Applying the first law, Eq. 5.11,

$$_1Q_2 = U_2 - U_1 + {}_1W_2$$

The work can be calculated from the relation

$$_1W_2 = \int_1^2 P \, dV$$

Since the pressure is constant

$$_1W_2 = P \int_1^2 dV = P(V_2 - V_1)$$

Therefore

$$_1Q_2 = U_2 - U_1 + P_2V_2 - P_1V_1 = H_2 - H_1$$

On a unit-mass basis we have

$$_1q_2 = h_2 - h_1$$

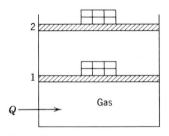

Thus, in a constant-pressure quasiequilibrium process, the heat transfer is equal to the change in enthalpy. Earlier in this chapter we noted that enthalpy had particular significance in the case of flow crossing the control surface. The reason it is of particular significance in a constant-pressure quasiequilibrium process is that the work done during the process is equal to the difference in the PV product for the final and initial states. This would not be true if the pressure had not been constant.

Fig. 5.16 The constant-pressure quasiequilibrium process.

Example 5.15

A cylinder fitted with a piston has a volume of 2 ft³ and contains steam at 60 lbf/in.², 300 F. Heat is transferred to the steam until the temperature is 500 F, while the pressure remains constant.

Determine the heat transfer, the work, and the change in internal energy for this process.

For this system changes in kinetic and potential energy are not significant. Therefore

$$_1Q_2 = m(u_2 - u_1) + {_1}W_2$$

$$_1W_2 = \int_1^2 P\, dV = P\int_1^2 dV = P(V_2 - V_1) = m(P_2v_2 - P_1v_1)$$

Therefore

$$_1Q_2 = m(u_2 - u_1) + m(P_2v_2 - P_1v_1) = m(h_2 - h_1)$$

$$m = \frac{V_1}{v_1} = \frac{2}{7.259} = 0.275 \text{ lbm}$$

$$h_1 = 1181.6 \qquad h_2 = 1283.0$$

$$_1Q_2 = 0.275(1283.0 - 1181.6) = 27.9 \text{ Btu}$$

$$_1W_2 = mP(v_2 - v_1) = \frac{0.275 \times 60 \times 144}{778}(9.403 - 7.259)$$

$$= 6.55 \text{ Btu}$$

Therefore

$$U_2 - U_1 = {_1}Q_2 - {_1}W_2 = 27.9 - 6.5 = 21.4 \text{ Btu}$$

This can be checked by finding u_1 and u_2

$$u_1 = h_1 - P_1 v_1 = 1181.6 - \frac{60 \times 144 \times 7.259}{778}$$

$$= 1101.0 \text{ Btu/lbm}$$

$$u_2 = h_2 - P_2 v_2 = 1283.0 - \frac{60 \times 144 \times 9.403}{778}$$

$$= 1178.6 \text{ Btu/lbm}$$

$$U_2 - U_1 = m(u_2 - u_1) = 0.275(1178.6 - 1101.0) = 21.4 \text{ Btu}$$

5.13 The Internal Energy, Enthalpy, and Specific Heat of Ideal Gases

At this point certain comments about the internal energy, enthalpy, and the constant-pressure and constant-volume specific heats of an ideal gas should be made. An ideal gas has been defined as a gas that has the equation of state

$$Pv = RT$$

It can be shown that for an ideal gas, the internal energy is a function of the temperature only. That is, for an ideal gas

$$u = f(T) \tag{5.60}$$

This means that an ideal gas at a given temperature has a certain definite specific internal energy u, regardless of the pressure.

In 1843 Joule demonstrated this fact when he conducted the following experiment, which is one of the classical experiments in thermodynamics. Two pressure vessels (Fig. 5.17), connected by a pipe and valve, were immersed in a bath of water. Initially vessel A contained air at 22 atm pressure and vessel B was highly evacuated. When thermal equilibrium was attained the valve was opened, allowing the pressures in A and B to

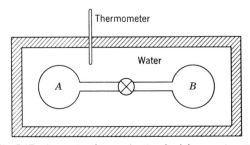

Fig. 5.17   Apparatus for conducting Joule's experiment.

equalize. No change in the temperature of the bath was detected during or after this process. Because there was no change in the temperature of the bath, Joule concluded that there had been no heat transferred to the air. Since the work was also zero, he concluded from the first law of thermodynamics that there was no change in the internal energy of the gas. Since the pressure and volume changed during this process, one concludes that internal energy is not a function of pressure and volume. Because air does not conform exactly to the definition of an ideal gas, a small change in temperature will be detected when very accurate measurements are made in Joule's experiment.

The relation between the internal energy u and the temperature can be established by using the definition of constant-volume specific heat given by Eq. 5.57.

$$C_v = \left(\frac{\partial u}{\partial T}\right)_v$$

Since the internal energy of an ideal gas is not a function of volume, for an ideal gas we can write

$$C_{vo} = \frac{du}{dT}$$

$$du = C_{vo}\, dT \tag{5.61}$$

where the subscript o denotes the specific heat of an ideal gas. For a given mass m

$$dU = mC_{vo}\, dT \tag{5.62}$$

From the definition of enthalpy and the equation of state of an ideal gas, it follows that

$$h = u + Pv = u + RT \tag{5.63}$$

Since R is a constant and u is a function of temperature only, it follows that the enthalpy, h, of an ideal gas is also a function of temperature only. That is,

$$h = f(T) \tag{5.64}$$

The relation between enthalpy and temperature is found from the constant-pressure specific heat as defined by Eq. 5.58.

$$C_p = \left(\frac{\partial h}{\partial T}\right)_P$$

Since the enthalpy of an ideal gas is a function of the temperature only, and is independent of the pressure, it follows that

$$C_{po} = \frac{dh}{dT}$$

$$dh = C_{po}\, dT \tag{5.65}$$

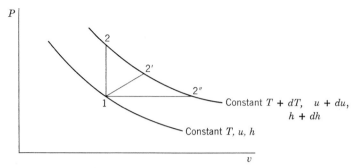

Fig. 5.18   Pressure-volume diagram for an ideal gas.

For a given mass m,

$$dH = mC_{po}\, dT \tag{5.66}$$

The consequences of Eqs. 5.61 and 5.65 are demonstrated by Fig. 5.18, which shows two lines of constant temperature. Since internal energy and enthalpy are functions of temperature only, these lines of constant temperature are also lines of constant internal energy and constant enthalpy. From state 1 the high temperature can be reached by a variety of paths, and in each case the final state is different. However, regardless of the path, the change in internal energy is the same, as is the change in enthalpy, for lines of constant temperature are also lines of constant u and constant h.

Because the internal energy and enthalpy of an ideal gas are functions of temperature only, it also follows that the constant-volume and constant-pressure specific heats are also functions of temperature only. That is

$$C_{vo} = f(T); \qquad C_{po} = f(T) \tag{5.67}$$

Since all gases approach ideal gas behavior as the pressure approaches zero, the ideal-gas specific heat for a given substance is often called the zero-pressure specific heat, and the zero-pressure constant-pressure specific heat is given the symbol C_{po}. The zero-pressure constant-volume specific heat is given the symbol C_{vo}. $\bar{C}_{po}$ as a function of temperature for a number of different substances is shown in Fig. 5.19. Empirical equations expressing $\bar{C}_{po}$ as a function of temperature have been developed for many substances, and Table A.9 in the Appendix gives a number of these.*

A very important relation between the constant-pressure and constant-volume specific heats of an ideal gas may be developed from the definition of enthalpy.

$$h = u + Pv = u + RT$$

* The equations given in Table A.9 involve three terms. A number of more accurate four-constant equations have been developed. K. A. Kobe and associates have presented a very complete summary in *Petroleum Refiner*, Jan. 1949 through Nov. 1954.

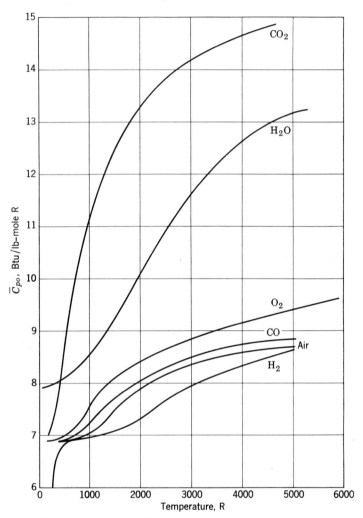

Fig. 5.19 Constant-pressure specific heats for a number of gases at zero pressure.

Differentiating, and substituting Eqs. 5.61 and 5.65, we have

$$dh = du + R\,dT$$

$$C_{po}\,dT = C_{vo}\,dT + R\,dT$$

Therefore

$$C_{po} - C_{vo} = R \tag{5.68}$$

On a mole basis this equation would be written

$$\bar{C}_{po} - \bar{C}_{vo} = \bar{R} \tag{5.69}$$

This tells us that the difference between the constant-pressure and constant-volume specific heats of an ideal gas is always constant, though both are a function of temperature. Thus, using the value of $\bar{C}_{po}$ from Table A.9, the constant-volume specific heat of oxygen, $\bar{C}_{vo}$, would be written

$$\bar{C}_{vo} = \bar{C}_{po} - \bar{R}$$

$$\bar{C}_{vo} = 11.515 - \frac{172}{\sqrt{T}} + \frac{1530}{T} - 1.986 \text{ Btu/lb mole-R}$$

$$= 9.529 - \frac{172}{\sqrt{T}} + \frac{1530}{T} \text{ Btu/lb mole-R}$$

The equations from Table A.9 can be substituted into Eqs. 5.61 and 5.65, and the change in internal energy and enthalpy then found by integration.

Example 5.16

Calculate the change of enthalpy as 1 lbm of oxygen is heated from 500 R to 2000 R, assuming ideal gas behavior.

Using the specific-heat equation from Table A.9, and integrating Eq. 5.65, we have

$$\bar{h}_2 - \bar{h}_1 = \int_{T_1}^{T_2} \bar{C}_{po} \, dT = \int_{T_1}^{T_2} \left(11.515 \, dT - \frac{172 \, dT}{T^{1/2}} + 1530 \frac{dT}{T} \right)$$

$$\bar{h}_2 - \bar{h}_1 = 11.515(T_2 - T_1) - 172 \times 2(T_2^{1/2} - T_1^{1/2}) + 1530 \ln \frac{T_2}{T_1}$$

$$\bar{h}_{2000} - \bar{h}_{500} = 17{,}280 - 7690 + 2120 = 11{,}710 \text{ Btu/lb mole}$$

$$h_{2000} - h_{500} = \frac{\bar{h}_{2000} - \bar{h}_{500}}{M} = \frac{11{,}710}{32} = 366 \text{ Btu/lbm}$$

The average specific heat for any process is defined by the relation

$$C_{p(av)} = \frac{\int_{T_1}^{T_2} C_p \, dT}{T_2 - T_1} \tag{5.70}$$

Thus, the average specific heat for Example 5.16 is

$$C_{p(av)} = \frac{366 \text{ Btu/lbm}}{(2000 - 500)R} = 0.244 \text{ Btu/lbm R}$$

The integration of specific heat equations can be very conveniently done on a digital computer. For this reason it is important to have accurate specific heat equations available. On the other hand, when a digital computer is not used, there is great value in having tables that give the zero-pressure enthalpy and internal energy of ideal gases as a function of temperature. Values of enthalpy as a function of temperature for a number of ideal gases are given in Table A.11, and for air in Table A.10.

Often, sufficiently accurate results are obtained by assuming that the specific heat is a constant. In this case it follows that

$$h_2 - h_1 = C_{po}(T_2 - T_1); \quad u_2 - u_1 = C_{vo}(T_2 - T_1)$$

Example 5.17

The centrifugal air compressor of a gas turbine receives air from the ambient atmosphere where the pressure is 14.5 lbf/in.² and the temperature is 80 F. At the discharge of the compressor the pressure is 54 lbf/in.², the temperature is 400 F, and the velocity is 300 ft/sec. The mass rate of flow into the compressor is 2000 lbm/min. Determine the power required to drive the compressor.

We consider a control volume around the compressor, and locate the control volume at some distance from the compressor so that the air crossing the control surface has a very low velocity and is essentially at ambient conditions. If we located our control volume directly across the inlet section it would be necessary to know the temperature and velocity at the compressor inlet. We assume an adiabatic steady-state, steady-flow process in which the change in potential energy and the inlet kinetic energy are zero. Therefore, the first law for this process, Eq. 5.50, reduces to

$$h_i = h_e + \frac{V_e^2}{2g_c} + w$$

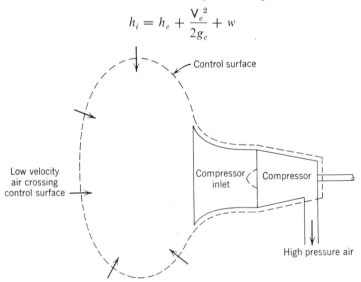

Fig. 5.20 Sketch for Example 5.17.

If we assume constant specific heat, from Table A.8 we have

$$-w = h_e - h_i + \frac{V_e^2}{2g_c} = C_{po}(T_e - T_i) + \frac{V_e^2}{2g_c}$$

$$= 0.24(400 - 80) + \frac{(300)^2}{2 \times 32.17 \times 778}$$

$$= 76.8 + 1.8 = 78.6 \text{ Btu/lbm}$$

$$-\dot{W}_{c.v.} = \frac{78.6(2000)}{42.4} = 3695 \text{ hp}$$

Power input = 3695 hp

If we use the values for the enthalpy of air that are given in the Air Tables (Table A.10), we have

$$T_i = 80 + 460 = 540 \text{ R} \qquad T_e = 400 + 460 = 860 \text{ R}$$
$$h_i = 129.06 \text{ Btu/lbm} \qquad h_e = 206.46 \text{ Btu/lbm}$$

$$-w = h_e - h_i + \frac{V_e^2}{2g_c}$$

$$= 206.46 - 129.06 + \frac{(300)^2}{2 \times 32.17 \times 728}$$

$$= 77.40 + 1.8 = 79.2 \text{ Btu/lbm}$$

$$-\dot{W}_{c.v.} = \frac{79.2(2000)}{42.4} = 3740 \text{ hp}$$

Example 5.18

A cylinder fitted with a piston has an initial volume of 2 ft³ and contains nitrogen at 20 lbf/in.², 80 F. The piston is moved, compressing the nitrogen until the pressure is 160 lbf/in.² and the temperature is 300 F. During this compression process heat is transferred from the nitrogen, and the work done on the nitrogen is 9.15 Btu. Determine the amount of this heat transfer.

We consider the nitrogen as our system, and assume that the nitrogen is an ideal gas. Changes in the kinetic and potential energy are negligible.

First law: $_1Q_2 = m(u_2 - u_1) + _1W_2$
Property relation: $Pv = RT$; $u = f(T)$

The mass of nitrogen is found from the equation of state with the value of R from Table A.8.

$$m = \frac{PV}{RT} = \frac{20 \times 144 \times 2}{55.15 \times 540} = 0.1868 \text{ lbm}$$

Assuming constant specific heat as given in Table A.8,

$$_1Q_2 = m\, C_{vo}(T_2 - T_1) + {}_1W_2$$
$$= 0.1868(0.177)(300 - 80) - 9.15$$
$$= 7.25 - 9.15 = -1.90 \text{ Btu.}$$

PROBLEMS

5.1 At a toy fair there are four types of power automobiles. A is battery operated; B has an electric motor that utilizes a-c current; C has a spring that can be wound with a key; and D has a charged capsule of CO_2 gas and operates like a rocket. Examine each of the automobiles as it operates for heat, work, and changes in internal energy. In each case consider the entire car as the system.

5.2 The average heat transfer from a person to the surroundings when he is not actively working is about 400 Btu/hr. Suppose that in an auditorium containing 1000 people the ventilation system fails.

(a) How much does the internal energy of the air in the auditorium increase during the first 15 minutes after the ventilation system fails?

(b) Considering the auditorium and all the people as a system, and assuming no heat transfer to the surroundings, how much does the internal energy of the system change? How do you account for the fact that the temperature of the air increases?

5.3 A sealed "bomb" containing certain chemicals is placed in a tank of water which is open to the atmosphere. When the chemicals react, heat is transferred from the bomb to the water, causing the temperature of the water to rise. A stirring device is used to circulate the water, and the power input to the rod driving the stirrer is 0.04 hp. In a 15-min period the heat transfer from the bomb is 1000 Btu and the heat transfer from the tank to the surrounding air is 50 Btu. Assuming no evaporation of water, determine the increase in the internal energy of the water.

5.4 A radiator of a steam heating system has a volume of 0.7 ft³. When the radiator is filled with dry saturated steam at a pressure of 20 lbf/in.² all valves to the radiator are closed. How much heat will have been transferred to the room when the pressure of the steam is 10 lbf/in.²?

5.5 A pressure vessel having a volume of 5 ft³ contains steam at the critical point. Heat is removed until the pressure is 400 lbf/in.² Determine the heat transferred from the steam.

5.6 A sealed tube has a volume of 2 in.³ and contains a certain fraction of liquid and vapor H_2O in equilibrium at 14.7 lbf/in.² The fraction of liquid and vapor is such that when heated the steam will pass through the critical point. Calculate the heat transfer when the steam is heated from the initial state at 14.7 lbf/in.² to the critical state.

5.7 A steam boiler has a total volume of 80 ft³. The boiler initially contains 60 ft³ of liquid water and 20 ft³ of vapor in equilibrium at 14.7 lbf/in.² The boiler is fired up and heat is transferred to the water and steam in the boiler.

Somehow, the valves on the inlet and discharge of the boiler are both left closed. The relief valve lifts when the pressure reaches 800 lbf/in.² How much heat was transferred to the water and steam in the boiler before the relief valve lifted?

5.8 A dewar vessel having a total volume of 100 gal contains liquid nitrogen at 1 atm pressure. The vessel is filled with 90 % liquid and 10 % vapor by volume. The dewar vessel is accidentally sealed off, so that as heat is transferred to the

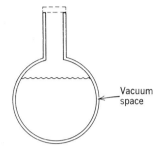

Vacuum
space

Fig. 5.21   Sketch for Problem 5.8.

liquid nitrogen across the vacuum space, the pressure will increase. It is anticipated that the inner vessel will rupture when the pressure reaches 60 lbf/in.² How long will it take to reach this pressure if the heat leak into the dewar vessel is 90 Btu/hr?

5.9 A rigid vessel having a volume of 20 ft³ is filled with ammonia at 100 lbf/in.², 200 F. Heat is transferred from the ammonia until it exists as saturated vapor. Calculate the heat transferred during this process.

5.10 Five lbm of water at 60 F is contained in a vertical cylinder by a frictionless piston of a mass such that the pressure of the water is 100 lbf/in.² Heat is

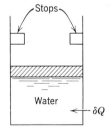

Stops

Water

δQ

Fig. 5.22   Sketch for Problem 5.10.

transferred slowly to the water, causing the piston to rise until it reaches the stops, at which point the volume inside the cylinder is 15 ft³. More heat is transferred to the water until it exists as saturated vapor.

(a) Find the final pressure in the cylinder and the heat transfer and work done during the process.

(b) Show this process on a T-V diagram.

5.11 Steam which is contained in a cylinder expands against a piston. Following are the conditions before and after expansion.

Before Expansion		After Expansion	
Pressure:	160 lbf/in.²	Pressure:	20 lbf/in.²
Temperature:	500 F	Volume:	0.6 ft³
Volume:	0.1 ft³		

The heat transfer during expansion $= -0.8$ Btu. Calculate the work done during this process.

5.12 A system is to be charged with ammonia. It is initially evacuated. A charging bottle filled with saturated liquid ammonia at 80 F is then connected to the system, and the ammonia flows into the system. The charging bottle remains connected and open to the system. The final temperature in the system is 80 F. The charging bottle has a volume of 0.4 ft³, and the system has volume of 10 ft³. What is the heat transfer to the ammonia?

5.13 Capsule A contains Freon-12 at the critical point and has a volume of 0.1 ft³. Volume B is initially evacuated. The capsule ruptures and the Freon

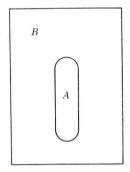

Fig. 5.23   Sketch for Problem 5.13.

fills the volume. The volume of $A + B$ is 1.0 ft³. After a certain amount of heat transfer takes place, the pressure is 100 lbf/in.²

Determine the amount of heat transferred to the Freon-12.

5.14 Tank A (Fig. 5.24) contains 1 lbm saturated Freon-12 vapor at a temperature of 80 F. The valve is then opened slightly and Freon flows slowly into

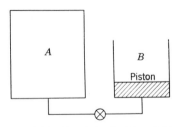

Fig. 5.24   Sketch for Problem 5.14.

the cylinder B. The mass of the piston is such that the pressure of the Freon-12 in cylinder B is 20 lbf/in.^{2} The process ends when the pressure in tank A has dropped to 20 lbf/in.^{2} During this process, heat is transferred to the Freon-12 so that the temperature remains constant at 80 F. Calculate the heat transfer during this process.

5.15 A cylinder fitted with a piston contains 5 lbm of H_2O at a pressure of 200 lbf/in.^{2} and a quality of 80%. The piston is restrained by a spring which is so arranged that for zero volume in the cylinder the spring is fully extended. The spring force is proportional to the spring displacement. The weight of the piston may be neglected so that the force on the spring is exactly balanced by the pressure forces on the H_2O.

Heat is transferred to the H_2O until its volume is 150% of the initial volume.

(a) What is the final pressure?

(b) What is the quality (if saturated) or temperature (if superheated) in the final state?

(c) Draw a P-V diagram and determine the work.

(d) Determine the heat transfer.

5.16 One lbm of steam is confined inside a spherical elastic membrane or balloon which supports an internal pressure proportional to its diameter. The initial condition of the steam is saturated vapor at 220F. Heat is transferred to the steam until the pressure reaches 20 lbf/in.^{2} Determine:

(a) The final temperature.

(b) The heat transfer.

5.17 Freon-12 vapor enters a compressor at 20 lbf/in.^{2}, 40 F, and the mass rate of flow is 5 lbm/min. What is the smallest diameter tubing that can be used if the velocity of refrigerant must not exceed 20 ft/sec?

5.18 Water flows from a large reservoir into a constant area duct as indicated in Fig. 5.25. At the duct inlet the velocity is constant over the area with a value V_0. Due to viscous effects the velocity distribution changes as the water

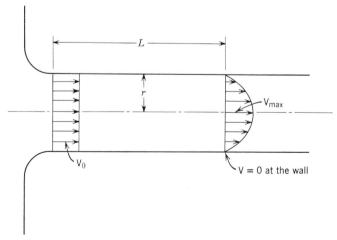

Fig. 5.25   Sketch for Problem 5.18.

flows down the duct, and at a distance L from the inlet the velocity distribution is parabolic with centerline velocity V_{max}. Find an expression for V_{max} in terms of V_0.

5.19 Water vapor is compressed in a centrifugal compressor. Dry saturated vapor at 100 F enters the compressor and the vapor leaves at 5 lbf/in.², 400 F. Heat is transferred from the vapor during the compression process at the rate of 2000 Btu/hr. The rate of flow of vapor is 300 lbm/hr. Calculate the horsepower required to drive the compressor.

5.20 Steam enters the nozzle of a turbine with a low velocity at a pressure of 400 lbf/in.², 600 F, and leaves the nozzle at 260 lbf/in.² at a velocity of 1540 ft/sec. The rate of flow of steam is 3000 lbm/hr. Calculate the quality or temperature of the steam leaving the nozzle and the exit area of the nozzle.

5.21 In a commercial refrigerator, Freon-12 enters the compressor as a saturated vapor at -10 F and leaves at a pressure of 200 lbf/in.² and temperature of 160 F. The mass rate of flow is 5 lbm/min and the heat loss from the compressor is 2 Btu/lbm of Freon-12. What horsepower is required to drive the compressor?

5.22 Recently, construction of a one-mile-high skyscraper was proposed. Suppose that in such a skyscraper heating steam is to be supplied to the top floor via a vertical pipe. Steam enters the pipe at ground level as dry saturated vapor at a pressure of 30 lbf/in.². At the top of the pipe the pressure is 15 lbf/in.², and the heat transfer from the steam as it flows up the pipe is 50 Btu/lbm. What is the quality of the steam at the top of the pipe?

5.23 Consider the steam turbine-driven water pump, which is shown schematically in Fig. 5.26. The enthalpy of the water is increased by 4 Btu/lbm

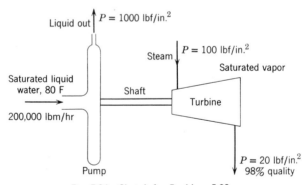

Fig. 5.26 Sketch for Problem 5.23.

during the pumping process. The initial state of the water and the initial and final states of the steam are as shown. Consider both the pumping process and expansion process adiabatic.

(*a*) What is the rate of steam flow required to drive the turbine?

(*b*) If the turbine is replaced with an electric motor, what capacity (hp) motor is required?

5.24 The following data are for a simple steam power plant of the type shown in Fig. 5.11.

Rate of steam flow = 200,000 lbm/hr

Power to pump = 400 hp

Pipe diameters:

Steam generator to turbine: 8 in.

Condenser to steam generator: 3 in.

Pressures and temperatures at various points in the cycle:

Location	Pressure	Quality or Temperature	Velocity
Entering turbine	800 lbf/in.²	900 F	
Leaving turbine, entering condenser	1.6 lbf/in.²	92%	600 ft/sec
Leaving condenser, entering pump	1.5 lbf/in.²	110 F	
Leaving pump	900 lbf/in.²		
Entering economizer	890 lbf/in.²	115 F	
Leaving economizer, entering steam generator	860 lbf/in.²	350 F	
Leaving steam generator	830 lbf/in.²	920 F	

Calculate:

(a) Power output of the turbine.

(b) Heat transfer per hour in condenser, economizer, and steam generator.

(c) Diameter of pipe connecting the turbine to the condenser.

(d) Gallons of cooling water per minute through the condenser if the temperature of the cooling water increases from 55 F to 75 F in the condenser.

5.25 A somewhat simplified flow diagram for the nuclear power plant shown in Fig. 1.5 is given in Fig. 5.27. The mass flow rates and state of the steam at various points in the cycle are shown in the table below. This cycle involves a number of "heaters." In these units, heat is transferred from steam which leaves the turbine at some intermediate pressure to liquid water which is being pumped from the condenser to the steam drum. The rate of heat transfer to the H_2O in the reactor is 537×10^6 Btu/hr.

(a) Assuming no heat transfer from the moisture separator between the high-pressure and low-pressure turbines, determine the enthalpy per pound of steam and the quality of the steam entering the low-pressure turbine.

(b) Determine the power output of the high-pressure turbine, assuming no heat transfer from the steam as it flows through the turbine.

(c) Determine the power output of the low-pressure turbine, assuming no heat transfer from the steam as it flows through the turbine.

(d) Determine the quality of the steam leaving the reactor.

(e) Determine the temperature of the steam leaving the intermediate-pressure heater, assuming no heat transfer from the heater to the surroundings.

(f) Determine the rate of heat transfer (Btu/hr) to the condenser cooling water.

(g) What is the ratio of the total power output of the two turbines to the heat transferred to the H_2O in the reactor?

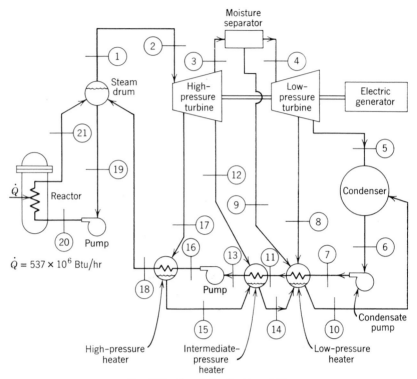

$\dot{Q} = 537 \times 10^6$ Btu/hr

Fig. 5.27 Sketch for Problem 5.25.

Point	$\dot{m}$—lbm/hr	P—lbf/in.²	T—F	h—Btu/lbm
1	600,000	1050	sat vap	
2	600,000	1000		1189
3	476,000	50		1082
4		45		
5		1		980
6	600,000	1	92	
7		60		60
8	22,000	5		1057
9	37,000	45		240
10		5		
11	600,000	55	155	
12	64,000	50		1082
13	600,000	48		
14				150
15	60,000	140	282	251
16	600,000	150		243
17	60,000	140		1115
18	600,000	1100		
19	11,000,000	1050	530	
20	11,000,000	1075		525
21	11,000,000	1060		

5.26 The following data are for a refrigeration cycle which has a hermetically sealed compressor and uses Freon-12 as a refrigerant.

	Pressure	Temperature
Leaving compressor	180 lbf/in.²	240 F
Entering condenser	178 lbf/in.²	220 F
Leaving condenser, entering expansion valve	175 lbf/in.²	100 F
Leaving expansion valve, entering evaporator	29 lbf/in.²	
Leaving evaporator	27 lbf/in.²	20 F
Entering compressor	25 lbf/in.²	40 F

Rate of flow of Freon = 200 lbm/hr
Power input to compressor = 2.5 hp

Calculate:
(a) The heat transfer per hour from the compressor.
(b) The heat transfer per hour from the Freon in the condenser.
(c) The heat transfer per hour to the Freon in the evaporator.

5.27 The following data are from the test of a large refrigeration unit utilizing ammonia as the refrigerant.

	Pressure	Temperature
Leaving compressor	260 lbf/in.²	
Entering condenser	250 lbf/in.²	200 F
Leaving condenser, entering expansion valve	240 lbf/in.²	105 F
Leaving expansion valve, entering the evaporator	35 lbf/in.²	
Leaving the evaporator, entering compressor	30 lbf/in.²	20 F

Assume no heat transfer from the compressor. The power input to the compressor is 140 hp. The capacity of the plant is 1,000,000 Btu/hr (i.e., the heat transfer to the refrigerant in the evaporator).
(a) Determine the rate of flow of the ammonia.
(b) What is the temperature of the ammonia leaving the compressor?
(c) What is the rate of heat transfer from the ammonia in the condenser?

5.28 A schematic diagram of a hydroelectric plant is shown in Fig. 5.28. Water enters the inlet conduit at the level of the lake, and work is done by the water in the hydraulic turbine. Assume no change in kinetic energy or internal energy u in the inlet conduit, and that the kinetic energy and internal energy of the water leaving the hydraulic turbine is the same as that in the inlet conduit. Calculate the power developed by the hydraulic turbine considering each of the three control volumes shown.

5.29 In a nuclear reactor steam generator, 2.94 ft³/min of water enters a $\frac{3}{4}$ in. diameter tube at a pressure of 1000 lbf/in.² and temperature of 100 F, and leaves the tube as a saturated vapor at 900 lbf/in.².
Find the heat transfer rate to the water in Btu/hr.

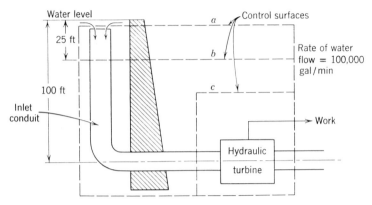

Fig. 5.28   Sketch for Problem 5.28.

5.30 Liquid ammonia at a temperature of 60 F and a pressure of 200 lbf/in.² is mixed in a steady-state, steady-flow process with saturated ammonia vapor at a pressure of 200 lbf/in.². The mass rates of flow of liquid and vapor are equal, and after mixing the pressure is 180 lbf/in.² and the quality is 85%. Determine the heat transfer per lbm of mixture.

5.31 Consider the following mixing process. Water which flows through a line at 2000 lbf/in.², 100 F at the rate of 50 lbm/min is throttled across a valve to 60 lbf/in.² and then enters a mixing chamber. 100 lbm/min of steam at 60 lbf/in.², 900 F enters the mixing chamber through another line. The steam and water are mixed and then leave the mixing chamber at 60 lbf/in.². Assuming the entire process to be adiabatic, determine the quality (if saturated) or the temperature (if superheated) of the exiting fluid.

5.32 In certain situations, when only superheated steam is available, a need for saturated steam may arise for a specific purpose. This can be accomplished in a desuperheater, in which case water is sprayed into the superheated steam in such amounts that the steam leaving the superheater is dry and saturated. The following data apply to such a desuperheater, which operates as a steady-flow process. Superheated steam at the rate of 2000 lbm/hr, at 400 lbf/in.², 600 F, enter the desuperheater. Water at 420 lbf/in.², 100 F, also enters the desuperheater. The dry saturated vapor leaves at 380 lbf/in.². Calculate the rate of flow of water.

5.33 Ammonia vapor flows through a pipe at a pressure of 100 lbf/in.² and a temperature of 80 F. Attached to the pipeline is an evacuated vessel having a volume of 1 ft³. The valve in the line to this evacuated vessel is opened, and the pressure in the vessel comes to 100 lbf/in.², at which time the valve is closed. If this process occurs adiabatically, how much ammonia flows into the vessel?

5.34 A tank having a volume of 200 ft³ contains saturated vapor steam at a pressure of 20 lbf/in.². Attached to this tank is a line in which vapor at 100 lbf/in.², 400 F, flows. Steam from this line enters the vessel until the pressure is 100 lbf/in.². If there is no heat transfer from the tank and the heat capacity of the tank is neglected, calculate the mass of steam that enters the tank.

5.35 Freon-12 is contained in a 1 ft³ tank at 80 F, 15 lbf/in.². It is desired to fill the tank 80% full of liquid (by volume) at this temperature. The tank is connected to a line flowing F-12 at 100 lbf/in.², 100 F, and the valve opened slightly.

(a) Calculate the final mass in the tank at 80 F.

(b) Determine the required heat transfer during the filling process if the temperature is to remain at 80 F.

5.36 In this problem we compare three different systems that involve flow into a vessel from a line in which steam at 100 lbf/in.², 500 F is flowing. In each case the process is adiabatic. Determine the final temperature of the steam in each of the following:

(a) The vessel is initially evacuated, and steam flows in until the pressure is 100 lbf/in.².

(b) Steam flows into a cylinder fitted with a piston which is restrained by a spring. Assume no pressure on the back side of the piston, and that the pressure

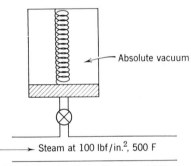

Fig. 5.29   Sketch for Problem 5.36b.

of the steam in the cylinder is proportional to the displacement. Steam flows into the cylinder until the pressure is 100 lbf/in.². (Fig. 5.29.)

(c) Steam flows into a cylinder with a piston which is so weighted that a constant pressure of 100 lbf/in.² is maintained in the cylinder. Steam flows into the cylinder causing the piston to rise. (Fig. 5.30.)

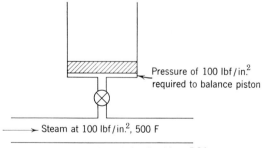

Fig. 5.30   Sketch for Problem 5.36c.

5.37 An insulated tank having a volume of 20 ft³ contains dry saturated steam at 800 lbf/in.². Steam is withdrawn through a line from the top of the tank until the pressure is 400 lbf/in.². Calculate the mass of steam that is with-drawn, assuming that at any moment the tank contains a homogeneous mixture of liquid and vapor, and that this homogeneous mixture is withdrawn from the tank. (A step-by-step solution is suggested for this problem.)

5.38 Occasionally a steam accumulator is used to drive a steam locomotive or for other purposes. Consider an accumulator that contains steam at 400 lbf/in.². Assume that the steam in the tank is dry and saturated and that only saturated vapor is withdrawn. The volume of the accumulator is 60 ft³. Steam is withdrawn from the accumulator until the pressure is reduced to 100 lbf/in.². What mass of vapor is withdrawn from the tank?

5.39 A pressure vessel having a volume of 30 ft³ contains saturated steam at 500 F. The vessel initially contains 50% vapor and 50% liquid by volume. Liquid is withdrawn slowly from the bottom of the tank, and heat is transferred to the tank in order to maintain constant temperature. Determine the heat transfer to the tank when half of the contents of the tank has been removed.

5.40 A popular demonstration involves making ice by pumping a vacuum over liquid water until the pressure is reduced to less than the triple-point pressure. Such an apparatus is shown schematically in Fig. 5.31. In this case

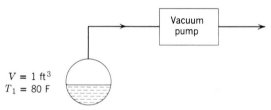

$V = 1 \text{ ft}^3$
$T_1 = 80 \text{ F}$

Fig. 5.31   Sketch for Problem 5.40.

the tank has a total volume of 1 ft³. Initially the tank contains 0.9 ft³ of satur-ated vapor (H_2O) and 0.1 ft³ of saturated liquid. The initial temperature is 80 F. Assume no heat transfer during this process.

(*a*) Determine what fraction of the initial mass will be pumped off when the liquid and vapor first reach 32 F.

(*b*) Determine what fraction of the initial mass can be solidified.

5.41 Consider the "do-it-yourself" power plant to be operated on the kitchen stove, shown in Fig. 5.32. A steam kettle having a volume of 1 ft³ contains 90%

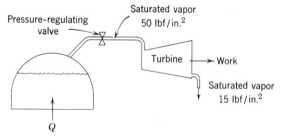

Fig. 5.32   Sketch for Problem 5.41.

liquid and 10% vapor (by volume) at 14.7 lbf/in.². The pressure-regulating valve is then adjusted to 50 lbf/in.², and heat is transferred to the water. When the pressure reaches 50 lbf/in.², saturated vapor flows from the kettle to the turbine. The steam leaves the turbine as saturated vapor at 15 lbf/in.². This process is continued until the kettle is filled with 10% liquid and 90% vapor by volume (at 50 lbf/in.²). There is no heat transfer from the turbine.

(a) Determine the total work done by the turbine during this process.

(b) Determine the total heat transfer during this process.

5.42 A throttling calorimeter is a device which is used to determine the quality of wet steam (i.e., steam which has a small amount of moisture present) flowing through a pipe. This device involves taking a small but continuous flow of steam from the pipe and throttling it in an adiabatic process to approximately atmospheric pressure. After this adiabatic throttling (constant enthalpy) process the pressure and temperature of the steam are measured, and thus the enthalpy of the wet steam in the line is known.

A throttling calorimeter is used to measure the quality of steam in a pipe in which the absolute pressure is 180 lbf/in.². A mercury manometer is used to measure the pressure in the calorimeter, and shows a pressure in the calorimeter of 2.5 in. Hg above atmospheric pressure. If a minimum of 10 degrees of superheat is required in the calorimeter, what is the minimum quality of steam that can be determined? The barometer reads 29.43 in. Hg.

5.43 Water at a pressure of 1200 lbf/in.², 300 F, is throttled to a pressure of 20 lbf/in.² in an adiabatic process. What is the quality after throttling?

5.44 Freon-12 at 180 lbf/in.², 100 F flows through the expansion valve in a vapor-compression refrigeration system. The pressure leaving the valve is 20 lbf/in.². Determine the quality of the Freon leaving the expansion valve. State clearly all assumptions you made in solving this problem.

5.45 Nitrogen is heated in a steady-state, steady-flow process. The initial pressure and temperature are 100 lbf/in.² and 100 F respectively. The final pressure is 80 lbf/in.² and the final temperature is 2000 F. Determine the heat transfer and the change of entropy during this process using the following data:

(a) The specific heat data given by the appropriate equation in Table A.9.

(b) Assume the specific heat to be constant at the value given in Table A.8.

5.46 Consider ten lbm of air that is initially at 14.7 lbf/in.², 100 F. Heat is transferred to the air until the temperature reaches 500 F. Determine the change of internal energy, the change in enthalpy, the heat transfer and the work for the following processes:

(a) Constant-volume process.

(b) Constant-pressure process.

5.47 Air contained in a cylinder fitted with a piston is compressed in a quasi-equilibrium process. During the compression process the relation between pressure and volume is $PV^{1.25}$ = constant. The mass of air in the cylinder is 0.2 lbm. The initial pressure is 20 lbf/in.², and the initial temperature is 60 F. The final volume is $\frac{1}{8}$ of the initial volume.

Determine the work and the heat transfer.

5.48 In an air liquefaction plant, air flows through an expansion engine at the rate of 600 lbm/hour. The pressure and temperature of the air entering the expansion engine is 220 lbf/in.², −80 F, and on leaving the pressure is 25 lbf/in.²

and the temperature is -170 F. The heat transfer to the air as it flows through the expansion engine is equal to 10% of the power output of the expansion engine.

Determine the power output and the heat transfer per hour from the expansion engine.

5.49 Air flows in a pipeline at a pressure of 100 lbf/in.² and a temperature of 80 F. Connected to this tank is an evacuated vessel. When the valve on this tank is opened, air flows into the tank until the pressure is 100 lbf/in.².

(*a*) If this process occurs adiabatically, what is the final temperature of the air?

(*b*) Determine a general expression that gives the relation between the temperature of a gas flowing into an evacuated vessel and the final temperature of the gas in the tank in terms of the thermodynamic properties of the gas.

5.50 (*a*) Air flows in a pipe in which frictional effects are present. At one point in the pipe the pressure is 100 lbf/in.², 200 F, and the velocity is 300 ft/sec. At a certain point down stream the pressure is 70 lbf/in.². Assuming no heat transfer during the process, determine the final velocity and temperature of the air. (*b*) What is the temperature change of an incompressible liquid as it flows through a pipe with a pressure drop due to frictional effects?

5.51 A steam turbine and nitrogen compressor are coupled together as indicated in Fig. 5.33.

The inlet conditions to the steam turbine are 600 lbf/in.² and 700 F and the exit conditions are 3 lbf/in.², $x = 0.95$. Heat transfer from the steam turbine can be neglected. The flow rate of steam is 1000 lbm/hr. The nitrogen enters the compressor at 15 lbf/in.², 60 F and leaves the aftercooler at 1500 lbf/in.², 100 F. The mass rate of flow through the compressor is 1500 lbm/hr. The steam turbine delivers 1.6 hp to the compressor and the balance to an electric power generator.

(*a*) Determine the power available from the turbine for driving the electric power generator.

(*b*) Determine the rate of heat transfer from the nitrogen as it flows through the compressor and aftercooler.

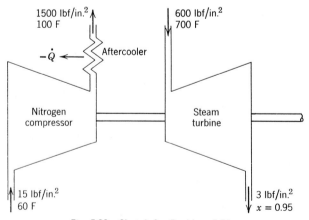

Fig. 5.33   Sketch for Problem 5.51.

5.52 One method of producing liquid nitrogen is to use the arrangement shown in Fig. 5.34. Nitrogen gas at 1500 lbf/in.², 80 F, flows through the heat exchanger, where it is cooled. As it flows across the expansion valve the pressure drops from 1500 lbf/in.² to 15 lbf/in.², and during this process some liquid is formed. The vapor flows out through the counterflow heat exchanger, and leaves at a temperature of 75 F. Assume no heat transfer between the surroundings and the nitrogen.

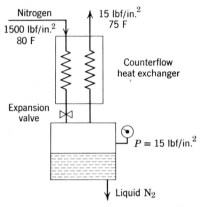

Fig. 5.34   Sketch for Problem 5.52.

(*a*) What fraction of the entering gas stream can be liquefied?

(*b*) What is the temperature difference between the two streams at that point in the heat exchanger where the high pressure stream is at a temperature of −150 F?

5.53 A schematic arrangement for a proposed procedure for producing fresh water from salt water which would operate in conjunction with a large steam power plant and utilize a flash evaporator is shown in Fig. 5.35. Cooling water at the rate of 2,500,000 lbm/hr enters the condenser, where its temperature is increased from 63 F to 85 F. It then enters a flash evaporator, where the pressure is reduced to that corresponding to a saturation temperature of 76.5 F. During this process some of the liquid flashes into vapor, and the remainder is pumped back to the sea. The vapor is then condensed at 74 F to form the desired fresh water. This takes place by utilizing the sea water which enters at 63 F and leaves at 69.5 F. Calculate:

(*a*) The amount of fresh water which is produced per hour. Assume that the mixture which is formed when the liquid at 80 F is throttled (as it enters the flash evaporator) is in equilibrium at 76.5 F, and that it is perfectly separated.

(*b*) The amount of cooling water which enters at 4.

5.54 A steam turbine driven generator is shown in Fig. 5.36. The turbine consists of a high-pressure turbine and a low-pressure turbine on the same shaft. The steam approaching the turbine in the steam line is at 600 lbf/in.², 800 F. Before entering the turbine the steam flows across a throttle valve causing a reduction in pressure to 500 lbf/in.². The rate of steam flow to the low-pressure turbine is 100,000 lbm/hr. The steam leaves the high-pressure turbine and enters the low-pressure turbine as saturated vapor at 40 lbf/in.². At this point

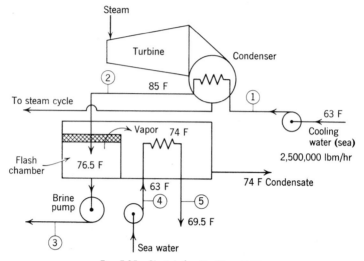

Fig. 5.35   Sketch for Problem 5.53.

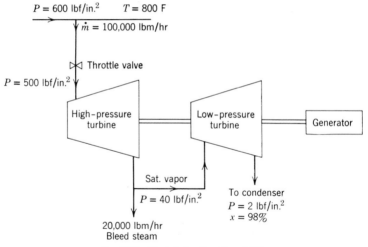

Fig. 5.36   Sketch for Problem 5.54.

20,000 lbm/hr are bled off to be used in a chemical process and the rest of the steam flows through the low-pressure turbine. The steam leaves the low-pressure turbine at 2 lbf/in.² pressure and a quality of 98% and flows to a condenser. Determine the power output of each turbine.

5.55 Consider the device shown in Fig. 5.37. Steam flows in a steam line at 100 lbf/in.², 500 F. From this steam line, steam flows through a steam turbine. The steam exhausts into large chamber having a volume of 1000 ft³. Initially, this chamber is evacuated. The turbine can operate until the pressure in the

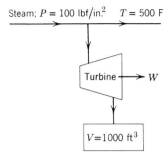

Steam; $P = 100$ lbf/in.^{2} $T = 500$ F

Turbine ⟶ W

$V = 1000$ ft^3

Fig. 5.37   Sketch for Problem 5.55.

chamber is 100 lbf/in.^{2}. At this point the steam temperature is 560 F. Assume the entire process to be adiabatic.

Determine the work done by the turbine during this process.

5.56 Experimental equipment consisting of 10 lbm of copper at 80 F is located inside an insulated, evacuated tank having a free volume of 1 ft^3. The valve is then opened slightly and Freon-12 from a line at 10 F, 50 lbf/in.^{2} flows into the tank. During this process, the pressure inside the tank is maintained

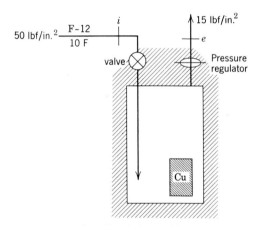

50 lbf/in.^{2} — F-12
10 F

i

15 lbf/in.^{2}

e

valve

Pressure regulator

Cu

Fig. 5.38   Sketch for Problem 5.56.

at 29.34 lbf/in.^{2} by a regulator which throttles vapor to 15 lbf/in.^{2} and exhausts it to the atmosphere. When the valve is closed, the tank contains 0.2 ft^3 of liquid and 0.8 ft^3 of vapor. The specific heat of copper is 0.1 Btu/lbm-R and it may be assumed that the specific heat of the tank walls is negligible.

Calculate the mass of Freon-12 that enters the tank and the mass exhausted to the atmosphere during the process.

5.57 An insulated and evacuated vessel of 1 ft^3 volume contains a capsule of water at 100 lbf/in.^{2}, 300 F. The volume of the capsule is 0.1 ft^3. The capsule breaks and the contents fill the entire volume. What is the final pressure?

5.58 The capacity and performance of small refrigeration compressors are frequently measured by an apparatus known as a calorimeter, which is shown schematically in Fig. 5.39. In this apparatus a water-cooled condenser is utilized, and the desired compressor discharge pressure is maintained by regulating the flow of cooling water. The evaporator is surrounded by a secondary fluid which is maintained at the ambient temperature by means of an electric heater. Thus, it may be assumed that there is no heat transfer from the secondary refrigerant to the surroundings, and that the heat transfer from the secondary

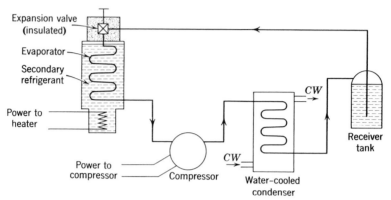

Fig. 5.39 Sketch for Problem 5.58.

refrigerant to the main refrigerant is equal to the electric input to the heater.

The test essentially involves measuring the power input to the compressor and to the heater while maintaining the prescribed pressures and temperatures throughout the cycle.

The following data were obtained from the test of a compressor rated at $\frac{1}{9}$ horsepower which utilizes Freon-12 as a refrigerant. Assume standard atmospheric pressure.

Pressure of Freon-12 in evaporator	39.04 in. Hg gage
Pressure of Freon-12 entering expansion valve	180 lbf/in.² gage
Temperature of Freon-12 entering expansion valve	104 F
Temperature of Freon-12 leaving evaporator	90 F
Ambient temperature	90 F
Power input to calorimeter	105 watts
Power input to compressor motor	125 watts

(*a*) How many lbm of Freon-12 does the compressor pump per hr?

(*b*) What is the ratio of refrigerating effect to work input? We shall note in the next chapter that this parameter is called the coefficient of performance.

(*c*) If the compressor pumped the same rate as determined in (*a*), but the liquid entered the expansion valve at a temperature of 90 F, what would the coefficient of performance be?

5.59 Usually a cryogenic fluid is stored in a vacuum insulated tank, Fig. 5.40. One way of discharging the fluid from such a tank is to withdraw some of the liquid from the storage tank and vaporize it in a heat exchanger, as shown in the

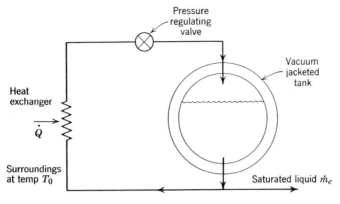

Fig. 5.40   Sketch for Problem 5.59.

sketch, and then feed the vapor to the top of the tank at such a rate as to maintain constant pressure. The heat transferred to the fluid is from the surroundings which are at temperature T_0. Suppose the fluid in the tank is saturated at a given pressure, and it is desired to withdraw fluid from the tank at this pressure at the rate of $\dot{m}_e$. Assume that the vapor leaving the heat exchanger and entering the storage tank is saturated vapor at the given pressure.

Determine heat transfer rate to the heat exchanger, $\dot{Q}$, as a function of the mass rate of liquid flow $\dot{m}_e$, and the thermodynamic properties of the fluid.

5.60 When a steam boiler is used in conjunction with a reactor in a nuclear power plant, the time required for a rapid blowdown is an important factor in safety considerations. In making this calculation it is necessary to know the pressure in the boiler as a function of the amount of liquid in the tank. To illustrate the procedure involved consider the following situation.

The boiler has a volume of 100 ft³. Initially it is half filled with liquid and half with vapor. The initial pressure is 200 lbf/in.². Assume that there is no heat transfer to the liquid or vapor during this process, and that the liquid and vapor are always in equilibrium.

Determine the pressure in the tank when the volume of the liquid is:
(a) $\frac{3}{8}$ of the volume of the boiler
(b) $\frac{1}{4}$ of the volume of the boiler
(c) $\frac{1}{8}$ of the volume of the boiler

5.61 Heat is transferred at a given rate to a mixture of liquid and vapor in equilibrium in a closed container. Determine the rate of change of temperature as a function of the thermodynamic properties of the liquid and vapor and the mass of liquid and the mass of vapor.

5.62 A spherical drop of liquid is suspended in an infinite atmosphere as shown in Fig. 5.41. Owing to differences in temperature it is exchanging heat with its surroundings. It also is losing mass by evaporation to the surroundings.

The instantaneous rate of heat transfer $\dot{Q}$ is expressed by

$$\dot{Q} = KA(T_o - T)$$

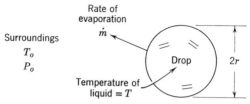

Fig. 5.41   Sketch for Problem 5.62.

where K is a constant and A is the surface area. The instantaneous rate of mass transfer is given by the symbol $\dot{m}$. It may be assumed that at a given instant of time the sphere is uniform in temperature and always at a pressure equal to that of the surroundings, P_o. The vapor of the evaporating liquid in the region adjacent to the drop is saturated.

Derive an expression for the instantaneous time rate of change of the drop temperature, $\partial T / \partial t$ in terms of the significant physical quantities.

6   The Second Law of Thermodynamics

The first law of thermodynamics states that during any cycle that a system undergoes, the cyclic integral of the heat is equal to the cyclic integral of the work. The first law, however, places no restrictions on the direction of flow of heat and work. A cycle in which a given amount of heat is transferred from the system and an equal amount of work is done on the system satisfies the first law just as well as a cycle in which the flows of heat and work are reversed. However, we know from our experience that the fact that a proposed cycle does not violate the first law does not insure that the cycle will actually occur. It is this kind of experimental evidence that has led to the formulation of the second law of thermodynamics. Thus a cycle will occur only if both the first and second laws of thermodynamics are satisfied.

In its broader significance the second law involves the fact that processes proceed in a certain direction but not in the opposite direction. A hot cup of coffee cools by virtue of heat transfer to the surroundings, but heat will not flow from the cooler surroundings to the hotter cup of coffee. Gasoline is used as a car drives up a hill, but on coasting down the hill, the fuel level in the gasoline tank cannot be restored to its original level. Such familiar observations as these, and a host of others, are evidence of the validity of the second law of thermodynamics.

We will first consider this second law for a system undergoing a cycle and in the next chapter will extend the principles to a system undergoing a change of state and to a control volume.

6.1   Heat Engines and Refrigerators

Consider the system and the surroundings previously cited in the development of the first law, as shown in Fig. 6.1. Let the gas constitute the system and, as in our discussion of the first law, let this system undergo a cycle in which work is first done on the system by the paddle wheel as the

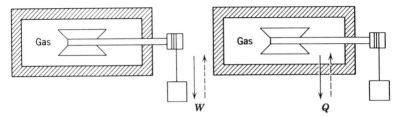

Fig. 6.1   A system that undergoes a cycle involving work and heat.

weight is lowered. Then let the cycle be completed by transferring heat to the surroundings.

We know from our experience, however, that we cannot reverse this cycle. That is, if we transfer heat to the gas, as shown by the dotted arrow, the temperature of the gas will increase, but the paddle wheel will not turn and raise the weight. With the given surroundings (the container, the paddle wheel, and the weight) this system can operate in a cycle in which the heat transfer and work are both negative, but it cannot operate in a cycle in which both the heat transfer and work are positive, even though this would not violate the first law.

Consider another cycle, which we know from our experience is impossible to actually accomplish. Let two systems, one at a high temperature and the other at a low temperature, undergo a process in which a quantity of heat is transferred from the high-temperature system to the low-temperature system. We know that this process can take place. We also know that the reverse process, in which heat is transferred from the low-temperature system to the high-temperature system, does not occur, and that it is impossible to complete the cycle by heat transfer only. This is illustrated in Fig. 6.2.

These two illustrations lead us to the consideration of the heat engine and refrigerator, which is also referred to as a heat pump. With the heat

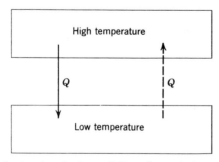

Fig. 6.2   An example showing the impossibility of completing a cycle by transferring heat from a low-temperature body to a high-temperature body.

engine we can have a system that operates in a cycle and has a net positive work and a net positive heat transfer. With the heat pump we can have a system that operates in a cycle and has heat transferred to it from a low-temperature body and heat transferred from it to a high-temperature body, though work is required to do this. Three simple heat engines and two simple refrigerators will be considered.

The first heat engine is shown in Fig. 6.3, and consists of a cylinder fitted with appropriate stops and a piston. Let the gas in the cylinder consititute the system. Initially the piston rests on the lower stops, with a weight on the platform. Let the system now undergo a process in which heat is transferred from some high-temperature body to the gas, causing it to expand and raise the piston to the upper stops. At this point the weight is removed. Now let the system be restored to its initial state by transferring heat from the gas to a low-temperature body, thus completing the cycle. Since the weight was raised during the cycle, it is evident that work was done by the gas during the cycle. From the first law we conclude that the net heat transfer was positive and equal to the work done during the cycle.

Such a device is called a heat engine, and the substance to which and from which heat is transferred is called the working substance or working fluid. A heat engine may be defined as a device that operates in a thermodynamic cycle and does a certain amount of net positive work as a result of heat transfer from a high-temperature body and to a low-temperature body. Often the term heat engine is used in a broader sense to include all devices that produce work, either through heat transfer or combustion, even though the device does not operate in a thermodynamic cycle. The

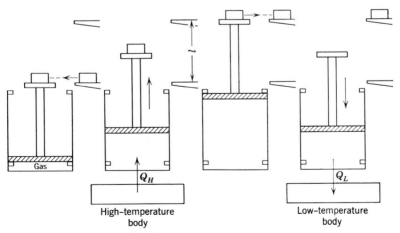

Fig. 6.3 A simple heat engine.

internal-combustion engine and the gas turbine are examples of such devices, and calling these heat engines is an acceptable use of the term. In this chapter, however, we are concened with the more restricted form of heat engine, as defined above, which operates on a thermodynamic cycle.

A simple steam power plant is an example of a heat engine in this restricted sense. Each component in this plant may be analyzed by a steady-state, steady-flow process, but considered as a whole it may be considered a heat engine (Fig. 6.4) in which water (steam) is the working fluid. An amount of heat, Q_H, is transferred from a high-temperature body, which may be the products of combustion in a furnace, a reactor, or a secondary fluid which in turn has been heated in a reactor. In Fig. 6.4 the turbine is shown schematically as driving the pump, indicating that what is significant is the net work that is delivered during the cycle. The quantity of heat Q_L is rejected to a low-temperature body, which is usually the cooling water in a condenser. Thus, the simple steam power plant is a heat engine in the restricted sense, for it has a working fluid, to which and from which heat is transferred, and which does a certain amount of work as it undergoes a cycle.

Another example of a heat engine is the thermoelectric power generation device that was discussed in Chapter 1 and shown schematically in Fig. 1.11. Heat is transferred from a high temperature body to the hot junction (Q_H) and heat is transferred from the cold junction to the surroundings (Q_L). Work is done in the form of electrical energy. Since there is no working fluid we usually do not think of this as a device that operates in a cycle. However, if one adopted a microscopic point of view one could think of a cycle as regards the flow of electrons. Furthermore, as in the case of the steam power plant, the state at each point in the thermoelectric power generator does not change with time under steady state conditions.

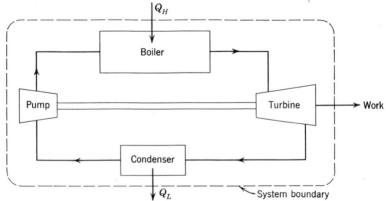

Fig. 6.4   A heat engine involving steady-state, steady-flow processes.

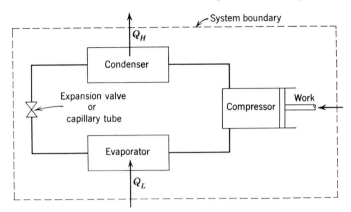

Fig. 6.5   A simple refrigeration cycle.

Thus, by means of a heat engine we are able to have a system operate in a cycle and have the net work and net heat transfer both positive, which we were not able to do with the system and surroundings of Fig. 6.1.

One should note that in using the symbols Q_H and Q_L we have departed from our sign connotation for heat, because for a heat engine Q_L is negative when the working fluid is considered as the system. In this chapter it will be advantageous to use the symbol Q_H to represent the heat transfer to or from the high-temperature body, and Q_L the heat transfer to or from the low-temperature body. The direction of the heat transfer will be evident in each case from the context.

At this point it is appropriate to introduce the concept of thermal efficiency of a heat engine. In general we say that efficiency is the ratio of output (the energy sought) to input (the energy that costs), but these must be clearly defined. At the risk of oversimplification we may say that in a heat engine the energy sought is the work, and the energy that costs money is the heat from the high-temperature source (indirectly, the cost of the fuel). Thermal efficiency is defined as:

$$\eta_{\text{thermal}} = \frac{W(\text{energy sought})}{Q_H(\text{energy that costs})} = \frac{Q_H - Q_L}{Q_H} = 1 - \frac{Q_L}{Q_H} \qquad (6.1)$$

The second cycle we were not able to complete was the one that involved the impossibility of transferring heat directly from a low-temperature body to a high-temperature body. This can of course be done with a refrigerator or heat pump. A vapor-compression refrigerator cycle, which was introduced in Chapter 1 and shown in Fig. 1.8, is also shown in Fig. 6.5. The working fluid is the refrigerant, such as a Freon or ammonia, which goes through a thermodynamic cycle. Heat is transferred to the refrigerant in the evaporator, where its pressure and temperature are low. Work is done on the refrigerant in the compressor and heat is transferred from it in the condenser, where its pressure and temperature are high. The pressure drop occurs as the refrigerant flows through the throttle valve or capillary tube.

Thus, in a refrigerator or heat pump we have a device that operates in a cycle, that requires work, and that accomplishes the objective of transferring heat from a low-temperature body to a high-temperature body.

The thermoelectric refrigerator, which was discussed in Chapter 1 and is shown schematically in Fig. 1.10, is another example of a device that meets our definition of a refrigerator. The work input to the thermoelectric refrigerator is in the form of electrical energy, and heat is transferred from the refrigerated space to the cold junction (Q_L) and from the hot junction to the surroundings (Q_H).

The "efficiency" of a refrigerator is expressed in terms of the coefficient of performance, which we designate with the symbol β. In the case of a refrigerator the objective (i.e., energy sought) is Q_L, the heat transferred from the refrigerated space, and the energy that costs is the work W. Thus the coefficient of performance, β,* is

$$\beta = \frac{Q_L(\text{energy sought})}{W(\text{energy that costs})} = \frac{Q_L}{Q_H - Q_L} = \frac{1}{Q_H/Q_L - 1} \qquad (6.2)$$

Before stating the second law, the concept of a thermal reservoir should be introduced. A thermal reservoir is a body to which and from which heat can be transferred indefinitely without change in the temperature of the reservoir. Thus, a thermal reservoir always remains at constant temperature. The ocean and the atmosphere approach this definition very closely. Frequently it will be useful to designate a high-temperature

---

* It should be noted that a refrigeration or heat pump cycle can be used with either of two objectives in mind. It can be used as a refrigerator, in which case the primary objective is Q_L, the heat transferred to the refrigerant from the refrigerated space. It also can be used as a heating system (in which case it usually is referred to as a heat pump) the objective being Q_H, the heat transferred from the refrigerant to the high-temperature body, which is the space to be heated. Q_L is transferred to the refrigerant from the ground, the atmospheric air, or well water. The coefficient of performance in this case, β' is

$$\beta' = \frac{Q_H \text{ (energy sought)}}{W \text{ (energy that costs)}} = \frac{Q_H}{Q_H - Q_L} = \frac{1}{1 - Q_L/Q_H}$$

It also follows that for a given cycle,

$$\beta' - \beta = 1$$

Unless otherwise specified, the term coefficient of performance will always refer to a refrigerator as defined by Eq. 6.2.

reservoir and a low-temperature reservoir. Sometimes a reservoir from which heat is transferred is called a source, and a reservoir to which heat is transferred is called a sink.

6.2 Second Law of Thermodynamics

On the basis of the matter considered in the previous section we are now ready to state the second law of thermodynamics. There are two classical statements of the second law, known as the Kelvin-Planck statement and the Clausius statement.

The Kelvin-Planck statement: It is impossible to construct a device that will operate in a cycle and produce no effect other than the raising of a weight and the exchange of heat with a single reservoir.

This statement ties in with our discussion of the heat engine, and, in effect, it states that it is impossible to construct a heat engine that operates in a cycle and receives a given amount of heat from a high-temperature body and does an equal amount of work. The only alternative is that some heat must be transferred from the working fluid at a lower temperature to a low-temperature body. Thus, work can be done by the transfer of heat only if there are two temperature levels involved, and heat is transferred from the high-temperature body to the heat engine and also from the heat engine to the low-temperature body. This implies that it is impossible to build a heat engine that has a thermal efficiency of 100 per cent.

The Clausius statement: It is impossible to construct a device that operates in a cycle and produces no effect other than the transfer of heat from a cooler body to a hotter body.

This statement is related to the refrigerator or heat pump, and in effect states that it is impossible to construct a refrigerator that operates without an input of work. This also implies that the coefficient of performance is always less than infinity.

In regard to these two statements, three observations should be made. The first is that both are negative statements. It is of course impossible to "prove" a negative statement. However, we can say that the second law of thermodynamics (like every other law of nature) rests on experimental evidence. Every relevant experiment that has been conducted has either directly or indirectly verified the second law, and no experiment has ever been conducted that contradicts the second law. The basis of the second law is therefore experimental evidence.

A second observation is that these two statements of the second law are equivalent. Two statements are equivalent if the truth of each statement implies the truth of the other, or if the violation of each statement implies the violation of the other. That a violation of the Clausius statement implies a violation of the Kelvin-Planck statement may be shown as follows. The device at the left in Fig. 6.6 is a refrigerator that requires no work, and thus violates the Clausius statement. Let an amount of heat Q_L be transferred from the low-temperature reservoir to this refrigerator, and let the same amount of heat Q_L be transferred to the high-temperature reservoir. Let an amount of heat Q_H, which is greater than Q_L, be transferred from the high-temperature reservoir to the heat engine, and let the engine reject the amount of heat Q_L as it does an amount of work W (which equals $Q_H - Q_L$). Since there is no net heat transfer to the low-temperature reservoir, the low-temperature reservoir, the heat engine, and the refrigerator can be considered together as a device that operates in a cycle and produces no effect other than the raising of a weight (work) and the exchange of heat with a single reservoir. Thus, a violation of the Clausius statement implies a violation of the Kelvin-Planck statement. The complete equivalence of these two statements is established when it is also shown that a violation of the Kelvin-Planck statement implies a violation of the Clausius statement. This is left as an exercise for the student.

The third observation is that frequently the second law of thermodynamics has been stated as the impossibility of constructing a perpetual motion machine of the second kind. A perpetual motion machine of the first kind would create work from nothing or create mass-energy, thus violating the first law. A perpetual motion machine of the second kind would violate the second law, and a perpetual-motion machine of the third kind would have no friction, and thus run indefinitely but would produce no work.

A heat engine that violated the second law could be made into a perpetual motion machine of the second kind as follows. Consider Fig. 6.7, which might be the power plant of a ship. An amount of heat Q_L is

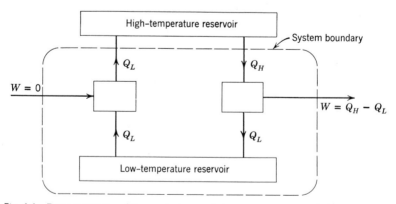

Fig. 6.6   Demonstration of the equivalence of the two statements of the second law.

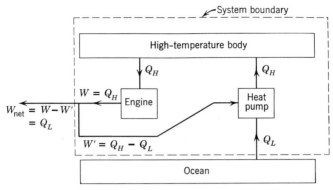

Fig. 6.7   A perpetual-motion machine of the second kind.

transferred from the ocean to a high-temperature body by means of a heat pump. The work required is W', and the heat transferred to the high-temperature body is Q_H; let the same amount of heat be transferred to a heat engine, which violates the Kelvin-Planck statement of the second law, and does an amount of work $W = Q_H$. Of this work an amount of work $Q_H - Q_L$ is required to drive the heat pump, leaving the net work ($W_{net} = Q_L$) available for driving the ship. Thus, we have a perpetual motion machine in the sense that work is done by utilizing freely available sources of energy such as the ocean or atmosphere.

6.3   The Reversible Process

The question that now logically arises is this. If it is impossible to have a heat engine of 100 per cent efficiency, what is the maximum efficiency one can have? The first step in the answer to this question is to define an ideal process, which is called a reversible process.

A reversible process for a system is defined as a process, which once having taken place, can be reversed and in so doing leave no change in either the system or surroundings.

Let us illustrate the significance of this definition for a gas contained in a cylinder that is fitted with a piston. Consider first Fig. 6.8, in which a gas (which we define as the system) at high pressure is restrained by a piston that is secured by a pin. When the pin is removed, the piston is raised and forced abruptly against the stops. Some work is done by the system, since the piston has been raised a certain amount. Suppose we wish to restore the system to its initial state. One way of doing this would be to exert a force on the piston, thus compressing the gas until the pin could again be inserted in the piston. Since the pressure on the face of the piston is greater on the return stroke than on the initial stroke, the work done on

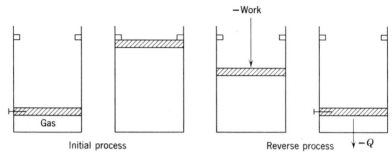

Fig. 6.8   An example of an irreversible process.

the gas in this reverse process is greater than the work done by the gas in the initial process. An amount of heat must be transferred from the gas during the reverse stroke in order that the system have the same internal energy it had originally. Thus, the system is restored to its initial state, but the surroundings have changed by virtue of the fact that work was required to force the piston down and heat was transferred to the surroundings. Thus, the initial process is an irreversible one because it could not be reversed without leaving a change in the surroundings.

In Fig. 6.9 let the gas in the cylinder comprise the system and let the piston be loaded with a number of weights. Let the weights be slid off horizontally one at a time, allowing the gas to expand and do work in raising the weights that remain on the piston. As the size of the weights is made smaller and their number is increased, we approach a process that can be reversed, for at each level of the piston during the reverse process there will be a small weight that is exactly at the level of the platform and thus can be placed on the platform without requiring work. In the limit, therefore, as the weights become very small, the reverse process can be accomplished in such a manner that both the system and surroundings are in exactly the same state they were initially. Such a process is a reversible process.

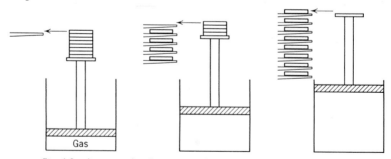

Fig. 6.9   An example of a process that approaches being reversible.

6.4 Factors That Render Processes Irreversible

There are many factors that make processes irreversible, four of which are considered in this section.

Friction. It is readily evident that friction makes a process irreversible, but a brief illustration may amplify the point. Let a block and an inclined plane comprise a system, Fig. 6.10, and let the block be pulled up the inclined plane by weights that are lowered. A certain amount of work is required to do this. Some of this work is required to overcome the friction between the block and the plane, and some is required to increase the potential energy of the block. The block can be restored to its initial position by removing some of the weights, thus allowing the block to slide down the plane. Some heat transfer from the system to the surroundings will no doubt be required to restore the block to its initial temperature. Since the surroundings are not restored to their initial state at the conclusion of the reverse process, we conclude that friction has rendered the process irreversible. Another type of frictional effect is that associated with the flow of viscous fluids in pipes and passages and in the movement of bodies through viscous fluids.

Unrestrained Expansion. The classic example of an unrestrained expansion is shown in Fig. 6.11, in which a gas is separated from a vacuum by a membrane. Consider the process that occurs when the membrane breaks and the gas fills the entire vessel. It can be shown that this is an irreversible process by considering the process that would be necessary to restore the system to its original state. This would involve compressing the gas and transferring heat from the gas until its initial state was reached. Since the work and heat transfer involve a change in the surroundings, the surroundings are not restored to their initial state, indicating that the unrestrained expansion was an irreversible process. The process described in Fig. 6.8 is also an example of an unrestrained expansion.

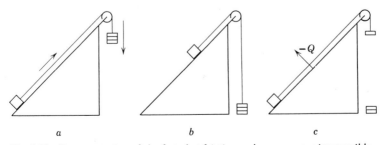

a   *b*   *c*

Fig. 6.10 Demonstration of the fact that friction makes processes irreversible.

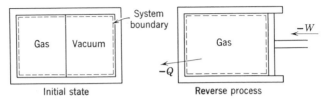

Fig. 6.11   Demonstration of the fact that unrestrained expansion makes processes irreversible.

In the reversible expansion of a gas there must be only an infinitesimal difference between the force exerted by the gas and the restraining force, so the rate at which the boundary moves will be infinitesimal. In accordance with our previous definition, this is a quasiequilibrium process. However, actual cases involve a finite difference in forces, which gives rise to a finite rate of movement of the boundary, and thus are irreversible in some degree.

Heat Transfer through a Finite Temperature Difference.   Consider as a system a high-temperature body and a low-temperature body, and let heat be transferred from the high-temperature body to the low-temperature body. The only way in which the system can be restored to its initial state is to provide refrigeration, which requires work from the surroundings, and some heat transfer to the surroundings will also be necessary. Because of the heat transfer and the work, the surroundings are not restored to their original state, indicating that the process was irreversible.

An interesting question now arises. Heat is defined as energy that is transferred due to a temperature difference. We have just shown that heat transfer through a temperature difference is an irreversible process. Therefore, how can we have a reversible heat-transfer process? A heat-transfer process approaches a reversible process as the temperature difference between the two bodies approaches zero. Therefore, we define a reversible heat-transfer process as one in which the heat is transferred through an infinitesimal temperature difference. We realize of course that to transfer a finite amount of heat through an infinitesimal temperature difference would require an infinite amount of time, or infinite area. Therefore, all actual heat-transfer processes are through a finite temperature difference and are therefore irreversible, and the greater the temperature difference the greater the irreversibility. We will find however, that the concept of reversible heat transfer is very useful in describing ideal processes.

Mixing of Two Different Substances.   This process is illustrated in Fig. 6.12 in which two different gases are separated by a membrane. Let the membrane break and a homogeneous mixture of oxygen and nitrogen fill

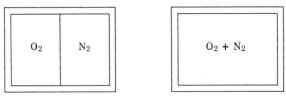

Fig. 6.12   Demonstration of the fact that the mixing of two different substances is an irreversible process.

the entire volume. This process will be considered in some detail in Chapter 11. We can say here that this may be considered as a special case of an unrestrained expansion, for each gas undergoes an unrestrained expansion as it fills the entire volume. A certain amount of work is necessary to separate these gases. Thus an air separation plant such as described in Chapter 1 requires an input of work in order that the separation may be accomplished.

Other Factors.   There are a number of other factors that make processes irreversible but they will not be considered in detail here. Hysteresis effects and the $I^2 R$ loss encountered in electrical circuits are both factors that make processes irreversible. A combustion process as it ordinarily takes place is also an irreversible process.

It is frequently advantageous to distinguish between internal and external irreversibility. Figure 6.13 shows two identical systems to which heat is transferred. Assuming each system to be a pure substance, the temperature remains constant during the heat-transfer process. In one the heat is transferred from a reservoir at a temperature $T + dT$, and in the other the reservoir is at a much higher temperature, $T + \Delta T$, than the system. The first is a reversible heat-transfer process and the second is an irreversible heat-transfer process. However, as far as the system itself is concerned, it passes through exactly the same states in both processes, which we assume are reversible. Thus, we can say in the second case that

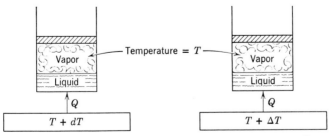

Fig. 6.13   Illustration of the difference between an internally and externally reversible process.

the process is internally reversible but externally irreversible because the irreversibility occurs outside the system.

One should also note the general interrelation of reversibility, equilibrium, and time. In a reversible process, the deviation from equilibrium is infinitesimal, and therefore it occurs at an infinitesimal rate. Since it is desirable that actual processes proceed at a finite rate, the deviation from equilibrium must be finite, and therefore the actual process is irreversible in some degree. The greater the deviation from equilibrium, the greater the irreversibility, and the more rapidly the process will occur. It should also be noted that the quasiequilibrium process, which was described in Chapter 2, is a reversible process, and hereafter the term reversible process will be used.

6.5   The Carnot Cycle

Having defined the reversible process and considered some factors that make processes irreversible, let us again pose the question raised in Section 6.3, namely, if the efficiency of all heat engines is less than 100 per cent, what is the most efficient cycle we can have? Let us answer this question for a heat engine that receives heat from a high-temperature reservoir and rejects heat to a low-temperature reservoir. Since we are dealing with reservoirs we recognize that both the high temperature and the low temperature are constant and remain constant regardless of the amount of heat transferred.

Let us assume that this heat engine, which operates between the given high-temperature and low-temperature reservoirs, operates in a cycle in which every process is reversible. If every process is reversible, the cycle is also reversible, and if the cycle is reversed, the heat engine becomes a refrigerator. In the next section we will show that this is the most efficient cycle that can operate between two constant-temperature reservoirs. It is called the Carnot cycle, and is named after a French engineer, Nicolas Leonard Sadi Carnot (1796–1832), who stated the second law of thermodynamics in 1824.

We now turn our attention to a consideration of the Carnot cycle. Figure 6.14 shows a power plant that is similar in many respects to a simple steam power plant and which we assume operates on the Carnot cycle. Assume the working fluid to be a pure substance, such as steam. Heat is transferred from the high-temperature reservoir to the water (steam) in the boiler. For this to be a reversible heat transfer, the temperature of the water (steam) must be only infinitesimally lower than the temperature of the reservoir. This also implies, since the temperature of the reservoir remains constant, that the temperature of the water must remain constant.

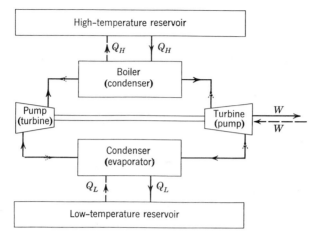

Fig. 6.14 Example of a heat engine that operates on a Carnot cycle.

Therefore, the first process in the Carnot cycle is a reversible isothermal process in which heat is transferred from the high-temperature reservoir to the working fluid. A change of phase from liquid to vapor at constant pressure is of course an isothermal process for a pure substance.

The next process occurs in the turbine. It occurs without heat transfer and is therefore adiabatic. Since all processes in the Carnot cycle are reversible, this must be a reversible adiabatic process, during which the temperature of the working fluid decreases from the temperature of the high-temperature reservoir to the temperature of the low-temperature reservoir.

In the next process heat is rejected from the working fluid to the low-temperature reservoir. This must be a reversible isothermal process in which the temperature of the working fluid is infinitesimally higher than that of low-temperature reservoir. During this isothermal process some of the steam is condensed.

The final process, which completes the cycle, is a reversible adiabatic process in which the temperature of the working fluid increases from the low temperature to the high temperature. If this were to be done with water (steam) as the working fluid, it would involve taking a mixture of liquid and vapor from the condenser and compressing it. (This would be very inconvenient in practice and therefore in all power plants the working fluid is completely condensed in the condenser, and the pump handles only the liquid phase.)

Since the Carnot heat engine cycle is reversible, every process could be reversed, in which case it would become a refrigerator. The refrigerator is shown by the dotted lines and parentheses in Fig. 6.14. The temperature of

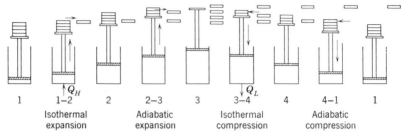

1	1–2	2	2–3	3	3–4	4	4–1	1
	Isothermal expansion		Adiabatic expansion		Isothermal compression		Adiabatic compression	

Fig. 6.15   Example of a gaseous system operating on a Carnot cycle.

the working fluid in the evaporator would be infinitesimally less than the temperature of the low-temperature reservoir, and in the condenser it is infinitesimally higher than that of the high-temperature reservoir.

It should be emphasized that the Carnot cycle can be executed in many different ways. Many different working substances can be used, such as a gas, a thermoelectric device, or a paramagnetic substance in a magnetic field such as was described in Chapter 4. There are also various possible arrangements of machinery. For example, a Carnot cycle can be devised that takes place entirely within a cylinder, using a gas as a working substance, as shown in Fig. 6.15.

The important point to be made here is that the Carnot cycle, regardless of what the working substance may be, always has the same four basic processes. These are:

(a) A reversible isothermal process in which heat is transferred to or from the high-temperature reservoir.

(b) A reversible adiabatic process in which the temperature of the working fluid decreases from the high temperature to the low temperature.

(c) A reversible isothermal process in which heat is transferred to or from the low-temperature reservoir.

(d) A reversible adiabatic process in which the temperature of the working fluid increases from the low temperature to the high temperature.

6.6   Two Propositions Regarding the Efficiency of a Carnot Cycle

There are two important propositions regarding the efficiency of a Carnot cycle:

First Proposition. It is impossible to construct an engine that operates between two given reservoirs and is more efficient than a reversible engine operating between the same two reservoirs.

The proof of this statement involves a "thought experiment." An initial assumption is made, and it is then shown that this assumption leads to impossible conclusions. The only possible conclusion is that the initial assumption was incorrect.

Let us assume that there is an irreversible engine operating between two given reservoirs that has a greater efficiency than a reversible engine operating between the same two reservoirs. Let the heat transfer to the irreversible engine be Q_H, the heat rejected be Q_L', and the work be W_{IE} (which equals $Q_H - Q_L'$) as shown in Fig. 6.16. Let the reversible engine operate as a refrigerator (since it is reversible this is possible) and let the heat transfer with the low-temperature reservoir be Q_L, the heat transfer with the high-temperature reservoir be Q_H, and the work required be W_{RE} (which equals $Q_H - Q_L$).

Since the initial assumption was that the irreversible engine is more efficient, it follows (because Q_H is the same for both engines) that $Q_L' < Q_L$ and $W_{IE} > W_{RE}$. Now the irreversible engine can drive the reversible engine and still deliver the net work W_{net} (which equals $W_{IE} - W_{RE} = Q_L - Q_L'$). However, if we consider the two engines and the high-temperature reservoir as a system, as indicated in Fig. 6.16, we have a system that operates in a cycle, exchanges heat with a single reservoir, and does a certain amount of work. However, this would constitute a violation of the second law and we conclude that our initial assumption (that the irreversible engine is more efficient than the reversible engine) is incorrect, and therefore we cannot have an irreversible engine that is more efficient than a reversible engine operating between the same two reservoirs.

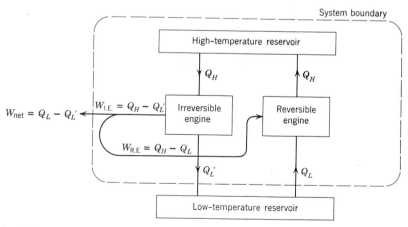

Fig. 6.16   Demonstration of the fact that the Carnot cycle is the most efficient cycle operating between two fixed temperature reservoirs.

Second Proposition. All engines that operate on the Carnot cycle between two given constant-temperature reservoirs have the same efficiency. The proof of this proposition is similar to the proof outlined above, and involves the assumption that there is one Carnot cycle that is more efficient than another Carnot cycle operating between the same temperature reservoirs. Let the Carnot cycle with the higher efficiency replace the irreversible cycle of the previous argument, and the Carnot cycle with the lower efficiency operate as the refrigerator. The proof proceeds with the same line of reasoning as in the first proposition. The details are left as an exercise for the student.

6.7 The Thermodynamic Temperature Scale

In discussing the matter of temperature in Chapter 2 it was pointed out that the zeroth law of thermodynamics provides a basis for temperature measurement, but that a temperature scale must be defined in terms of a particular thermometer substance and device. A temperature scale that is independent of any particular substance, which might be called an absolute temperature scale, would be most desirable. In the last paragraph we noted that the efficiency of a Carnot cycle is independent of the working substance and depends only on the temperature. This fact provides the basis for such an absolute temperature scale, which we will call the thermodynamic temperature scale.

The concept of this temperature scale may be developed with the aid of Fig. 6.17, which shows three reservoirs and three engines that operate on

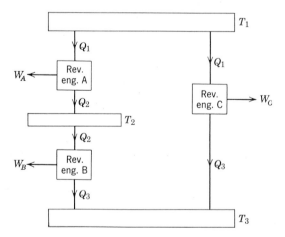

Fig. 6.17   Arrangement of heat engines to demonstrate the thermodynamic temperature scale.

the Carnot cycle. T_1 is the highest temperature, T_3 is the lowest temperature, and T_2 is an intermediate temperature, and the engines operate between the various reservoirs as indicated. Q_1 is the same for both A and C, and since we are dealing with reversible cycles, Q_3 is the same for B and C.

Since the efficiency of a Carnot cycle is a function of only the temperature we can write

$$\eta_{\text{thermal}} = 1 - \frac{Q_L}{Q_H} = \psi(T_L, T_H) \tag{6.3}$$

where ψ designates a functional relation.

Let us apply this to the three Carnot cycles of Fig. 6.17.

$$\frac{Q_1}{Q_2} = \psi(T_1, T_2)$$

$$\frac{Q_2}{Q_3} = \psi(T_2, T_3)$$

$$\frac{Q_1}{Q_3} = \psi(T_1, T_3)$$

Since,

$$\frac{Q_1}{Q_3} = \frac{Q_1 Q_2}{Q_2 Q_3}$$

it follows that

$$\psi(T_1, T_3) = \psi(T_1, T_2) \times \psi(T_2, T_3) \tag{6.4}$$

Note that the left side is a function of T_1 and T_3 (and not T_2) and therefore the right side of this equation must also be a function of T_1 and T_3, (and not T_2). From this we can conclude that the form of the function ψ must be such that

$$\psi(T_1, T_2) = \frac{f(T_1)}{f(T_2)}$$

$$\psi(T_2, T_3) = \frac{f(T_2)}{f(T_3)}$$

for in this way $f(T_2)$ will cancel from the product of $\psi(T_1, T_2) \times \psi(T_2, T_3)$. Therefore, we conclude that

$$\frac{Q_1}{Q_3} = \psi(T_1, T_3) = \frac{f(T_1)}{f(T_3)} \tag{6.5}$$

In general terms,

$$\frac{Q_H}{Q_L} = \frac{f(T_H)}{f(T_L)} \tag{6.6}$$

Now there are several functional relations which will satisfy this equation. The one that has been selected, which was originally proposed by Lord Kelvin, for the thermodynamic scale of temperature, is the relation

$$\frac{Q_H}{Q_L} = \frac{T_H}{T_L} \qquad (6.7)$$

With absolute temperatures so defined the efficiency of a Carnot cycle may be expressed in terms of the absolute temperatures.*

$$\eta_{\text{thermal}} = 1 - \frac{Q_L}{Q_H} = 1 - \frac{T_L}{T_H} \qquad (6.8)$$

This means that if the the thermal efficiency of a Carnot cycle operating between two given constant-temperature reservoirs is known, the ratio of the two absolute temperatures is also known.

It should be noted that Equation 6.7 gives us a ratio of absolute temperatures, but it does not give us information about the magnitude of the degree. Let us first consider a qualitative approach to this matter and then a more rigorous statement.

Suppose we had a heat engine operating on the Carnot cycle that received heat at the temperature of the steam point and rejected heat at the temperature of the ice point. (Since a Carnot cycle involves only reversible processes, it is impossible to construct such a heat engine and perform the proposed experiment. However, we can follow the reasoning as a "thought

---

* Lord Kelvin also proposed a logarithmic scale of the form

$$\frac{Q_H}{Q_L} = \frac{e^{``T_H"}}{e^{``T_L"}}$$

where "T_H" and "T_L" designate the absolute temperatures on this proposed logarithmic scale. This relation can also be written

$$\ln \frac{Q_H}{Q_L} = ``T_H" - ``T_L"$$

The form Kelvin actually proposed was

$$\log_{10} \frac{Q_H}{Q_L} = ``T_H" - ``T_L"$$

Thus, the relation between the scale in use and the proposed logarithmic scale is

$$``T" = \log_{10} T + L$$

where L is a constant that determines the level of temperature that corresponds to zero on the logarithmic scale. On this logarithmic scale temperatures range from $-\infty$ to $+\infty$, whereas on the thermodynamic scale in use they vary from 0 to $+\infty$ for ordinary systems.

experiment" and gain a further understanding of the thermodynamic temperature scale.) If the efficiency of such an engine could be measured, it would be found to be 26.80 per cent. Therefore, from Eq. 6.7

$$\eta_{th} = 1 - \frac{T_L}{T_H} = 1 - \frac{T_{ice\,point}}{T_{steam\,point}} = 0.2680$$

$$\frac{T_{ice\,point}}{T_{steam\,point}} = 0.7320$$

This gives us one equation involving the two unknowns T_H and T_L. The second equation comes from an arbitrary decision regarding the magnitude of the degree on the thermodynamic temperature scale. If we wish to have the magnitude of the degree on the absolute scale correspond to the magnitude of the degree on the Fahrenheit scale, we can write,

$$T_{steam\,point} - T_{ice\,point} = 180$$

This scale, the absolute Fahrenheit scale, is referred to as the Rankine scale, and temperatures on this scale are designated by R.

Solving these two equations simultaneously we find

$$T_{steam\,point} = 671.67\ R \qquad T_{ice\,point} = 491.67\ R$$

It follows that temperatures on the Fahrenheit and Rankine scales are related as follows:

$$T(^\circ F) + 459.67 = T(^\circ R)$$

The absolute scale related to the Celsius scale is the Kelvin scale, designated by K. On both these scales there are 100 degrees between the ice point and the steam point. Therefore, if we wished to use our engine operating on the Carnot cycle between the steam point and the ice point we would have the relations:

$$T_{steam\,point} - T_{ice\,point} = 100$$

$$\frac{T_{ice\,point}}{T_{steam\,point}} = 0.7320$$

Solving these two equations simultaneously we find

$$T_{steam\,point} = 373.15\ K \qquad T_{ice\,point} = 273.15\ K$$

It follows that

$$T(^\circ C) + 273.15 = T(^\circ K)$$

As already noted, the measurement of efficiencies of Carnot cycles is, however, not a practical way to approach the problem of temperature measurement on the thermodynamic scale of temperature. The actual approach used is based on the ideal gas thermometer and an assigned value for the triple point of water. At the Tenth Conference on Weights and Measures, which was held in 1954, the temperature of the triple point of water was assigned the value 273.16 K. (The triple point of water is approximately 0.01 C above the ice point. The ice point is defined as the temperature of a mixture of ice and water at a pressure of 1 atm of air which is saturated with water vapor.)

Let us now briefly consider the ideal gas scale of temperature. This scale is based upon the fact that as the pressure of a gas approaches zero, its equation of state approaches the ideal gas equation of state, namely,

$$Pv = RT$$

Consider how an ideal gas might be used to measure temperature in a constant-volume gas thermometer, which is shown schematically in Fig. 6.18. Let the gas bulb be placed in the location where the temperature is to be measured, and let the mercury column be so adjusted that the level of mercury stands at the reference mark A. Thus the volume of the gas remains constant. Assume that the gas in the capillary tube is at the same temperature as the gas in the bulb. Then the pressure of the gas, which is indicated by the height L of the mercury column, is an indication of the temperature.

Let the pressure that is associated with the temperature of the triple point of water (273.16 K) also be measured and let us designate this

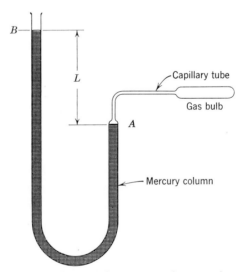

Fig. 6.18   Schematic diagram of a constant-volume gas thermometer.

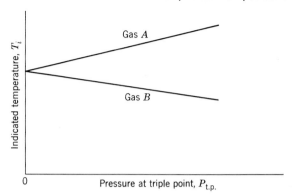

Fig. 6.19 Sketch showing how the ideal-gas temperature is determined.

pressure $P_{t.p.}$ Then, from the definition of an ideal gas, any other temperature T could be determined from a pressure measurement P by the relation

$$T = 273.16 \left(\frac{P}{P_{t.p.}} \right)$$

The temperature so measured is referred to as the ideal-gas temperature, and it can be shown that the temperature so measured is exactly equal to the thermodynamic temperature.

From a practical point of view we have the problem that no gas behaves exactly like an ideal gas. However, we do know that as the pressure approaches zero, the behavior of all gases approaches that of an ideal gas. Suppose then, that a series of measurements is made with varying amounts of gas in the gas bulb. This means that the pressure measured at the triple point, and also the pressure at any other temperature, will vary. If the indicated temperature T_i (obtained by assuming that the gas is ideal) is plotted against the pressure of gas with the bulb at the triple point of water, a curve like the one shown in Fig. 6.19 is obtained. When this curve is extrapolated to zero pressure, the correct ideal-gas temperature is obtained. Different curves might result from different gases, but they would all indicate the same temperature at zero pressure.

We have outlined only the general features and principles for measuring temperature on the ideal gas scale of temperatures. Precision work in this field is difficult and laborious, and there are only a few laboratories in the world where this precision work is carried on. The International Scale of Temperature, which was presented in Chapter 2, closely approximates the thermodynamic temperature scale and is much easier to work with in actual temperature measurement.

The significance of absolute zero can be indicated by considering a Carnot cycle heat engine that receives a given amount of heat from a given high temperature reservoir. As the temperature at which heat is rejected from the cycle is lowered, the work increases and the amount of heat rejected decreases. In the limit, the heat rejected is zero, and the temperature of the reservoir corresponding to this limit is absolute zero.

Similarly, in the case of a Carnot cycle refrigerator, the amount of work required to produce a given amount of refrigeration increases as the temperature of the refrigerated space decreases. Absolute zero represents the limiting temperature that can be achieved, and the amount of work required to produce a finite amount of refrigeration approaches infinity as the temperature at which refrigeration is provided approaches zero.

PROBLEMS

6.1 Determine the thermal efficiency of the power plant described in Problem 5.24.

6.2 Calculate the coefficient of performance of the refrigeration cycle described in Problem 5.26.

6.3 Prove that a device that violates the Kelvin-Planck statement of the second law also violates the Clausius statement of the second law.

6.4 Suggest a number of factors that would make the cycle described in Problem 5.24 an irreversible cycle.

6.5 One thousand Btu of heat are transferred from a reservoir at 600 F to an engine that operates on the Carnot cycle. The engine rejects heat to a reservoir at 80 F. Determine the thermal efficiency of the cycle and the work done by the engine.

6.6 A refrigerator that operates on a Carnot cycle is required to transfer 10,000 Btu/min from a reservoir at −20 F to the atmosphere at 80 F. What is the power required?

6.7 The maximum allowable temperature of the working fluid is usually determined by metallurgical considerations. In a certain power plant this temperature is 1300 F. Nearby is a river in which the water has a temperature of 48 F. What is the maximum possible efficiency for this power plant?

6.8 An inventor claims to have developed a refrigeration unit which maintains the refrigerated space at 20 F while operating in a room where the temperature is 80 F, and which has a coefficient of performance of 8.5. How do you evaluate his claim? How would you evaluate his claim of a coefficient of performance of 8.0?

6.9 It is proposed to heat a house using a heat pump. The heat transfer from the house is 50,000 Btu/hr. The house is to be maintained at 75 F while the outside air is at a temperature of 20 F. What is the minimum power required to drive the heat pump?

6.10 A home is to be maintained at a temperature of 70 F by means of a "heat pump" pumping heat from the atmosphere. Heat losses through the walls of the home are estimated at 1200 Btu per hour per F temperature difference between the atmosphere and the inside of the home.

(*a*) If the atmospheric temperature is 40 F, what is the minimum work (Btu/hr) required to drive the pump?

(*b*) It is proposed to use the same heat pump to cool the home in summer. For the same room temperature, the same heat loss rate per degree F through the walls, and the same work rate input to the pump, what is the maximum permissible atmospheric temperature?

6.11 It is desired to produce refrigeration at −10 F.   A reservoir is available at a temperature of 300 F and the ambient temperature is 90 F.   Thus work can be done by a heat engine operating between the 300 F reservoir and the ambient, and this work can be used to drive the refrigerator.   Determine the ratio of the heat transferred from the high temperature reservoir to the heat transferred from the refrigerated space, assuming all processes to be reversible.

6.12 Helium has the lowest normal boiling point of any of the elements, namely 4.2 K.   At this temperature it has an enthalpy of evaporation of 19.9 cal/gm mole.

A Carnot refrigeration cycle is to be used in the production of 1 gm mole of liquid helium at 4.2 K from saturated vapor at the same temperature.   What is the work input to the refrigerator and the coefficient of performance of this refrigeration cycle?   Assume an ambient temperature of 300 K.

6.13 Temperatures of 0.01 K can be achieved by a technique known as magnetic cooling.   In this process a strong magnetic field is imposed on a paramagnetic salt which is maintained at 1 K by transferring heat to liquid helium which is boiling at very low pressure.   The salt is then thermally isolated from the helium, the magnetic field is removed, and the temperature drops.

Assume that 1×10^{-3} calories are to be removed from the paramagnetic salt at an average temperature of 0.1 K, and that the necessary refrigeration is produced by a Carnot refrigeration cycle.   What is the work input to the refrigerator and the coefficient of performance of this refrigeration cycle?   Assume an ambient temperature of 300 K.

6.14 The lowest temperature which has been achieved at the present time (1965) is about 1×10^{-6} K.   Achieving this temperature involved an additional stage to that described in Problem 6.13, namely nuclear cooling.   This is similar to magnetic cooling, but involves the magnetic moment associated with the nucleus rather than that associated with certain ions in the paramagnetic salt.

Suppose that 10^{-8} Btu were to be removed from a specimen at an average temperature of 10^{-5} K (10^{-8} Btu is about the amount of energy associated with the dropping of a pin through a distance of $\frac{1}{8}$ in., and is about equal to the energy transferred as heat at this temperature in some experiments).   If this amount of refrigeration at an average temperature of 1×10^{-5} K is produced by a Carnot refrigeration cycle, determine the work input and the coefficient of performance of the refrigeration cycle.   Assume an ambient temperature of 300 K.

6.15 Consider an engine in outer space which operates on the Carnot cycle. The only way in which heat can be transferred from the engine is by radiation. The rate at which heat is radiated is proportional to the fourth power of the absolute temperature and the area of the radiating surface.   Show that for a given power output and a given T_H, the area of the radiator will be a minimum when $T_L/T_H = \frac{3}{4}$.

7 Entropy

Up to this point in our consideration of the second law of thermodynamics we have dealt only with thermodynamic cycles. Although this is a very important and useful approach, we are in many cases concerned with processes rather than cycles. Thus, we might be interested in the second-law analysis of processes we encounter daily, such as the combustion process in an automobile engine, the cooling of a cup of coffee, or the chemical processes that take place in our bodies. It would also be most desirable to be able to deal with the second law quantitatively as well as qualitatively.

In our consideration of the first law, we initially stated the law in terms of a cycle, but then defined a property, the internal energy, which enabled us to use the first law quantitatively for processes. Similarly we have stated the second law for a cycle, and we will now find that the second law leads to another property, entropy, which enables us to treat the second law quantitatively for processes. Energy and entropy are both abstract concepts that man has devised to aid in describing certain observations. As we noted in Chapter 2, thermodynamics can be described as the science of energy and entropy. The significance of this statement will now become increasingly evident.

7.1 Inequality of Clausius

The first step in our consideration of the property we call entropy is to establish the inequality of Clausius, which is

$$\oint \frac{\delta Q}{T} \le 0$$

The inequality of Clausius is a corollary or consequence of the second law of thermodynamics, and will be demonstrated to be valid for all possible cycles. This includes both reversible and irreversible heat engines and refrigerators. Since any reversible cycle can be represented by a series of Carnot cycles, in this analysis we need only consider a Carnot cycle that leads to the inequality of Clausius.

Consider first a reversible (Carnot) heat engine cycle, operating between reservoirs at temperatures T_H and T_L, as shown in Fig. 7.1.

For this cycle, the cyclic integral of the heat transfer, $\oint \delta Q$, is greater than zero.

$$\oint \delta Q = Q_H - Q_L > 0$$

Since T_H and T_L are constant, it follows from the definition of the absolute temperature scale and the fact that this is a reversible cycle that

$$\oint \frac{\delta Q}{T} = \frac{Q_H}{T_H} - \frac{Q_L}{T_L} = 0$$

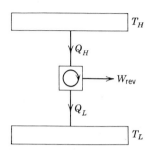

Fig. 7.1   Reversible heat engine cycle for demonstration of the inequality of Clausius.

If $\oint \delta Q$, the cyclic integral of δQ, is made to approach zero (by making T_H approach T_L), while the cycle remains reversible, the cyclic integral of $\delta Q/T$ remains zero. Thus we conclude that for all reversible heat engine cycles

$$\oint \delta Q \geq 0$$

and

$$\oint \frac{\delta Q}{T} = 0$$

Now consider an irreversible cyclic heat engine operating between the same T_H and T_L as the reversible engine of Fig. 7.1, and receiving the same quantity of heat Q_H. Comparing the irreversible cycle with the reversible one, we conclude from the second law, that

$$W_{\text{irr}} < W_{\text{rev}}$$

Since $Q_H - Q_L = W$ for both the reversible and irreversible cycles, we conclude that

$$Q_H - Q_{L_{\text{irr}}} < Q_H - Q_{L_{\text{rev}}}$$

and therefore

$$Q_{L_{\text{irr}}} > Q_{L_{\text{rev}}}$$

Consequently, for the irreversible cyclic engine,

$$\oint \delta Q = Q_H - Q_{L_{\text{irr}}} > 0$$

$$\oint \frac{\delta Q}{T} = \frac{Q_H}{T_H} - \frac{Q_{L_{\text{irr}}}}{T_L} < 0$$

Suppose that we cause the engine to become more and more irreversible while keeping Q_H, T_H, and T_L fixed. The cyclic integral of δQ then approaches zero, while that for $\delta Q/T$ becomes a progressively larger negative value. In the limit, as the work output goes to zero,

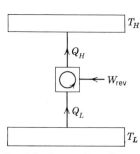

$$\oint \delta Q = 0$$

$$\oint \frac{\delta Q}{T} < 0$$

Thus we conclude that for all irreversible heat engine cycles

$$\oint \delta Q \geq 0$$

$$\oint \frac{\delta Q}{T} < 0$$

Fig. 7.2   Reversible refrigeration cycle for demonstration of the inequality of Clausius.

To complete the demonstration of the inequality of Clausius we must perform similar analyses for both reversible and irreversible refrigeration cycles. For the reversible refrigeration cycle shown in Fig. 7.2,

$$\oint \delta Q = -Q_H + Q_L < 0$$

and

$$\oint \frac{\delta Q}{T} = -\frac{Q_H}{T_H} + \frac{Q_L}{T_L} = 0$$

As the cyclic integral of δQ is made to approach zero reversibly (T_H approaching T_L), the cyclic integral of $\delta Q/T$ remains at zero. In the limit,

$$\oint \delta Q = 0$$

$$\oint \frac{\delta Q}{T} = 0$$

Thus for all reversible refrigeration cycles

$$\oint \delta Q \leq 0$$

$$\oint \frac{\delta Q}{T} = 0$$

Finally let an irreversible cyclic refrigerator operate between temperatures T_H and T_L and receive the same amount of heat Q_L as the reversible refrigerator of Fig. 7.2. From the second law, we conclude that the work input required will be greater for the irreversible refrigerator, or

$$W_{irr} > W_{rev}$$

Since $Q_H - Q_L = W$ for each cycle, it follows that

$$Q_{H_{irr}} - Q_L > Q_{H_{rev}} - Q_L$$

and therefore

$$Q_{H_{irr}} > Q_{H_{rev}}$$

That is, the heat rejected by the irreversible refrigerator to the high-temperature reservoir is greater than the heat rejected by the reversible refrigerator. Therefore, for the irreversible refrigerator,

$$\oint \delta Q = -Q_{H_{irr}} + Q_L < 0$$

$$\oint \frac{\delta Q}{T} = -\frac{Q_{H_{irr}}}{T_H} + \frac{Q_L}{T_L} < 0$$

By making this machine progressively more irreversible while keeping Q_L, T_H, and T_L constant, the cyclic integrals of δQ and $\delta Q/T$ both become larger in the negative direction. Consequently, a limiting case as the cyclic integral of δQ approaches zero does not exist for the irreversible refrigerator.

Thus for all irreversible refrigeration cycles,

$$\oint \delta Q < 0$$

$$\oint \frac{\delta Q}{T} < 0$$

Summarizing, we note that, as regards the sign of $\oint \delta Q$, we have considered all possible reversible cycles (that is, $\oint \delta Q \lessgtr 0$), and for each of these reversible cycles

$$\oint \frac{\delta Q}{T} = 0$$

We have also considered all possible irreversible cycles for the sign of $\oint \delta Q$ (that is, $\oint \delta Q \lessgtr 0$), and for all these irreversible cycles

$$\oint \frac{\delta Q}{T} < 0$$

Thus for all cycles we can write

$$\oint \frac{\delta Q}{T} \leq 0 \qquad\qquad (7.1)$$

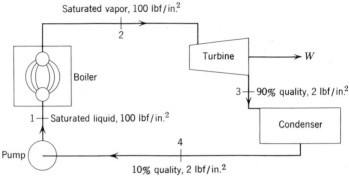

Fig. 7.3 A simple steam power plant that demonstrates the inequality of Clausius.

where the equality holds for reversible cycles and the inequality for irreversible cycles. This relation, Eq. 7.1, is known as the inequality of Clausius.

The significance of the inequality of Clausius may be illustrated by considering the simple steam power plant cycle shown in Fig. 7.3. This cycle is slightly different from the usual cycle for steam power plants in that the pump handles a mixture of liquid and vapor in such proportions that saturated liquid leaves the pump and enters the boiler. Suppose that someone reports that the pressure and quality at various points in the cycle are as given in Fig. 7.3. Does this cycle satisfy the inequality of Clausius?

Heat is transferred in two places, the boiler and the condenser. Therefore

$$\oint \frac{\delta Q}{T} = \int \left(\frac{\delta Q}{T}\right)_{\text{boiler}} + \int \left(\frac{\delta Q}{T}\right)_{\text{condenser}}$$

Since the temperature remains constant in both the boiler and condenser this may be integrated as follows:

$$\oint \frac{\delta Q}{T} = \frac{1}{T_1} \int_1^2 \delta Q + \frac{1}{T_3} \int_3^4 \delta Q = \frac{{}_1Q_2}{T_1} + \frac{{}_3Q_4}{T_3}$$

Let us consider a 1-lb mass as the working fluid.

$${}_1q_2 = h_2 - h_1 = 888.8 \text{ Btu/lbm}; \qquad T_1 = 327.8 \text{ F}$$
$${}_3q_4 = h_4 - h_3 = 196.2 - 1014.0 = -817.8 \text{ Btu/lbm}; \quad T_3 = 126.1 \text{ F}$$

Therefore

$$\oint \frac{\delta Q}{T} = \frac{888.8}{327.8 + 459.7} = \frac{817.8}{126.1 + 459.7} = -0.267 \text{ Btu/lbm-R}$$

Thus this cycle satisfies the inequality of Clausius, which is equivalent to saying that it does not violate the second law of thermodynamics.

7.2 Entropy—A Property of a System

By the use of Eq. 7.1 and Fig. 7.4 it may be shown that the second law of thermodynamics leads to a property of a system which we call entropy. Let a system undergo a reversible process from state 1 to state 2 along path A, and let the cycle be completed along path B, which is also reversible.

Since this is a reversible cycle we can write

$$\oint \frac{\delta Q}{T} = 0 = \int_{1A}^{2A} \frac{\delta Q}{T} + \int_{2B}^{1B} \frac{\delta Q}{T}$$

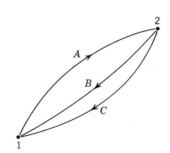

Now consider another reversible cycle, which has the same initial process, but let the cycle be completed along path C. For this cycle we can write

$$\oint \frac{\delta Q}{T} = 0 = \int_{1A}^{2A} \frac{\delta Q}{T} + \int_{2C}^{1C} \frac{\delta Q}{T}$$

Subtracting the second equation from the first we have

Fig. 7.4 Two reversible cycles demonstrating the fact that entropy is a property of a substance.

$$\int_{2B}^{1B} \frac{\delta Q}{T} = \int_{2C}^{1C} \frac{\delta Q}{T}$$

Since the $\int \delta Q/T$ is the same for all reversible paths between states 2 and 1, we conclude that this quantity is independent of the path and is a function of the end states only, and is therefore a property. This property is called entropy, and is designated S. It follows that entropy may be defined as a property of a substance in accordance with the relation

$$dS \equiv \left(\frac{\delta Q}{T}\right)_{rev} \tag{7.2}$$

Entropy is an extensive property, and the entropy per unit mass, is designated s. It is important to note that entropy is defined here in terms of a reversible process.

The change in the entropy of a system as it undergoes a change of state may be found by integrating Eq. 7.2. Thus

$$S_2 - S_1 = \int_1^2 \left(\frac{\delta Q}{T}\right)_{rev} \tag{7.3}$$

In order to perform this integration, the relation between T and Q must be known, and illustrations will be given subsequently. The important point to note here is that since entropy is a property, the change in the entropy of a substance in going from one state to another is the same for all processes, both reversible and irreversible, between these two states. Equation 7.3 enables us to find the change in entropy only along a reversible path. However, once it has been evaluated, this is the magnitude of the entropy change for all processes between these two states, because entropy is a property of a substance.

Equation 7.3 enables us to determine changes of entropy, but tells us nothing about absolute values of entropy. However, from the third law of thermodynamics, which is discussed in Chapter 12, it follows that the entropy of all pure substances can be assigned the value of zero at the absolute zero of temperature. This gives rise to absolute values of entropy and is particularly important when chemical reactions are involved.

However, when no change of composition is involved, it is quite adequate to give values of entropy relative to some arbitrarily selected reference state. This is the procedure followed in most tables of thermodynamic properties, such as the steam tables and ammonia tables. Therefore, until absolute entropy is introduced in Chapter 12, values of entropy will always be given relative to some arbitrary reference state.

A word should be added here regarding the role of T as an integrating factor. We noted in Chapter 4 that Q is a path function, and therefore δQ is an inexact differential. However, since $(\delta Q/T)_{rev}$ is a thermodynamic property, it is an exact differential. From a mathematical perspective we note that an inexact differential may be converted to an exact differential by the introduction of an integrating factor. Therefore, $1/T$ serves as the integrating factor in converting the inexact differential δQ to the exact differential $\delta Q/T$ for a reversible process.

7.3   The Entropy of a Pure Substance

Entropy is an extensive property of a system. Values of specific entropy (entropy per unit mass) are tabulated in tables of thermodynamic properties in the same manner as specific volume and specific enthalpy. The units of specific entropy in the steam tables, Freon-12 tables, and ammonia tables are Btu/lbm-R, and the values are given relative to an arbitrary reference state. In the steam tables the entropy of saturated liquid at 32 F is given the value of zero. For most refrigerants, such as Freon-12 and ammonia, the entropy of saturated liquid at -40 F is assigned the value of zero.

We will in general use the term "entropy" to refer to both total entropy and entropy per unit mass, since the context or appropriate symbol will clearly indicate the precise meaning of the term.

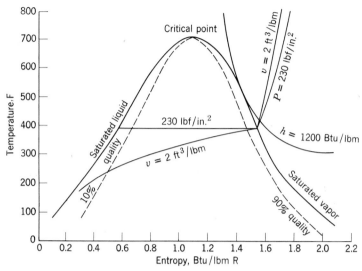

Fig. 7.5   Temperature-entropy diagram for steam.

In the saturation region the entropy may be calculated using the quality, the relations being similar to those for specific volume and enthalpy.

$$s = (1 - x)s_f + xs_g$$
$$s = s_f + xs_{fg} \qquad (7.4)$$
$$s = s_g - (1 - x)s_{fg}$$

The entropy of a compressed liquid is tabulated in the same manner as the other properties. These properties are primarily a function of the temperature, and are not greatly different from those for saturated liquid at the same temperature. Table 4 of Keenan and Keyes' steam tables, which is summarized in Table A.1.4 of the Appendix, gives the correction for the entropy of compressed liquid water in the same manner as for other properties, as has been discussed previously.

The thermodynamic properties of a substance are often shown on a temperature-entropy diagram, and an enthalpy-entropy diagram, which is also called a Mollier diagram, after Richard Mollier (1863–1935) of Germany. Figures 7.5 and 7.6 show the essential elements of temperature-entropy and enthalpy-entropy diagrams for steam. The general features of such diagrams are the same for all pure substances. A more complete temperature-entropy diagram for steam is shown in Fig. 9 of the steam tables.

These diagrams are valuable both as a means of presenting thermo-dynamic data and also because they enable one to visualize the changes of

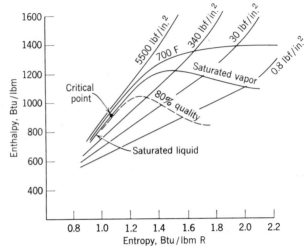

Fig. 7.6   Enthalpy-entropy diagram for steam.   (Not to scale.)

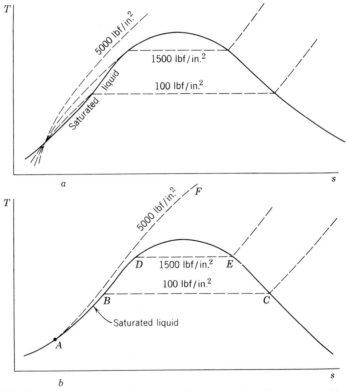

Fig. 7.7   Temperature-entropy diagram to show properties of a compressed liquid.

state that occur in various processes, and as our study progresses the student should acquire facility in visualizing thermodynamic processes on these diagrams. The temperature-entropy diagram is particularly useful for this purpose.

One more observation should be made here concerning the compressed-liquid lines on the temperature-entropy diagram for water. Reference to Table 4 of the steam tables (Appendix, Table A.1.4) indicates that the entropy correction is negative at all the listed temperatures except at 32 F. If these corrections are considerably magnified they appear as shown in Fig. 7.7a. It can be shown that each constant-pressure line crosses the saturated-liquid line at the point of maximum density, which is about 39 F for water (the exact temperature at which maximum density occurs varies with pressure). For temperatures less than the temperature at which the density is a maximum, the entropy correction is positive. It is important to understand the general shape of these lines when showing the pumping process for liquids.

Having made this observation for water, it should be stated that for most substances the magnitude of the entropy correction is so small that usually a process in which liquid is heated at constant pressure is shown as coinciding with the saturated-liquid line until the saturation temperature is reached (Fig. 7.7b). Thus, if water at 1500 lbf/in² is heated from 32 F to the saturation temperature, it would be shown by line ABD, which coincides with the saturated-liquid line.

7.4 Entropy Change in Reversible Processes

Having established the fact that entropy is a thermodynamic property of a system, its significance in various processes will now be considered. In this section we will limit ourselves to systems that undergo reversible processes, and consider the Carnot cycle, reversible heat-transfer processes, and reversible adiabatic processes.

Let the working fluid of a heat engine operating on the Carnot cycle comprise the system. The first process is the isothermal transfer of heat to the working fluid from the high-temperature reservoir. For this we can write

$$S_2 - S_1 = \int_1^2 \left(\frac{\delta Q}{T}\right)_{rev}$$

Since this is a reversible process in which the temperature of the working fluid remains constant, it can be integrated to give

$$S_2 - S_1 = \frac{1}{T_H} \int_1^2 \delta Q = \frac{{}_1Q_2}{T_H}$$

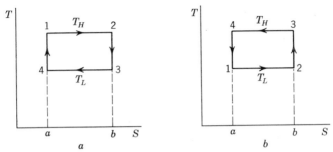

Fig. 7.8   The Carnot cycle on the temperature-entropy diagram.

This process is shown in Fig. 7.8a, and the area under line 1-2, area 1-2-b-a-1, represents the heat transferred to the working fluid during the process.

The second process of a Carnot cycle is a reversible adiabatic one. From the definition of entropy,

$$dS = \left(\frac{\delta Q}{T}\right)_{rev}$$

it is evident that the entropy remains constant in a reversible adiabatic process. A constant-entropy process is called an isentropic process. Line 2-3 represents this process, and this process is concluded at state 3 when the temperature of the working fluid reaches T_L.

The third process is the reversible isothermal process in which heat is transferred from the working fluid to the low-temperature reservoir. For this we can write

$$S_4 - S_3 = \int_3^4 \left(\frac{\delta Q}{T}\right)_{rev} = \frac{{}_3Q_4}{T_L}$$

Since during this process the heat transfer is negative (as regards the working fluid) the entropy of the working fluid decreases during this process. Also, since the final process 4-1, which completes the cycle, is a reversible adiabatic process (and therefore isentropic), it is evident that the entropy decrease in process 3-4 must exactly equal the entropy increase in process 1-2. The area under line 3-4, area 3-4-a-b-3, represents the heat transferred from the working fluid to the low-temperature reservoir.

Since the net work of the cycle is equal to the net heat transfer, it is evident that area 1-2-3-4-1 represents the net work of the cycle. The efficiency of the cycle may also be expressed in terms of areas.

$$\eta_{th} = \frac{W_{net}}{Q_H} = \frac{\text{area 1-2-3-4-1}}{\text{area 1-2-b-a-1}}$$

Some statements made earlier about efficiencies may now be understood graphically. For example, increasing T_H while T_L remains constant increases the efficiency. Decreasing T_L as T_H remains constant increases the efficiency. It is also evident that the efficiency approaches 100 per cent as the absolute temperature at which heat is rejected approaches zero.

If the cycle is reversed, we have a refrigerator or heat pump, and the Carnot cycle for a refrigerator is shown in Fig. 7.8b. Notice in this case that the entropy of the working fluid increases at T_L, since heat is transferred to the working fluid at T_L. The entropy decreases at T_H due to heat transfer from the working fluid.

Let us next consider reversible heat-transfer processes. Actually we are concerned here with processes that are internally reversible, i.e., processes that involve no irreversibilities within the boundary of the system. For such processes the heat transfer to or from a system can be shown as an area on a temperature-entropy diagram. For example, consider the change of state from saturated liquid to saturated vapor at constant pressure. This would correspond to the process 1-2 on the T-s diagram of Fig. 7.9 (note that absolute temperature is required here), and the area 1-2-b-a-1 represents the heat transfer. Since this is a constant-pressure process, the heat transfer per unit mass is equal to h_{fg}. Thus,

$$s_2 - s_1 = s_{fg} = \frac{1}{m} \int_1^2 \left(\frac{\delta Q}{T}\right)_{rev} = \frac{1}{mT} \int_1^2 \delta Q = \frac{1q_2}{T} = \frac{h_{fg}}{T}$$

This relation gives a clue as to how s_{fg} is calculated for tabulation in tables of thermodynamic properties. For example, consider steam at 100 lbf/in.^{2}

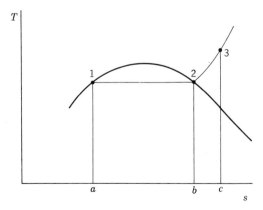

Fig. 7.9   A temperature-entropy diagram to show areas which represent heat transfer for an internally reversible process.

From the steam tables we have

$$h_{fg} = 888.8 \text{ Btu/lbm}$$
$$T = 327.81 + 459.67 = 787.48$$

Therefore,

$$s_{fg} = \frac{h_{fg}}{T} = \frac{888.8}{787.48} = 1.1286 \text{ Btu/lbm-R}$$

This is the value listed for s_{fg} in the steam tables.

If heat is transferred to the saturated vapor at constant pressure, the steam is superheated along line 2-3. For this process we can write

$$_2q_3 = \frac{1}{m} \int_2^3 \delta Q = \int_2^3 T\,ds$$

Since T is not constant this cannot be integrated unless we know a relation between temperature and entropy. However, we do realize that the area under line 2-3, area 2-3-c-b-2, represents $\int_2^3 T\,ds$, and therefore represents the heat transferred during this reversible process.

The important conclusion to draw here is that for processes that are internally reversible, the area underneath the process line on a temperature-entropy diagram represents the quantity of heat transferred. This is not true for irreversible processes, as will be demonstrated later.

There are many situations in which essentially adiabatic processes take place. We have already noted that in such cases the ideal process, which is a reversible adiabatic process, is isentropic. We shall consider here an example of a reversible adiabatic process for a system and consider in a later section the reversible adiabatic process for a control volume. We shall also note in a later section of this chapter that by comparing an actual process with the ideal or isentropic process we have a basis for defining the efficiency of certain classes of machines.

Example 7.1

Consider a cylinder fitted with a piston which contains saturated Freon-12 vapor at 20 F. Let this vapor be compressed in a reversible adiabatic process until the pressure is 150 lbf/in². Determine the work per pound of Freon-12 for this process.

From the first law we conclude that

$$_1q_2 = u_2 - u_1 + {_1}w_2 = 0$$
$$_1w_2 = u_1 - u_2$$

State 1 is specified by the statement of the problem and therefore the initial entropy is known. We also conclude, from the second law that since the process is reversible and adiabatic, $s_1 = s_2$. Therefore we know entropy and pressure in the final state, which is sufficient to specify the final state, since we are dealing with a pure substance.

From the Freon-12 tables

$$u_1 = h_1 - P_1 v_1 = 79.385 - \frac{35.736 \times 144 \times 1.0988}{778} = 72.11 \text{ Btu/lbm}$$

$$s_1 = s_2 = 0.16719 \text{ Btu/lbm-R}$$

$$P_2 = 150 \text{ lbf/in.}^2$$

Therefore, from the superheat tables for Freon-12

$$T_2 = 122.9 \text{ F}; \qquad h_2 = 90.330; \qquad v_2 = 0.28270$$

$$u_2 = 90.330 - \frac{150 \times 144 \times 0.28270}{778} = 82.48 \text{ Btu/lbm}$$

$$_1 W_2 = u_1 - u_2 = 72.11 - 82.48 = -10.37 \text{ Btu/lbm}$$

7.5 Two Important Thermodynamic Relations

At this point we will derive two important thermodynamic relations for a simple compressible substance. These relations are

$$T \, dS = dU + P \, dV$$
$$T \, dS = dH - V \, dP$$

The first of these relations can be derived by considering a simple compressible substance in the absence of motion or gravitational effects. The first law for a change of state under these conditions can be written

$$\delta Q = dU + \delta W$$

The equations we are deriving here deal first of all with those changes of state in which the state of the substance can be identified at all times. Thus we must consider a quasiequilibrium process, or, to use the term introduced in the last chapter, a reversible process. For a reversible process of a simple compressible substance we can write

$$\delta Q = T \, dS \quad \text{and} \quad \delta W = P \, dV$$

Substituting these relations into the first law equation we have

$$T \, dS = dU + P \, dV \qquad (7.5)$$

which is the equation we set out to derive. Note that this equation was derived by assuming a reversible process, and thus this equation can be integrated for any reversible process, for during such a process the state of the substance can be identified at any point during the process. We also note that Eq. 7.5 deals only with properties. Suppose we have an irreversible process taking place between given initial and final states. The properties of a substance depend only on the state, and therefore the change in the properties during a given change of state are the same for an irreversible process as for a reversible process. Therefore Eq. 7.5 is often applied to an irreversible process between two given states, but the integration of Eq. 7.5 is performed along a reversible path between the same two states.

Since enthalpy is defined as

$$H = U + PV$$

it follows that

$$dH = dU + P \, dV + V \, dP$$

Substituting this relation into Eq. 7.5 we have

$$T \, dS = dH - V \, dP \tag{7.6}$$

which is the second equation that we set out to derive.

These equations can also be written for a unit mass,

$$T \, ds = du + P \, dv \tag{7.7}$$
$$T \, ds = dh - v \, dP$$

or on a mole basis,

$$T \, d\bar{s} = d\bar{u} + P \, d\bar{v} \tag{7.8}$$
$$T \, d\bar{s} = d\bar{h} - \bar{v} \, dP$$

These equations will be used extensively in certain subsequent sections of this book.

If we consider substances of fixed composition other than a simple compressible substance we can write other "$T \, dS$" equations than those given above for a simple compressible substance. In Chapter 4, Eq. 4.13, we noted that for a reversible process we can write the following expression for work.

$$\delta W = P \, dV - \mathcal{T} \, dL - \mathcal{S} \, dA - \mu_0 V \mathcal{H} \, d\mathcal{M} - \mathcal{E} \, dZ + \cdots$$

It follows that a more general expression for the "$T \, dS$" equation would be

$$T \, dS = dU + P \, dV - \mathcal{T} \, dL - \mathcal{S} \, dA - \mu_0 V \mathcal{H} \, d\mathcal{M} - \mathcal{E} \, dZ + \cdots \tag{7.9}$$

7.6 Entropy Change of a System During an Irreversible Process

Consider a system which undergoes the cycles shown in Fig. 7.10. The cycle made up of the reversible processes A and B is a reversible cycle. Therefore we can write

$$\oint \frac{\delta Q}{T} = \int_{1A}^{2A} \frac{\delta Q}{T} + \int_{2B}^{1B} \frac{\delta Q}{T} = 0$$

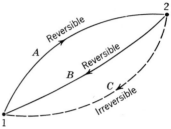

The cycle made up of the reversible process A and the irreversible process C is an irreversible cycle. Therefore, for this cycle the inequality of Clausius may be applied, giving the result

Fig. 7.10 Entropy change of a system during an irreversible process.

$$\oint \frac{\delta Q}{T} = \int_{1A}^{2A} \frac{\delta Q}{T} + \int_{2C}^{1C} \frac{\delta Q}{T} < 0$$

Subtracting the second equation from the first and rearranging, we have

$$\int_{2B}^{1B} \frac{\delta Q}{T} > \int_{2C}^{1C} \frac{\delta Q}{T}$$

Since path B is reversible, and since entropy is a property,

$$\int_{2B}^{1B} \frac{\delta Q}{T} = \int_{2B}^{1B} dS = \int_{2C}^{1C} dS$$

Therefore,

$$\int_{2C}^{1C} dS > \int_{2C}^{1C} \frac{\delta Q}{T}$$

For the general case we can write

$$dS \geq \frac{\delta Q}{T}$$

$$S_2 - S_1 \geq \int_1^2 \frac{\delta Q}{T} \tag{7.10}$$

In these equations the equality holds for a reversible process and the inequality for an irreversible process.

This is one of the most important equations of thermodynamics and is used to develop a number of concepts and definitions. In essence this equation states the influence of irreversibility on the entropy of a system.

Thus, if an amount of heat δQ is transferred to a system at temperature T in a reversible process the change of entropy is given by the relation

$$dS = \frac{\delta Q}{T}$$

However, if while the amount of heat δQ is transferred to the system at temperature T there are any irreversible effects occurring, the change of entropy will be greater than for the reversible process, for we would write

$$dS > \frac{\delta Q}{T}$$

Equation 7.10 holds when $\delta Q = 0$ or when $\delta Q < 0$ as well as when $\delta Q > 0$. If δQ is negative, the entropy will tend to decrease as the result of the heat transfer. However, the influence of irreversibilities is still to increase the entropy of the system, and from the absolute numerical perspective we can still write for $\delta Q < 0$,

$$dS \geq \frac{\delta Q}{T}$$

7.7 Lost Work

The significance of the change of entropy for an irreversible process can be amplified by introducing the concept of lost work, to which we give the symbol LW. This concept can be described with the aid of Fig. 7.11, in which a gas is separated from a vacuum by a membrane. Let the membrane have a small rupture so that the gas fills the entire volume, and let the necessary heat transfer take place so that the final temperature is the same as the initial temperature. (How much heat transfer would be necessary if this were an ideal gas?). Since the work is zero for this process we conclude from the first law that

$$\delta Q = dU$$

We would like to compare this irreversible process with a reversible process between the same two states. This could be achieved by having

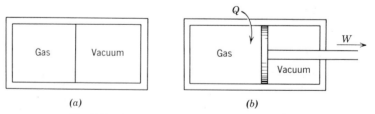

(a)   (b)

Fig. 7.11   A process that demonstrates lost work.

the gas expand against a frictionless piston while heat is transferred to the gas in the amount necessary to maintain constant temperature. For this process we conclude from the first law that

$$\delta Q = dU + \delta W$$

and, since this is a reversible process we can write

$$\delta Q = T\,dS \quad \text{and} \quad \delta W = P\,dV$$

The major difference between these two processes is that in the irreversible process the work is zero, whereas in the reversible process the greatest possible work is done. Thus, we might speak of the lost work for an irreversible process. Every irreversible process has associated with it a certain amount of lost work. In Fig. 7.11 we have shown the two extreme cases, a reversible process and one in which the work is zero. Between these two extremes are processes that have various degrees of irreversibility, i.e., the lost work may vary from zero to some maximum value. For a simple compressible substance we can therefore write

$$P\,dV = \delta W + \delta LW \tag{7.11}$$

where δLW is the lost work and δW the actual work.

Substituting the relation (Eq. 7.5)

$$T\,dS = dU + P\,dV$$

into Eq. 7.11 we have

$$T\,dS = dU + \delta W + \delta LW$$

But, from the first law

$$\delta Q = dU + \delta W$$

Therefore,

$$T\,dS = \delta Q + \delta LW$$

and

$$dS = \frac{\delta Q + \delta LW}{T} \tag{7.12}$$

Thus, we have an expression for the change of entropy for an irreversible process as an equality, whereas in the last section we had the inequality

$$dS \geq \frac{\delta Q}{T} \tag{7.13}$$

In a reversible process the lost work is zero and therefore both Eqs. 7.12 and 7.13 reduce to

$$dS = \left(\frac{\delta Q}{T}\right)_{\text{rev}}$$

for a reversible process.

Some important conclusions can now be drawn from Eqs. 7.12 and 7.13. First of all, there are two ways in which the entropy of a system can be increased, namely, by transferring heat to it and by having it undergo an irreversible process. Since the lost work cannot be less than zero, there is only one way in which the entropy of a system can be decreased, and that is to transfer heat from the system.

Secondly, the change in entropy of a system can be separated into the change due to heat transfer and the change due to internal irreversibilities. Frequently the increase in entropy due to irreversibilities is called the irreversible production of entropy.

Finally, as we have already noted, for an adiabatic process $\delta Q = 0$, and in this case the increase in entropy is always associated with the irreversibilities.

One other point, which involves the representation of irreversible processes on P-V and T-S diagrams, should be made. The work for an irreversible process is not equal to $\int P\, dV$ and the heat transfer is not equal to $\int T\, dS$. Therefore, the area underneath the path does not represent work and heat on the P-V and T-S diagrams, respectively. In fact, in many cases we are not certain of the exact state through which a system passes when it undergoes an irreversible process. For this reason it is advantageous to show irreversible processes as dotted lines and reversible processes as solid lines. Thus, the area underneath the dotted line will never represent work or heat. For example, the processes of Fig. 7.11 would be shown on P-V and T-S diagrams as in Fig. 7.12.

Figure 7.12a shows an irreversible process, and since the heat transfer and work for this process is zero, the area underneath the dashed line has

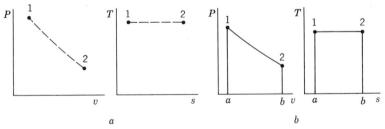

Fig. 7.12   Reversible and irreversible processes on pressure-volume and temperature-entropy diagrams.

no significance. Figure 7.12*b* shows the reversible process, and area 1–2–*b*–*a*–1 represents the work on the *P-V* diagram and the heat transfer on the *T-S* diagram.

7.8   The Second Law of Thermodynamics for a Control Volume

The second law of thermodynamics can be applied to a control volume by a similar procedure to that used in writing the first law for the control volume. The second law for a system has been stated (Eq. 7.10) in the form

$$dS \geq \frac{\delta Q}{T}$$

For a finite change in entropy, ΔS, that occurs during a time interval δt we can write

$$\frac{\Delta S}{\delta t} \geq \frac{1}{\delta t}\left(\frac{\delta Q}{T}\right) = \left(\frac{\dot{Q}}{T}\right)_{av} \tag{7.14}$$

where $(\dot{Q}/T)_{av}$ represents the average value over the time interval δt.

Consider the system and control volume shown in Fig. 7.13. During time δt the mass δm_i enters the control volume, the mass δm_e leaves, an amount of heat δQ is transferred to the system across an element of area where the surface temperature is T, and the work δW is done by the system.

Let

$S_t =$ the entropy in the control volume at time t

$S_{t+\delta t} =$ the entropy in the control volume at time $t + \delta t$

Then

$S_1 = S_t + s_i\,\delta m_i =$ entropy of the system at time t

$S_2 = S_{t+\delta t} + s_e\,\delta m_e =$ entropy of the system at time $t + \delta t$

Therefore

$$\frac{\Delta S}{\delta t} = \frac{S_2 - S_1}{\delta t} = \frac{[S_{t+\delta t} - S_t]}{\delta t} + \frac{[s_e\,\delta m_e - s_i\,\delta m_i]}{\delta t} \geq \left(\frac{\dot{Q}}{T}\right)_{av} \tag{7.15}$$

The quantity $[s_e\,\delta m_e - s_i\,\delta m_i]$ of Eq. 7.15 represents the net flow of entropy out of the control volume during δt as the result of the flow of the masses δm_e and δm_i across the control surface.

Since, from Eq. 5.20,

$$\delta m_e - \delta m_i = \left[\int_A \rho V_r \cos \alpha\, dA\right]_{av} \delta t$$

it follows that

$$s_e \, \delta m_e - s_i \, \delta m_i = \left[\int_A s\rho V_r \cos\alpha \, dA \right]_{av} \delta t \qquad (7.16)$$

On dividing this equation by δt we have an expression for the average rate at which entropy flows across the control surface during δt.

$$\frac{s_e \, \delta m_e - s_i \, \delta m_i}{\delta t} = \left[\int_A s\rho V_r \cos\alpha \, dA \right]_{av} \qquad (7.17)$$

The quantity $(S_{t+\delta t} - S_t)$ of Eq. 7.15, which represents the change of entropy within the control volume during δt, can be written in terms of a volume integral.

$$S_{t+\delta t} - S_t = \delta \int_V s\rho \, dV \qquad (7.18)$$

During the time interval δt the average rate of change of entropy within the control volume is

$$\frac{S_{t+\delta t} - S_t}{\delta t} = \frac{\delta}{\delta t} \int_V s\rho \, dV \qquad (7.19)$$

The significance of the term $(\dot{Q}/T)_{av}$ in Eq. 7.14 must be carefully considered when applied to a control volume. When we write this term for a system that is in thermodynamic equilibrium we are considering a quantity of mass at a uniform temperature T. As noted before, in the case of a control volume we deviate from a strictly classical concept of thermodynamics, and are prepared to consider a variation in temperature throughout the control volume. As a consequence we must consider each element of area on the surface across which heat flows, and the surface temperature of this area. The reason is that when dealing with the second law the important variable is not δQ or $\dot{Q}$, but $\delta Q/T$ or $\dot{Q}/T$, where T is the temperature of the mass to which heat is transferred. Therefore, in applying the relation, Eq. 7.14,

$$\frac{\Delta S}{\delta t} \geq \left(\frac{\dot{Q}}{T}\right)_{av}$$

to the system and control volume shown in Fig. 7.13, we should write

$$\left(\frac{\dot{Q}}{T}\right)_{av} = \left[\int_A \left(\frac{\dot{Q}/A}{T}\right) dA \right]_{av} \qquad (7.20)$$

where the integration is performed over the entire control surface and T is surface temperature. Therefore, substituting Eqs. 7.17, 7.19, and 7.20 into Eq. 7.15, we have

$$\frac{\delta}{\delta t} \int_V s\rho \, dV + \left[\int_A s\rho V_r \cos\alpha \, dA \right]_{av} \geq \left[\int_A \left(\frac{\dot{Q}/A}{T}\right) dA \right]_{av} \qquad (7.21)$$

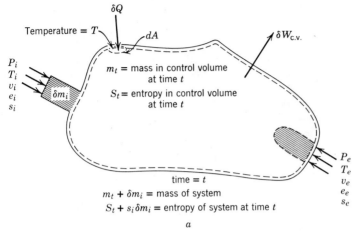

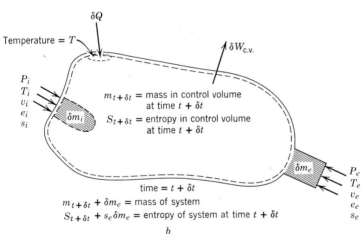

Fig. 7.13   Schematic diagram for a second law analysis of a control volume.

As δt approaches zero we can establish the limits for each of the terms in Eq. 7.21, and on substituting these limits we have a rate equation form of the second law for a control volume:

$$\lim_{\delta t \to 0} \frac{\delta}{\delta t} \int_V s\rho \, dV = \frac{d}{dt} \int_V s\rho \, dV \tag{7.22}$$

$$\lim_{\delta t \to 0} \left[\int_A s\rho \mathsf{V}_r \cos \alpha \, dA \right]_{av} = \int_A s\rho \mathsf{V}_r \cos \alpha \, dA \tag{7.23}$$

$$\lim_{\delta t \to 0} \left[\int_A \left(\frac{\dot{Q}/A}{T} \right) dA \right]_{av} = \int_A \left(\frac{\dot{Q}/A}{T} \right) dA \tag{7.24}$$

where $\dot{Q}/A$ is the flux of heat transfer at an element of area where the surface temperature is T. We also note that as δt approaches zero the boundaries of the system and the control volume coincide, and therefore the term

$$\int_A \left(\frac{\dot{Q}/A}{T}\right) dA$$

applies to the control volume, and we write

$$\int_A \left(\frac{\dot{Q}_{c.v.}/A}{T}\right) dA$$

Substituting these limits that are approached as δt approaches zero into Eq. 7.21, we have the rate form of the second law for a control volume

$$\frac{d}{dt} \int_V s\rho \, dV + \int_A s\rho \mathsf{V}_r \cos \alpha \, dA \geq \int_A \left(\frac{\dot{Q}_{c.v.}/A}{T}\right) dA \qquad (7.25)$$

For the steady-state, steady-flow process, which has been defined in Section 5.9, we conclude that there is no change with time of the entropy per unit mass at any point within the control volume, and therefore the first term of Eq. 7.25 equals zero. That is

$$\frac{d}{dt} \int_V s\rho \, dV = 0 \qquad (7.26)$$

and for the steady-state, steady-flow process,

$$\int_A s\rho \mathsf{V}_r \cos \alpha \, dA \geq \int_A \left(\frac{\dot{Q}_{c.v.}/A}{T}\right) dA \qquad (7.27)$$

If in addition we assume that there are a number of areas on the control surface over which the mass flux and the state of the mass crossing the control surface are uniform and constant with respect to time we can write,

$$\sum \dot{m}_e s_e - \sum \dot{m}_i s_i \geq \int_A \left(\frac{\dot{Q}_{c.v.}/A}{T}\right) dA \qquad (7.28)$$

If in a steady-state, steady-flow process there is only one area over which mass enters the control volume at a uniform rate and only one area over which mass leaves the control volume at a uniform rate we can write

$$\dot{m}(s_e - s_i) \geq \int_A \left(\frac{\dot{Q}_{c.v.}/A}{T}\right) dA \qquad (7.29)$$

For an adiabatic process with these assumptions it follows that

$$s_e \geq s_i \qquad (7.30)$$

where the equality holds for a reversible adiabatic process.

For the uniform-state, uniform-flow process, which was described in Section 5.10, the second law for a control volume, Eq. 7.25, can be written in the following form.

$$\frac{d}{dt}[ms]_{\text{c.v.}} + \sum \dot{m}_e s_e - \sum \dot{m}_i s_i \geq \int_A \left(\frac{\dot{Q}_{\text{c.v.}}/A}{T}\right) dA \qquad (7.31)$$

If this is integrated over the time interval t we have

$$\int_0^t \frac{d}{dt}[ms]_{\text{c.v.}} \, dt = [m_2 s_2 - m_1 s_1]_{\text{c.v.}}$$

$$\int_0^t (\sum \dot{m}_e s_e) \, dt = \sum m_e s_e; \qquad \int_0^t (\sum \dot{m}_i s_i) \, dt = \sum m_i s_i \qquad (7.32)$$

Therefore, for this period of time t we can write the second law for the uniform-state, uniform-flow process as

$$[m_2 s_2 - m_1 s_1]_{\text{c.v.}} + \sum m_e s_e - \sum m_i s_i \geq \int_0^t \left[\int_A \left(\frac{\dot{Q}_{\text{c.v.}}/A}{T}\right) dA\right] dt \qquad (7.33)$$

However, since in this process the temperature is uniform throughout the control volume, the integral on the right reduces to

$$\int_0^t \left[\int_A \left(\frac{\dot{Q}_{\text{c.v.}}/A}{T}\right) dA\right] dt = \int_0^t \left[\frac{1}{T} \int_A \left(\frac{\dot{Q}_{\text{c.v.}}}{A}\right) dA\right] dt = \int_0^t \left(\frac{\dot{Q}_{\text{c.v.}}}{T}\right) dt$$

and therefore the second law for the uniform-flow, uniform-state process can be written

$$[m_2 s_2 - m_1 s_1]_{\text{c.v.}} + \sum m_e s_e - \sum m_i s_i \geq \int_0^t \left(\frac{\dot{Q}_{\text{c.v.}}}{T}\right) dt \qquad (7.34)$$

By introducing the lost work we can write this as an equality. In doing so, we note that since the temperature is uniform throughout the control volume at any instant of time,

$$\int_0^t \left[\int_V \left(\frac{L\dot{W}_{\text{c.v.}}/V}{T}\right) dV\right] dt = \int_0^t \left[\frac{1}{T} \int_V \left(\frac{L\dot{W}_{\text{c.v.}}}{V}\right) dV\right] dt$$

$$= \int_0^t \left(\frac{L\dot{W}_{\text{c.v.}}}{T}\right) dt$$

Therefore,

$$[m_2 s_2 - m_1 s_1]_{\text{c.v.}} + \sum m_e s_e - \sum m_i s_i = \int_0^t \left(\frac{\dot{Q}_{\text{c.v.}} + L\dot{W}_{\text{c.v.}}}{T}\right) dt \qquad (7.35)$$

Example 7.2

Steam enters a steam turbine at a pressure of 100 lbf/in.², a temperature of 500 F, and a velocity of 200 ft/sec. The steam leaves the turbine at a pressure of 20 lbf/in.² and a velocity of 600 ft/sec. Determine the work per pound of steam flowing through the turbine, assuming the process to be reversible and adiabatic.

In solving a problem such as this it is usually advisable to draw a schematic diagram of the apparatus, and to show the process or, in the case of irreversible process, the various states involved on a T-s diagram. The next step in the solution is to write the continuity equation, the first and second laws of thermodynamics, and the property relation as they apply to the particular problem.

The schematic diagram and a T-s diagram are shown in Fig. 7.14. The various equations that apply to this process are:

Continuity eq.: $$\dot{m}_e = \dot{m}_i = \dot{m}$$

First law: $$h_i + \frac{V_i^2}{2g_c} = w + h_e + \frac{V_e^2}{2g_c}$$

Second law: $$s_e = s_i$$

Property relation: Steam tables
From the steam tables.

$$h_i = 1279.1 \text{ Btu/lbm} \qquad s_i = 1.7085 \text{ Btu/lbm-R}$$

The two properties known in the final state are pressure and entropy.

$$P_e = 20 \text{ lbf/in.}^2 \qquad s_e = s_i = 1.7085 \text{ Btu/lbm-R}$$

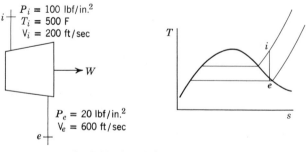

Fig. 7.14   Sketch for Example 7.2.

Therefore, the quality and enthalpy of the steam leaving the turbine can be determined.

$$s_e = 1.7085 = s_g - (1 - x)_e s_{fg} = 1.7319 - (1 - x)_e 1.3962$$

$$(1 - x)_e = \frac{0.0234}{1.3962} = 0.01676$$

$$h_e = h_g - (1 - x)_e h_{fg} = 1156.3 - 0.01676(960.1) = 1140.2 \text{ Btu/lbm}$$

Therefore, the work per pound of steam for this isentropic process may be found using the equation for the first law as given above

$$w = 1279.1 - 1140.2 + \frac{(200)^2 - (600)^2}{2 \times 32.17 \times 778} = 132.5 \text{ Btu/lbm}$$

Example 7.3

Consider the reversible adiabatic flow of steam through a nozzle. Steam enters the nozzle at 100 lbf/in.², 500 F, with a velocity of 100 ft/sec. The pressure of the steam at the nozzle exit is 40 lbf/in.². Determine the exit velocity of the steam from the nozzle, assuming a reversible, adiabatic, steady-state, steady-flow process.

This process is shown schematically and on a T-s diagram in Fig. 7.15. Since this is a steady state, steady-flow process in which the work, the heat transfer, and the changes in potential energy are zero, we can write,

Continuity eq.: $$\dot{m}_e = \dot{m}_i = \dot{m}$$

First law: $$h_i + \frac{V_i^2}{2g_c} = h_e + \frac{V_e^2}{2g_c}$$

Second law: $$s_e = s_i$$

Property relation: Steam tables

$$h_i = 1279.1 \text{ Btu/lbm}; \qquad s_i = 1.7085 \text{ Btu/lbm-R}$$

The two properties that we know in the final state are

$$s_e = s_i = 1.7085 \text{ Btu/lbm-R}; \qquad P_e = 40 \text{ lbf/in.}^2$$

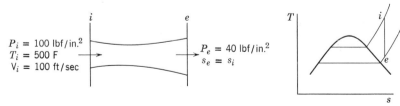

$P_i = 100$ lbf/in.²
$T_i = 500$ F
$V_i = 100$ ft/sec

$P_e = 40$ lbf/in.²
$s_e = s_i$

Fig. 7.15   Sketch for Example 7.3.

Therefore,

$$h_e = 1193.8 \text{ Btu/lbm}$$

Substituting into the equation for the first law as given above we have,

$$\frac{V_e^2}{2g_c} = h_i - h_e + \frac{V_i^2}{2g_c}$$

$$= 1279.1 - 1193.8 + \frac{100 \times 100}{2 \times 32.17 \times 778} = 85.5 \text{ Btu/lbm}$$

$$V_e = \sqrt{2 \times 32.17 \times 778 \times 85.5} = 2070 \text{ ft/sec}$$

Example 7.4

An inventor reports that he has a refrigeration compressor that receives saturated Freon-12 vapor at 0 F and delivers the vapor at 150 lbf/in.², 120 F. The compression process is adiabatic. Does the process described violate the second law?

Since this is a steady-state, steady-flow, adiabatic process we can write:

Second law: $\qquad\qquad s_e \geq s_i$

Property relation: Freon-12 tables
From the Freon-12 tables,

$s_e = 0.16629$ Btu/lbm R; $s_i = 0.16888$ Btu/lbm R. Therefore, $s_e < s_i$, whereas, for this process, the second law requires that $s_e \geq s_i$. The process described would involve a violation of the second law, and would not be possible.

7.9　The Reversible Adiabatic, Steady-State, Steady-Flow Process

An expression can be derived for the work in a reversible adiabatic, steady-state, steady-flow process which is of great help in understanding the significant variables in such a process. We have noted that when a steady-state, steady-flow process involves a single flow of fluid into and out of the control volume, the first law can be written, Eq. 5.50,

$$q + h_i + \frac{V_i^2}{2g_c} + Z_i \frac{g}{g_c} = w + h_e + \frac{V_e^2}{2g_c} + Z_e \frac{g}{g_c}$$

and the second law, Eq. 7.29, is

$$\dot{m}(s_e - s_i) \geq \int_A \left(\frac{\dot{Q}_{\text{c.v.}}/A}{T} \right) dA$$

If the process is reversible and adiabatic,

$$s_e = s_i$$

and it follows from the property relation

$$T \, ds = dh - v \, dP$$

that

$$h_e - h_i = \int_i^e v \, dP \qquad (7.36)$$

Substituting these relations into Eq. 5.50 and noting that $q = 0$ we have

$$w = (h_i - h_e) + \frac{(V_i^2 - V_e^2)}{2g_c} + (Z_i - Z_e)\frac{g}{g_c}$$

$$= -\int_i^e v \, dP + \frac{(V_i^2 - V_e^2)}{2g_c} + (Z_i - Z_e)\frac{g}{g_c} \qquad (7.37)$$

If in addition we assume that the changes in kinetic and potential energy are zero we have

$$w = -\int_i^e v \, dP \qquad (7.38)$$

From this equation we conclude that the work required to accomplish a reversible adiabatic, steady-state, steady-flow compression process depends on the specific volume of the fluid during the process. To further amplify this point, consider the simple steam power plant shown in Fig. 7.16. Suppose this is an ideal power plant, with no pressure drop in the piping, the boiler, or the condenser. Thus the pressure increase in the pump is equal to the pressure decrease in the turbine. Neglecting kinetic and potential energy changes, the work done in each of these processes is given by Eq. 7.38. Since the pump handles liquid, which has a very small specific volume as compared to the vapor that flows through the turbine,

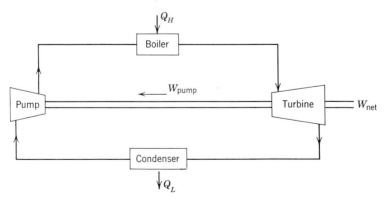

Fig. 7.16   Simple steam power plant.

the power input to the pump is much less than the power output of the turbine, the difference being the net power output of the power plant.

This same line of reasoning can be qualitatively applied to actual devices that involve steady-state, steady-flow processes, even though the processes are not exactly reversible and adiabatic.

If we consider a reversible adiabatic, steady-state, steady-flow process in which the work is zero (such as flow through a nozzle) and the fluid is incompressible (v = constant), Eq. 7.37 can be integrated to give

$$v(P_e - P_i) + \frac{(V_e^{\,2} - V_i^{\,2})}{2g_c} + (Z_e - Z_i)\frac{g}{g_c} = 0 \tag{7.39}$$

This is known as the Bernoulli equation, (after Daniel Bernoulli) and is a very important equation in fluid mechanics.

Example 7.5

Calculate the work per pound to pump water isentropically from 100 lbf/in.², 80 F to 1000 lbf/in.².

From the steam tables, $v_1 = 0.01608$ ft³/lbm. Assuming the specific volume to remain constant and using Eq. 7.38 we have,

$$-w = \int_1^2 v \, dP = v(P_2 - P_1) = 0.01608(1000 - 100) \times \frac{144}{778}$$

$$= 2.68 \text{ Btu/lbm}$$

7.10 Entropy Change of an Ideal Gas

Two very useful equations for computing the entropy change of an ideal gas can be developed from Eq. 7.7 by substituting Eqs. 5.61 and 5.65, as follows:

$$T \, ds = du + P \, dv$$

For an ideal gas

$$du = C_{vo} \, dT \qquad \text{and} \qquad \frac{P}{T} = \frac{R}{v}$$

Therefore,

$$ds = C_{vo} \frac{dT}{T} + \frac{R \, dv}{v} \tag{7.40}$$

$$s_2 - s_1 = \int_1^2 C_{vo} \frac{dT}{T} + R \ln \frac{v_2}{v_1} \tag{7.41}$$

Similarly

$$T \, ds = dh - v \, dP$$

For an ideal gas

$$dh = C_{po}\, dT \qquad \text{and} \qquad \frac{v}{T} = \frac{R}{P}$$

Therefore,

$$ds = C_{po}\frac{dT}{T} - R\frac{dP}{P} \tag{7.42}$$

$$s_2 - s_1 = \int_1^2 C_{po}\frac{dT}{T} - R\ln\frac{P_2}{P_1} \tag{7.43}$$

In order to integrate Eqs. 7.41 and 7.43, the relation between specific heat and temperature must be known. It follows from Eqs. 7.41 and 7.43 that when C_{po} and C_{vo} are assumed constant that the change in entropy is given by the relations

$$s_2 - s_1 = C_{po}\ln T_2/T_1 - R\ln P_2/P_1 = C_{vo}\ln T_2/T_1 + R\ln v_2/v_1$$

The empirical specific heat equations of Table A.9 can be used, as illustrated by Example 7.6.

Example 7.6

Consider the same example as cited previously, in which oxygen is heated from 500 R to 2000 R. Assume that during this process the pressure dropped from 30 lbf/in.^{2} to 20 lbf/in.^{2}. Calculate the change in entropy per lbm.

Using Eq. 7.43 and the appropriate equation from Table A.9

$$\bar{s}_2 - \bar{s}_1 = \int_{T_1}^{T_2}\left(11.515\frac{dT}{T} - \frac{172\,dT}{T^{3/2}} + \frac{1530\,dT}{T^2}\right) - \bar{R}\int_{P_1}^{P_2}\frac{dP}{P}$$

$$= 11.515\ln\frac{2000}{500} + 2 \times 172\left[\frac{1}{\sqrt{2000}} - \frac{1}{\sqrt{500}}\right]$$

$$- 1530\left[\frac{1}{2000} - \frac{1}{500}\right] - 1.986\ln\frac{20}{30}$$

$$= 15.98 - 7.70 + 2.29 + 0.80 = 11.37 \text{ Btu/lb mole-R}$$

$$s_2 - s_1 = \frac{\bar{s}_2 - \bar{s}_1}{M} = \frac{11.37}{32.00} = 0.356 \text{ Btu/lbm-R}$$

Changes in entropy that take into account the variation of specific heat with temperature can also be found from the *Gas Tables*. The method used is developed from Eq. 7.42. The entropy in an arbitrary reference state, where the temperature is T_0 and the pressure is 1 atm, is assumed to be zero. Therefore, at a given temperature T and pressure P (expressed in atmospheres) the entropy s is found from Eq. 7.42 to be

$$s = \int_{T_0}^{T} C_{po} \frac{dT}{T} - R \ln P$$

In the *Gas Tables* the quantity ϕ is defined as

$$\phi = \int_{T_0}^{T} C_{po} \frac{dT}{T}$$

Then, the change of entropy between states 1 and 2 is

$$s_2 - s_1 = \phi_2 - \phi_1 - R \ln \frac{P_2}{P_1} \tag{7.44}$$

This equation, as well as Eqs. 7.41 and 7.43, holds for all processes, both reversible and irreversible. The value of ϕ for air is given in Table A.10 of the Appendix.

Example 7.7

Calculate the change in entropy per pound as air is heated from 540 R to 1200 R while the pressure drops from 50 lbf/in.² to 40 lbf/in.².
From Table A.10,

$$\phi_1 = 0.6008 \text{ Btu/lbm-R} \qquad \phi_2 = 0.7963 \text{ Btu/lbm-R}$$

Using Eq. 7.44,

$$s_2 - s_1 = 0.7963 - 0.6008 - \frac{53.34}{778} \ln \frac{40}{50} = 0.2108 \text{ Btu/lbm-R}$$

The *Gas Tables* can be used for reversible adiabatic processes by employing the relative pressure P_r and relative specific volume v_r. The definition of these terms and the derivation follow.
For the reversible adiabatic process

$$T\, ds = dh - v\, dP = 0$$

Therefore

$$dh = C_{po}\, dT = v\, dP = RT \frac{dP}{P}$$

$$\frac{dP}{P} = \frac{C_{po}}{R} \frac{dT}{T}$$

Let this equation be integrated between a reference state having a temperature T_0 and a pressure P_0, and a given arbitrary state having a temperature T and a pressure P. Then

$$\ln \frac{P}{P_0} = \frac{1}{R} \int_{T_0}^{T} C_{po} \frac{dT}{T}$$

The right side of this equation is a function of temperature only. The relative pressure P_r is defined as

$$\ln P_r \equiv \ln \frac{P}{P_0} = \frac{1}{R} \int_{T_0}^{T} C_{po} \frac{dT}{T} = \frac{\phi}{R} \qquad (7.45)$$

Thus, a value of P_r can be tabulated as a function of temperature.

If we consider two states, 1 and 2, along a constant-entropy line it follows from Eq. 7.45 that

$$\frac{P_1}{P_2} = \left(\frac{P_{r1}}{P_{r2}}\right)_{s=\text{constant}} \qquad (7.46)$$

This equation states that the ratio of the relative pressures for two states having the same entropy is equal to the ratio of the absolute pressures.

The development of the relative specific volume is similar, and the ratio of the relative specific volumes v_r, in an isentropic process is equal to the ratio of the specific volumes. That is,

$$\frac{v_1}{v_2} = \left(\frac{v_{r1}}{v_{r2}}\right)_{s=\text{constant}} \qquad (7.47)$$

Example 7.8

Air expands in an air turbine from a pressure of 50 lbf/in.² and a temperature of 600 F to an exhaust pressure of 20 lbf/in.². Assume the process to be reversible and adiabatic, with negligible changes in kinetic and potential energy. Calculate the work per pound of air flowing through the turbine.

Since this is a steady-state, steady-flow reversible adiabatic process we can write

Continuity eq.: $\qquad\qquad \dot{m}_e = \dot{m}_i = \dot{m}$

First law: $\qquad\qquad\quad h_i = h_e + w$

Second law: $\qquad\qquad s_e = s_i$

Property relation: *Gas Tables.*
From Table A.10,

$$T_i = 1060 \text{ R}; \qquad h_i = 255.96 \text{ Btu/lbm}; \qquad (P_r)_i = 15.203$$

From Eq. 7.46

$$(P_r)_e = (P_r)_i \times \frac{P_e}{P_i} = 15.203 \times \frac{20}{50} = 6.081$$

From Table A.10,

$$T_e = 822 \text{ R}; \qquad h_e = 197.18$$

Therefore

$$w = h_i - h_e = 255.96 - 197.18 = 58.8 \text{ Btu/lbm}$$

At this point it is advantageous to introduce the specific heat ratio k, which is defined as the ratio of the constant-pressure to the constant-volume specific heat at zero pressure.

$$k = \frac{C_{po}}{C_{vo}} \qquad (7.48)$$

Since the difference between C_{po} and C_{vo} is a constant (Eq. 5.68) and since C_{po} and C_{vo} are functions of temperature, it follows that k is also a function of temperature. However, when we consider the specific heat to be constant, k is also constant.

From the definition of k and and Eq. 5.68 it follows that

$$C_{vo} = \frac{R}{k-1}; \qquad C_{po} = \frac{kR}{k-1} \qquad (7.49)$$

Some very useful and simple relations for the reversible adiabatic process can be developed when the specific heats are assumed to be constant.

For the reversible adiabatic process, $ds = 0$. Therefore,

$$T \, ds = du + P \, dv = C_{vo} \, dT + P \, dv = 0$$

From the equation of state for an ideal gas,

$$dT = \frac{1}{R} (P \, dv + v \, dP)$$

Therefore,

$$\frac{C_{vo}}{R} (P \, dv + v \, dP) + P \, dv = 0$$

Substituting Eq. 7.49 into this expression and rearranging,

$$\frac{1}{k-1} (P \, dv + v \, dP) + P \, dv = 0$$

$$v \, dP + kP \, dv = 0$$

$$\frac{dP}{P} + k \frac{dv}{v} = 0$$

Since k is constant when the specific heat is constant, this equation can be integrated under these conditions to give

$$Pv^k = \text{constant} \qquad (7.50)$$

Equation 7.50 holds for all reversible adiabatic processes involving an ideal gas with constant specific heat. It is usually advantageous to express this constant in terms of the initial and final states.

$$Pv^k = P_1v_1{}^k = P_2v_2{}^k = \text{constant} \tag{7.51}$$

From this equation and the ideal gas equation of state the following expressions relating the initial and final states of an isentropic process can be derived.

$$\frac{P_2}{P_1} = \left(\frac{v_1}{v_2}\right)^k = \left(\frac{V_1}{V_2}\right)^k \tag{7.52}$$

$$\frac{T_2}{T_1} = \left(\frac{P_2}{P_1}\right)^{(k-1)/k} = \left(\frac{v_1}{v_2}\right)^{k-1} \tag{7.53}$$

With the assumption of constant specific heat some convenient equations can be derived for the work done by an ideal gas during an adiabatic process. Consider first a system consisting of an ideal gas that undergoes a process in which work is done only at the moving boundary.

$$_1Q_2 = m(u_2 - u_1) + {}_1W_2 = 0$$
$$_1W_2 = -m(u_2 - u_1) = -mC_{vo}(T_2 - T_1)$$
$$= \frac{mR}{1-k}(T_2 - T_1) = \frac{P_2V_2 - P_1V_1}{1-k} \tag{7.54}$$

Consider an ideal gas that undergoes a steady-state, steady-flow adiabatic process in which changes of kinetic and potential energy are negligible. In this case

$$w = h_1 - h_2 = C_{po}(T_1 - T_2)$$
$$= \frac{kR}{k-1}(T_1 - T_2) = \frac{k}{k-1}(P_1v_1 - P_2v_2) \tag{7.55}$$

It should be noted that Eqs. 7.54 and 7.55 apply to adiabatic processes only. Since no assumption was made regarding reversibility, they apply to both reversible and irreversible processes. Frequently Eq. 7.54 is derived for reversible processes by starting with the relation $_1W_2 = \int_1^2 P\,dV$ for the system.

7.11   The Reversible Polytropic Process for an Ideal Gas

When a gas undergoes a reversible process in which there is heat transfer, the process frequently takes place in such a manner that a plot of $\log P$ vs. $\log V$ is a straight line as shown in Fig. 7.17. For such a process $PV^n = \text{constant}$.

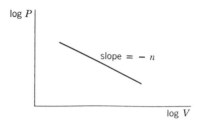

Fig. 7.17   Example of a polytropic process.

This is called a polytropic process. An example is the expansion of the combustion gases in the cylinder of a water-cooled reciprocating engine. If the pressure and volume during a polytropic process are measured during the expansion stroke, as might be done with an engine indicator, and the logarithms of the pressure and volume are plotted, the result would be similar to Fig. 7.17. From this figure it follows that

$$\frac{d \ln P}{d \ln V} = -n$$

$$d \ln P + n d \ln V = 0$$

If n is a constant (which implies a straight line on the $\log P$ vs. $\log V$ plot), this can be integrated to give the following relation:

$$PV^n = \text{constant} = P_1 V_1^n = P_2 V_2^n \qquad (7.56)$$

From this it is evident that the following relations can be written for a polytropic process.

$$\frac{P_2}{P_1} = \left(\frac{V_1}{V_2}\right)^n$$

$$\frac{T_2}{T_1} = \left(\frac{P_2}{P_1}\right)^{(n-1)/n} = \left(\frac{V_1}{V_2}\right)^{n-1} \qquad (7.57)$$

For a system consisting of an ideal gas, the work done at the moving boundary during a reversible polytropic process can be derived from the relations $_1W_2 = \int_1^2 P\, dV$ and $PV^n = \text{constant}$.

$$_1W_2 = \int_1^2 P\, dV = \text{constant} \int_1^2 \frac{dV}{V^n}$$

$$= \frac{P_2 V_2 - P_1 V_1}{1 - n} = \frac{mR(T_2 - T_1)}{1 - n} \qquad (7.58)$$

In a similar manner an expression can be derived for the work done in a steady-state, steady-flow reversible process with negligible changes in kinetic and potential energies, from the relations $w = -\int_i^e v \, dP$ and $Pv^n = \text{constant} = C^n$.

$$w = -\int_i^e v \, dP = -C \int_i^e \frac{dP}{P^{1/n}}$$

$$= -\frac{n}{n-1}(P_e v_e - P_i v_i) = -\frac{nR}{n-1}(T_e - T_i) \qquad (7.59)$$

The polytropic processes for various values of n are shown in Fig. 7.18 on P-v and T-s diagrams. The values of n for some familiar processes are given below.

Isobaric process	$n = 0$
Isothermal process	$n = 1$
Isentropic process	$n = k$
Isometric process	$n = \infty$

Example 7.9

Nitrogen is compressed in a reversible process in a cylinder from 14.7 lbf/in.², 60 F to 60 lbf/in.². During the compression process the relation between pressure and volume is $PV^{1.3} = \text{constant}$. Calculate the work and heat transfer per pound, and show this process on P-v and T-s diagrams.

$$P_1 = 14.7 \text{ lbf/in.}^2; \qquad P_2 = 60 \text{ lbf/in.}^2$$
$$T_1 = 520 \text{ R}$$

T_2 can be calculated from Eq. 7.57

$$\frac{T_2}{T_1} = \left(\frac{P_2}{P_1}\right)^{(n-1)/n} = \left(\frac{60}{14.7}\right)^{(1.3-1)/1.3} = 1.383$$

$$T_2 = 520 \times 1.383 = 719 \text{ R}$$

For this process the work can be found using Eq. 7.58.

$$_1W_2 = \frac{R(T_2 - T_1)}{1 - n} = \frac{55.15(719 - 520)}{(1 - 1.3)778} = -47.0 \text{ Btu/lbm}$$

The heat transfer can be calculated using the first law. Let us assume C_{v0} to be constant over this range in temperature.

$$_1q_2 = u_2 - u_1 + {}_1W_2 = C_{v0}(T_2 - T_1) + {}_1W_2$$
$$= 0.177(719 - 520) - 47.0 = -11.8 \text{ Btu/lbm}$$

This process is shown on the P-v and T-s diagrams of Fig. 7.19.

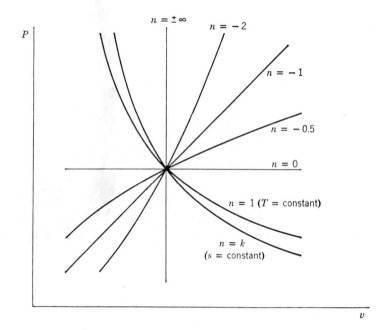

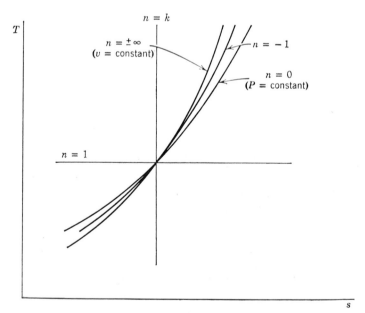

Fig. 7.18   Polytropic processes on P-v and τ-s diagrams.

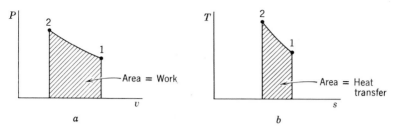

Fig. 7.19   Diagram for Example 7.9.

The reversible isothermal process for an ideal gas is of particular interest. In this case

$$PV = \text{constant} = P_1V_1 = P_2V_2 \qquad (7.60)$$

The work done at the boundary of a simple compressible system during a reversible isothermal process can be found by integrating the equation

$$_1W_2 = \int_1^2 P \, dV$$

The integration is as follows:

$$_1W_2 = \int_1^2 P \, dV = \text{constant} \int_1^2 \frac{dV}{V} = P_1V_1 \ln \frac{V_2}{V_1} = P_1V_1 \ln \frac{P_1}{P_2}$$

$$_1W_2 = mRT \ln \frac{V_2}{V_1} = mRT \ln \frac{P_1}{P_2} \qquad (7.61)$$

For the reversible isothermal steady-state, steady-flow process with negligible changes in kinetic and potential energy the work is calculated from Eq. 7.38

$$w = -\int_i^e v \, dP = -\text{constant} \int_i^e \frac{dP}{P} = -P_i v_i \ln \frac{P_e}{P_i} \qquad (7.62)$$

Since there is no change in internal energy or enthalpy in an isothermal process, the heat transfer is equal to the work (neglecting changes in kinetic and potential energy). Therefore, we could have derived Eqs. 7.61 and 7.62 by calculating the heat transfer.

For example, using Eq. 7.5

$$\int_1^2 T \, ds = {}_1q_2 = \int_1^2 du + \int_1^2 P \, dv$$

But $du = 0$ and $Pv = \text{constant} = P_1v_1 = P_2v_2$

$$_1q_2 = \int_1^2 P \, dv = P_1v_1 \ln \frac{v_2}{v_1}$$

which yields the same result as Eq. 7.61.

7.12 Principle of the Increase of Entropy

In this section we consider the total change in the entropy of a system and its surroundings when the system undergoes a change of state. This consideration leads to the principle of the increase of entropy.

Consider the process shown in Fig. 7.20, in which a quantity of heat δQ is transferred from the surroundings at temperature T_0 to the system at temperature T, and let the work done by the system during this process be δW. For this process we can apply Eq. 7.10 to the system and write

$$dS_{\text{system}} \geq \frac{\delta Q}{T}$$

For the surroundings δQ is negative and we can write

$$dS_{\text{surr}} = \frac{-\delta Q}{T_0}$$

The total change of entropy is therefore

$$dS_{\text{system}} + dS_{\text{surr}} \geq \frac{\delta Q}{T} - \frac{\delta Q}{T_0}$$

$$\geq \delta Q\left(\frac{1}{T} - \frac{1}{T_0}\right) \tag{7.63}$$

Since $T_0 > T$, the quantity $\left(\dfrac{1}{T} - \dfrac{1}{T_0}\right)$ is positive and we conclude that

$$dS_{\text{system}} + dS_{\text{surr}} \geq 0$$

If $T > T_0$, the heat transfer is from the system to the surroundings, and both δQ and the quantity $\left(\dfrac{1}{T} - \dfrac{1}{T_0}\right)$ are negative, thus yielding the same result.

Thus we conclude that for all possible processes that a system in a given surroundings can undergo,

$$dS_{\text{system}} + dS_{\text{surr}} \geq 0 \tag{7.64}$$

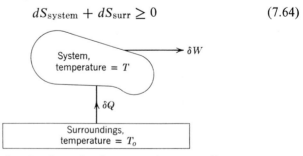

Fig. 7.20 Entropy change for the system plus surroundings.

where the equality holds for reversible processes and the inequality for irreversible processes. Since all macroscopic processes that occur are to some degree irreversible, there is always a net increase in the entropy of the system plus its surroundings. If a system is isolated from its surroundings there is of course no change in the entropy of the surroundings, and all of the entropy increase would occur in the system. Thus we can write

$$dS_{\text{isolated system}} \geq 0 \qquad (7.65)$$

Equations 7.64 and 7.65 lead to a statement of the principle of the increase of entropy, namely, that the entropy of an isolated system, or the entropy of a system and its surroundings will continually increase, or, in the limit remain constant. There is no way in which the entropy of an isolated system or the entropy of a system and its surroundings can decrease. It also follows that only those processes will occur that have associated with them a net increase of the entropy of the system and its surroundings. This applies to the combustion of fuel in our automobile engines, to the cooling of our coffee, and to the processes that take place in our body.

The same general conclusion is reached in the case of a control volume. To demonstrate this, consider a control volume, Fig. 7.21, which exchanges both mass and heat with the surroundings. At the point in the surroundings where the heat transfer occurs the temperature is T_0. From Eq. 7.25 the second law for this process is

$$\frac{d}{dt}\int_V s\rho \, dV + \int_A s\rho V_r \cos \alpha \, dA \geq \int_A \left(\frac{\dot{Q}_{\text{c.v.}}/A}{T} \right) dA$$

We recall that the first term represents the rate of change of entropy within the control volume, and the second term is the net entropy flow

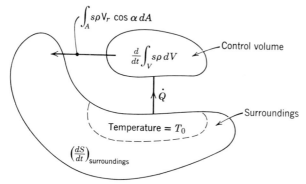

Fig. 7.21 Entropy change for a control volume plus surroundings.

out of the control volume as the result of the mass flow. Therefore, for the surroundings we can write

$$\left(\frac{dS}{dt}\right)_{\text{surr}} = \int_A s\rho V_r \cos\alpha \, dA - \frac{\dot{Q}_{\text{c.v.}}}{T_0}$$

Adding these two equations we have

$$\frac{d}{dt}\int_V s\rho \, dV + \left(\frac{dS}{dt}\right)_{\text{surr}} \geq \int_A \left(\frac{\dot{Q}_{\text{c.v.}}/A}{T}\right) dA - \frac{\dot{Q}_{\text{c.v.}}}{T_0} \tag{7.66}$$

Since $\dot{Q}_{\text{c.v.}} > 0$ when $T_0 > T$, and $\dot{Q}_{\text{c.v.}} < 0$ when $T_0 < T$, it follows that

$$\frac{d}{dt}\int_V s\rho \, dV + \left(\frac{dS}{dt}\right)_{\text{surr}} \geq 0 \tag{7.67}$$

Example 7.10

Suppose 1 lbm of saturated water vapor at 212 F is condensed to saturated liquid at 212 F in a constant-pressure process by heat transfer to the surrounding air, which is at 80 F. What is the net increase in entropy of the system plus surroundings?

For the system, from the steam tables

$$\Delta S_{\text{system}} = -s_{fg} = -1.4446 \text{ Btu/lbm-R}$$

Considering the surroundings

$$Q_{\text{to surroundings}} = h_{fg} = 970.3 \text{ Btu/lbm}$$

$$\Delta S_{\text{surr}} = \frac{Q}{T_0} = \frac{970.3}{540} = 1.7980 \text{ Btu/lbm-R}$$

$$\Delta S_{\text{system}} + \Delta S_{\text{surr}} = -1.4446 + 1.7968 = 0.3522 \text{ Btu/lbm-R}$$

This increase in entropy is in accordance with the principle of the increase of entropy, and tells, as does our experience, that this process can take place.

It is interesting to note how this heat transfer from the water to the surroundings might have taken place reversibly. Suppose that an engine operating on the Carnot cycle received heat from the water and rejected heat to the surroundings, as shown in Fig. 7.22. The decrease in the entropy of the water is equal to the increase in the entropy of the surroundings.

$$\Delta S_{\text{system}} = -1.4446 \text{ Btu/lbm-R}$$

$$\Delta S_{\text{surr}} = 1.4446 \text{ Btu/lbm-R}$$

$$Q_{\text{to surroundings}} = T_0 \Delta S = 540(1.4446) = 780.1 \text{ Btu/lbm}$$

$$W = Q_H - Q_L = 970.3 - 780.1 = 190.2 \text{ Btu/lbm}$$

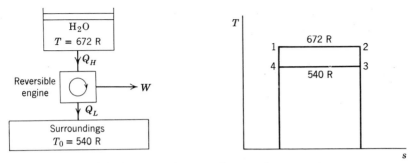

Fig. 7.22   Reversible heat transfer with the surroundings.

Since this is a reversible cycle, the engine could be reversed and operated as a heat pump. For this cycle the work input to the heat pump would be 190.2 Btu/lbm.

This principle of the increase of entropy is a most important aspect of the second law of thermodynamics, and will be developed further in Chapter 8 where the concepts of availability and irreversibility are introduced.

7.13   Efficiency

In Chapter 6 we noted that the second law of thermodynamics led to the concept of thermal efficiency for a heat engine cycle, namely

$$\eta_{th} = \frac{W_{net}}{Q_H}$$

where W_{net} is the net work of the cycle and Q_H is the heat transfer from the high-temperature body.

In this chapter we have extended our consideration of the second law to processes, and this leads us now to consider the efficiency of a process. For example, we might be interested in the efficiency of a turbine in a steam power plant, or the compressor in a gas turbine engine.

In general we can say that the efficiency of a machine in which a process takes place involves a comparison between the actual performance of the machine under given conditions and the performance that would have been achieved in an ideal process. It is in the definition of this ideal process that the second law becomes a major consideration. For example, a steam turbine is intended to be an adiabatic machine. The only heat transfer is the unavoidable heat transfer that takes place between the given turbine and the surroundings. Also, we note that for a given steam turbine operating in a steady-state, steady-flow manner, the state of the steam entering the turbine and the exhaust pressure are fixed. Therefore the ideal process would be a reversible adiabatic process, which is an isentropic process, between the inlet state and the turbine exhaust pressure. If we denote the actual work done per unit mass of steam flow through the turbine as w_a and the work that would have been done in a reversible adiabatic process between the inlet state and the turbine exhaust pressure as w_s the efficiency of the turbine is defined as

$$\eta_{\text{turbine}} = \frac{w_a}{w_s} \qquad (7.68)$$

The same relation would hold for a gas turbine.

A few other examples may help to clarify this point. In a nozzle the objective is to have the maximum kinetic energy leaving the nozzle for the given inlet conditions and exhaust pressure. The nozzle is also an adiabatic device and therefore the ideal process is a reversible adiabatic or isentropic process. The efficiency of a nozzle is the ratio of the actual kinetic energy leaving the nozzle, $V_a^2/2g_c$, to the kinetic energy for an isentropic process between the same inlet conditions and exhaust pressure, namely, $V_s^2/2g_c$

$$\eta_{\text{nozzle}} = \frac{V_a^2/2g_c}{V_s^2/2g_c} \qquad (7.69)$$

In compressors for air or other gases, there are two ideal processes to which the actual performance can be compared. If no effort is made to cool the gas during compression (that is, when the process is adiabatic), the ideal process is a reversible adiabatic or isentropic process between the given inlet state and exhaust pressure. If we denote the work per unit mass of gas flow through the compressor for this isentropic process as w_s, and the actual work as w_a (the actual work input will be greater than the work input for an isentropic process), the efficiency is defined by the relation

$$\eta_{\text{adiabatic compressor}} = \frac{w_s}{w_a} \qquad (7.70)$$

If an attempt is made to cool the air during compression by use of a water jacket or fins, the ideal process is considered a reversible isothermal process. If w_t is the work for the reversible isothermal process between the given inlet state and exhaust pressure, and w_a the actual work, the efficiency is defined by the relation

$$\eta_{\text{cooled compressor}} = \frac{w_t}{w_a} \qquad (7.71)$$

Thus we note that the efficiency of a device that involves a process (rather than a cycle) involves a comparison of the actual performance to that which would be achieved in a related, but well defined ideal process.

Example 7.11

A steam turbine receives steam at a pressure of 100 lbf/in.^{2}, 500 F. The steam leaves the turbine at a pressure of 2 lbf/in.^{2}. The work output of the turbine is measured and is found to be 172 Btu per pound of steam flowing through the turbine. Determine the efficiency of the turbine.

The efficiency of the turbine is given by Eq. 7.68,

$$\eta_{turbine} = \frac{w_a}{w_s}$$

Thus a determination of the turbine efficiency involves a calculation of the work which would be done in an isentropic process between the given inlet state and final pressure. For this isentropic process:

Continuity eq.: $\qquad\qquad \dot{m}_1 = \dot{m}_2 = \dot{m}$

First law: $\qquad\qquad\qquad h_1 = h_{2s} + w_s$

Second law: $\qquad\qquad\quad s_1 = s_{2s}$

Property relation: Steam tables

$$h_1 = 1279.1; \qquad s_1 = 1.7085$$

$$s_{2s} = s_1 = 1.7085 = 1.9200 - (1 - x)_{2s} 1.7451$$

$$(1 - x)_{2s} = \frac{0.2115}{1.7451} = 0.1210$$

$$h_{2s} = 1116.2 - 0.1210(1022.2) = 992.4$$

$$w_s = h_1 - h_{2s} = 1279.1 - 992.4 = 286.7 \text{ Btu/lbm}$$

$$w_a = 172 \text{ Btu/lbm}$$

$$\eta_{turbine} = \frac{w_a}{w_s} = \frac{172}{286.7} = 0.60 = 60\%$$

7.14 Some General Comments Regarding Entropy

It is quite possible at this point that a student may have a good grasp of the material that has been covered, and yet he may have only a vague understanding of the significance of entropy. In fact, the question "What is entropy?" is frequently raised by students with the implication that no one really knows! This section has been included in an attempt to give insight into the qualitative and philosophical aspects of the concept of entropy, and to illustrate the broad application of entropy to many different disciplines.

First of all, we recall that the concept of energy rises from the first law of thermodynamics and the concept of entropy from the second law of thermodynamics. Actually it is just as difficult to answer the question "What is energy?" as it is to answer the question "What is entropy?" However, since we regularly use the term energy and are able to relate this term to phenomena that we observe every day, the word energy has a definite meaning to us and thus serves as an effective vehicle for thought and communication. The word entropy could serve in the same capacity. If, when we observed a highly irreversible process (such as cooling coffee by placing an ice cube in it), we said, "That surely increases the entropy," we would soon be as familiar with the word *entropy* as we are with the word *energy*. In many cases when we speak about a higher efficiency we are actually speaking about accomplishing a given objective with a smaller total increase in entropy.

A second point to be made regarding entropy is that frequently entropy is associated with probability. From this point of view the net increase in entropy that occurs during an irreversible process can be associated with a change of state from a less probable state to a more probable state. For example, to use a previous example, one is more likely to find gas on both sides of the ruptured membrane of Fig. 6.11 than to find a gas on one side and a vacuum on the other. Thus, when the membrane ruptures, the direction of the process is from a less probable state to a more probable state and associated with this process is an increase in entropy. Similarly, the more probable state is that a cup of coffee will be at the same temperature as its surroundings than at a higher (or lower) temperature. Therefore, as the coffee cools as the result of a transferring of heat to the surroundings, there is a change from a less probable to a more probable state, and associated with this is an increase in entropy.

The final point to be made is that the second law of thermodynamics and the principle of the increase of entropy have philosophical implications. Does the second law of thermodynamics apply to the universe as a whole? Are there processes unknown to us that occur somewhere in the universe, such as "continual creation," that have a decrease in entropy associated with them, and thus offset the continual increase in entropy that is associated with the natural processes that are known to us? If the second law is valid for the universe (we of course do not know if the universe can be considered as an isolated system) how did it get in the state of low entropy? On the other end of the scale, if all processes known to us have an increase in entropy associated with them, what is the future of the natural world as we know it?

Quite obviously it is impossible to give conclusive answers to these questions on the basis of the second law of thermodynamics alone. However, the authors see the second law of thermodynamics as man's description of the prior and continuing work of a creator, who also holds the answer to the future destiny of man and the universe.

PROBLEMS

7.1 Plot to scale a temperature-entropy diagram for Freon-12, showing the following lines:
(a) Saturated liquid and saturated vapor.
(b) 20 lbf/in.^{2} and 200 lbf/in.^{2} constant-pressure lines.
(c) 90 Btu/lbm and 100 Btu/lbm constant-enthalpy lines.
(d) 1 ft^3/lbm constant-specific volume line.

7.2 A heat engine operates on the Carnot cycle and receives 500 Btu from a reservoir at 1000 F, and rejects heat at 80 F.
(a) Show the cycle on a T-s diagram, considering the working fluid as the system.
(b) Calculate the work and efficiency of the cycle.
(c) Calculate the change in entropy of the high-temperature and low-temperature reservoirs.
(d) Suppose the engine operates on the cycle indicated above, but the temperature of the high-temperature reservoir is increased to 1500 F. (Heat is then transferred from the reservoir at 1500 F to the working fluid at 1000 F.) The low-temperature reservoir remains at 80 F. Determine the entropy change for each reservoir.

7.3 A Carnot cycle utilizes steam as the working fluid, and has an efficiency of 20%. Heat is transferred to the working fluid at 400 F and during this process the working fluid changes from saturated liquid to saturated vapor.
(a) Show this cycle on a T-s diagram that includes the saturated-liquid and saturated-vapor lines.
(b) Calculate the quality at the beginning and end of the heat-rejection process.
(c) Calculate the work per lbm of steam.

7.4 A Carnot cycle heat pump (refrigerator) has ammonia as the working fluid. Heat is transferred from the ammonia at 100 F, and during this process the ammonia changes from saturated vapor to saturated liquid. Heat is transferred to the working fluid at 0 F.
(a) Show this cycle on a T-s diagram.
(b) What is the quality at the beginning and end of the isothermal process at 0 F?
(c) What is the coefficient of performance of this cycle as a refrigerator?

7.5 A pressure vessel contains steam at 160 lbf/in.^{2}, 700 F. A valve at the top of the pressure vessel is opened, allowing steam to escape. Assume that at any instant the steam that remains in the pressure vessel has undergone a reversible adiabatic process. Determine the fraction of steam that has escaped when the steam remaining in the pressure vessel is saturated vapor.

7.6 A cylinder fitted with a piston is filled with steam at 100 lbf/in.², 500 F. The steam expands in a reversible adiabatic process until the pressure is 20 lbf/in.². The initial volume of the steam in the cylinder is 1 ft³. Determine the work done during this process.

7.7 Ammonia at 40 lbf/in.², 20 F is compressed in a cylinder by a piston to a pressure of 240 lbf/in.² in a reversible adiabatic process. Determine the work of compression per lbm of ammonia.

7.8 A cylinder fitted with a piston contains one pound of Freon-12 at 15 lbf/in.², 200 F. The piston is slowly moved and the necessary heat transfer takes place so that the Freon-12 is compressed in a reversible isothermal process until the Freon-12 exists as saturated vapor.

(a) Show the process on a temperature-entropy diagram that is approximately to scale.

(b) Calculate the final pressure and specific volume of the Freon-12.

(c) Determine the work and the heat transfer for this process.

7.9 A mass of 100 lbm is held in position in a length of 5 in. diameter tube by a pin. Below this mass is a volume of 0.5 ft³ of steam at 800 lbf/in.², 800 F. The pin is released and the mass is accelerated upwards, leaving the top of the

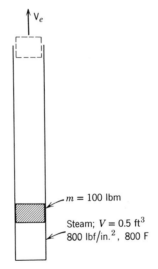

V_e

$m = 100$ lbm

Steam; $V = 0.5$ ft³
800 lbf/in.², 800 F

Fig. 7.23   Sketch for Problem 7.9.

tube with a certain velocity. If the steam undergoes a reversible adiabatic expansion, until a pressure of 100 lbf/in.² is reached, what is the exit velocity of the mass?

7.10 Solve Problem 4.7 without using the relation $_1W_2 = \int_1^2 P\, dV$.

7.11 A centrifugal compressor receives dry saturated water vapor at 50 F and compresses it to 4 lbf/in.². The volume rate of flow into the compressor is 1000 ft³/min. Assuming the compression process to be reversible and adiabatic, determine the power required to drive the compressor.

7.12 A refrigerator utilizes Freon-12 as the refrigerant and handles 200 lbm/hr. The Freon enters the compressor at 30 lbf/in.², 20 F, and leaves at 175 lbf/in.². What hp motor will be required to drive the compressor if the compression process is reversible and adiabatic?

7.13 A steam turbine receives steam at 100 lbf/in.², 500 F. The steam expands in a reversible adiabatic process and leaves the turbine at 14.7 lbf/in.². The power output of the turbine is 20,000 hp. What is the rate of steam flow in lbm/hr to the turbine?

7.14 A design for a turbine has been proposed involving the reversible, isothermal, steady flow of steam through the turbine. Saturated vapor at 100 lbf/in.² enters the turbine and the steam leaves at 20 lbf/in.². Determine the work per lbm of steam flowing through the turbine.

7.15 Steam enters a turbine at a pressure of 800 lbf/in.² and a temperature of 1000 F. At the exit of the turbine the pressure is 2 lbf/in.² and the entropy is 0.2 Btu/lbm-R greater than at the inlet. The inlet and exit velocities are essentially the same, and the process is adiabatic.

What is the mass rate of flow of steam (lbm/minute) that is required to produce a power output of 20,000 hp?

7.16 Steam at 400 lbf/in.², 600 F expands through a nozzle to 300 lbf/in.² at the rate of 20,000 lbm/hr. If the process occurs isentropically and the initial velocity is low, calculate:

(*a*) The velocity leaving the nozzle.

(*b*) The exit area of the nozzle.

7.17 A diffuser is a device in which a fluid flowing at high velocity is decelerated in such a way that the pressure increases during the process. Steam at 20 lbf/in.², 300 F enters the diffuser with a velocity of 2000 ft/sec and leaves with a velocity of 200 ft/sec. If the process is reversible and occurs without heat transfer, what is the final pressure and temperature of the steam? A Mollier diagram may be helpful in solving this problem.

7.18 In a steam power plant water enters the pump at 20 lbf/in.², 120 F, and leaves at 1400 lbf/in.². Calculate the work per lbm for this process if it occurs isentropically.

7.19 A centrifugal pump delivers liquid oxygen to a rocket engine at the rate of 100 lbm/sec. The oxygen enters the pump as saturated liquid at one atmosphere pressure, and the discharge pressure is 500 lbf/in.². Determine the power required to drive the pump if the process is reversible and adiabatic.

7.20 Tank *A* initially contains 10 lbm of steam at 100 lbf/in.², 600 F, and is connected through a valve to a cylinder fitted with a frictionless piston, as shown

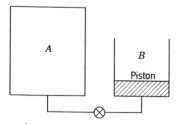

Fig. 7.24   Sketch for Problem 7.20.

in Fig. 7.24. A pressure of 20 lbf/in.² is required to balance the weight of the piston.

The connecting valve is opened until the pressure in *A* equals 20 lbf/in.². Assume the entire process to be adiabatic, and that the steam that finally remains in *A* has undergone a reversible adiabatic process.

Determine the work done against the piston and the final temperature of the steam in cylinder *B*.

7.21 Repeat Problem 7.20, but let the piston initially rest on stops so that the initial volume of the cylinder *B* is 10 ft³, as shown in Fig. 7.25. Assume that this volume is initially evacuated.

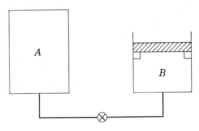

Fig. 7.25   Sketch for Problem 7.21.

7.22 Air at 200 lbf/in.², 1800 F expands in a reversible adiabatic process to 20 lbf/in.². Using data given in the Air Tables (Table A.10) determine the following:

The final temperature.
The final specific volume.
The change in internal energy per lbm.
The change in enthalpy per lbm.
The work done per lbm by the air during this expansion.
(*a*) Assume that the air is contained in a cylinder fitted with a piston.
(*b*) Assume a steady-state, steady-flow process.

7.23 Repeat Problem 7.22 assuming constant specific heat for the air as given in Table A.8.

7.24 A Carnot engine has 1 lbm of air as the working fluid. Heat is received at 1200 R and rejected at 500 R. At the beginning of the heat addition process the pressure is 100 lbf/in.², and during this process the volume triples. Calculate the net cycle work per lbm of air.

7.25 Twenty ft³ of air at a pressure of 58 lbf/in.² and a temperature of 520 R expand reversibly in a cylinder to a pressure of 14.7 lbf/in.². The final volume is 78.9 ft³. Assuming constant specific heat for this process calculate:

(*a*) The heat transfer during the expansion.
(*b*) The change of entropy during this process.

7.26 A tank of 20 ft³ volume contains air at 100 lbf/in.², 80 F. A valve on the tank is opened and the pressure in the tank drops quickly to 20 lbf/in.². If the air that remains in the tank has undergone a reversible adiabatic process, calculate the final mass of air in the tank.

7.27 Nitrogen, at the rate of 1000 ft³/min is compressed adiabatically in an axial flow compressor (steady flow) from 14.0 lbf/in.² to 50 lbf/in.². The temperature entering the compressor is 70 F and leaving the compressor it is 340 F. The velocity of the nitrogen entering the compressor is 500 ft/sec and leaving it is 20 ft/sec. Calculate the shaft hp of the compressor.

7.28 Nitrogen expands in a nozzle from a pressure of 100 lbf/in.² to 60 lbf/in.². The initial temperature is 200 F and the velocity entering the nozzle is 200 ft/sec. The rate of flow of nitrogen is 2000 lbm/hr. Calculate the exit area of the nozzle if the flow is reversible and adiabatic.

7.29 Helium which is contained in a cylinder fitted with a piston expands reversibly according to the relation $PV^{1.5}$ = constant. The initial volume of the helium is 2 ft³, the initial pressure is 70 lbf/in.², and the initial temperature is 400 R. After expansion the pressure is 20 lbf/in.². Calculate the work done and heat transfer during the expansion.

7.30 Air is compressed in a reversible steady-state, steady-flow process from 15 lbf/in.², 100 F to 100 lbf/in.². Calculate the work of compression per pound, the change of entropy, and the heat transfer per pound of air compressed, assuming the following processes.

(*a*) Isothermal.
(*b*) Polytropic, $n = 1.25$.
(*c*) Adiabatic.
(*d*) Show all these processes on a *P-v* and a *T-s* diagram.

7.31 Starting with the relation $w = -\int_{i}^{e} v\, dP$, show that the work done per lbm of fluid flow in a steady-state, steady-flow, reversible adiabatic process, involving an ideal gas with constant specific heat, and with no changes in kinetic or potential energy, is given by the relation

$$w = \frac{kRT_i}{k-1}\left[1 - \left(\frac{P_e}{P_i}\right)^{(k-1)/k}\right]$$

7.32 An ideal gas with constant specific heat enters a nozzle with a velocity V_i and leaves with a velocity V_e after undergoing a reversible adiabatic expansion. Show that the velocity leaving is given by the relation

$$V_e = \sqrt{V_i^2 + \frac{2g_c kRT_i}{k-1}\left[1 - \left(\frac{P_e}{P_i}\right)^{(k-1)/k}\right]}$$

7.33 A large tank having a volume of 20 ft³ is connected to a small tank having a volume of 5 ft³. The large tank contains air initially at 100 lbf/in.², 80 F and the small tank is initially evacuated. A valve in the connecting pipe between the two tanks is suddenly opened and is closed when the tanks come to pressure equilibrium. The air in the large tank may be assumed to have undergone a reversible process and the entire process is adiabatic. What is the final mass of air in the small tank? What is the final temperature of the air in the small tank?

7.34 Water at 70 F is pumped from a lake to an elevated storage tank. The average elevation of the water in the tank is 100 ft above the surface of the lake, and the volume of the tank is 10,000 gal. Initially the tank contains air at 14.7 lbf/in.^{2}, 70 F, and the tank is closed so that the air is compressed as the water enters the bottom of the tank. The pump is operated until the tank is three-quarters full. The temperature of the air and water remain constant at 70 F. Determine the work input to the pump.

7.35 In 1819 Desormes and Clement measured the value of the specific heat ratio k for air in the following manner. The air in a large pressure vessel was maintained at a pressure P_1, slightly above atmospheric pressure, and both the air and the vessel were at atmospheric temperature. The valve in a line connecting the vessel to the atmosphere was quickly opened until the pressure in the tank equaled the atmospheric pressure P_o, at which moment the valve was closed. After the vessel and the air had again come to thermal equilibrium with the atmosphere (the atmospheric temperature remains constant), the final pressure in the vessel, P_2, was noted. Find an expression for k in terms of P_1, P_2, and P_o. It may be assumed that there is no heat transfer to the air during the time when air is escaping from the vessel.

7.36 A neophyte engineer has a problem to solve which involves the entropy of superheated steam at pressures below 1 lbf/in.^{2}, but he finds that the steam table which he has does not give the properties of superheated steam below this pressure.

(*a*) How would you advise him to proceed?

(*b*) What assumptions does this procedure involve?

(*c*) Set up, in accordance with the assumptions made, a line similar to the 1 lbf/in.^{2} line in Table A.1.3 which gives v, h, and s at 0.5 lbf/in.^{2} at temperatures of 200 F, 500 F, 1000 F.

7.37 A contact feedwater heater for heating the water going into a boiler operates on the principle of mixing steam and water. For the change of state shown in Fig. 7.26, calculate the increase in entropy per hr, assuming a steady-flow adiabatic process.

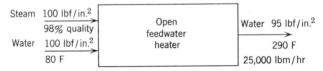

Fig. 7.26   Sketch for Problem 7.37.

7.38 Steam at 100 lbf/in.^{2}, 500 F is flowing in a line. Connected to the line is a 50 ft^3 tank containing steam at 14.7 lbf/in.^{2}, 350 F. The valve is opened, allowing steam to flow into the tank until the final pressure in the tank is 100 lbf/in.^{2} During this process, heat is transferred from the tank at such a rate that the temperature of its contents remains constant at 350 F. The surroundings are at a constant temperature of 80 F.

(*a*) Find the mass of steam that flows into the tank, and the heat transferred during the process.

(*b*) Find the change in entropy of the control volume (tank) during the process.

(*c*) Show that this process does not violate the second law of thermodynamics.

7.39 In a refrigeration plant liquid ammonia enters the expansion valve at 200 lbf/in.^{2}, 80 F. The pressure leaving the expansion valve is 40 lbf/in.^{2}, and changes in kinetic energy are negligible. What is the increase in entropy per lbm? Show this process on a temperature-entropy diagram.

7.40 Freon-12 flows through a capillary tube. The entering state is 150 lbf/in.², 80 F, the pressure leaving is 30 lbf/in.², and the process is adiabatic. What is the increase in entropy per lbm of Freon-12 flowing through the capillary tube? Show the initial and final states on a T-s diagram.

7.41 A salesman reports that he has a steam turbine available that delivers 3800 hp. The steam enters the turbine at 100 lbf/in.², 500 F and leaves the turbine at a pressure of 2 lbf/in.², and the required rate of steam flow is 30,000 lbm/hr.

(*a*) How do you evaluate his claim?

(*b*) Suppose he changed his claim and said the required steam flow was 34,000 lbm/hr.

7.42 The equipment shown in Fig. 7.27 is used to fill bottles of Freon-12 for shipping. The shipping bottles are initially evacuated. Each bottle contains 100 lbm of Freon-12 when it is filled, at which time the volume of liquid Freon-12 is 85% of the total, and the volume of vapor is 15% of the total. Heat is transferred from the bottle during the filling process so that the temperature of the Freon-12 when the filling process has been completed is 80 F. The compression process is adiabatic.

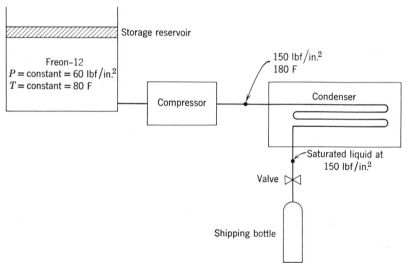

Fig. 7.27   Sketch for Problem 7.42.

(*a*) Determine the volume of a shipping bottle.
(*b*) Determine the work of compression for filling one bottle.
(*c*) Determine the heat transfer in the condenser for filling one bottle.
(*d*) Determine the heat transfer from the bottle for filling one bottle.
(*e*) If all the heat transfer from the condenser and bottle is to the surroundings at a temperature of 80 F, determine the net increase in entropy of the system and the surroundings for the filling of one bottle.

(*f*) Prove that the compression process indicated does not violate the second law of thermodynamics.

7.43 Steam enters a turbine at 100 lbf/in.², 800 F, and exhausts at 20 lbf/in.², 400 F. Any heat transfer is with the surroundings at 80 F, and changes in kinetic and potential energy are negligible. It is claimed that this turbine produces 100 hp with a mass flow of 1800 lbm/hr. Does this process violate the second law of thermodynamics?

7.44 Steam flowing steadily in a line at 1000 lbf/in.², 700 F, 20 ft/sec, is expanded in a nozzle to 200 lbf/in.² in an irreversible, isothermal process during which 200 Btu of heat are transferred per lbm of steam from a large reservoir at 800 F. The surroundings are at 14.7 lbf/in.², 77 F. Calculate:

(*a*) Exit velocity from the nozzle

(*b*) The net increase of entropy per lbm of steam.

7.45 It is desired to quickly cool a given quantity of material to 40 F. The required heat transfer is 1000 Btu. One possibility is to immerse it in a mixture of ice and water, in which case the heat transfer from the material results in the melting of ice. Another possibility is to cool the material by evaporating Freon-12 at 0 F, in which case the heat transfer results in changing Freon-12 from saturated liquid to saturated vapor. A third possibility is to do the same with liquid nitrogen at one atmosphere pressure.

(*a*) Calculate the change of entropy of the cooling medium in each of the three cases.

(*b*) What is the significance of these results?

7.46 Consider the scheme shown in Fig. 7.28 for raising a weight by heat transfer from the reservoir at 300 F to the Freon-12. The pressure on the Freon-12 due to the weight plus the atmosphere is 200 lbf/in.² Initially the temperature of the Freon-12 is 160 F and its volume is 0.4 ft³. Heat is transferred until the temperature of the Freon-12 is 300 F.

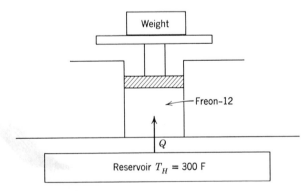

Fig. 7.28   Sketch for Problem 7.46.

(*a*) Determine the heat transfer and work for this process.

(*b*) Determine the net change of entropy.

(*c*) Devise a scheme for accomplishing this with no net change of entropy.

7.47 A steam turbine receives 18,000 lbm of steam per hr at 400 lbf/in.², 600 F and exhausts steam at 2 lbf/in.² The efficiency of the turbine is 78%. Determine the power output of the turbine and the increase of entropy per pound of steam flowing through the turbine.

7.48 Air enters the compressor of a gas turbine at 14.0 lbf/in.², 60 F at the rate of 4000 ft³/min, and leaves at 60 lbf/in.² The process is adiabatic, and changes in kinetic and potential energy are negligible. Calculate the power required to drive this compressor assuming:

(a) That the process is reversible.

(b) That the compressor has an efficiency of 82%.

SUPPLEMENTARY PROBLEMS

7.49 A 5 ft³ tank containing steam at 1 atm. pressure, 1% quality, is fitted with a relief valve. Heat is transferred to the tank from a large source at 500 F. When the pressure in the tank reaches 300 lbf/in.², the relief valve opens, saturated vapor at 300 lbf/in.² is throttled across the valve and discharged at atmospheric pressure. The process continues until the quality in the tank is 90%.

(a) Calculate the mass discharged from the tank.

(b) Determine the heat transfer to the tank during the process.

(c) Considering a control volume that contains the tank and valve, calculate the entropy change within the control volume and that of the surroundings. Show that the process does not violate the second law.

7.50 The 2 ft³ tank shown in Fig. 7.29 is to be filled with Freon-12 for use as a constant-temperature bath in a research project. At the initial state 1 the tank is evacuated, and the desired conditions after filling are $T_2 = -40$ F, with liquid occupying $\frac{3}{4}$ of the volume of the tank and vapor $\frac{1}{4}$ of the volume. The

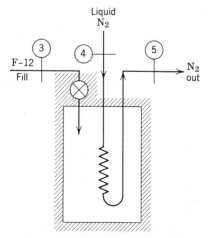

Fig. 7.29   Sketch for Problem 7.50.

Freon in the fill line, point 3, is at 100 lbf/in.², 100 F. A supply of liquid nitrogen, to be used as the cooling medium during the filling process, enters at point
4 as saturated liquid at 15 lbf/in.², passes through a coil and leaves at point 5
as a gas at 15 lbf/in.², −40 F. It may be assumed that the pressures and temperatures at points 3, 4, and 5 remain constant throughout the process, and
also that the tank and lines are well insulated.   Calculate:

(a) The mass of Freon-12 in the tank at the final state.
(b) The enthalpy change of the nitrogen, per lbm, between points 4 and 5.
(c) The total mass of nitrogen required for the process.
(d) The net entropy change for the process.

7.51 Consider the two tanks A and B as shown in Fig. 7.30, each tank having
a volume of 1 ft³. Tank A contains saturated vapor Freon-12 at 100 F, and B
contains F-12 at 0 F, 15 lbf/in.² Tank B, the line connecting the tanks, and the
valve are heavily insulated. The valve is opened slightly and then closed when
the two tanks have come to the same pressure. During the process, heat is

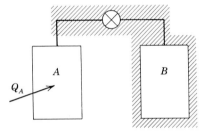

Fig. 7.30   Sketch for Problem 7.51.

exchanged between the surroundings and tank A such that the F-12 inside A
at any time is at 100 F.

Calculate the final pressure, the final temperature in tank B, the heat transferred during the process, and the net entropy change.

7.52 Liquids are often transferred from a tank by pressurization with a gas.
Consider the problem shown in Fig. 7.31. Tanks A and B both contain Freon-12.

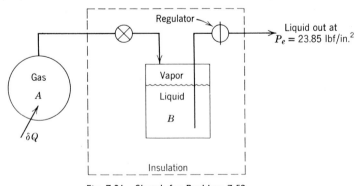

Fig. 7.31   Sketch for Problem 7.52.

Tank A has a volume of 3.2 ft^3, and B a volume of 2.5 ft^3. The Freon in A is initially at 80 F, saturated vapor, and that in B is at -40 F with a quality of 0.01. The valve is opened slightly, allowing Freon to flow from A to B. When the pressure in B has built up to 23.85 lb/in.^{2}, liquid begins to flow out. The liquid transfer continues until the pressure in A has dropped to 23.85 lbf/in.^{2} During the process, heat is transferred to the gas inside tank A such that its temperature always remains at 80 F, but tank B is insulated. Determine

(a) The quality in tank B at the end of the process.

(b) The mass of liquid transferred from tank B.

(c) The net entropy change, assuming that the surroundings are at 80 F.

7.53 Two tanks, A and B, contain steam in the amounts and at the condition indicated in Fig. 7.32. The tanks are connected to a common cylinder fitted with a piston of such a weight that a pressure of 200 lbf/in.^{2} is required to support it. Initially the piston is at the bottom of the cylinder.

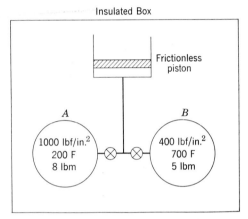

Fig. 7.32   Sketch for Problem 7.53.

Calculate the change of enthalpy, internal energy, and entropy of all the steam if the valves are opened and all the steam comes to a uniform pressure and temperature. Assume negligible volume in the pipes and valves and assume no heat transfer between the containing walls and the steam.

7.54 A spherical balloon initially 6 in. in diameter and containing Freon-12 at 15 lbf/in.^{2} is connected to an uninsulated 1 ft^3 tank containing Freon-12 at 80 lbf/in.^{2} Both are at 80 F, the temperature of the surroundings.

The valve connecting the two is then opened very slightly and left open until the pressures become equal. During the process, heat is transferred with the surroundings such that the temperature of all the Freon remains at 80 F. It may also be assumed that the balloon diameter is proportional to the pressure inside the balloon at any point during the process. Calculate:

(a) The final pressure.

(b) Work done by the Freon during the process.

(c) Heat transfer to the Freon during the process.

(d) Net entropy change for the process.

7.55 An insulated cylinder is divided into two compartments A and B by a

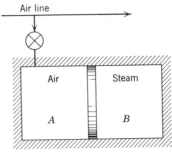

Fig. 7.33   Sketch for Problem 7.55.

frictionless nonconducting piston. Compartment A contains air at 14.7 lbf/in.^{2}, 80 F and B contains saturated water vapor at 14.7 lbf/in.^{2} Each side has an initial volume of 1 ft^3. Side A is connected by a valve to a line in which air flows at 100 lbf/in.^{2}, 80 F.

The valve is opened slightly and air from the line flows into A until the pressure reaches 100 lbf/in.^{2} Calculate the final temperature in each of the compartments and the mass entering A.

7.56 Consider the system shown in Fig. 7.34. Tank A has a volume of 10 ft^3 and initially contains air at 100 lbf/in.^{2}, 100 F. Cylinder B is fitted with a frictionless piston resting on the bottom, at which position the spring is fully extended. The piston has a cross-sectional area of 100 in.^{2} and mass of 100 lbm, and the spring constant K_s is 100 lbf/in. Atmospheric pressure is 14.7 lbf/in.^{2}

The valve is opened and air flows into the cylinder until the pressures in A and B become equal, after which the valve is closed. During this process, the air finally remaining in A may be considered to have undergone a reversible adiabatic process, and the entire process is adiabatic. The spring force is proportional to the displacement.

Determine the final pressure in the system and the temperature in cylinder B.

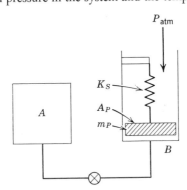

Fig. 7.34   Sketch for Problem 7.56.

7.57 At one time a certain scientist felt that the equivalent of the following process violated the second law of thermodynamics. (See Fig. 7.35.) Initially compartments A and B, which are separated by a frictionless nonconducting piston of negligible mass, each contain 1 mole of nitrogen at 1 atm pressure. The initial temperature in compartment A is 200 F and in compartment B it is 100 F. Heat is transferred from a constant-temperature reservoir at 200 F to the nitrogen in compartment B until it reaches a temperature of 200 F. During the heat transfer process the piston will move as necessary to maintain the same pressure in both compartments.

(*a*) Determine the final temperature in compartment A.

(*b*) Prove that even though the final temperature in compartment A is greater than 200 F this process does not violate the second law.

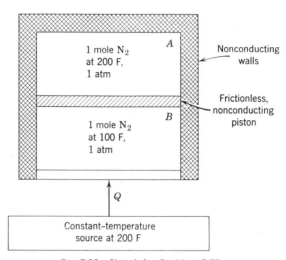

Fig. 7.35   Sketch for Problem 7.57.

7.58 A frictionless, thermally conducting piston separates the air and water in the cylinder shown in Fig. 7.36. The initial volume of A and B are equal, the volume of each being 10 ft³. The initial pressure in both A and B is 100 lbf/in.² The volume of the liquid in B is 2% of the total volume of B. Heat is transferred to both A and B until all the liquid in B evaporates.

(*a*) Determine the total heat transfer during this process.

(*b*) Determine the work done by the piston on the air and the heat transfer to the air.

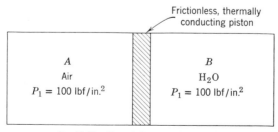

Fig. 7.36   Sketch for Problem 7.58.

7.59 A cylinder shown in Fig. 7.37 is so constructed that compartments A and B are separated by metal partition, and compartment A is fitted with a frictionless piston. Assume that the temperatures in compartments A and B differ only by an infinitesimal. Compartment A initially contains 100 lbm of air at 200 lbf/in.^{2}, 300 F. Compartment B contains 40 lbm of liquid H_2O and 5 lbm of vapor H_2O at 300 F. The piston is moved to the right until the pressure in compartment A reaches 300 lbf/in.^{2} Assume no heat transfer except across the metal partition. Determine the total change of entropy and internal energy.

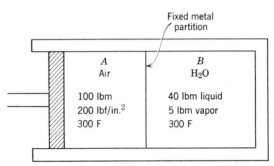

Fig. 7.37   Sketch for Problem 7.59.

7.60 A tank of volume V_T is filled with air at the initial condition P_1 and T_1. It is to be evacuated with a vacuum pump. The atmospheric pressure is P_a.

(a) Calculate the work of evacuation as a function of the pressure in the tank, and plot a curve of work of evacuation vs pressure.

(b) Considering the pump to handle a constant volume per unit time, determine horsepower as a function of pressure in the tank and horsepower as a function of time.

Assume both the tank and the pump to operate under isothermal conditions, and assume that the pumping process is reversible.

8 *Irreversibility and Availability*

We now turn our attention to irreversibility and availability, two additional concepts that have found increasing use in recent years. These concepts are particularly applicable in the analysis of complex thermodynamic systems, for with the aid of a digital computer, irreversibility and availability are very powerful tools in design and optimization studies of such systems.

8.1 Reversible Work

In order to introduce the concepts of reversible work and irreversibility, let us consider Fig. 8.1. Figure 8.1a shows a control volume undergoing a uniform-state, uniform-flow process. There may be irreversibilities present as the process takes place, and this sketch represents an actual uniform-state, uniform-flow process with irreversibilities present. The work crossing the control surface during the process is $W_{c.v.}$ and the heat transfer is $Q_{c.v.}$. All of the heat transfer is with the surroundings at temperature T_0.

Figure 8.1b shows an identical control volume, with exactly the same quantities and states of fluid entering and leaving the control volume as in Fig. 8.1a, and exactly the same change of state within the control volume. In contrast to Fig. 8.1a, however, in this case all processes are reversible. Thus Fig. 8.1b represents an ideal process (somewhat similar to the Carnot cycle as far as cycles are concerned) to which the actual process of Fig. 8.1a can be compared. The work and heat crossing the control surface for this ideal process will be different than in Fig. 8.1a (which involved irreversibilities) and these quantities are designated $(W_{c.v.})_{rev}$ and $(Q_{c.v.})_{rev}$. In order that the heat transfer between the control volume and the surroundings may occur reversibly when there is a difference in the temperature in the control volume and the surroundings, it is necessary that this heat transfer take place through a reversible heat

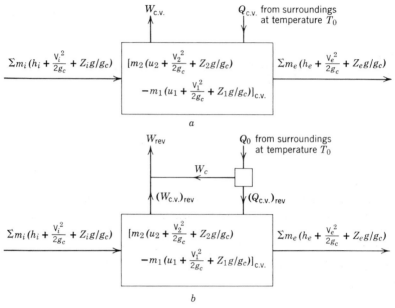

Fig. 8.1   Two uniform-state, uniform-flow processes to demonstrate the concept of reversible work.

engine. The work output of this reversible heat engine is designated W_c. The sum of the work crossing the control surface for the reversible case and the work output of the reversible engine is called the reversible work and is designated W_{rev}. That is,

$$W_{rev} = (W_{c.v.})_{rev} + W_c \qquad (8.1)$$

The difference between this reversible work W_{rev}, and that done in the first case, $W_{c.v.}$, when irreversible processes may occur is called the irreversibility, which is designated I.

$$I = W_{rev} - W_{c.v.} \qquad (8.2)$$

Quite obviously, when all processes take place in a completely reversible manner, the irreversibility is zero.

While we could calculate the reversible work for each problem that we might consider, it is advantageous at this point to develop a general expression for the reversible work. Let us therefore consider the reversible process shown in Fig. 8.1b. We have assumed a uniform-state, uniform-flow process for this control volume. This process was described in

Section 5.10, and for this process the first law can be written, Eq. 5.54, as

$$(Q_{\text{c.v.}})_{\text{rev}} + \sum m_i \left(h_i + \frac{V_i^2}{2g_c} + Z_i \frac{g}{g_c} \right)$$

$$= (W_{\text{c.v.}})_{\text{rev}} + \sum m_e \left(h_e + \frac{V_e^2}{2g_c} + Z_e \frac{g}{g_c} \right)$$

$$+ \left[m_2 \left(u_2 + \frac{V_2^2}{2g_c} + Z_2 \frac{g}{g_c} \right) - m_1 \left(u_1 + \frac{V_1^2}{2g_c} + Z_1 \frac{g}{g_c} \right) \right]_{\text{c.v.}} \quad (8.3)$$

The significance of each of these terms is shown in Fig. 8.1b.

Since all processes are to be reversible, the heat transfer with the surroundings must also be reversible. Therefore, if the temperature within the control volume is different from the surroundings, this heat transfer must take place through a reversible heat engine. This is also shown schematically in Fig. 8.1b, and the work done by the reversible engine is designated W_c.

For the reversible engine the work, W_c, we can write:

First law: $\qquad\qquad W_c = Q_0 - (Q_{\text{c.v.}})_{\text{rev}}$

Second law: Since $\quad \dfrac{Q_0}{T_0} = \displaystyle\int_0^t \left(\frac{\dot{Q}_{\text{c.v.}}}{T} \right)_{\text{rev}} dt$

it follows that

$$W_c = T_0 \int_0^t \left(\frac{\dot{Q}_{\text{c.v.}}}{T} \right)_{\text{rev}} dt - (Q_{\text{c.v.}})_{\text{rev}} \quad (8.4)$$

The second law for the uniform-state, uniform-flow process, Eq. 7.34, for this reversible process is

$$m_2 s_2 - m_1 s_1 + \sum m_e s_e - \sum m_i s_i = \int_0^t \left(\frac{\dot{Q}_{\text{c.v.}}}{T} \right)_{\text{rev}} dt \quad (8.5)$$

Substituting this into Eq. 8.4 we have

$$W_c = T_0 [m_2 s_2 - m_1 s_1 + \sum m_e s_e - \sum m_i s_i] - (Q_{\text{c.v.}})_{\text{rev}} \quad (8.6)$$

We can now substitute the expression for $(W_{\text{c.v.}})_{\text{rev}}$ from Eq. 8.3 and for W_c from Eq. 8.6 into Eq. 8.1.

$$W_{\text{rev}} = (Q_{\text{c.v.}})_{\text{rev}} + \sum m_i \left(h_i + \frac{V_i^2}{2g_c} + Z_i \frac{g}{g_c} \right)$$

$$- \sum m_e \left(h_e + \frac{V_e^2}{2g_c} + Z_e \frac{g}{g_c} \right)$$

$$- \left[m_2 \left(u_2 + \frac{V_2^2}{2g_c} + Z_2 \frac{g}{g_c} \right) - m_1 \left(u_1 + \frac{V_1^2}{2g_c} + Z_1 \frac{g}{g_c} \right) \right]_{\text{c.v.}}$$

$$+ T_0 [m_2 s_2 - m_1 s_1 + \sum m_e s_e - \sum m_i s_i] - (Q_{\text{c.v.}})_{\text{rev}}$$

On rearranging this equation, we have

$$W_{\text{rev}} = \sum m_i\left(h_i - T_0 s_i + \frac{V_i^2}{2g_c} + Z_i\frac{g}{g_c}\right)$$
$$- \sum m_e\left(h_e - T_0 s_e + \frac{V_e^2}{2g_c} + Z_e\frac{g}{g_c}\right)$$
$$- \left[m_2\left(u_2 - T_0 s_2 + \frac{V_2^2}{2g_c} + Z_2\frac{g}{g_c}\right)\right.$$
$$\left.- m_1\left(u_1 - T_0 s_1 + \frac{V_1^2}{2g_c} + Z_1\frac{g}{g_c}\right)\right]_{\text{c.v.}} \qquad (8.7)$$

Note that $(Q_{\text{c.v.}})_{\text{rev}}$ cancels and does not appear in Eq. 8.7.

Thus we have an expression for the reversible work of a control volume that exchanges heat with the surroundings at temperature T_0. Note that the reversible work is a function of T_0, the temperature of the surroundings.

Let us now consider two special cases, namely, a system (fixed mass) and a steady-state, steady-flow process for a control volume.

For a system there is no flow across the control surface, and therefore, considering Eq. 8.7,

$$\sum m_i\left(h_i - T_0 s_i + \frac{V_i^2}{2g_c} + Z_i\frac{g}{g_c}\right) = 0;$$
$$\sum m_e\left(h_e - T_0 s_e + \frac{V_e^2}{2g_c} + Z_e\frac{g}{g_c}\right) = 0$$

Thus, for a system the reversible work is

$$\left(\frac{W_{\text{rev}}}{m}\right)_{1\quad 2} = {}_1 w_{\text{rev }2}$$
$$= \left[\left(u_1 - T_0 s_1 + \frac{V_1^2}{2g_c} + Z_1\frac{g}{g_c}\right) - \left(u_2 - T_0 s_2 + \frac{V_2^2}{2g_c} + Z_2\frac{g}{g_c}\right)\right]$$
$$(8.8)$$

For a steady-state, steady-flow process we note on consideration of Eq. 8.7 that

$$\left[m_2\left(u_2 - T_0 s_2 + \frac{V_2^2}{2g_c} + Z_2\frac{g}{g_c}\right) - m_1\left(u_1 - T_0 s_1 + \frac{V_1^2}{2g_c} + Z_1\frac{g}{g_c}\right)\right]_{\text{c.v.}} = 0$$

Therefore, for a steady-state, steady-flow process

$$W_{\text{rev}} = \sum m_i\left(h_i - T_0 s_i + \frac{V_i^2}{2g_c} + Z_i\frac{g}{g_c}\right)$$
$$- \sum m_e\left(h_e - T_0 s_e + \frac{V_e^2}{2g_c} + Z_e\frac{g}{g_c}\right) \qquad (8.9)$$

When there is a single flow of fluid into and out of the control volume in a steady-state, steady-flow process we can write

$$\frac{W_{\text{rev}}}{m} = w_{\text{rev}} = \left(h_i - T_0 s_i + \frac{V_i^2}{2g_c} + Z_i \frac{g}{g_c} \right)$$
$$- \left(h_e - T_0 s_e + \frac{V_e^2}{2g_c} + Z_e \frac{g}{g_c} \right) \quad (8.10)$$

Each expression for reversible work involves the temperature of the surroundings, T_0. Therefore in solving problems this information must be available. Unless otherwise stated we will use 77 F (25 C) for the temperature of the surroundings. This temperature has been selected because thermochemical data are frequently given relative to this base and it is also a reasonable temperature to assume for the surroundings. One must keep in mind that one should use the actual temperature of the surroundings when this information is available.

8.2 Irreversibility

In the last section we considered the two control volumes shown in Fig. 8.1, and noted that the irreversibility is defined as

$$I = W_{\text{rev}} - W_{\text{c.v.}}$$

We also derived Eq. 8.7, which was a general expression for the reversible work for a control volume undergoing a uniform-state, uniform-flow process. We can also derive a general expression for irreversibility. We do so by noting that an expression for $W_{\text{c.v.}}$ can be found by applying the first law to the control volume that involves the irreversible process in Fig. 8.1a. From Eq. 5.54

$$W_{\text{c.v.}} = \sum m_i \left(h_i + \frac{V_i^2}{2g_c} + Z_i \frac{g}{g_c} \right) - \sum m_e \left(h_e + \frac{V_e^2}{2g_c} + Z_e \frac{g}{g_c} \right)$$
$$- \left[m_2 \left(u_2 + \frac{V_2^2}{2g_c} + Z_2 \frac{g}{g_c} \right) - m_1 \left(u_1 + \frac{V_1^2}{2g_c} + Z_1 \frac{g}{g_c} \right) \right]_{\text{c.v.}} + Q_{\text{c.v.}}$$
$$(8.11)$$

Substituting the expression for W_{rev} from Eq. 8.7 and for $W_{\text{c.v.}}$ from Eq. 8.11 into Eq. 8.2 we have

$$I = \sum m_e T_0 s_e - \sum m_i T_0 s_i + m_2 T_0 s_2 - m_1 T_0 s_1 - Q_{\text{c.v.}} \quad (8.12)$$

This is a general expression for the irreversibility in a uniform-state, uniform-flow process. Once again we consider two particular cases, namely, the system and the steady-state, steady-flow process. For the system,

$$\sum m_e T_0 s_e = 0; \qquad \sum m_i T_0 s_i = 0; \qquad m_2 = m_1 = m$$

and Eq. 8.12 reduces to

$$_1 I_2 = m T_0 (s_2 - s_1) - {_1}Q_2 \tag{8.13}$$

For the steady-state, steady-flow process,

$$m_2 T_0 s_2 = m_1 T_0 s_1$$

and Eq. 8.12 reduces to

$$I = \sum m_e T_0 s_e - \sum m_i T_0 s_i - Q_{\text{c.v.}} \tag{8.14}$$

When there is a single flow into and out of the control volume in a steady-state, steady-flow process we can write

$$I = m T_0 (s_e - s_i) - Q_{\text{c.v.}} \tag{8.15}$$

Example 8.1

a. Considering Fig. 8.2, tank A has a volume of 100 ft³ and initially contains Freon-12 at a pressure of 10 lbf/in.² and a temperature of 80 F. The compressor evacuates tank A and charges tank B. Tank B is initially evacuated and is of such a volume that the final pressure of the Freon-12 in tank B is 80 lbf/in.² when the temperature reaches its final value of 80 F. The temperature of the surroundings is 80 F. Determine the minimum work input to the compressor.

b. After tank B is charged and tank A is evacuated, a by-pass valve around the compressor is left open, and the two tanks come to a uniform pressure at a temperature of 80 F. Determine the irreversibility for this process. The solution is as follows:

a. Consider a system consisting of the two tanks and the connecting piping. For this system there is no change in volume. Since changes in

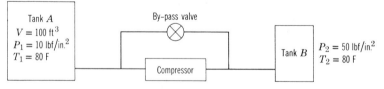

Fig. 8.2   Sketch for Example 8.1.

kinetic and potential energy are not significant, Eq. 8.8 reduces to

$$_1(w_{\text{rev}})_2 = (u_1 - u_2) - T_0(s_1 - s_2)$$

$$u_1 = h_1 - P_1V_1 = 89.596 - \frac{10 \times 144 \times 4.7248}{778} = 80.95 \text{ Btu/lbm}$$

$$s_1 = 0.20746 \text{ Btu/lbm-R}$$

$$u_2 = 86.316 - \frac{80 \times 144 \times 0.52795}{778} = 78.40 \text{ Btu/lbm}$$

$$s_2 = 0.16885 \text{ Btu/lbm-R}$$

$$_1(w_{\text{rev}})_2 = (80.95 - 78.40) - 540(0.20746 - 0.16885)$$
$$= 2.55 - 20.85 = -18.30 \text{ Btu/lbm}$$

$$m = \frac{V_1}{v_1} = \frac{100}{4.7248} = 22.4 \text{ lbm}$$

$$_1(W_{\text{rev}})_2 = 22.4(-18.3) = -412 \text{ Btu}$$

Note that the reversible work is a negative number. This means that the minimum work input to the compressor to accomplish this change of state is 412 Btu. If there are any irreversibilities this work input will increase, say to 500 Btu. Thus the reversible work can still be thought of as the maximum work, inasmuch as −412 is a larger number than −500.

b. When the Freon-12 flows from tank B to tank A through the by-pass valve, we recognize that this is an irreversible process. We could calculate this irreversibility either by calculating the reversible work from Eq. 8.8 and the irreversibility from Eq. 8.2 or we could calculate the irreversibility directly from Eq. 8.13. Let us do both calculations in order to gain further insight into these concepts. The state of the Freon-12 in tank B is designated state 2 as above, and the final state is designated state 3.

We must first find the final pressure in the system. The two properties we know are specific volume and temperature. The volume of tank B is found from the results of part a.

$$V_B = mv_{2B} = 22.4(0.52795) = 11.82 \text{ ft}^3$$
$$V_3 = V_A + V_B = 100 + 11.82 = 111.82 \text{ ft}^3$$
$$v_3 = \frac{V_3}{m} = \frac{111.82}{22.4} = 4.98 \text{ ft}^3/\text{lbm}$$

By interpolation from the Freon-12 table, $P_3 = 9.73 \text{ lbf/in.}^2$

$$h_3 = 89.585 \text{ Btu/lbm} \qquad s_3 = 0.20809 \text{ Btu/lbm-R}.$$

$$u_3 = 89.585 - \frac{9.73 \times 144 \times 4.48}{778} = 76.62 \text{ Btu/lbm}$$

From Eq. 8.8,

$$_2(W_{rev})_3 = u_2 - u_3 - T_0(s_2 - s_3)$$
$$= 78.40 - 76.62 - 540(0.16885 - 0.20809)$$
$$= 22.96 \text{ Btu/lbm}$$
$$_2(W_{rev})_3 = 22.4(22.96) = 514 \text{ Btu}$$

The irreversibility can now be calculated from Eq. 8.2.

$$_2I_3 = {}_2(W_{rev})_3 - {}_2W_3 = 514 - 0 = 514 \text{ Btu}$$

The irreversibility can also be calculated from Eq. 8.13.

$$_2I_3 = mT_0(s_3 - s_2) - {}_2Q_3$$

In order to determine $_2Q_3$ we apply the equation for the first law to this process.

$$_2Q_3 = m(u_3 - u_2) + {}_2W_3$$
$$= 22.4(76.62 - 78.40) + 0 = -39.9 \text{ Btu.}$$
$$_2I_3 = 22.4 \times 540(0.20809 - 0.16885) - (-39.9) = 514 \text{ Btu.}$$

Example 8.2

Steam at 400 lbf/in.², 600 F enters a steam turbine. The exhaust pressure is 2 lbf/in.². The process is adiabatic and the efficiency of the turbine is 70%.

Determine the reversible work and the irreversibility per pound of steam flowing through the turbine for the actual change of state that takes place.

The change of state that takes place is designated by i and e on Fig. 8.3. The state that would have been achieved in a reversible adiabatic process

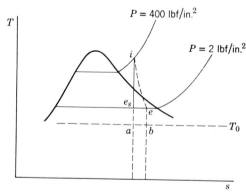

Fig. 8.3 Sketch for Example 8.2.

is designated e_s. The efficiency of a turbine is defined as, Eq. 7.68,

$$\eta_{\text{turbine}} = \frac{w_a}{w_s}$$

To find w_s we use the first law for a steady-state, steady-flow process.

$$h_i = w_s + h_{e_s}$$
$$h_i = 1306.9; \qquad s_i = 1.5894$$
$$s_i = s_{es} = 1.5894 = 1.9200 - (1 - x)_{es} 1.7451$$

$$(1 - x)_{es} = \frac{0.3306}{1.7451} = 0.1897$$

$$h_{es} = 1116.2 - 0.1879(1022.2) = 922.4 \text{ Btu/lbm}$$
$$w_s = 1306.9 - 922.4 = 384.5 \text{ Btu/lbm}$$
$$w_a = \eta(w_s) = 0.7(384.5) = 269.3 \text{ Btu/lbm}$$

We can now find the enthalpy and entropy at the turbine exit. Applying the steady-state, steady-flow energy equation to the actual turbine,

$$h_i = h_e + w_a$$
$$h_e = 1306.9 - 269.3 = 1037.6 \text{ Btu/lbm}$$
$$1037.6 = 1116.2 - (1 - x)_e 1022.2$$
$$(1 - x)_e = 0.077$$
$$s_e = 1.9200 - 0.077(1.7451) = 1.7858 \text{ Btu/lbm-R}$$

We can find the reversible work from Eq. 8.10.

$$w_{\text{rev}} = (h_i - h_e) - T_0(s_i - s_e)$$
$$= (1306.9 - 1037.6) - 537(1.5894 - 1.7858)$$
$$= 269.3 + 105.6 = 374.9 \text{ Btu/lbm}$$

$$\frac{I}{m} = w_{\text{rev}} - w_a = 374.9 - 269.3 = 105.6 \text{ Btu/lbm}$$

The irreversibility could also be calculated from Eq. 8.15.

$$\frac{I}{m} = T_0(s_e - s_i) - q$$
$$= 537(1.7858 - 1.5894) - 0 = 105.6 \text{ Btu/lbm}$$

In solving a problem such as this we could find the reversible work from first principles, without using the equations that have been derived in this chapter. Thus the reversible work could have been found by finding the

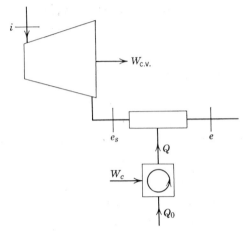

Fig. 8.4   Sketch for Example 8.2.

reversible work between states i and e_s and then between states e_s and e and adding these together to give the reversible work. This would appear as shown in Fig. 8.4. We have found the work between states i and e_s above.

$$w_s = h_i - h_{es} = 384.5 \text{ Btu/lbm}$$

The process between e_s and e involves a constant pressure heat transfer to the steam, and this can be accomplished reversibly by use of a heat pump which receives heat from the surroundings and rejects heat to the steam. The work input to this heat pump per unit mass flow, w_c, is equal to area $abee_s$ in Fig. 8.3.

$$w_c = (T_e - T_0)(s_e - s_{es})$$
$$= (586 - 537)(1.7858 - 1.5894) = 9.6 \text{ Btu/lbm}.$$

Then

$$w_{rev} = w_s - w_c = 384.5 - 9.6 = 374.9 \text{ Btu/lbm}$$

Thus, in deriving the expressions for reversible work and irreversibility we have only generalized the calculations, and one can always determine these quantities by applying the fundamentals directly to a given problem.

8.3   Availability

What is the maximum reversible work that can be done by a system in a given state? In Section 8.1 we developed an expression for the reversible work for a given change of state of a system. But the question that arises is, what final state will make this reversible work the maximum?

The answer to this question is that when a system is in equilibrium with the environment, no spontaneous change of state will occur, and the system will not be capable of doing any work. Therefore, if a system in a given state undergoes a completely reversible process until it reaches a state in which it is in equilibrium with the environment, the maximum reversible work will have been done by the system.

If a system is in equilibrium with the surroundings, it must certainly be in pressure and temperature equilibrium with the surroundings—that is, at pressure P_0 and temperature T_0. It must also be in chemical equilibrium with the surroundings, which implies that no further chemical reaction will take place. Equilibrium with the surroundings also requires that the system have zero velocity and minimum potential energy. Similar requirements could be set forth regarding magnetic, electrical, and surface effects if these are relevant to a given problem.

The same general remarks can be made in regard to a quantity of mass that undergoes a steady-state, steady-flow process. With a given state for the mass entering the control volume, the reversible work will be a maximum when this mass leaves the control volume in equilibrium with the surroundings. This means that as the mass leaves the control volume it must be at the pressure and temperature of the surroundings, in chemical equilibrium with the surroundings, and have minimum potential energy, and zero velocity. (The mass leaving the control volume must of necessity have some velocity but it can be made to approach zero.)

Let us first consider the availability associated with a steady-state, steady-flow process. In Eq. 8.10 we noted that when we consider a single flow,

$$w_{rev} = \left(h_i - T_0 s_i + \frac{V_i^2}{2g_c} + Z_i \frac{g}{g_c} \right) - \left(h_e - T_0 s_e + \frac{V_e^2}{2g_c} + Z_e \frac{g}{g_c} \right)$$

This reversible work will be a maximum when the mass leaving the control volume is in equilibrium with the surroundings. If we designate this state in which the fluid is in equilibrium with the surroundings with subscript 0, the reversible work will be a maximum when $h_e = h_0$, $s_e = s_0$, $V_e = 0$, and $Z_e = Z_0$. Designating this maximum reversible work per unit mass flow as the availability per unit mass flow, and assigning this the symbol ψ, we have

$$\psi = \left(h - T_0 s + \frac{V^2}{2g_c} + Z \frac{g}{g_c} \right) - \left(h_0 - T_0 s_0 + Z_0 \frac{g}{g_c} \right) \quad (8.16)$$

The initial state is designated without a subscript to indicate that this is the availability associated with a substance in any state as it enters a control volume in a steady-state, steady-flow process. It also follows that the reversible work per unit mass flow between any two states is equal to the decrease in availability between these two states.

$$w_{rev} = \psi_i - \psi_e \qquad (8.17)$$

If we have more than one flow into and out of the control volume in a steady-state, steady-flow process we can write

$$W_{rev} = \sum m_i \, \psi_i - \sum m_e \, \psi_e \qquad (8.18)$$

The availability associated with a system is developed in a similar way, except for one factor. When the volume of a system increases, some work is done by the system against the surroundings, and this is not available for doing useful work.

To simplify this analysis let us also assume that the change in kinetic and potential energy of the system is negligible. In this case w_{rev}, as given by Eq. 8.8, is

$$_1(w_{rev})_2 = (u_1 - T_0 s_1) - (u_2 - T_0 s_2)$$

If the final state is in equilibrium with the surroundings $u_2 = u_0$ and $s_2 = s_0$. In this case the reversible work is a maximum. If we designate this maximum reversible work as $(w_{rev})_{max}$, and write it without subscript to indicate a general state we have

$$(w_{rev})_{max} = (u - T_0 s) - (u_0 - T_0 s_0) \qquad (8.19)$$

The availability per unit mass for a system is equal to this maximum reversible work minus the work done against the surroundings. This work done against the surroundings, W_{surr} is

$$W_{surr} = P_0(V_0 - V) = -m P_0(v - v_0) \qquad (8.20)$$

The availability per unit mass for a system in the absence of kinetic and potential energy changes is designated ϕ

$$\begin{aligned}
\phi &= (w_{rev})_{max} - w_{surr} \\
\phi &= (u - T_0 s) - (u_0 - T_0 s_0) + P_0(v - v_0) \\
\phi &= (u + P_0 v - T_0 s) - (u_0 + P_0 v_0 - T_0 s_0) \\
\phi &= (u - u_0) + P_0(v - v_0) - T_0(s - s_0)
\end{aligned} \qquad (8.21)$$

It follows that

$$_1(w_{rev})_2 = \phi_1 - \phi_2 - P_0(v_1 - v_2) + \frac{V_1^2 - V_2^2}{2g_c} + (Z_1 - Z_2)\frac{g}{g_c} \qquad (8.22)$$

The use of availability and irreversibility in an actual thermodynamic problem is shown in Fig. 8.5. A theoretical analysis was made of a reciprocating internal-combustion automotive engine to see what happened

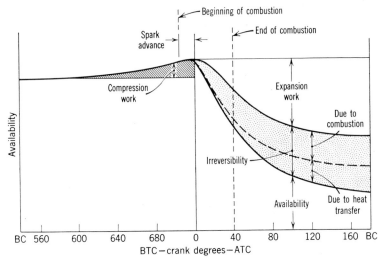

Fig. 8.5   Availability vs. crank angle of the charge in a spark-ignited internal combustion
engine. From D. J. Patterson and G. J. Van Wylen, "A Digital Computer
Simulation for Spark Ignited Engine Cycles," *SAE Progress in Technology Series*, 7,
p. 88. Published by SAE Inc., New York, 1964.

to the availability of the air-fuel mixture that entered the engine and
where the irreversibility occurred during the process. The abscissa on
Fig. 8.5 is crank angle, the left side representing bottom dead center when
the cylinder is assumed to be filled with an air-fuel mixture having the
availability indicated on the ordinate. As the compression process takes
place, the availability of this mixture increases as the result of the work
done in compressing the mixture. When the piston passes top dead center
the expansion process takes place. The beginning and end of combustion
are also indicated on the diagram. During the combustion and expansion
process irreversibilities occur. Those that are associated with the combustion process itself and those associated with heat transfer to the cooling
water or surroundings are both indicated. The work done during the
expansion process and availability at the end of the expansion are indicated
on the right ordinate. Note that this availability that remains in the
cylinder at the end of the expansion stroke is exhausted to the atmosphere.

The less the irreversibility associated with a given change of state, the
greater the work that will be done (or the less work that will be required).
This is significant in at least two regards. The first is that availability is
one of our natural resources. This availability is found in such forms as
oil reserves, coal reserves, and uranium reserves. Suppose we wish to
accomplish a given objective that requires a certain amount of work. If
this work is produced reversibly while drawing on one of the availability

reserves, the decrease in availability would be exactly equal to the reversible work. However, since there are irreversibilities involved in producing this required amount of work, the actual work will be less than the reversible work, and the decrease in availability will be greater (by the amount of the irreversibility) than if this work had been produced reversibly. Thus the more irreversibilities we have in all of our processes, the greater will be the decrease in our availability reserves.* The conservation and effective use of these availability reserves is an important responsibility for all of us.

The second reason that it is desirable to accomplish a given objective with the smallest irreversibility is an economic one. Work costs money, and in many cases a given objective can be accomplished at less cost when the irreversibility is less. It should be noted, however, that many factors enter into the total cost of accomplishing a given objective, and an optimization process that involves consideration of many factors is often necessary in arriving at the most economical design. For example, in a heat transfer process, the smaller the temperature difference across which the heat is transferred, the less the irreversibility. However, for a given rate of heat transfer, a smaller temperature difference will require a larger (and therefore more expensive) heat exchanger, and these various factors must all be considered in the development of the optimum and most economical design.

Example 8.3

A steam turbine, Fig. 8.6, receives 200,000 lbm of steam per hour at 400 lbf/in.², 600 F. At the point in the turbine where the pressure is 60 lbf/in.², steam is bled off for use in processing equipment at the rate of 50,000 lbm/hr. The temperature of this bled steam is 300 F. The balance of the steam leaves the turbine at 2 lbf/in.², 90 per cent quality. The heat transfer to the surroundings is 500,000 Btu/hr. Determine the availability per pound of the steam entering and at both points at which steam leaves the turbine and the reversible work per pound of steam for the given change of state.

Let us designate the states as shown in Fig. 8.6. The availability at any point for the steam entering or leaving the turbine is given by Eq. 8.16.

$$\psi = (h - h_0) - T_0(s - s_0) + \frac{V^2}{2g_c} + (Z - Z_0)\frac{g}{g_c}.$$

Since changes in kinetic and potential energy are not involved in this

---

* In many popular talks reference is made to our energy reserves. From a thermodynamic point of view availability reserves would be a much more acceptable term. There is much energy in the atmosphere and the ocean, but relatively little availability.

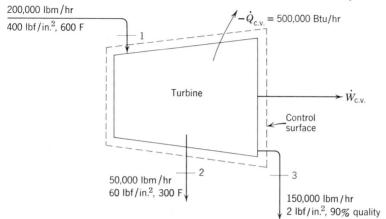

Fig. 8.6   Sketch for Example 8.3.

problem this equation reduces to

$$\psi = (h - h_0) - T_0(s - s_0)$$

At the pressure and temperature of the surroundings, namely, 14.7 lbf/in.², 77 F, the water is a slightly compressed liquid, and the properties of the water are essentially equal to those for saturated liquid at 77 F.

$h_0 = 45.0$ Btu/lbm; $s_0 = 0.0876$ Btu/lbm-R

$\psi_1 = (1306.9 - 45.0) - 537(1.5894 - 0.0876) = 1261.9 - 806.5$
$= 455.4$ Btu/lbm

$\psi_2 = (1181.6 - 45.0) - 537(1.6492 - 0.0876) = 1136.6 - 838.6$
$= 298.0$ Btu/lbm

$\psi_3 = (1014.0 - 45.0) - 537(1.7455 - 0.0876) = 969.0 - 890.3$
$= 78.7$ Btu/lbm

The reversible work can be found from Eq. 8.9.

$$\frac{W_{rev}}{m_1} = \psi_1 - \frac{m_2}{m_1}\psi_2 - \frac{m_3}{m_1}\psi_3$$

$$\frac{W_{rev}}{m_1} = 455.4 - 0.25(298.0) - 0.75(78.7) = 321.8 \text{ Btu/lbm}$$

Example 8.4

A lead storage battery of the type used in an automobile is able to deliver 1440 watt-hours of electrical energy. This energy is available for starting the car.

Suppose we wish to use compressed air for doing an equivalent amount of work in starting the car. The compressed air is to be stored at 1000 lbf/in.^{2}, 77 F. What volume of tank would be required to have the compressed air have an availability of 1440 watt-hours?

$$1440 \text{ watt hours} = 1.440 \times 3412 = 4910 \text{ Btu.}$$

Let us first find the availability of air at 1000 lbf/in.^{2}, 77 F. From Eq. 8.21,

$$\phi = (u - u_0) - T_0(s - s_0) + P_0(v - v_0)$$

$$v = \frac{RT}{P} = \frac{53.34 \times 537}{1000 \times 144} = 0.1975 \text{ ft}^3/\text{lbm}$$

$$v_0 = \frac{RT_0}{P_0} = \frac{53.34 \times 537}{14.7 \times 144} = 13.38 \text{ ft}^3/\text{lbm}$$

$$\phi = 0 - 537\left(\frac{-53.34}{778} \ln \frac{1000}{14.7}\right) + \frac{14.7 \times 144}{778}(0.1975 - 13.38)$$

$$= 0 + 155.3 - 35.9 = 119.4 \text{ Btu/lbm}$$

In order to have an availability of 4910 Btu, the mass of air is

$$m = \frac{4910}{119.4} = 41.1 \text{ lbm}$$

$$V = \frac{mRT}{P} = \frac{41.1 \times 53.34 \times 537}{1000 \times 144} = 8.21 \text{ ft}^3$$

8.4 Consideration of Processes That Involve Heat Transfer with a Body Other than the Atmosphere

Up to this point we have considered processes in which the only heat transfer is with the surroundings. Since many processes do involve heat transfer with bodies at a temperature above or below the temperature of the surroundings, a few remarks should be made regarding them.

The simplest way of handling such processes is to consider two (or more) sub-systems, one comprising the body from which heat is transferred, and the other the body to which heat is transferred. These two sub-systems comprise the system under consideration and the reversible work, availability and irreversibility for the system will be the sum of these quantities for the sub-systems. The same procedure could be used in the case of a control volume. The two examples that follow illustrate this approach. The first involves the irreversible transfer of heat and the second involves reversible heat transfer.

Example 8.5

In a boiler, heat is transferred from the products of combustion to the steam. The temperature of the products of combustion decreases from 2000 F to 1000 F while the pressure remains constant at 1 atm. The average constant-pressure specific heat of the products of combustion is 0.26 Btu/lbm-R. The water enters at 100 lbf/in.², 300 F and leaves at 100 lbf/in.², 500 F. Determine the reversible work and the irreversibility for this process per pound of water evaporated.

We select the control volume shown in Fig. 8.7. Thus we are considering a steady-state, steady-flow process that involves the flow of products and flow of water across the control surface.

Assuming the products to be an ideal gas with constant specific heat, the change of entropy of the products for this constant-pressure process is given by the relation:

$$(s_e - s_i)_{prod} = C_{po} \ln \frac{T_e}{T_i}$$

For this control volume we can write the following governing equations:

Continuity eq.:
$$(\dot{m}_i)_{H_2O} = (\dot{m}_e)_{H_2O} \qquad (a)$$
$$(\dot{m}_i)_{prod} = (\dot{m}_e)_{prod} \qquad (b)$$

First law: (A steady-state, steady-flow process)

$$(\dot{m}_i h_i)_{H_2O} + (\dot{m}_i h_i)_{prod} = (\dot{m}_e h_e)_{H_2O} + (\dot{m}_e h_e)_{prod} \qquad (c)$$

Second law: (The process is adiabatic for the control volume shown)

$$(\dot{m}_e s_e)_{H_2O} + (\dot{m}_e s_e)_{prod} \geq (\dot{m}_i s_i)_{H_2O} + (\dot{m}_i s_i)_{prod} \qquad (d)$$

From Eqs. a, b, and c, we can calculate ratio of the mass flow of products to the mass flow of water.

$$\dot{m}_{prod}(h_i - h_e)_{prod} = \dot{m}_{H_2O}(h_e - h_i)_{H_2O}$$

$$\frac{\dot{m}_{prod}}{\dot{m}_{H_2O}} = \frac{(h_e - h_i)_{H_2O}}{(h_i - h_e)_{prod}} = \frac{1009.5}{0.26(2000 - 1000)} = 3.885$$

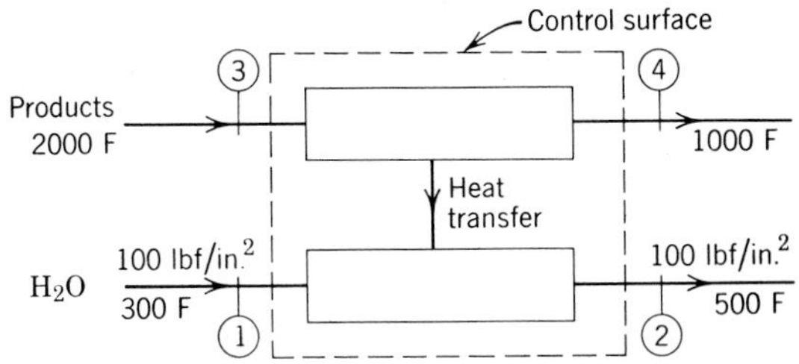

Fig. 8.7   Sketch for Example 8.5.

To find the reversible work we find w_{rev} for the water and for the products and add these together.

We first calculate w_{rev} for the change of state of the water

$$(w_{rev})_{H_2O} = (h_1 - h_2) - T_0(s_1 - s_2)$$
$$= (269.6 - 1279.1) - 537(0.4369 - 1.7085)$$
$$= -326 \text{ Btu/lbm}$$

Next we consider the products.

$$(w_{rev})_{prod} = \frac{\dot{m}_{prod}}{\dot{m}_{H_2O}} [(h_3 - h_4) - T_0(s_3 - s_4)]$$

(States 3 and 4 designate the initial and final states of the products.)

$$(w_{rev})_{prod} = 3.885\left[0.26(2000 - 1000) - 537\left(0.26 \ln \frac{2460}{1460}\right)\right]$$
$$= 728 \text{ Btu/lbm H}_2\text{O}$$

$$w_{rev} = 728 - 326 = 402 \text{ Btu/lbm H}_2\text{O}$$

$$\frac{\dot{i}}{\dot{m}_{H_2O}} = w_{rev} - w = 402 - 0 = 402 \text{ Btu/lbm H}_2\text{O}$$

It is also of interest to determine the net change of entropy. The change in the entropy of the water is

$$(s_2 - s_1)_{H_2O} = 1.7085 - 0.4369 = 1.2716 \text{ Btu/lbm H}_2\text{O-R}$$

The change in the entropy of the products is

$$(s_4 - s_3)_{prod} = -3.885 \times 0.26 \ln \frac{2460}{1460} = -0.524 \text{ Btu/lbm H}_2\text{O-R}$$

Thus, there is a net increase in entropy during the process. The irreversibility could also have been calculated from Eq. 8.14:

$$\dot{i} = \sum \dot{m}_e T_0 s_e - \sum \dot{m}_i T_0 s_i - \dot{Q}_{c.v.}$$

For the control volume selected, $\dot{Q}_{c.v.} = 0$, and therefore,

$$\frac{\dot{i}}{\dot{m}_{H_2O}} = T_0(s_2 - s_1)_{H_2O} + \frac{\dot{m}_{prod}}{\dot{m}_{H_2O}} (s_4 - s_3)_{prod}$$
$$= 537(1.2716) + 537(-0.524) = 402 \text{ Btu/lbm H}_2\text{O}$$

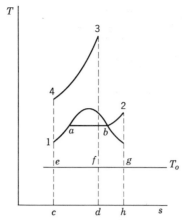

Fig. 8.8 Temperature-entropy diagram for Example 8.5.

These two processes are shown on the T–s diagram of Fig. 8.8. Line 3–4 represents the process for the 3.885 lbm of products. Area 3–4–c–d–3 represents the heat transferred from the 3.885 lbm of products of combustion, and area 3–4–e–f–3 represents the reversible work for the given change in state of these products. Area 1–a–b–2–h–c–1 represents the heat transferred to the water, and this is equal to area 3–4–c–d–3 which represents the heat transferred from the products of combustion. Area 1–a–b–2–g–c–1 represents the reversible work for the given change in state of the water. The difference between area 3–4–e–f–3 (the reversible work for the products) and area 1–a–b–2–g–e–1 (the reversible work for the water) represents the net reversible work. It is readily shown that this net reversible work is equal to area f–g–h–d–f, or $T_0(\Delta s)_{\text{net}}$. Since the actual work is zero, this area also represents the irreversibility, which agrees with our calculation above.

It is essential to note that when the change of state involving heat transfer takes place reversibly, the net change in entropy is zero, and therefore the decrease in the entropy of the body from which heat is transferred must be equal to the increase in entropy of the body to which heat is transferred. This is best demonstrated by considering an example similar to Example 8.5.

Example 8.6

Repeat Example 8.5, but assume that the heat transfer is entirely reversible, i.e., that the heat transfer takes place through a reversible engine.

Schematically this would involve heat transfer from the products of combustion to reversible engines that reject heat to the water, as shown in Fig. 8.9.

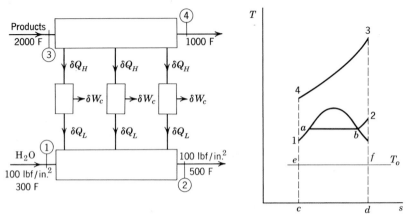

Fig. 8.9   Diagram for Example 8.6.

We again write the governing equations:

Continuity eq.: $\quad\quad\quad\quad (\dot{m}_i)_{H_2O} = (\dot{m}_e)_{H_2O}$

$$(\dot{m}_i)_{prod} = (\dot{m}_e)_{prod}$$

First law:

$$(\dot{m}_i h_i)_{H_2O} + (\dot{m}_i h_i)_{prod} = (\dot{m}_e h_e)_{H_2O} + (\dot{m}_e h_e)_{prod} + \dot{W}_{c.v.}$$

Second law: Since this is a reversible adiabatic process,

$$(\dot{m}_e s_e)_{H_2O} + (\dot{m}_e s_e)_{prod} = (\dot{m}_i s_i)_{H_2O} + (\dot{m}_i s_i)_{prod}$$

From the continuity equation and second law we can determine flow of products per unit flow of water.

$$(s_2 - s_1)_{H_2O} + \frac{\dot{m}_{prod}}{\dot{m}_{H_2O}}(s_4 - s_3)_{prod} = 0$$

$$\frac{\dot{m}_{prod}}{\dot{m}_{H_2O}}(s_3 - s_4)_{prod} = (1.7085 - 0.4369)$$

$$\frac{\dot{m}_{prod}}{\dot{m}_{H_2O}}\left(0.26 \times \ln\frac{2460}{1460}\right) = 1.2716$$

$$\frac{\dot{m}_{prod}}{\dot{m}_{H_2O}} = \frac{1.2716}{0.26 \times 0.521} = 9.39$$

We now calculate the reversible work for the change of state of the water and the products:

$$(w_{rev})_{H_2O} = (h_1 - h_2) - T_0(s_1 - s_2)$$

$$(w_{rev})_{prod} = [(h_3 - h_4) - T_0(s_3 - s_4)]\frac{\dot{m}_{prod}}{\dot{m}_{H_2O}}$$

But, since

$$(s_2 - s_1)_{H_2O} = \frac{\dot{m}_{prod}}{\dot{m}_{H_2O}} (s_3 - s_4)_{prod}$$

it follows that

$$w_{rev} = (h_1 - h_2) + \frac{\dot{m}_{prod}}{\dot{m}_{H_2O}} (h_3 - h_4)$$

We note that this net reversible work is exactly equal to the work which would be determined from the first law. We would expect this, of course, since the process is completely reversible.

$$w_{rev} = (269.6 - 1279.1) + 9.39 \times 0.26(2000 - 1000)$$

$$= 1431.9 \text{ Btu/lbm } H_2O$$

Since the net change in entropy is zero, the T–s diagram is as shown in Fig. 8.9. Area 3–4–c–d–3 represents the heat transferred from the products to the engines, and area 1–a–b–2–d–c–1 represents the heat received by the water. Area 3–4–1–a–b–2–3 represents the work done by the heat engines, which is equal to the reversible work for this process.

8.5 Processes Involving Chemical Reactions

Although chemical reactions will not be considered in detail until Chapter 12 some preliminary remarks regarding availability in such processes can be made here. In the first place, we observe that the reactants are often in pressure and temperature equilibrium with the surroundings before the reaction takes place, and the same is true of the products after the reaction. An automobile engine would be an example of such a process if we visualized the products being cooled to atmospheric temperature before being discharged from the engine.

Let us first consider for a system the implications of temperature equilibrium with the surroundings during a chemical reaction in a system. The temperature of the system T is equal to T_0, the temperature of the surroundings. Therefore, from Eq. 8.8 we can write (noting that in this case $T_0 = T$),

$$_1(w_{rev})_2 = \left(u_1 - T_1 s_1 + \frac{V_1{}^2}{2g_c} + Z_1 \frac{g}{g_c} \right) - \left(u_2 - T_2 s_2 + \frac{V_2{}^2}{2g_c} + Z_2 \frac{g}{g_c} \right)$$

The quantity $(U - TS)$ is a thermodynamic property of a substance and is called the Helmholtz function. It is an extensive property and we designate it by the symbol A. Thus

$$A = U - TS$$
$$a = u - Ts$$

(8.23)

Therefore, when a system undergoes a change of state while in temperature equilibrium with the surroundings, the reversible work is given by the relation

$$_1(w_{\text{rev}})_2 = \left(a_1 + \frac{\text{V}_1{}^2}{2g_c} + Z_1 \frac{g}{g_c}\right) - \left(a_2 + \frac{\text{V}_2{}^2}{2g_c} + Z_2 \frac{g}{g_c}\right)$$

In those cases where the kinetic and potential energy changes are not significant, this reduces to

$$_1(W_{\text{rev}})_2 = A_1 - A_2 = m(a_1 - a_2) \tag{8.24}$$

Let us now consider a system that undergoes a chemical reaction while in both pressure and temperature equilibrium with the surroundings. The availability function ϕ for a system has been defined as

$$\phi = (u + P_0 v - T_0 s) - (u_0 + P_0 v_0 - T_0 s_0)$$

If $P = P_0$ and $T = T_0$, then

$$\phi = (u + Pv - Ts) - (u_0 + P_0 v_0 - T_0 s_0)$$
$$\phi = (h - Ts) - (h_0 - T_0 s_0) \tag{8.25}$$

The quantity $h - Ts$ is a thermodynamic property and is termed the Gibbs function, designated by the symbol g.

$$G = H - TS$$
$$g = h - Ts \tag{8.26}$$

Introducing the Gibbs function into Eq. 8.25 we have, when a system is in pressure and temperature equilibrium with the surroundings.

$$\phi = g - g_0$$

From Eq. 8.22 it follows that under these same conditions

$$_1(w_{\text{rev}})_2 = (g_1 - g_2) - P_0(v_1 - v_2) + \frac{\text{V}_1{}^2 - \text{V}_2{}^2}{2g_c} + (Z_1 - Z_2)\frac{g}{g_c} \tag{8.27}$$

The Gibbs function is also of significance in a steady-state, steady-flow process that takes place in temperature equilibrium with the surroundings. Since in this case $T_i = T_e = T_0$, Eq. 8.9 reduces to

$$W_{\text{rev}} = m_i\left(h_i - T_i s_i + \frac{\text{V}_i{}^2}{2g_c} + Z_i \frac{g}{g_c}\right) - m_e\left(h_e - T_e s_e + \frac{\text{V}_e{}^2}{2g_c} + Z_e \frac{g}{g_c}\right)$$

Introducing the Gibbs function we have

$$W_{\text{rev}} = m_i\left(g_i + \frac{\text{V}_i{}^2}{2g_c} + Z_i \frac{g}{g_c}\right) - m_e\left(g_e + \frac{\text{V}_e{}^2}{2g_c} + Z_e \frac{g}{g_c}\right) \tag{8.28}$$

Thus we have introduced two new properties, the Helmholtz function, A, and the Gibbs function, G. Both these functions are very important in the thermodynamics of chemical reactions and will be used extensively in later chapters of this book.

PROBLEMS

Unless otherwise stated assume that the surroundings are at 1 atm pressure, 77 F.

8.1 Consider a steam turbine that has a throttling governor. (That is, the power output of the turbine is controlled by throttling the inlet steam.) The steam in the pipeline flowing to the turbine has a pressure of 800 lbf/in.² and a temperature of 1000 F. At a certain load the steam is throttled in an adiabatic process to 600 lbf/in.² Calculate the reversible work and irreversibility per lbm of steam for this process. Show the initial and final states of the steam on a *T-s* diagram.

8.2 Freon-12 enters the expansion valve of a refrigerator at a pressure of 150 lbf/in.² and a temperature of 80 F. It leaves the expansion valve at a temperature of 10 F. Calculate the reversible work and irreversibility for this process. Do you think it would be worth while to attempt to replace the irreversible throttling process with a reversible process in order to reduce the work required for operating the compressor?

8.3 Air enters the compressor of a gas turbine at 14.0 lbf/in.², 60 F, with a velocity of 400 ft/sec. The air leaves the compressor at a pressure of 60 lbf/in.², 400 F, and a velocity of 200 ft/sec. The process is adiabatic. Calculate the reversible work and irreversibility per lbm of air for this process.

8.4 Air enters the compressor of a gas turbine at 10.0 lbf/in.², 20 F and leaves the compressor at 35 lbf/in.² The compressor has an efficiency of 82%. Determine the work of compression per lbm of air, the reversible work for the actual change of state, and irreversibility per lbm of air.

8.5 Determine the reversible work and the irreversibility for the process described in Problem 5.11. The temperature of the surroundings is 77 F.

8.6 Determine the reversible work and the irreversibility for the process described in Problem 5.14. The temperature of the surroundings is 80 F.

8.7 Steam flows in a pipe at 200 lbf/in.², 500 F. An evacuated vessel having a volume of 10 ft³ is attached to this line through a valve, which is initially closed. The valve is opened and steam flows into the vessel until the pressure reaches 100 lbf/in.², at which point the valve is closed.
Determine the irreversibility, assuming no heat transfer during the process.

8.8 A 10 ft³ tank containing saturated vapor Freon-12 at 20 F is connected to a line flowing liquid Freon-12 at 80 F, 140 lbf/in.² The valve is then opened and Freon flows into the tank. During the process, heat is transferred with the surroundings at 80 F such that when the valve is closed the tank contains 50% liquid, 50% vapor, by volume, at 80 F. Calculate the heat transfer and the irreversibility for this process.

8.9 Compressed air is used to start a diesel engine. The air is stored at 300 lbf/in.², 77 F in a tank having a volume of 20 ft³, and it can be used for starting until the pressure is 40 lbf/in.^{2} It can be assumed that during the starting process the temperature of the air remains at 77 F. What is the work available for starting the engine?

8.10 What is the minimum work required to change 1 lbm of oxygen from 15 lbf/in.^{2}, 80 F to saturated liquid at 1 atm pressure? Sketch an apparatus which would be used in such a process and show the process on a temperature entropy diagram.

8.11 Suppose nitrogen is to be liquefied by the process of Problem 5.52. Assume that a reversible isothermal compressor is used to compress the air from 15.0 lbf/in.^{2}, 80 F to 1500 lbf/in.^{2} before the high pressure nitrogen enters the heat exchanger.

(a) What is the required work input to liquefy 1 lbm of nitrogen?

(b) What is the irreversibility per pound of nitrogen liquefied?

8.12 A pressure vessel has a volume of 30 ft^3 and contains air at 200 lbf/in.^{2}, 350 F. The air is cooled to 77 F by heat transfer to the surroundings at 77 F. Calculate the availability in the initial and final states and the irreversibility of this process.

8.13 Liquid nitrogen at 1 atm pressure is to be vaporized and delivered to a pipeline at 500 lbf/in.^{2}, 0 F. Three possible schemes for doing this are shown in Fig. 8.10. The first scheme involves pumping the liquid and then vaporizing

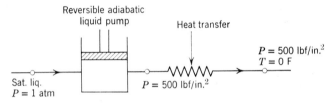

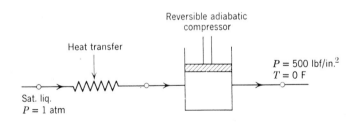

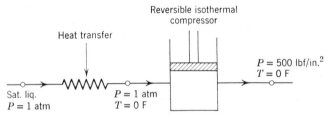

Fig. 8.10   Sketch for Problem 8.13.

it. The second involves vaporizing the liquid and superheating it just enough so that it would leave a reversible adiabatic compressor at 500 lbf/in.², 0 F. The third involves vaporizing it and superheating it to 0 F, followed by a reversible isothermal compressor.

(a) What is the availability of liquid nitrogen at 1 atm pressure?

(b) What is the minimum work necessary to deliver 1 lbm of nitrogen at 500 lbf/in.², 0 F?

Show a schematic arrangement of how you would do this with this minimum work input.

(c) Determine the work and the irreversibility per pound of nitrogen delivered for each of the three suggested ways of accomplishing this.

8.14 A pressure vessel of 10 ft³ capacity contains air at 500 lbf/in.², 77 F. A valve on the vessel is opened and the air escapes as the pressure drops to 200 lbf/in.² Assume no heat transfer during this process and that the gas remaining in the tank has undergone a reversible process. Calculate:

(a) The initial availability of the air in the vessel

(b) The availability of the air in the tank immediately after the expansion process.

(c) After some time the air that remains in the tank comes to a temperature of 77 F as a result of heat transfer from the surroundings. The volume of the air remains constant during this process. Determine the availability of the air in the tank in this final state.

8.15 Water is used as the working fluid in a power plant utilizing a nuclear reactor. A schematic diagram for this power plant is shown in Fig. 8.11. The

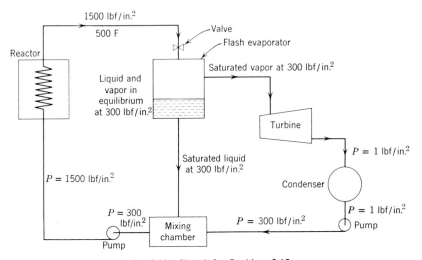

Fig. 8.11   Sketch for Problem 8.15.

compressed liquid that leaves the reactor enters the flash evaporator, where the pressure is reduced. That fraction of the water which flashes into steam flows to the turbine, while that which remains liquid flows to the mixing chamber.

Calculate the following quantities:

(a) The work done by the turbine per lbm of water leaving the reactor. Assume a reversible adiabatic turbine.

(b) The availability of the water leaving the reactor.

(c) The irreversibility in the flash evaporator per lbm of water entering.

(d) The irreversibility in the mixing chamber per lbm of water leaving.

8.16 Figure 8.12 shows a closed feedwater heater used in a steam power plant. Determine the irreversibility per lbm of feedwater leaving the heater at 380 lbf/in.², 200 F.

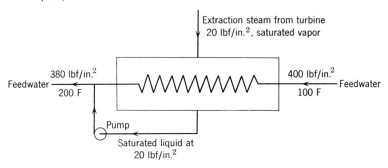

Fig. 8.12   Sketch for Problem 8.16.

8.17 Consider two identical blocks of metal, each having a mass of 10 lbm and a specific heat of 0.1 Btu/lbm-R. One has an initial temperature of 2000 R and the other an initial temperature of 500 R. The blocks are brought to the same temperature in a reversible process. Determine the final temperature of the blocks and the net work.

8.18 Consider the blocks of metal in Problem 8.17. The blocks are placed in thermal communication and allowed to come to temperature equilibrium. Determine the final temperature of the blocks and the irreversibility for the process. Show the processes of Problems 8.17 and 8.18 on a T-S diagram.

8.19 Two blocks of metal, each having a mass of 10 lbm and a specific heat of 0.1 Btu/lbm-R, are at a temperature of 100 F. A reversible refrigerator receives heat from one block and rejects heat to the other. Calculate the work required to cause a temperature difference of 200 F between the two blocks.

8.20 One lbm of water at 14.7 lbf/in.² undergoes a change of state from saturated liquid to saturated vapor in a steady-state, steady-flow process. Calculate the irreversibility for the following cases.

(a) This change of state occurs as a result of heat transfer from a constant-temperature reservoir at 1000 F.

(b) This change of state is effected by an electric resistance heater.

8.21 At a certain location the temperature of the water supply is 50 F. Ice is to be made from this water supply by the process shown in Fig. 8.13. The final temperature of the ice is 10 F, and the final temperature of the water that is used as cooling water in the condenser is 80 F.

What is the minimum work required to produce one ton of ice?

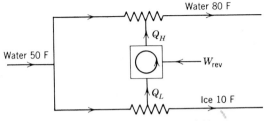

Fig. 8.13   Sketch for Problem 8.21.

8.22 Consider the process described in Problem 7.58. Calculate the irreversibility for this process assuming that the required heat transfer to the air and H_2O is from a reservoir at 1000 F.

8.23 An air preheater is used to cool the products of combustion from a furnace while heating the air to be used for combustion. The rate of flow of products is 100,000 lbm/hr, and the products are cooled from 600 F to 400 F, and for the products at this temperature $C_p = 0.26$ Btu/lbm-R. The rate of air flow is 93,000 lbm/hr, the initial air temperature is 100 F, and for the air $C_p = 0.24$ Btu/lbm-R.

(a) What is the initial and final availability of the products (Btu/hr)?

(b) What is the irreversibility for this process?

(c) Suppose this heat transfer from the products took place reversibly through heat engines. What would be the final temperature of the air? What power would be developed by the heat engines?

8.24 One mole of carbon dust is burned with 1 mole of oxygen to form 1 mole of carbon dioxide in a steady-flow process. The temperature of the carbon and oxygen before combustion is 77 F and the temperature of the carbon dioxide after combustion is also 77 F. The heat transferred during the process is $-169,297$ Btu, and the entropy of the carbon dioxide after combustion is 0.709 Btu/lb mole-R higher than the entropy of carbon and oxygen before combustion. Calculate the reversible work and the irreversibility for this process.

9 Some Power and Refrigeration Cycles

Some power plants, such as the simple steam power plant, which we have considered several times, operate in a cycle. That is, the working fluid undergoes a series of processes and finally returns to the initial state. In other power plants, such as the internal combustion engine and gas turbine the working fluid does not go through a thermodynamic cycle, even though the engine itself may operate in a mechanical cycle. In this case the working fluid has a different composition or is in a different state at the conclusion of the process than at the beginning. Such equipment is sometimes said to operate on the open cycle (the word cycle is really a misnomer), whereas the steam power plant operates on a closed cycle. The same distinction between open and closed cycles can be made regarding refrigeration devices. For both the open- and closed-cycle type of apparatus, however, it is advantageous to analyze the performance of an idealized closed cycle similar to the actual cycle. Such a procedure is particularly advantageous in determining the influence of certain variables on performance. For example, the spark-ignition internal combustion engine is usually approximated by the Otto cycle. From an analysis of the Otto cycle one concludes that increasing the compression ratio increases the efficiency. This is also true for the actual engine, even though the Otto cycle efficiencies may deviate significantly from the actual efficiencies.

This chapter is concerned with these idealized cycles, both for power and refrigeration apparatus. The working fluids considered are both vapors and ideal gases. An attempt will be made to point out how the processes in actual apparatus deviate from the ideal. Consideration is also given to certain modifications of the basic cycles which are intended to improve performance. These involve the use of such devices as regenerators, multistage compressors and expanders, and intercoolers. The order in which the cycles will be considered is: (1) vapor power cycles, (2) vapor refrigeration cycles, (3) air-standard power cycles, and (4) air-standard refrigeration cycles.

VAPOR POWER CYCLES

9.1 The Rankine Cycle

The ideal cycle for a simple steam power plant is the Rankine cycle, shown in Fig. 9.1.

The processes that comprise the cycle are:

1–2: Reversible adiabatic pumping process in the pump.

2–3: Constant-pressure transfer of heat in the boiler.

3–4: Reversible adiabatic expansion in the turbine (or other prime mover such as a steam engine).

4–1: Constant-pressure transfer of heat in the condenser.

The Rankine cycle also includes the possibility of superheating the vapor, as cycle 1–2–3′–4′–1.

If changes of kinetic and potential energy are neglected, heat transfer and work may be represented by various areas on the T-s diagram. The heat transferred to the working fluid is represented by area a–2–2′–3–b–a, and the heat transferred from the working fluid by area a–1–4–b–a. From the first law we conclude that the area representing the work is the difference between these two areas, namely, area 1–2–2′–3–4–1. The thermal efficiency is defined by the relation

$$\eta_{th} = \frac{w_{net}}{q_H} = \frac{\text{area } 1\text{–}2\text{–}2'\text{–}3\text{–}4\text{–}1}{\text{area } a\text{–}2\text{–}2'\text{–}3\text{–}b\text{–}a} \qquad (9.1)$$

In analyzing the Rankine cycle it is helpful to think of efficiency as depending on the average temperature at which heat is supplied and the average temperature at which heat is rejected. Any changes that increase the average temperature at which heat is supplied or decrease the average temperature at which heat is rejected will increase the Rankine cycle efficiency.

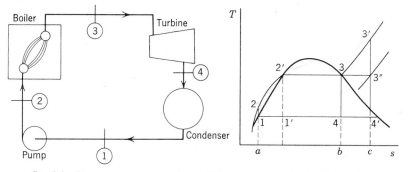

Fig. 9.1 Simple steam power plant which operates on the Rankine cycle.

It should be stated that in analyzing the ideal cycles in this chapter the changes in kinetic and potential energies from one point in the cycle to another are neglected. In general this is a reasonable assumption for the actual cycles.

It is readily evident that the Rankine cycle has a lower efficiency than a Carnot cycle with the same maximum and minimum temperatures as a Rankine cycle, because the average temperature between 2 and 2′ is less than the temperature during evaporation. We might well ask, why choose the Rankine cycle as the ideal cycle? Why not select the Carnot cycle 1′–2′–3–4–1′? At least two reasons can be given. The first involves the pumping process. State 1′ is a mixture of liquid and vapor, and great difficulties are encountered in building a pump that will handle the mixture of liquid and vapor at 1′ and deliver saturated liquid at 2′. It is much easier to completely condense the vapor and handle only liquid in the pump, and the Rankine cycle is based on this fact. The second reason involves superheating the vapor. In the Rankine cycle the vapor is superheated at constant pressure, process 3–3′. In the Carnot cycle all the heat transfer is at constant temperature, and therefore the vapor is superheated in process 3–3″. Note, however, that during this process the pressure is dropping, which means that the heat must be transferred to the vapor as it undergoes an expansion process in which work is done. This also is very difficult to achieve in practice. Thus, the Rankine cycle is the ideal cycle that can be approximated in practice. In the sections that follow we will consider some variations on the Rankine cycle that enable one to more closely approach the Carnot-cycle efficiency.

Before discussing the influence of certain variables on the performance of the Rankine cycle, an example is given.

Example 9.1

Determine the efficiency of a Rankine cycle utilizing steam as the working fluid in which the condenser pressure is 1 lbf/in.². The boiler pressure is 300 lbf/in.². The steam leaves the boiler as saturated vapor.

In solving Rankine-cycle problems we will let w_p denote the work into the pump per pound of fluid flowing and q_L the heat rejected from the working fluid per pound of fluid flowing.

In solving this problem we consider, in succession, a control surface around the pump, the boiler, the turbine, and the condenser. In each case the property relation used is the steam table.

Consider a control surface around the pump.

First law: $w_p = h_2 - h_1$

Second law: $s_2 = s_1$

Since
$$s_2 = s_1, \qquad h_2 - h_1 = \int_1^2 v\, dP$$

Therefore, assuming the fluid to be incompressible,

$$w_p = v(P_2 - P_1) = 0.01614(300 - 1)\tfrac{144}{778} = 0.893 \text{ Btu/lbm}$$

$$h_2 = h_1 + w_p = 69.7 + 0.9 = 70.6 \text{ Btu/lbm}.$$

Next consider a control surface around the boiler.

First law: $q_H = h_3 - h_2 = 1202.8 - 70.6 = 1132.2$ Btu/lbm

Consider a control surface around the turbine.

First law: $w_t = h_3 - h_4$

Second law: $s_3 = s_4$

We can determine the quality at state 4 as follows:

$$s_3 = s_4 = 1.5104 = [s_g - (1 - x)s_{fg}]_4$$
$$= 1.9782 - (1 - x)_4 1.8456$$

$$(1 - x)_4 = \frac{0.4678}{1.8456} = 0.2535$$

$$h_4 = [h_g - (1 - x)h_{fg}]_4$$
$$= 1106.0 - 0.2535(1036.3)$$
$$= 843.3 \text{ Btu/lbm}$$

$$w_t = 1202.8 - 843.3 = 359.5 \text{ Btu/lbm}$$

Finally, consider a control surface around the condenser.

First law: $q_L = h_4 - h_1$
$$= 843.3 - 69.7 = 773.6 \text{ Btu/lbm}$$

We can now calculate the thermal efficiency

$$\eta_{\text{th}} = \frac{w_{\text{net}}}{q_H} = \frac{q_H - q_L}{q_H} = \frac{w_t - w_p}{q_H} = \frac{359.5 - 0.9}{1132.2} = 31.7\%$$

We could also write an expression for thermal efficiency in terms of properties at various points in the cycle

$$\eta_{\text{th}} = \frac{(h_3 - h_2) - (h_4 - h_1)}{h_3 - h_2} = \frac{(h_3 - h_4) - (h_2 - h_1)}{h_3 - h_2}$$

$$= \frac{1132.2 - 773.6}{1132.2} = \frac{359.5 - 0.9}{1132.2} = 31.7\%$$

9.2 Effect of Pressure and Temperature on Rankine Cycle

Let us first consider the effect of exhaust pressure and temperature on the Rankine cycle. This effect is shown on the *T-s* diagram of Fig. 9.2.

Let the exhaust pressure drop from P_4 to P_4', with the corresponding decrease in temperature at which heat is rejected. The net work is increased by area 1–4–4′–1′–2′–2–1 (shown by the cross hatching). The heat transferred to the steam is increased by area a'–2′–2–a–a'. Since these two areas are approximately equal, the net result is an increase in cycle efficiency. This is also evident from the fact that the average temperature at which heat is rejected is decreased. Note however, that lowering the back pressure causes an increase in the moisture content in the steam leaving the turbine. This is a significant factor because if the moisture in the low-pressure stages of the turbine exceeds about 10 per cent, not only is there a decrease in turbine efficiency, but also erosion of the turbine blades may be a very serious problem.

Next consider the effect of superheating the steam in the boiler, as shown in Fig. 9.3. It is readily evident that the work is increased by area 3–3′–4′–4–3, and the heat transferred in the boiler is increased by area 3–3′–b′–b–3. Since this ratio of these two areas is greater than the ratio of net work to heat supplied for the rest of the cycle, it is evident that for given pressures, superheating the steam increases the Rankine-cycle efficiency. This would also follow from the fact that the average temperature at which heat is transferred to the steam is increased. Note also that when the steam is superheated the quality of the steam leaving the turbine increases.

Finally, the influence of the maximum pressure of the steam must be considered, and this is shown in Fig. 9.4. In this analysis the maximum temperature of the steam, as well as the exhaust pressure, is held constant.

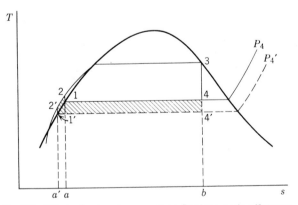

Fig. 9.2   Effect of exhaust pressure on Rankine-cycle efficiency.

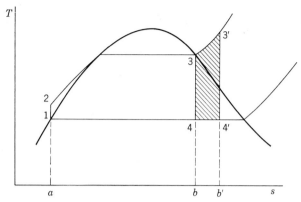

Fig. 9.3   Effect of superheating on Rankine-cycle efficiency.

The heat rejected decreases by area b'–$4'$–4–b–b'. The net work increases by the amount of the single crosshatching and decreases by the amount of the double crosshatching. Therefore the net work tends to remain the same, but the heat rejected decreases, and therefore the Rankine-cycle efficiency increases with an increase in maximum pressure. Note that in this case also the average temperature at which heat is supplied increases with an increase in pressure. The quality of the steam leaving the turbine decreases as the maximum pressure increases.

To summarize this section we can say that the Rankine-cycle efficiency can be increased by lowering the exhaust pressure, increasing the pressure during heat addition, and by superheating the steam. The quality of the

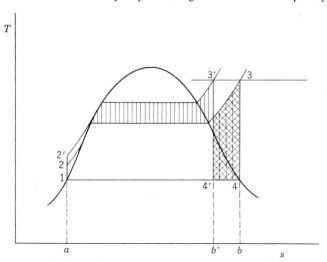

Fig. 9.4   Effect of boiler pressure on Rankine-cycle efficiency.

steam leaving the turbine is increased by superheating the steam, and decreased by lowering the exhaust pressure and by increasing the pressure during heat addition.

Example 9.2

In a Rankine cycle steam leaves the boiler and enters the turbine at 600 lbf/in.², 800 F. The condenser pressure is 1 lbf/in.². Determine the cycle efficiency.

To determine the cycle efficiency we must calculate the turbine work, the pump work, and the heat transfer to the steam in the boiler. We do this by considering a control surface around each of these components and assuming steady-state, steady-flow processes.

a. A control surface around the pump.

First law: $w_p = h_2 - h_1$

Second law: $s_2 = s_1$

Since

$$s_2 = s_1, \qquad h_2 - h_1 = \int_1^2 v \, dP = v(P_2 - P_1)$$

Therefore,

$$w_p = v(P_2 - P_1) = 0.01614(600 - 1) \times \tfrac{144}{778} = 1.8 \text{ Btu/lbm}$$
$$h_1 = 69.70$$
$$h_2 = 69.7 + 1.8 = 71.5 \text{ Btu/lbm.}$$

b. A control surface around the turbine.

First law: $w_t = h_3 - h_4$

Second law: $s_4 = s_3$
$$h_3 = 1407.7 \quad s_3 = 1.6343$$
$$s_3 = s_4 = 1.6343 = 1.9783 - (1 - x)_4 \, 1.8456$$
$$(1 - x)_4 = 0.1865$$
$$h_4 = 1106.0 - 0.1865(1036.3) = 913.3$$
$$w_t = h_3 - h_4 = 1407.7 - 913.3 = 494.4 \text{ Btu/lbm}$$
$$w_{net} = w_t - w_p = 494.4 - 1.8 = 492.6 \text{ Btu/lbm}$$

c. A control surface around the boiler.

$$q_H = h_3 - h_2 = 1407.7 - 71.5 = 1336.2 \text{ Btu/lbm}$$

$$\eta_{th} = \frac{w_{net}}{q_H} = \frac{492.6}{1336.2} = 36.9\%$$

d. The net work could also be determined by calculating the heat rejected in the condenser, q_L, and noting, from the first law, that the net work for the cycle is equal to the net heat transfer.

Considering a control surface around the condenser,

$$q_L = h_4 - h_1 = 913.3 - 69.7 = 843.6 \text{ Btu/lbm}$$

Therefore,

$$w_{\text{net}} = q_H - q_L = 1336.2 - 843.6 = 492.6 \text{ Btu/lbm}$$

9.3 The Reheat Cycle

In the last paragraph we noted that the efficiency of the Rankine cycle could be increased by increasing the pressure during the addition of heat. However, this also increases the moisture content of the steam in the low-pressure end of the turbine. The reheat cycle has been developed to take advantage of the increased efficiency with higher pressures, and yet avoid excessive moisture in the low-pressure stages of the turbine. This cycle is shown schematically and on a T-s diagram in Fig. 9.5. The unique feature of this cycle is that the steam is expanded to some intermediate pressure in the turbine, and is then reheated in the boiler, after which it expands in the turbine to the exhaust pressure. It is evident from the T-s diagram that there is very little gain in efficiency from reheating the steam, because the average temperature at which heat is supplied is not greatly changed. The chief advantage is in decreasing the moisture content in the low-pressure stages of the turbine to a safe value. Note also, that if metals could be found that would enable one to superheat the steam to 3', the simple Rankine cycle would be more efficient than the reheat cycle, and there would be no need for the reheat cycle.

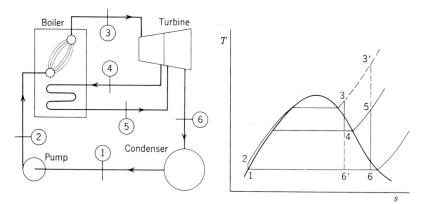

Fig. 9.5 The ideal reheat cycle.

Example 9.3

Consider a reheat cycle utilizing steam. Steam leaves the boiler and enters the turbine at 600 lbf/in.², 800 F. After expansion in the turbine to 60 lbf/in.², the steam is reheated to 800 F and then expanded in the low-pressure turbine to 1 lbf/in.². Determine the cycle efficiency.

Designating the states in accordance with Fig. 9.5 we proceed as follows: Consider a control surface around the turbine.

First law: $w_t = (h_3 - h_4) + (h_5 - h_6)$
Second law: $s_4 = s_3$
$$s_6 = s_5$$

To find w_t we proceed as follows:

$$h_3 = 1407.7 \qquad s_3 = 1.6343$$
$$s_4 = s_3 = 1.6343 = 1.6438 - (1 - x)_4 \, 1.2168$$
$$(1 - x)_4 = 0.0078$$
$$h_4 = 1177.6 - 0.0078(915.5) = 1170.5$$
$$h_5 = 1430.5 \quad s_5 = 1.9015$$
$$s_5 = s_6 = 1.9015 = 1.9782 - (1 - x)_6 \, 1.8456$$
$$(1 - x)_6 = 0.0416$$
$$h_6 = 1106.0 - 0.0416(1036.8) = 1062.9$$
$$w_t = (h_3 - h_4) + (h_5 - h_6)$$
$$w_t = (1407.7 - 1170.5) + (1430.5 - 1062.9) = 604.8 \;\; \text{Btu/lbm}$$

Consider a control surface around the pump.

First law: $w_p = h_2 - h_1$
Second law: $s_2 = s_1$
Since
$$s_2 = s_1, \qquad h_2 - h_1 = \int_1^2 v \, dP = v(P_2 - P_1)$$
Therefore,
$$w_p = v(P_2 - P_1) = 0.01614(600 - 1)\tfrac{144}{778} = 1.8 \;\text{Btu/lbm.}$$
$$h_2 = 69.7 + 1.8 = 71.5 \;\text{Btu/lbm}$$

Consider a control surface around the boiler.

$$q_H = (h_3 - h_2) + (h_5 - h_4)$$
$$q_H = (1407.7 - 71.5) + (1430.5 - 1170.5) = 1596.2 \;\text{Btu/lbm}$$
$$w_{net} = w_t - w_p = 604.8 - 1.8 = 603.0 \;\text{Btu/lbm}$$

$$\eta_{th} = \frac{w_{net}}{q_H} = \frac{603.0}{1596.2} = 37.8\%$$

Note by comparison with Example 9.2 that the gain in efficiency from reheating is relatively small, but that the moisture content leaving the turbine is decreased as a result of reheating from 18.6 per cent to 4.2 per cent.

9.4 The Regenerative Cycle

Another important variation from the Rankine cycle is the regenerative cycle, which involves the use of feedwater heaters. The basic concepts of this cycle can be demonstrated by considering the Rankine cycle without superheat as shown in Fig. 9.6. During the process between states 2 and 2' the working fluid is heated while in the liquid phase, and the average temperature of the working fluid is much lower during this process than during the vaporization process 2'–3. This causes the average temperature at which heat is supplied in the Rankine cycle to be lower than in the Carnot cycle 1'–2'–3–4–1', and consequently the efficiency of the Rankine cycle is less than that of the corresponding Carnot cycle. In the regenerative cycle the working fluid enters the boiler at some state between 2 and 2', and consequently the average temperature at which heat is supplied is increased.

Consider first an idealized regenerative cycle, shown in Fig. 9.7. The unique feature of this cycle compared to the Rankine cycle is that after leaving the pump, the liquid circulates around the turbine casing, counter-flow to the direction of vapor flow in the turbine. Thus, it is possible to transfer heat from the vapor as it flows through the turbine to the liquid flowing around the turbine. Let us assume for the moment that this is a

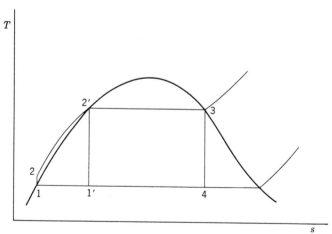

Fig. 9.6   Temperature-entropy diagram showing the relationship between Carnot-cycle efficiency and Rankine-cycle efficiency.

reversible heat transfer; that is, at each point the temperature of the vapor is only infinitesimally higher than the temperature of the liquid. In this case line 4–5 on the *T-s* diagram of Fig. 9.7, which represents the states of the vapor flowing through the turbine, is exactly parallel to line 1–2–3, which represents the pumping process (1–2) and the states of the liquid flowing around the turbine. Consequently areas 2–3–b–a–2 and 5–4–d–c–5 are not only equal but congruous, and these areas respectively represent the heat transferred to the liquid and from the vapor. Note also that heat is transferred to the working fluid at constant temperature in process 3–4, and area 3–4–d–b–3 represents this heat transfer. Heat is transferred from the working fluid in process 5–1, and area 1–5–c–a–1 represents this heat transfer. Note that this area is exactly equal to area 1′–5′–d–b–1′, which is the heat rejected in the related Carnot cycle 1′–3–4–5′–1′. Thus, this idealized regenerative cycle has an efficiency exactly equal to the efficiency of the Carnot cycle with the same heat-supply and heat-rejection temperatures.

Quite obviously this idealized regenerative cycle is not practical. First of all, it would not be possible to effect the necessary heat transfer from the vapor in the turbine to the liquid feedwater. Furthermore, the moisture content of the vapor leaving the turbine is considerably increased as a result of the heat transfer, and the disadvantage of this has been noted previously. The practical regenerative cycle involves the extraction of some of the vapor after it has partially expanded in the turbine and the use of feedwater heaters, as shown in Fig. 9.8.

Steam enters the turbine at state 5. After expansion to state 6, some of the steam is extracted and enters the feedwater heater. The steam that is not extracted is expanded in the turbine to state 7 and is then condensed in the condenser. This condensate is pumped into the feedwater heater where it mixes with the steam extracted from the turbine. The proportion of

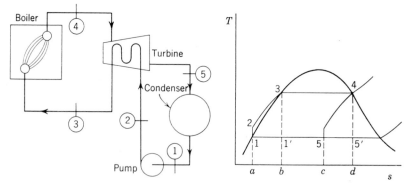

Fig. 9.7   The ideal regenerative cycle.

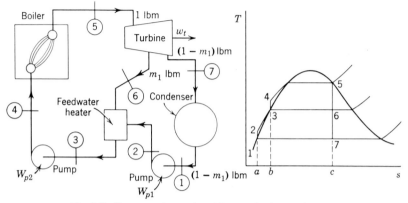

Fig. 9.8 Regenerative cycle with open feedwater heater.

steam extracted is just sufficient to cause the liquid leaving the feedwater heater to be saturated at state 3. Note that the liquid has not been pumped to the boiler pressure, but only to the intermediate pressure corresponding to state 6. Another pump is required to pump the liquid leaving the feedwater heater to boiler pressure. The significant point is that the average temperature at which heat is supplied has been increased.

This cycle is somewhat difficult to show on a T-s diagram because the mass of steam flowing through the various components is not the same. The T-s diagram of Fig. 9.7 simply shows the state of the fluid at the various points.

Area 4–5–c–b–4 in Fig. 9.8 represents the heat transferred per pound mass of working fluid. Process 7–1 is the heat-rejection process, but since not all the steam passes through the condenser, area 1–7–c–a–1 represents the heat transfer per pound mass flowing through the condenser, which does not represent the heat transfer per pound mass of working fluid entering the turbine. Note also that between states 6 and 7 only part of the steam is flowing through the turbine. The example that follows illustrates the calculations involved in the regenerative cycle.

Example 9.4

Consider a regenerative cycle utilizing steam as the working fluid. Steam leaves the boiler and enters the turbine at 600 lbf/in.^{2}, 800 F. After expansion to 60 lbf/in.^{2} some of the steam is extracted from the turbine for the purpose of heating the feedwater in an open feedwater heater. The pressure in the feedwater heater is 60 lbf/in.^{2} and the water leaving it is saturated liquid at 60 lbf/in.^{2} The steam not extracted expands to 1 lbf/in.^{2} Determine the cycle efficiency.

The line diagram and T-s diagram for this cycle are shown in Fig. 9.8.

From Examples 9.2 and 9.3 we have the following properties:

$$h_5 = 1407.7 \qquad h_6 = 1170.5 \qquad h_7 = 913.3 \qquad h_1 = 69.70$$

Consider a control surface around the low pressure pump.

First law: $w_{p1} = (h_2 - h_1)$

Second law: $s_2 = s_1$

Therefore,

$$h_2 - h_1 = \int_1^2 v \, dP = v(P_2 - P_1)$$

$$w_{p1} = v(P_2 - P_1) = 0.01614(60 - 1)\tfrac{144}{778} = 0.2 \text{ Btu/lbm}$$

$$h_2 = h_1 + w_p = 69.7 + 0.2 = 69.9$$

$$h_3 = 262.1$$

Consider a control surface around the turbine.

First law: $w_t = (h_5 - h_6) + (1 - m_1)(h_6 - h_7)$

Second law: $s_5 = s_6 = s_7$

It follows that, as has been calculated in Examples 9.2 and 9.3,

$$h_6 = 1170.5; \quad h_7 = 913.3$$

Next consider a control surface around the feedwater heater.

First law: $m_1(h_6) + (1 - m_1)h_2 = h_3$

$$m_1(1170.5) + (1 - m_1)69.9 = 262.1$$

$$m_1 = \frac{262.1 - 69.9}{1170.5 - 69.9} = 0.1747$$

We can now calculate the turbine work.

$$
\begin{aligned}
w_t &= (h_5 - h_6) + (1 - m_1)(h_6 - h_7) \\
&= (1407.7 - 1170.5) + (1 - 0.1747)(1170.5 - 913.3) = 449.4
\end{aligned}
$$

Consider a control surface around the boiler.

$$q_H = h_5 - h_4 = 1407.7 - 263.8 = 1143.9$$

Consider a control surface around the high pressure pump.

First law: $w_{p2} = (h_4 - h_3)$

Second law: $s_4 = s_3$

$$w_{p2} = v(P_4 - P_3) = 0.01738(600 - 60)\tfrac{144}{778} = 1.7 \text{ Btu/lbm}$$

$$w_{net} = w_t - (1 - m_1)w_{p1} - w_{p2} = 449.4 - 0.825(0.2) - 1.7 = 447.5$$

$$\eta_{th} = \frac{w_{net}}{q_H} = \frac{447.5}{1143.9} = 39.1\%$$

Note the increase in efficiency over the Rankine cycle of Example 9.2.

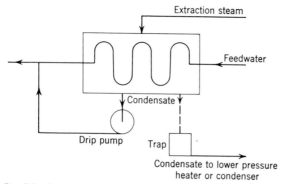

Fig. 9.9   Schematic arrangement for a closed feedwater heater.

Up to this point the discussion and example have tacitly assumed that the extraction steam and feedwater are mixed in the feedwater heater. Another much-used type of feedwater heater, known as a closed heater, is one in which the steam and feedwater do not mix, but rather heat is transferred from the extracted steam as it condenses on the outside of tubes as the feedwater flows through the tubes. In a closed heater, a schematic sketch of which is shown in Fig. 9.9, the steam and feedwater may be at considerably different pressures. The condensate may be pumped into the feedwater line, or it may be removed through a trap (a device that permits liquid but no vapor to flow to a region of lower pressure) to a lower pressure heater or to the main condenser.

Open feedwater heaters have the advantage of being less expensive and having better heat-transfer characteristics compared to closed feedwater heaters. They have the disadvantage of requiring a pump to handle the feedwater between each heater.

In many power plants a number of stages of extraction are used, though only rarely more than five. The number is, of course, determined by economic considerations. It is evident that by using a very large number of extraction stages and feedwater heaters, the cycle efficiency would approach that of the idealized regenerative cycle of Fig. 9.7, where the feedwater enters the boiler as saturated liquid at the maximum pressure. However, in practice this could not be economically justified because the savings effected by the increase in efficiency would be more than offset by the cost of additional equipment (feedwater heaters, piping, etc.).

A typical arrangement of the main components in an actual power plant is shown in Fig. 9.10. Note that one open feedwater heater is a deaerating feedwater heater, and this has the dual purpose of heating and removing the air from the feedwater. Unless the air is removed excessive corrosion occurs in the boiler. Note also that the condensate from the

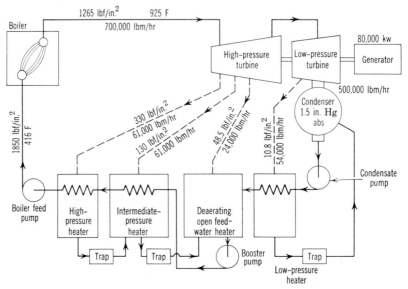

Fig. 9.10 Arrangement of heaters in an actual power plant utilizing regenerative feedwater heaters.

high-pressure heater drains (through a trap) to the intermediate heater, and the intermediate heater drains to the deaerating feedwater heater. The low-pressure heater drains to the condenser.

In many cases an actual power plant combines one reheat stage with a number of extraction stages. The principles already considered are readily applied to such a cycle.

9.5 Deviation of Actual Cycles from Ideal Cycles

Before leaving the matter of vapor power cycles, a few comments are in order regarding the ways in which an actual cycle deviates from an ideal cycle. (The losses associated with the combustion process are considered in a later chapter.) The most important of these are as follows.

Piping Losses. Pressure drop due to frictional effects and heat transfer to the surroundings are the most important piping losses. Consider for example the pipe connecting the turbine to the boiler. If only frictional effects occurred, the states a and b in Fig. 9.11 would represent the states of the steam leaving the boiler and entering the turbine respectively. Note that this causes an increase in entropy. Heat transferred to the surroundings at constant pressure can be represented by process bc. This effect causes a decrease in entropy. Both the pressure drop and heat transfer

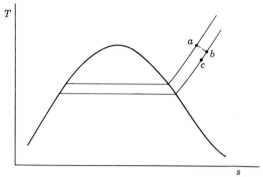

Fig. 9.11   Temperature-entropy diagram showing effect of losses between boiler and turbine.

cause a decrease in the availability of the steam entering the turbine, and the irreversibility of this process can be calculated by the methods outlined in Chapter 8.

A similar loss is the pressure drop in the boiler. Because of this pressure drop, the water entering the boiler must be pumped to a much higher pressure than the desired steam pressure leaving the boiler, and this requires additional pump work.

Turbine Losses.   The losses in the turbine are primarily those associated with the flow of the working fluid through the turbine. Heat transfer to the surroundings also represents a loss, but this is usually of secondary importance. The effects of these two losses are the same as those outlined for piping losses, and the process might be as represented in Fig. 9.12, where 4_s represents the state after an isentropic expansion and state 4 represents the actual state leaving the turbine. The governing procedures

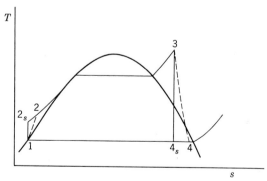

Fig. 9.12   Temperature-entropy diagram showing effect of turbine and pump inefficiencies on cycle performance.

may also cause a loss in the turbine, particularly if a throttling process is used to govern the turbine.

The efficiency of the turbine has been defined (in Chapter 7) as

$$\eta_t = \frac{w_t}{h_3 - h_{4s}}$$

where the states are as designated in Fig. 9.12.

Pump Losses.   The losses in the pump are similar to those of the turbine, and are primarily due to the irreversibilities associated with the fluid flow. Heat transfer is usually a minor loss.

The pump efficiency is defined as

$$\eta_p = \frac{h_{2s} - h_1}{w_p}$$

where the states are as shown in Fig. 9.12, and w_p is the actual work input per pound of fluid.

Condenser Losses.   The losses in the condenser are relatively small. One of these minor losses is the cooling below the saturation temperature of the liquid leaving the condenser. This represents a loss because additional heat transfer is necessary to bring the water to its saturation temperature.

The influence of these losses on the cycle is illustrated in the following example, which should be compared to Example 9.2.

Example 9.5

A steam power plant operates on a cycle with pressures and temperatures as designated in Fig. 9.13. The efficiency of the turbine is 86 per cent and the efficiency of the pump is 80 per cent. Determine the thermal efficiency of this cycle.

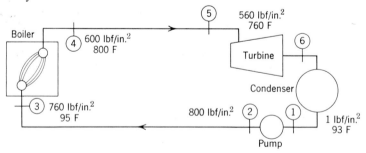

Fig. 9.13   Schematic diagram for Example 9.5.

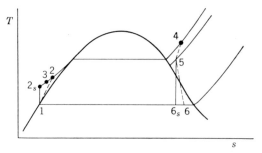

Fig. 9.14 Temperature-entropy diagram for Example 9.5.

From the steam tables

$$h_1 = 61.0$$
$$h_3 = 63.0 + 2.1 = 65.1$$
$$h_4 = 1407.7 \qquad s_4 = 1.6343$$
$$h_5 = 1387.3 \qquad s_5 = 1.6251$$

This cycle is shown on the T-s diagram of Fig. 9.14.

Consider a control surface around the turbine.
First law: $w_t = h_6 - h_5$
Second law: $s_{6s} = s_5$

$$\eta_t = \frac{w_t}{h_5 - h_{6s}} = \frac{h_5 - h_6}{h_5 - h_{6s}}$$
$$s_{6s} = s_5 = 1.6251 = 1.9782 - (1 - x)_{6s} \, 1.8456$$

$$(1 - x)_{6s} = \frac{0.3531}{1.8456} = 0.1912$$

$$h_{6s} = 1106.0 - 0.1912(1036.3) = 907.8$$
$$w_t = \eta_t(h_5 - h_{6s}) = 0.86(1387.3 - 907.8)$$
$$= 0.86(479.5) = 412.3 \text{ Btu/lbm}$$

Consider a control surface around the pump.
First law: $w_p = h_2 - h_1$
Second law: $s_{2s} = s_1$

$$\eta_p = \frac{h_{2s} - h_1}{w_p} = \frac{h_{2s} - h_1}{h_2 - h_1}$$

Since

$$s_{2s} = s_1, \qquad h_{2s} - h_1 = v(P_2 - P_1)$$

Therefore,

$$w_p = \frac{h_{2s} - h_1}{\eta_p} = \frac{v(P_2 - P_1)}{\eta_p} = \frac{0.01615(800 - 1)144}{0.8 \times 778}$$

$$= \frac{2.4}{0.8} = 3.0 \text{ Btu/lbm}$$

$$w_{\text{net}} = w_t - w_p = 412.3 - 3.0 = 409.3 \text{ Btu/lbm}$$

If we apply the first law to a control surface around the boiler, we have

$$q_H = h_4 - h_3 = 1407.7 - 65.1 = 1342.6 \text{ Btu/lbm}$$

$$\eta_{\text{th}} = \frac{409.3}{1342.6} = 30.4\%$$

This compares to an efficiency of 36.9 per cent for the Rankine efficiency of the similar cycle of Example 9.2.

VAPOR REFRIGERATION CYCLES

9.6 Vapor Compression Refrigeration Cycles

The ideal cycle for vapor compression refrigeration is shown in Fig. 9.15 as cycle 1–2–3–4–1. Saturated vapor at low pressure enters the compressor and undergoes a reversible adiabatic compression, 1–2. Heat is then rejected at constant pressure in process 2–3, and the working fluid leaves the condenser as saturated liquid. An adiabatic throttling process follows, process 3–4, and the working fluid is then evaporated at constant pressure, process 4–1, to complete the cycle.

The similarity between this cycle and the Rankine cycle is evident, for it is essentially the same cycle in reverse, except that an expansion valve replaces the pump. This throttling process is irreversible, whereas the

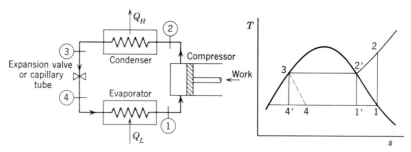

Fig. 9.15   The ideal vapor-compression refrigeration cycle.

pumping process of the Rankine cycle is reversible. The deviation of this ideal cycle from the Carnot cycle 1'-2'-3-4'-1' is evident from the T-s diagram. The reason for the deviation is that it is much more expedient to have a compressor handle only vapor than a mixture of liquid and vapor as would be required in process 1'-2' of the Carnot cycle. It is virtually impossible to compress (at a reasonable rate) a mixture such as that represented by state 1' and maintain equilibrium between the liquid and vapor, because there must be a heat and mass transfer across the phase boundary. It is also much simpler to have the expansion process take place irreversibly through an expansion valve than to have an expansion device that receives saturated liquid and discharges a mixture of liquid and vapor, as would be required in process 3-4'. For these reasons the ideal cycle for vapor-compression refrigeration is as shown in Fig. 9.15 by cycle 1-2-3-4-1.

As we saw in Chapter 6, the performance of a refrigeration cycle is given in terms of the coefficient of performance, β, which is defined for a refrigeration cycle as

$$\beta = \frac{q_L}{w_c} \qquad (9.2)$$

The capacity of a refrigeration plant is usually given in tons of refrigeration. This term had its origin in the ice-making industry, where cooling capacity was given in terms of tons of ice melting per day. The unit is now defined as

$$1 \text{ ton refrigeration} = 288{,}000 \text{ Btu of refrigeration/day}$$
$$= 12{,}000 \text{ Btu of refrigeration/hr}$$

Example 9.6

Consider an ideal refrigeration cycle that utilizes Freon-12 as the working fluid. The temperature of the refrigerant in the evaporator is 0 F and in the condenser it is 100 F. The refrigerant is circulated at the rate of 200 lbm/hr. Determine the coefficient of performance and the capacity of the plant in tons of refrigeration.

From the thermodynamic tables for Freon-12 we find the following properties for the states as designated in Fig. 9.15.

$$h_1 = 77.271 \qquad s_1 = 0.16888 \qquad P_2 = 131.86$$

Consider a control surface around the compressor.

First law: $w_c = h_2 - h_1$
Second law: $s_2 = s_1$
Therefore,

$$s_2 = s_1 = 0.16888, \text{ and } h_2 = 90.306$$
$$w_c = h_2 - h_1 = 90.306 - 77.271 = 13.035$$

Considering a control surface around the expansion valve, we conclude from the first law that

$$h_3 = h_4 = 31.100$$

Finally, consider a control surface around the evaporator.

First law: $q_L = h_1 - h_4 = 77.271 - 31.100 = 46.171$

Therefore,

$$\beta = \frac{q_L}{w_c} = \frac{46.171}{13.035} = 3.55$$

$$\text{Capacity} = \frac{46.171 \times 200}{12,000} = 0.768 \text{ tons.}$$

9.7 Working Fluids for Vapor-Compression Refrigeration Systems

A much larger number of different working fluids (refrigerants) are utilized in vapor-compression refrigeration systems than in vapor power cycles. Ammonia and sulfur dioxide were important in the early days of vapor-compression refrigeration. Today, however, the main refrigerants are the halogenated hydrocarbons, which are marketed under the trade names of Freon and Genatron. For example, dichlorodifluoromethane (CCl_2F_2) is known as Freon-12 and Genatron-12. Two important considerations in selecting a refrigerant are the temperature at which refrigeration is desired and the type of equipment to be used.

Since the refrigerant undergoes a change of phase during the heat-transfer process, the pressure of the refrigerant will be the saturation pressure during the heat-supply and heat-rejection processes. Low pressures mean large specific volumes and correspondingly large equipment. High pressures mean smaller equipment but it must be designed to withstand higher pressure. In particular, the pressures should be well below the critical pressure. For extremely low temperature applications a binary fluid system may be used in a manner analogous to the mercury-steam cycle described in Problem 9.16.

The type of compressor used has a particular bearing on the refrigerant. Reciprocating compressors are best adapted to low specific volumes, which means higher pressures, whereas centrifugal compressors are most suitable for low pressures and high specific volumes.

It is also important that the refrigerants used in domestic appliances be nontoxic. Other important characteristics are tendency to cause corrosion, miscibility with compressor oil, dielectric strength, stability, and cost. Also, for given temperatures during evaporation and condensation, not all refrigerants have the same coefficient of performance for the ideal cycle. It is, of course, desirable to utilize the refrigerant with the highest coefficient of performance, other factors permitting.

9.8   Deviation of the Actual Vapor-Compression Refrigeration Cycle from the Ideal Cycle

The actual refrigeration cycle deviates from the ideal cycle primarily because of pressure drops associated with fluid flow and heat transfer to or from the surroundings. The actual cycle might approach the one shown in Fig. 9.16.

The vapor entering the compressor will probably be superheated. During the compression process there are irreversibilities and heat transfer either to or from the surroundings, depending on the temperature of the refrigerant and the surroundings. Therefore, the entropy might increase or decrease during this process, for the irreversibility and heat transfer to the refrigerant cause an increase in entropy, and heat transfer from the refrigerant causes a decrease in entropy. These possibilities are represented by the two dotted lines 1–2 and 1–2'. The pressure of the liquid leaving the condenser will be less than the pressure of the vapor entering, and the temperature of the refrigerant in the condenser will be somewhat above that of the surroundings to which heat is being transferred. Usually the temperature of the liquid leaving the condenser is lower than the saturation temperature, and it might drop somewhat more in the piping between the condenser and expansion valve. This represents a gain, however, because as a result of this heat transfer the refrigerant enters the evaporator with a lower enthalpy, thus permitting more heat transfer to the refrigerant in the evaporator.

There is some drop in pressure as the refrigerant flows through the evaporator. It may be slightly superheated as it leaves the evaporator, and due to heat transfer from the surroundings the temperature will increase in the piping between the evaporator and compressor. This heat

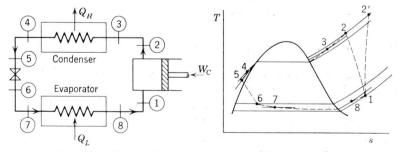

Fig. 9.16   The actual vapor-compression refrigeration cycle.

transfer represents a loss, because it increases the work of the compressor as a result of the increased specific volume of the fluid entering it.

Example 9.7

A refrigeration cycle utilizes Freon-12 as the working fluid. Following are the properties of the various points of the cycle designated in Fig. 9.16.

$$P_1 = 18 \text{ lbf/in.}^2 \qquad T_1 = 20 \text{ F}$$
$$P_2 = 180 \text{ lbf/in.}^2 \qquad T_2 = 220 \text{ F}$$
$$P_3 = 175 \text{ lbf/in.}^2 \qquad T_3 = 180 \text{ F}$$
$$P_4 = 170 \text{ lbf/in.}^2 \qquad T_4 = 110 \text{ F}$$
$$P_5 = 168 \text{ lbf/in.}^2 \qquad T_5 = 104 \text{ F}$$
$$P_6 = P_7 = 20 \text{ lbf/in.}^2 \qquad x_6 = x_7$$
$$P_8 = 19 \text{ lbf/in.}^2 \qquad T_8 = 0 \text{ F}$$

The heat transfer from the Freon-12 during the compression process is 2.0 Btu/lbm. Determine the coefficient of performance of this cycle.

From the Freon-12 tables the following properties are found.

$$h_1 = 80.527 \qquad\qquad h_2 = 106.896$$
$$h_5 = h_6 = h_7 = 32.067 \qquad h_8 = 77.621$$

Consider a control surface around the compressor.

First law: $q + h_1 = h_2 + w$

$$w_c = -w = h_2 - h_1 - q$$
$$= 106.896 - 80.527 - (-2) = 28.4 \text{ Btu/lbm}$$

To find q_L, consider a control surface around the evaporator.

$$q_L = h_8 - h_7 = 77.621 - 32.067 = 45.6$$

Therefore,

$$\beta = \frac{q_L}{w_c} = \frac{45.6}{28.4} = 1.61$$

9.9 The Ammonia-Absorption Refrigeration Cycle

The ammonia-absorption refrigeration cycle differs from the vapor compression cycle in the manner in which compression is achieved. In the absorption cycle the low-pressure ammonia vapor is absorbed in water and the liquid solution is pumped to a high pressure by a liquid pump. Figure 9.17 shows a schematic arrangement of the essential elements of such a system.

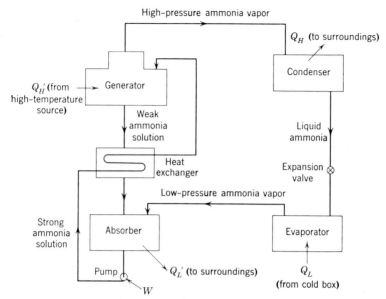

Fig. 9.17 The ammonia-absorption refrigeration cycle.

The low-pressure ammonia vapor leaving the evaporator enters the absorber where it is absorbed in the weak ammonia solution. This process takes place at a temperature slightly above that of the surroundings and heat must be transferred to the surroundings during this process. The strong ammonia solution is then pumped through a heat exchanger to the generator where a higher pressure and temperature are maintained. Under these conditions ammonia vapor is driven from the solution as a result of heat transfer from a high-temperature source. The ammonia vapor goes to the condenser where it is condensed, as in a vapor-compression system, and then to the expansion valve and evaporator. The weak ammonia solution is returned to the absorber through the heat exchanger.

The distinctive feature of the absorption system is that very little work input is required because the pumping process involves a liquid. This follows from the fact that for a reversible steady-flow process with negligible changes in kinetic and potential energy, the work is equal to $-\int v \, dP$, and the specific volume of the liquid is much less than the specific volume of the vapor. On the other hand, a relatively high-temperature source of heat must be available (200 F to 400 F). The equipment involved in an absorption system is somewhat greater than in a vapor-compression system and it can usually be economically justified only in those cases where a suitable source of heat is available that would otherwise be wasted.

This cycle brings out the important principle that since the work in a reversible steady-flow process with negligible changes in kinetic and potential energy is $-\int v\,dP$, a compression process should take place with the smallest possible specific volume.

AIR-STANDARD POWER CYCLES

9.10 Air-Standard Cycles

Many work-producing devices (engines) utilize a working fluid that is always a gas. The spark-ignition automotive engine is a familiar example, and the same is true of the Diesel engine and conventional gas turbine. In all of these engines there is a change in the composition of the working fluid, because during combustion it changes from air and fuel to combustion products. For this reason these engines are called internal combustion engines. In contrast to this the steam power plant may be called an external-combustion engine, because heat is transferred from the products of combustion to the working fluid. External-combustion engines using a gaseous working fluid (usually air) have been built. To date they have had very limited application, but the use of the gas turbine cycle in conjunction with a nuclear reactor has been investigated extensively.

Because the working fluid does not go through a complete thermodynamic cycle in the engine (even though the engine operates in a mechanical cycle) the internal-combustion engine operates on the so-called open cycle. However, in order to analyze internal-combustion engines it is advantageous to devise closed cycles that closely approximate the open cycles. One such approach is the air-standard cycle, which is based on the following assumptions:

(*a*) A fixed mass of air is the working fluid throughout the entire cycle, and the air is always an ideal gas. Thus there is no inlet process or exhaust process.

(*b*) The combustion process is replaced by a heat-transfer process from an external source.

(*c*) The cycle is completed by heat transfer to the surroundings (in contrast to the exhaust and intake process of an actual engine).

(*d*) All processes are internally reversible.

(*e*) The additional assumption is usually made that air has a constant specific heat.

The main value of the air-standard cycle is to enable us to examine qualitatively the influence of a number of variables on performance. The results obtained from the air-standard cycle, such as efficiency and mean effective pressure, will differ a great deal from those of the actual engine. The emphasis, therefore, in our consideration of the air-standard cycle will be primarily on the qualitative aspects.

The term "mean effective pressure," which is used in conjunction with reciprocating engines, is defined as the pressure which, if it acted on the piston during the entire power stroke, would do an amount of work equal to that actually done on the piston. The work for one cycle is found by multiplying this mean effective pressure by the area of the piston (minus the area of the rod on the crank end of a double-acting engine) and by the stroke.

9.11 The Air-Standard Carnot Cycle

The air-standard Carnot cycle is shown on the P-v and T-s diagrams of Fig. 9.18. Such a cycle could be achieved in either a reciprocating or steady-flow device, as shown in the same figure.

In Chapter 6 it was noted that the efficiency of a Carnot cycle depends only on the temperatures at which heat is supplied and rejected, and is

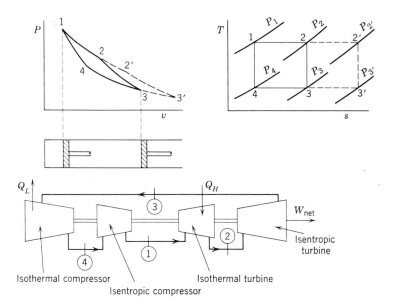

Fig. 9.18 The air-standard Carnot cycle.

given by the relation

$$\eta_{\text{th}} = 1 - \frac{T_L}{T_H} = 1 - \frac{T_4}{T_1} = 1 - \frac{T_3}{T_2}$$

where the subscripts refer to Fig. 9.18. The efficiency may also be expressed by the pressure ratio or compression ratio during the isentropic processes. This follows from the fact that

$$\text{Isentropic pressure ratio} = r_{\text{ps}} = \frac{P_1}{P_4} = \frac{P_2}{P_3} = \left(\frac{T_3}{T_2}\right)^{k/(1-k)}$$

$$\text{Isentropic compression ratio} = r_{\text{vs}} = \frac{V_4}{V_1} = \frac{V_3}{V_2} = \left(\frac{T_3}{T_2}\right)^{1/(1-k)}$$

Therefore

$$\eta_{\text{th}} = 1 - r_{\text{ps}}^{(1-k)/k} = 1 - r_{\text{vs}}^{1-k} \quad (9.3)$$

One other important variable in the air-standard Carnot cycle is the amount of heat transferred to the working fluid per cycle. It is evident from Fig. 9.18 that increasing the heat transfer per cycle at a given T_H causes a larger change in volume during the cycle, and this causes a lower mean effective pressure in a reciprocating engine. In fact, for air-standard Carnot cycles having a minimum pressure between 1 and 10 atm and a reasonable heat transfer per cycle, the mean effective pressure is so low that it would scarcely overcome friction forces.

Another practical difficulty of the Carnot cycle, which applies to both the reciprocating and steady-flow types of cycle, is the difficulty of transferring heat during the isothermal expansion and compression processes. It is virtually impossible to even approach this in an actual machine operating at a reasonable rate of speed. Thus, the air-standard Carnot cycle is not practical. Nonetheless it is of value as a standard for comparison with other cycles, and in a later paragraph we will consider the ideal gas turbine cycle with intercooling and reheating and note how its efficiency approaches that of the corresponding Carnot cycle.

Example 9.8

In an air-standard Carnot cycle heat is transferred to the working fluid at 2000 R, and heat is rejected at 500 R. The heat transfer to the working fluid at 2000 R is 50 Btu/lbm. The minimum pressure in the cycle is 1 atm. Assuming constant specific heat of air, determine the cycle efficiency and the mean effective pressure.

Designating the states as in Fig. 9.18 we have

$$P_3 = 14.7 \text{ lbf/in.}^2 \qquad\qquad T_3 = T_4 = 500 \text{ R}$$
$$T_1 = T_2 = 2000 \text{ R}$$

$$\frac{T_2}{T_3} = \left(\frac{P_2}{P_3}\right)^{(k-1)/k} = 4 \qquad \therefore \ \frac{P_2}{P_3} = 128$$

$$P_2 = 14.7(128) = 1882 \text{ lbf/in.}^2$$

Consider the process that occurs between states 1 and 2.

$$_1q_2 = RT \ln \frac{V_2}{V_1} = RT \ln \frac{P_1}{P_2} = \frac{53.34 \times 2000}{778} \ln \frac{P_1}{P_2} = 50 \text{ Btu/lbm}$$

Therefore,

$$\frac{P_1}{P_2} = 1.44 \qquad\qquad P_1 = 1882(1.44) = 2710 \text{ lbf/in.}^2$$

$$\frac{T_1}{T_4} = \left(\frac{P_1}{P_4}\right)^{(k-1)/k} = 4 \qquad \therefore \ \frac{P_1}{P_4} = 128$$

$$P_4 = \frac{2710}{128} = 21.2 \text{ lbf/in.}^2$$

$$\eta_{\text{th}} = 1 - \frac{T_L}{T_H} = 1 - \frac{500}{2000} = 0.75$$

The product of mean effective pressure and the piston displacement is equal to the net work.

$$\text{mep } (v_3 - v_1) = w_{\text{net}} = \eta_{\text{th}} \times {}_1q_2 = 37.5 \text{ Btu/lbm}$$

$$v_3 = \frac{RT_3}{P_3} = \frac{53.34 \times 500}{14.7 \times 144} = 12.6 \text{ ft}^3/\text{lbm}$$

$$v_1 = \frac{RT_1}{P_1} = \frac{53.34 \times 2000}{2710 \times 144} = 0.273 \text{ ft}^3/\text{lbm}$$

$$\text{mep} = \frac{37.5 \times 778}{(12.6 - 0.273)} = 2360 \text{ lbf/ft}^2 = 16.4 \text{ lbf/in.}^2$$

This is a much lower mean effective pressure than can be effectively utilized in a reciprocating engine.

9.12 The Air-Standard Otto Cycle

The air-standard Otto cycle is an ideal cycle that approximates a spark-ignition internal-combustion engine. This cycle is shown on the P-v and T-s diagrams of Fig. 9.19. Process 1–2 is an isentropic compression

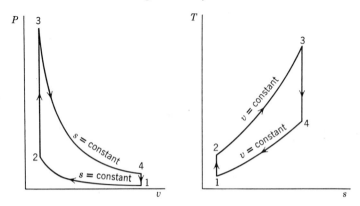

Fig. 9.19   The air-standard Otto cycle.

of the air as the piston moves from crank-end dead center to head-end dead center. Heat is then added at constant volume while the piston is momentarily at rest at head-end dead center. (This process corresponds to the ignition of the fuel-air mixture by the spark and the subsequent burning in the actual engine.) Process 3–4 is an isentropic expansion, and process 4–1 is the rejection of heat from the air while the piston is at crank-end dead center.

The thermal efficiency of this cycle is found as follows, assuming constant specific heat of air.

$$\eta_{\text{th}} = \frac{Q_H - Q_L}{Q_H} = 1 - \frac{Q_L}{Q_H} = 1 - \frac{mC_v(T_4 - T_1)}{mC_v(T_3 - T_2)}$$

$$= 1 - \frac{T_1\,(T_4/T_1 - 1)}{T_2\,(T_3/T_2 - 1)}$$

We note further that

$$\frac{T_2}{T_1} = \left(\frac{V_1}{V_2}\right)^{k-1} = \left(\frac{V_4}{V_3}\right)^{k-1} = \frac{T_3}{T_4}$$

Therefore,

$$\frac{T_3}{T_2} = \frac{T_4}{T_1}$$

and

$$\eta_{\text{th}} = 1 - \frac{T_1}{T_2} = 1 - (r_v)^{1-k} = 1 - \frac{1}{r_v^{k-1}} \qquad (9.4)$$

where r_v = compression ratio = $\dfrac{V_1}{V_2} = \dfrac{V_4}{V_3}$

The important thing to note is that the efficiency of the air-standard Otto cycle is a function only of the compression ratio, and that the

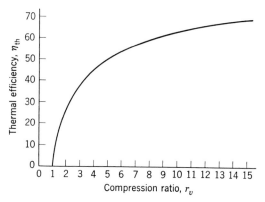

Fig. 9.20 Thermal efficiency of the Otto cycle as a function of compression ratio.

efficiency is increased by increasing the compression ratio. Figure 9.20 is a plot of the air-standard cycle thermal efficiency vs. compression ratio. It is also true of an actual spark-ignition engine that the efficiency can be increased by increasing the compression ratio. The trend toward higher compression ratios is prompted by the effort to obtain higher thermal efficiency. In the actual engine there is an increased tendency towards detonation of the fuel as compression ratio is increased. Detonation is characterized by an extremely rapid burning of the fuel and strong pressure waves present in the engine cylinder which give rise to the so-called spark knock. Therefore, the maximum compression ratio that can be used is fixed by the fact that detonation must be avoided. The advance in compression ratios over the years in the actual engine has been made possible by developing fuels with better antiknock characteristics.

Some of the most important ways in which the actual open-cycle spark-ignition engine deviates from the air-standard cycle are as follows:

(a) The specific heats of the actual gases increase with an increase in temperature.

(b) The combustion process replaces the heat-transfer process at high temperature, and combustion may be incomplete.

(c) Each mechanical cycle of the engine involves an inlet and an exhaust process, and due to the pressure drop through the valves a certain amount of work is required to charge the cylinder with air and exhaust the products of combustion.

(d) There will be considerable heat transfer between the gases in the cylinder and the cylinder walls.

(e) There will be irreversibilities associated with pressure and temperature gradients.

Example 9.9

The compression ratio in an air-standard Otto cycle is 8. At the beginning of the compression stroke the pressure is 14.7 lbf/in.² and the temperature is 60 F. The heat transfer to the air per cycle is 800 Btu/lbm air. Determine:

(a) The pressure and temperature at the end of each process of the cycle.
(b) The thermal efficiency.
(c) The mean effective pressure.

Designating the states as in Fig. 9.19 we have

$$P_1 = 14.7 \text{ lbf/in.}^2 \qquad\qquad T_1 = 520 \text{ R}$$

$$v_1 = \frac{53.34 \times 520}{14.7 \times 144} = 13.08 \text{ ft}^3/\text{lbm}$$

$$\frac{T_2}{T_1} = \left(\frac{V_1}{V_2}\right)^{k-1} = 8^{0.4} = 2.3 \qquad T_2 = 2.3(520) = 1197 \text{ R}$$

$$\frac{P_2}{P_1} = \left(\frac{V_1}{V_2}\right)^{k} = 8^{1.4} = 18.4 \qquad P_2 = 18.4(14.7) = 270.3 \text{ lbf/in.}^2$$

$$v_2 = \frac{13.08}{8} = 1.637 \text{ ft}^3/\text{lbm}$$

$$_2q_3 = C_v(T_3 - T_2) = 800 \text{ Btu/lbm}$$

$$T_3 - T_2 = \frac{800}{0.171} = 4690 \text{ R} \qquad T_3 = 1197 + 4690 = 5887 \text{ R}$$

$$\frac{T_3}{T_2} = \frac{P_3}{P_2} = \frac{5887}{1197} = 4.92 \qquad P_3 = 4.92(270.3) = 1331 \text{ lbf/in.}^2$$

$$\frac{T_3}{T_4} = \left(\frac{V_4}{V_3}\right)^{k-1} = 8^{0.4} = 2.3 \qquad T_4 = \frac{5887}{2.3} = 2558 \text{ R}$$

$$\frac{P_3}{P_4} = \left(\frac{V_4}{V_3}\right)^{k} = 8^{1.4} = 18.4 \qquad P_4 = \frac{1331}{18.4} = 73.0 \text{ lbf/in.}^2$$

$$\eta_{\text{th}} = 1 - \frac{1}{r_v^{k-1}} = 1 - \frac{1}{8^{0.4}} = 1 - \frac{1}{2.3} = 1 - 0.435 = 0.565$$

This can be checked by finding the heat rejected.

$$_4q_1 = C_v(T_1 - T_4) = 0.171(520 - 2558) = -348 \text{ Btu/lbm}$$

$$\therefore \eta_{th} = 1 - \frac{348}{800} = 1 - 0.435 = 0.565$$

$$w_{net} = 800 - 348 = 452 \text{ Btu/lbm} = (v_1 - v_2) \text{ mep}$$

$$\text{mep} = \frac{452 \times 778}{(13.08 - 1.637)144} = 213.5 \text{ lbf/in.}^2$$

Note how much higher this mean effective pressure is than for the Carnot cycle of Ex. 9.8. A low mean effective pressure means a large piston displacement for a given power output, and a large piston displacement means high frictional losses in an actual engine. In fact, the mean effective pressure of the Carnot cycle of Ex. 9.8 would scarcely overcome the friction in an actual engine.

9.13 The Air-Standard Diesel Cycle

The air-standard Diesel cycle is shown in Fig. 9.21. This is the ideal cycle for the Diesel engine, which is also called the compression-ignition engine.

In this cycle the heat is transferred to the working fluid at constant pressure. This process corresponds to the injection and burning of the fuel in the actual engine. Since the gas is expanding during the heat addition in the air-standard cycle, the heat transfer must be just sufficient

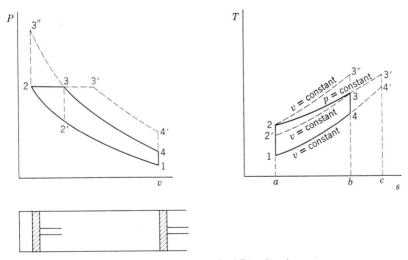

Fig. 9.21   The air-standard Diesel cycle.

to maintain constant pressure. When state 3 is reached the heat addition ceases and the gas undergoes an isentropic expansion, process 3–4, until the piston reaches crank-end dead center. As in the air-standard Otto cycle, a constant-volume rejection of heat at crank-end dead center replaces the exhaust and intake processes of the actual engine.

The efficiency of the Diesel cycle is given by the relation

$$\eta_{th} = 1 - \frac{Q_L}{Q_H} = 1 - \frac{C_v(T_4 - T_1)}{C_p(T_3 - T_2)} = 1 - \frac{T_1(T_4/T_1 - 1)}{kT_2(T_3/T_2 - 1)} \quad (9.5)$$

It is important to note that the isentropic compression ratio is greater than the isentropic expansion ratio in the Diesel cycle. Also, for a given state before compression and a given compression ratio (i.e., given states 1 and 2) the cycle efficiency decreases as the maximum temperature increases. This is evident from the T-s diagram, because the constant-pressure and constant-volume lines converge, and increasing the temperature from 3 to 3′ requires a large addition of heat (area 3–3′–c–b–3) and results in a relatively small increase in work (area 3–3′–4′–4–3).

There are a number of comparisons between the Otto cycle and the Diesel cycle, but here we will note only two. Consider Otto cycle 1–2–3″–4–1 and Diesel cycle 1–2–3–4–1, which have the same state at the beginning of the compression stroke and the same piston displacement and compression ratio. It is evident from the T-s diagram that the Otto cycle has the higher efficiency. In practice, however, the Diesel engine can operate on a higher compression ratio than the spark-ignition engine. The reason is that in the spark-ignition engine an air-fuel mixture is compressed, and detonation (spark knock) becomes a serious problem if too high a compression ratio is used. This problem does not exist in the Diesel engine because only air is compressed during the compression stroke. The development of higher octane fuels has permitted the use of higher compression ratios in spark-ignition engines.

Therefore, we might compare an Otto cycle with a Diesel cycle and in each case select a compression ratio that might be achieved in practice. Such a comparison can be made by considering Otto cycle 1–2′–3–4–1 and Diesel cycle 1–2–3–4–1. The maximum pressure and temperature is the same for both cycles, which means that the Otto cycle has a lower compression ratio than the Diesel cycle. It is evident from the T-s diagram that in this case the Diesel cycle has the higher efficiency. Thus, the conclusions drawn from a comparison of these two cycles must always be related to the basis on which the comparison has been made.

The actual compression-ignition open cycle differs from the air-standard Diesel cycle in much the same way that the spark-ignition open cycle differs from the air-standard Otto cycle.

Example 9.10

An air-standard Diesel cycle has a compression ratio of 15, and the heat transferred to the working fluid per cycle is 800 Btu/lbm. At the beginning of the compression process the pressure is 14.7 lbf/in.² and the temperature is 60 F. Determine:

(a) The pressure and temperature at each point in the cycle.
(b) The thermal efficiency.
(c) The mean effective pressure.

Designating the cycle as in Fig. 9.21 we have

$$P_1 = 14.7 \text{ lbf/in.}^2 \qquad T_1 = 520 \text{ R}$$

$$v_1 = \frac{53.34 \times 520}{14.7 \times 144} = 13.08 \text{ ft}^3/\text{lbm}$$

$$v_2 = \frac{v_1}{15} = \frac{13.08}{15} = 0.872 \text{ ft}^3/\text{lbm}$$

$$\frac{T_2}{T_1} = \left(\frac{V_1}{V_2}\right)^{k-1} = 15^{0.4} = 2.955$$

$$T_2 = 2.955(520) = 1535 \text{ R}$$

$$\frac{P_2}{P_1} = \left(\frac{V_1}{V_2}\right)^{k} = 15^{1.4} = 44.2$$

$$P_2 = 44.2(14.7) = 650 \text{ lbf/in.}^2$$

$$q_H = {}_2q_3 = C_p(T_3 - T_2) = 800 \text{ Btu/lbm}$$

$$T_3 - T_2 = \frac{800}{0.24} = 3333 \text{ R}$$

$$T_3 = 3333 + 1535 = 4868 \text{ R}$$

$$\frac{V_3}{V_2} = \frac{T_3}{T_2} = \frac{4868}{1535} = 3.17$$

$$v_3 = 3.17(0.872) = 2.77 \text{ ft}^3/\text{lbm}$$

$$\frac{T_3}{T_4} = \left(\frac{V_4}{V_3}\right)^{k-1} = \left(\frac{13.08}{2.83}\right)^{0.4} = 1.860 \qquad T_4 = \frac{4868}{1.860} = 2620 \text{ R}$$

$$q_L = {}_4q_1 = C_v(T_1 - T_4) = 0.171(520 - 2620) = -359 \text{ Btu/lbm}$$

$$w_{\text{net}} = 800 - 359 = 441 \text{ Btu/lbm}$$

$$\eta_{\text{th}} = \frac{w_{\text{net}}}{q_H} = \frac{441}{800} = 0.551$$

$$\text{mep} = \frac{w_{\text{net}}}{v_1 - v_2} = \frac{441 \times 778}{(13.08 - 0.87)144} = 195 \text{ lbf/in.}^2$$

9.14 The Ericsson and Stirling Cycles

We shall briefly consider these two cycles, not so much because of their extensive use, but rather because they serve to demonstrate how a regenerator can often be incorporated in a cycle to give a significant increase in efficiency. This principle finds extensive application in turbines as well as in certain reciprocating devices. The Stirling cycle is shown on the P-v and T-s diagrams of Fig. 9.22. Heat is transferred to the working fluid during the constant-volume process 2–3 and during the isothermal expansion process 3–4. Heat is rejected during the constant-volume process 4–1 and during the isothermal compression process 1–2. The significance of this cycle in conjunction with a regenerator is discussed in the next paragraph.

The Ericsson cycle is shown on the P-v and T-s diagrams of Fig. 9.23. This cycle differs from the Stirling cycle in that the constant-volume processes of the Stirling cycle are replaced by constant-pressure processes. In both cycles there is an isothermal compression and expansion.

The importance of both cycles is the possibility of including a regenerator; by so doing the air-standard Stirling and Ericsson cycles may have an efficiency equal to that of a Carnot cycle operating between the same temperatures. This may be demonstrated by considering Fig. 9.24, in which the Ericsson cycle is accomplished in a device that is essentially a gas turbine. If we assume an ideal heat-transfer process in the regenerator, i.e., no pressure drop and an infinitesimal temperature difference between the two streams, and reversible compression and expansion processes, then this device operates on the Ericsson cycle.

Note that the heat transfer to the gas between states 2 and 3, area 23ba2, is exactly equal to the heat transfer from the gas between states 4 and 1 area 14dc1. Thus Q_H all takes place in the isothermal turbine between states 3 and 4, and Q_L takes place in the isothermal compressor between

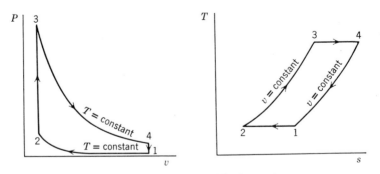

Fig. 9.22   The air-standard Stirling cycle.

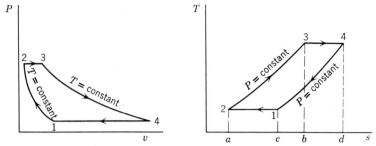

Fig. 9.23 The air-standard Ericsson cycle.

states 1 and 2. Since all the heat is supplied and rejected isothermally, the efficiency of this cycle will equal the efficiency of a Carnot cycle operating between the same temperatures. A similar cycle could be developed which would approximate the Stirling cycle.

The difficulties in achieving such a cycle are primarily those associated with heat transfer. It is difficult to achieve an isothermal compression or expansion in a machine operating at a reasonable speed, and there will be pressure drops in the regenerator and a temperature difference between the two streams flowing through the regenerator. However, the gas turbine with intercooling and regenerators, which is described in Section 9.17, is a practical attempt to approach the Ericsson cycle. There have also been attempts to approach the Stirling cycle with the use of regenerators.

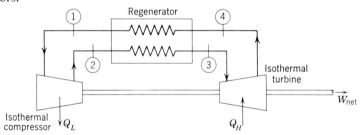

Fig. 9.24 Schematic arrangement of an engine operating on the Ericsson cycle and utilizing a regenerator.

9.15 The Brayton Cycle

The air-standard Brayton cycle is the ideal cycle for the simple gas turbine. The simple open-cycle gas turbine utilizing an internal-combustion process and the simple closed-cycle gas turbine, which utilizes heat-transfer processes, are both shown schematically in Fig. 9.25. The air-standard Brayton cycle is shown on the P-v and T-s diagrams of Fig. 9.26.

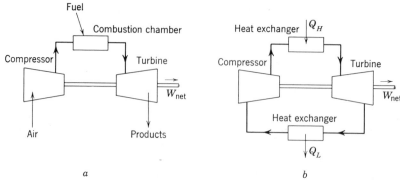

Fig. 9.25   A gas turbine operating on the Brayton cycle. (a) Open cycle. (b) Closed cycle.

The efficiency of the air-standard Brayton cycle is found as follows:

$$\eta_{th} = 1 - \frac{Q_L}{Q_H} = 1 - \frac{C_p(T_4 - T_1)}{C_p(T_3 - T_2)} = 1 - \frac{T_1(T_4/T_1 - 1)}{T_2(T_3/T_2 - 1)}$$

We note, however, that

$$\frac{P_3}{P_4} = \frac{P_2}{P_1} \qquad \therefore \; \frac{P_3}{P_2} = \frac{P_4}{P_1}$$

$$\frac{P_2}{P_1} = \left(\frac{T_2}{T_1}\right)^{k/(k-1)} = \frac{P_3}{P_4} = \left(\frac{T_3}{T_4}\right)^{k/(k-1)}$$

$$\frac{T_3}{T_4} = \frac{T_2}{T_1} \qquad \therefore \; \frac{T_3}{T_2} = \frac{T_4}{T_1} \quad \text{and} \quad \frac{T_3}{T_2} - 1 = \frac{T_4}{T_1} - 1$$

$$\eta_{th} = 1 - \frac{T_1}{T_2} = 1 - \frac{1}{(P_2/P_1)^{(k-1)/k}} \tag{9.6}$$

The efficiency of the air-standard Brayton cycle is therefore a function of isentropic pressure ratio; Fig. 9.27 shows a plot of efficiency vs. pressure

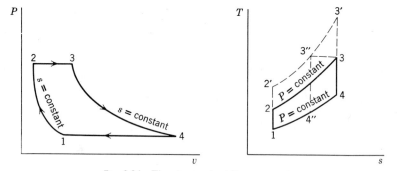

Fig. 9.26   The air-standard Brayton cycle.

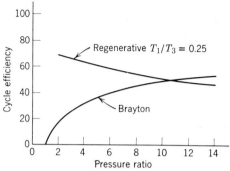

Fig. 9.27   Cycle efficiency as a function of pressure ratio for the Brayton and regenerative cycles.

ratio. The fact that efficiency increases with pressure ratio is evident from the *T-s* diagram of Fig. 9.26, because increasing the pressure ratio will change the cycle from 1–2–3–4–1 to 1–2′–3′–4–1. The latter cycle has a greater heat supply and the same heat rejected as the original cycle, and therefore it has a greater efficiency. Note further that the latter cycle has a higher maximum temperature (T_3') than the original cycle (T_3). In an actual gas turbine the maximum temperature of the gas entering the turbine is fixed by metallurgical considerations. Therefore, if we fix the temperature T_3 and increase the pressure ratio, the resulting cycle is 1–2′–3″–4″–1. This cycle would have a higher efficiency than the original cycle, but the work per pound of working fluid is thereby changed.

With the advent of nuclear reactors the closed-cycle gas turbine has become more important. Heat is transferred, either directly or via a second fluid, from the fuel in the nuclear reactor to the working fluid in the gas turbine. Heat is rejected from the working fluid to the surroundings.

The actual gas-turbine engine differs from the ideal cycle primarily because of irreversibilities in the compressor and turbine, and because of pressure drop in the flow passages and combustion chamber (or in the heat exchanger of a closed-cycle turbine). Thus, the state points in a simple open-cycle gas turbine might be as shown in Fig. 9.28.

The efficiencies of the compressor and turbine are defined in relation to isentropic processes. Designating the states as in Fig. 9.28, the definitions of compressor and turbine efficiencies are as follows:

$$\eta_{\text{comp}} = \frac{h_{2s} - h_1}{h_2 - h_1} \qquad (9.7)$$

$$\eta_{\text{turb}} = \frac{h_3 - h_4}{h_3 - h_{4s}} \qquad (9.8)$$

One other important feature of the Brayton cycle is the large amount of compressor work (also called back work) compared to the turbine work. Thus, the compressor might require from 40 per cent to 80 per cent of the output of the turbine. This is particularly important when the actual cycle is considered, because the effect of the losses is to require a larger amount of compression work from a smaller amount of turbine work, and thus the over-all efficiency drops very rapidly with a decrease in the efficiencies of the compressor and turbine. In fact, if these efficiencies drop below about 60 per cent, all the work of the turbine will be required to drive the compressor, and the over-all efficiency will be zero. This is in sharp contrast to the Rankine cycle, where only 1 or 2 per cent of the turbine work is required to drive the pump. The reason for this is that for a reversible steady-state, steady-flow process with negligible change in kinetic and potential energy, the work is equal to $-\int v \, dP$. Because we are pumping a liquid in the Rankine cycle, the specific volume is very low compared to the specific volume of the gas in a gas turbine. This matter is illustrated in the following examples.

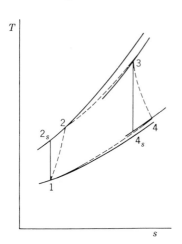

Fig. 9.28   Effect of inefficiencies on the gas-turbine cycle.

Example 9.11

In an air-standard Brayton cycle the air enters the compressor at 14.7 lbf/in.², 60 F. The pressure leaving the compressor is 70 lbf/in.² and the maximum temperature in the cycle is 1600 F. Determine:

(a) The pressure and temperature at each point in the cycle.
(b) The compressor work, turbine work, and cycle efficiency.
Designating the points as in Fig. 9.26 we have

$$P_1 = P_4 = 14.7 \text{ lbf/in.}^2 \qquad T_1 = 520 \text{ R}$$

$$P_2 = P_3 = 70 \text{ lbf/in.}^2 \qquad T_3 = 2060 \text{ R}$$

In the solution we consider successively a control surface around the compressor, the turbine, and the two heat exchangers. For the property relation we assume that air is an ideal gas with constant specific heat.
Control surface: Compressor

First law: $w_c = h_2 - h_1$. (Note that the compressor work w_c is here defined as work input to the compressor.)

Second law: $s_2 = s_1$

Therefore

$$\left(\frac{P_2}{P_1}\right)^{(k-1)/k} = \left(\frac{70}{14.7}\right)^{0.286} = \frac{T_2}{T_1} = 1.563, \qquad T_2 = 1.563(520) = 814\ R$$

$$w_c = h_2 - h_1 = C_p(T_2 - T_1) = 0.24(814 - 520)$$
$$= 70.6\ \text{Btu/lbm}$$

Control surface: Turbine

First Law: $w_t = h_3 - h_4$

Second Law: $s_3 = s_4$

Therefore,

$$\left(\frac{P_3}{P_4}\right)^{(k-1)/k} = \left(\frac{70}{14.7}\right)^{0.286} = \frac{T_3}{T_4} = 1.563 \qquad T_4 = \frac{2060}{1.563} = 1318\ R$$

$$w_t = h_3 - h_4 = C_p(T_3 - T_4) = 0.24(2060 - 1318)$$
$$= 178.1\ \text{Btu/lbm}$$

$$w_{net} = w_t - w_c = 178.1 - 70.6 = 107.5\ \text{Btu/lbm}$$

From a first law analysis of the two heat exchangers we have

$$q_H = h_3 - h_2 = C_p(T_3 - T_2) = 0.24(2060 - 814) = 299.0\ \text{Btu/lbm}$$
$$q_L = h_4 - h_1 = C_p(T_4 - T_1) = 0.24(1318 - 520) = 191.5\ \text{Btu/lbm}$$

$$\eta_{th} = \frac{w_{net}}{q_H} = \frac{107.5}{299.0} = 36.0\%$$

This may be checked by using Eq. 9.6

$$\eta_{th} = 1 - \frac{1}{(P_2/P_1)^{(k-1)/k}} = 1 - \frac{1}{(70/14.7)^{0.286}} = 1 - \frac{1}{1.563}$$

$$= 1 - 0.64 = 36.0\%$$

Example 9.12

Consider a gas turbine with air entering the compressor under the same conditions as in Example 9.11, and leaving at a pressure of 70 lbf/in.² The maximum temperature is 1600 F. Assume a compressor efficiency of 80 per cent, a turbine efficiency of 85 per cent, and a pressure drop between the compressor and turbine of 2 lbf/in.² Determine the compressor work, turbine work, and cycle efficiency.

Designating the states as in Fig. 9.28 and proceeding as we did in Example 9.11 we have

Control surface: Compressor

First law: $w_c = h_2 - h_1$

Second law: $s_{2s} = s_1$

$$\eta_c = \frac{h_{2s} - h_1}{h_2 - h_1}$$

$$\left(\frac{P_2}{P_1}\right)^{(k-1)/k} = \frac{T_{2s}}{T_1} = \left(\frac{70}{14.7}\right)^{0.286} = 1.563 \qquad T_{2s} = 1.563(520) = 814 \text{ R}$$

$$\eta_c = \frac{h_{2s} - h_1}{h_2 - h_1} = \frac{T_{2s} - T_1}{T_2 - T_1} = \frac{814 - 520}{T_2 - T_1} = 0.80$$

$$T_2 - T_1 = \frac{294}{0.80} = 367 \text{ R} \qquad T_2 = 520 + 367 = 887 \text{ R}$$

$$w_c = h_2 - h_1 = C_p(T_2 - T_1) = 0.24(887 - 520)$$
$$= 87.9 \text{ Btu/lbm}$$

Control surface: Turbine

First law: $w_t = h_3 - h_4$

Second law: $s_3 = s_{4s}$

$$\eta_{\text{th}} = \frac{h_3 - h_4}{h_3 - h_{4s}}$$

$$P_3 = P_2 - \text{pressure drop} = 70 - 2 = 68 \text{ lbf/in.}^2$$

$$\left(\frac{P_3}{P_4}\right)^{(k-1)/k} = \frac{T_3}{T_{4s}} = \left(\frac{68}{14.7}\right)^{0.286} = 1.550 \qquad T_{4s} = \frac{2060}{1.550} = 1330 \text{ R}$$

$$\eta_t = \frac{h_3 - h_4}{h_3 - h_{4s}} = \frac{T_3 - T_4}{T_3 - T_{4s}} = 0.85$$

$$T_3 - T_4 = 0.85(2060 - 1330) = 620 \text{ R}$$

$$T_4 = 2060 - 620 = 1440 \text{ R}$$

$$w_t = h_3 - h_4 = C_p(T_3 - T_4) = 0.24(2060 - 1440) = 148.8$$

$$w_{\text{net}} = w_t - w_c = 148.8 - 87.9 = 60.9 \text{ Btu/lbm}$$

Control surface: Combustion Chamber

First law: $q_H = h_3 - h_2 = C_p(T_3 - T_2)$
$$= 0.24(2060 - 887) = 281.6 \text{ Btu/lbm}$$

$$\eta_{\text{th}} = \frac{w_{\text{net}}}{q_H} = \frac{60.9}{281.6} = 21.6\%$$

The following comparisons can be made between Examples 9.11 and 9.12.

	w_c	w_t	w_{net}	q_H	η_{th}
Example 9.11 (Ideal)	70.6	177.8	107.2	299.0	36.0
Example 9.12 (Actual)	87.9	148.8	60.9	281.6	21.6

As stated previously the result of the irreversibilities is to decrease the turbine work and increase the compressor work. Since the net work is the difference between these two it decreases very rapidly as compressor and turbine efficiencies decrease. The development of compressors and turbines of high efficiency is therefore an important aspect of the development of gas turbines.

Note also that in the ideal cycle (Example 9.11) about 40 per cent of the turbine work is required to drive the compressor and 60 per cent is delivered as net work. In the actual turbine (Example 9.12) 59 per cent of the turbine work is required to drive the compressor and 41 per cent is delivered as net work. Thus, if the net power of this unit is to be 10,000 hp, a 25,000-hp turbine and a 15,000-hp compressor are required. This demonstrates the statement that a gas turbine has a high back-work ratio.

9.16 The Simple Gas-Turbine Cycle with Regenerator

The efficiency of the gas-turbine cycle may be improved by introducing a regenerator. The simple open-cycle gas-turbine cycle with regenerator is shown in Fig. 9.29, and the corresponding ideal air-standard cycle with

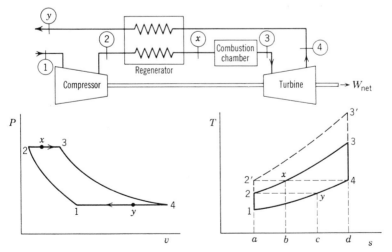

Fig. 9.29 The ideal regenerative cycle.

regenerator is shown on the P-v and T-s diagrams. Note that in cycle 1–2–x–3–4–y–1, the temperature of the exhaust gas leaving the turbine in state 4 is higher than the temperature of the gas leaving the compressor. Therefore, heat can be transferred from the exhaust gases to the high-pressure gases leaving the compressor. If this is done in a counterflow heat exchanger, which is known as a regenerator, the temperature of the high-pressure gas leaving the regenerator, T_x, may, in the ideal case, have a temperature equal to T_4, the temperature of the gas leaving the turbine. In this case heat transfer from the external source is necessary only to increase the temperature from T_x to T_3, and this heat transfer is represented by area x–3–d–b–x. Area y–1–a–c–y represents the heat rejected.

The influence of pressure ratio on the simple gas-turbine cycle with regenerator is shown by considering cycle 1–2′–3′–4–1. In this cycle the temperature of the exhaust gas leaving the turbine is just equal to the temperature of the gas leaving the compressor; therefore there is no possibility of utilizing a regenerator. This may be shown more exactly by determining the efficiency of the ideal gas-turbine cycle with regenerator.

The efficiency of this cycle with regeneration is found as follows, where the states are as given in Fig. 9.29.

$$\eta_{\text{th}} = \frac{w_{\text{net}}}{q_H} = \frac{w_t - w_c}{q_H}$$

$$q_H = C_p(T_3 - T_x)$$

$$w_t = C_p(T_3 - T_4)$$

But for the ideal regenerator $T_4 = T_x$, and therefore $q_H = w_t$. Therefore,

$$\eta_{\text{th}} = 1 - \frac{w_c}{w_t} = 1 - \frac{C_p(T_2 - T_1)}{C_p(T_3 - T_4)}$$

$$= 1 - \frac{T_1(T_2/T_1 - 1)}{T_3(1 - T_4/T_3)} = 1 - \frac{T_1}{T_3} \frac{[(P_2/P_1)^{(k-1)/k} - 1]}{[1 - (P_1/P_2)^{(k-1)/k}]}$$

$$\eta_{\text{th}} = 1 - \frac{T_1}{T_3}\left(\frac{P_2}{P_1}\right)^{(k-1)/k}$$

Thus, we see that for the ideal cycle with regeneration the thermal efficiency depends not only upon the pressure ratio, but also upon the ratio of the minimum to maximum temperature. We also note, in contrast to the Brayton cycle, that the efficiency decreases with an increase in pressure ratio. The thermal efficiency vs. pressure ratio for this cycle is plotted in Fig. 9.27 for a value of

$$\frac{T_1}{T_3} = 0.25$$

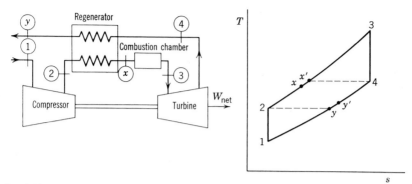

Fig. 9.30 Temperature-entropy diagram to illustrate the definition of regenerator efficiency.

The effectiveness or efficiency of a regenerator is given by the term regenerator efficiency. This may best be defined by reference to Fig. 9.30. State x represents the high-pressure gas leaving the regenerator. In the ideal regenerator there would be only an infinitesimal temperature difference between the two streams, and the high-pressure gas would leave the regenerator at temperature T_x', and $T_x' = T_4$. In an actual regenerator, which must operate with a finite temperature difference, T_x, the actual temperature leaving the regenerator is therefore less than T_x'. The regenerator efficiency is defined by

$$\eta_{\text{reg}} = \frac{h_x - h_2}{h_x' - h_2}$$

If the specific heat is assumed to be constant, the regenerator efficiency is also given by the relation

$$\eta_{\text{reg}} = \frac{T_x - T_2}{T_x' - T_2}$$

It should also be pointed out that a higher efficiency can be achieved by using a regenerator with greater heat-transfer area. However, this also increases the pressure drop, which represents a loss, and both the pressure drop and the regenerator efficiency must be considered in determining which regenerator gives maximum thermal efficiency for the cycle. From an economic point of view, the cost of the regenerator must be weighed against the saving that can be effected by its use.

Example 9.13

If an ideal regenerator is incorporated into the cycle of Example 9.11, determine the thermal efficiency of the cycle.

Designating the states as in Fig. 9.30,

$$T_x = T_4 = 1318 \text{ R}$$

$$q_H = h_3 - h_x = C_p(T_3 - T_x) = 0.24(2060 - 1318) = 178 \text{ Btu/lbm}$$

$$w_{net} = 107.2 \text{ Btu/lbm} \quad \text{(from Example 9.11)}$$

$$\eta_{th} = \frac{107.2}{178} = 60.4\%$$

9.17   The Ideal Gas-Turbine Cycle Using Multistage Compression with Intercooling, Multistage Expansion with Reheating, and Regenerator

In Section 9.14 it was pointed out that when an ideal regenerator was incorporated into the Ericsson cycle, an efficiency equal to the efficiency of the corresponding Carnot cycle could be attained. It was also pointed out that it is impossible to even closely approach in practice the reversible isothermal compression and expansion required in the Ericsson cycle.

The practical approach to this cycle is to use multistage compression with intercooling between stages, multistage expansion with reheat between stages, and a regenerator. Figure 9.31 shows a cycle with two stages of compression and two stages of expansion. The air-standard cycle is shown on the corresponding T-s diagram. It may be shown that for this cycle the maximum efficiency is obtained if equal pressure ratios are maintained across the two compressors and the two turbines. In this ideal cycle it is assumed that the temperature of the air leaving the intercooler, T_3, is equal to the temperature of the air entering the first stage of compression, T_1, and that the temperature after reheating, T_8, is equal to the temperature entering the first turbine, T_6. Further, in the ideal cycle it is assumed that the temperature of the high-pressure air leaving the regenerator, T_5, is equal to the temperature of the low-pressure air leaving the turbine, T_9.

If a large number of stages of compression and expansion are used, it is evident that the Ericsson cycle is approached. This is shown in Fig. 9.32. In practice the economical limit to the number of stages is usually two or three. The turbine and compressor losses and pressure drops that have already been discussed would be involved in any actual unit employing this cycle.

There are a variety of ways in which the turbines and compressors using this cycle can be utilized. Two possible arrangements for closed cycles are shown in Fig. 9.33. One advantage frequently sought in a given arrangement is ease of control of the unit under various loads. Detailed discussion of this point, however, is beyond the scope of this text.

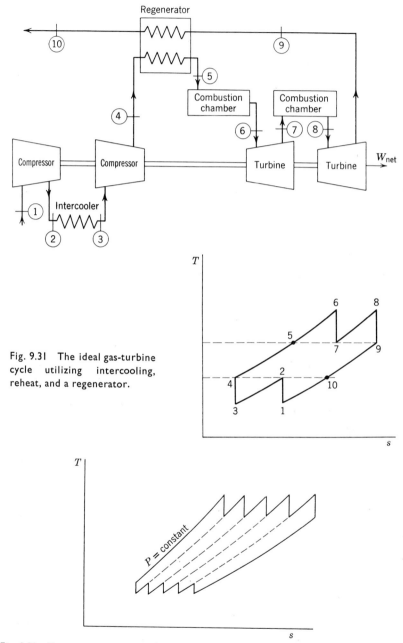

Fig. 9.31   The ideal gas-turbine cycle utilizing intercooling, reheat, and a regenerator.

Fig. 9.32   Temperature-entropy diagram which shows how the gas-turbine cycle with many stages approaches the Ericsson cycle.

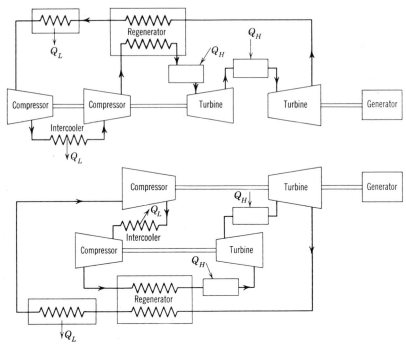

Fig. 9.33   Some arrangements of components that may be utilized in stationary gas-turbine power plants.

9.18   The Air-Standard Cycle for Jet Propulsion

The last air-standard power cycle we will consider is utilized in jet propulsion. In this cycle the work done by the turbine is just sufficient to drive the compressor—the gases are expanded in the turbine to a pressure such that the turbine work is just equal to the compressor work.

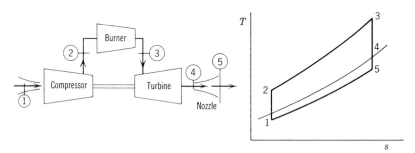

Fig. 9.34   The ideal gas-turbine cycle for a jet engine.

The exhaust pressure of the turbine will then be above that of the surroundings, and the gas can be expanded in a nozzle to the pressure of the surroundings. Since the gases leave at a high velocity, the change in momentum the gases undergo results in a thrust upon the aircraft in which the engine is installed. The air-standard cycle for this is shown in Fig. 9.34.

Since all the principles involved in this cycle have already been covered, the example that follows will conclude our consideration of air-standard power cycles.

Example 9.14

Consider an ideal cycle in which air enters the compressor at 14.7 lbf/in.², 60 F. The pressure leaving the compressor is 70 lbf/in.² and the maximum temperature is 1600 F. The air expands in the turbine to such a pressure that the turbine work is just equal to the compressor work. On leaving the turbine the air expands in a reversible adiabatic process in a nozzle to 14.7 lbf/in.² Determine the velocity of the air leaving the nozzle.

From Example 9.11 we have the following, where the states are as designated in Fig. 9.34.

$$P_1 = 14.7 \text{ lbf/in.}^2 \qquad T_1 = 520 \text{ R}$$

$$P_2 = 70 \text{ lbf/in.}^2 \qquad T_2 = 814 \text{ R}$$

$$w_c = 70.6 \text{ Btu/lbm}$$

$$P_3 = 70 \text{ lbf/in.}^2 \qquad T_3 = 2060 \text{ R}$$

$$w_c = w_t = C_p(T_3 - T_4)$$

$$= 70.6 \text{ Btu/lbm}$$

$$T_3 - T_4 = \frac{70.6}{0.24} = 294 \text{ R}$$

$$T_4 = 2060 - 294 = 1766 \text{ R}$$

$$\frac{T_3}{T_4} = \left(\frac{P_3}{P_4}\right)^{(k-1)/k} = \frac{2060}{1766} = 1.167$$

$$\frac{P_3}{P_4} = 1.715 \qquad P_4 = \frac{70}{1.715} = 40.8 \text{ lbf/in.}^2$$

Next consider a control surface around the nozzle. Let us assume that the velocity of the air entering the nozzle is low.

First law:
$$h_4 = h_5 + \frac{V_5{}^2}{2g_c}$$

Second law: $s_4 = s_5$

Therefore (from Example 9.11), $T_5 = 1318$ R

$$V_5^2 = 2g_c C_p(T_4 - T_5)$$
$$V_5^2 = 2 \times 32.17 \times 778 \times 0.24(1766 - 1318)$$
$$V_5 = 2318 \text{ ft/sec}$$

AIR-STANDARD REFRIGERATION CYCLE

9.19 The Air-Standard Refrigeration Cycle

The final section of this chapter concerns the air-standard refrigeration cycle. Its main use in practice is in the liquefaction of air and other gases and in certain special situations that require refrigeration.

The simplest form of the air-standard refrigeration cycle, which is essentially the reverse of the Brayton cycle, is shown in Fig. 9.35. The compressor and expander might be either reciprocating or rotary. After compression from 1 to 2, the air is cooled as a result of heat transfer to the surroundings at temperature T_0. The air is then expanded in process 3–4 to the pressure entering the compressor, and the temperature drops to T_4 in the expander. Heat may then be transferred to the air until temperature T_L is reached. The work for this cycle is represented by area 1–2–3–4–1, and the refrigeration effect is represented by area 4–1–b–a–4. The coefficient of performance is the ratio of these two areas.

In practice this cycle has been utilized for the cooling of aircraft in an open cycle, a simplified form of which is shown in Fig. 9.36. Upon leaving the expander the cool air is blown directly into the cabin thus providing the cooling effect where needed.

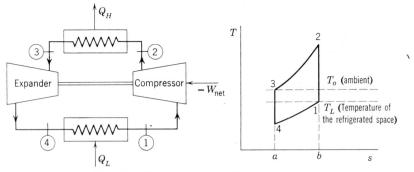

Fig. 9.35   The air-standard refrigeration cycle.

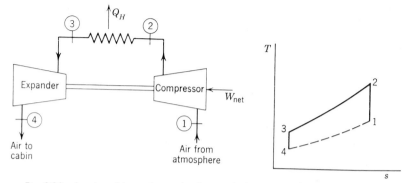

Fig. 9.36   An air refrigeration cycle that might be utilized for aircraft cooling.

When counterflow heat exchangers are incorporated, very low ' tem-peratures can be obtained. This is essentially the cycle used in low-pressure air liquefaction plants and in other liquefaction devices such as the Collins helium liquefier. The ideal cycle in this case is as shown in Fig. 9.37. It is evident that the expander operates at very low temperature, which presents unique problems to the designer in regard to lubrication and materials.

Example 9.15

Consider the simple air-standard refrigeration cycle of Fig. 9.35. Air enters the compressor at 14.7 lbf/in.², 0 F, and leaves at 80 lbf/in.² Air enters the expander at 60 F. Determine:

(a) The coefficient of performance for this cycle.

(b) The rate at which air must enter the compressor in order to provide one ton of refrigeration.

$$P_1 = P_4 = 14.7 \text{ lbf/in.}^2; \quad T_1 = 460 \text{ R}$$
$$P_2 = P_3 = 80.0 \text{ lbf/in.}^2; \quad T_3 = 520 \text{ R}$$

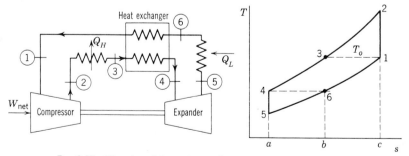

Fig. 9.37   The air refrigeration cycle utilizing a heat exchanger.

Control surface: Compressor

First law: $w_c = h_2 - h_1$

Second law: $s_1 = s_2$

Therefore,

$$\frac{T_2}{T_1} = \left(\frac{P_2}{P_1}\right)^{(k-1)/k} = \left(\frac{80}{14.7}\right)^{0.286} = 1.624$$

$T_2 = 460(1.624) = 747$ R

$w_c = h_2 - h_1 = C_p(T_2 - T_1) = 0.24(747 - 460) = 68.9$ Btu/lbm

(w_c designates work into the compressor)

Control surface: Expander

First law: $w_t = h_3 - h_4$

Second law: $s_3 = s_4$

$T_3 = 520$ R

$$\frac{T_3}{T_4} = \left(\frac{P_3}{P_4}\right)^{(k-1)/k} = \left(\frac{80}{14.7}\right)^{0.286} = 1.624$$

$$T_4 = \frac{520}{1.624} = 320 \text{ R}$$

$w_t = h_3 - h_4 = 0.24(520 - 320) = 48.0$ Btu/lbm

(w_t designates work done by expander)

From the first law as applied to a control surface around each of the heat exchangers we conclude that

$q_H = h_2 - h_3 = C_p(T_2 - T_3) = 0.24(747 - 520) = 54.5$ Btu/lbm

$q_L = h_1 - h_4 = C_p(T_1 - T_4) = 0.24(460 - 320) = 33.6$ Btu/lbm

$w_{net} = w_c - w_t = 68.9 - 48.0 = 20.9$ Btu/lbm

$$\beta = \frac{q_L}{w_{net}} = \frac{33.6}{20.9} = 1.61$$

1 ton of refrigeration $= 12,000$ Btu/hr $= 200$ Btu/min

$$\frac{\text{lbm air/min}}{\text{ton refrigeration}} = \frac{200}{33.6} = 5.95$$

PROBLEMS

9.1 In a Rankine cycle utilizing steam the steam enters the turbine at 400 lbf/in.^{2},$^\prime$ 600 F. Determine the thermal efficiency of the cycle and the moisture content leaving the turbine for exhaust pressures of 14.7 lbf/in.², 5 lbf/in.², 2 lbf/in.², 1 lbf/in.² Plot thermal efficiency vs. exhaust pressure for the given inlet conditions to the turbine.

9.2 A Rankine cycle has an exhaust pressure of 2 lbf/in.² Determine the thermal efficiency and moisture content leaving the turbine for an inlet temperature of 600 F and the following inlet pressures: 100 lbf/in.², 200 lbf/in², 400 lbf/in.², saturated vapor at 600 F. Plot thermal efficiency vs. turbine inlet pressure for the given turbine inlet temperature and exhaust pressure.

9.3 A Rankine cycle has an exhaust pressure of 2 lbf/in.² and a pressure entering the turbine of 400 lbf/in.² Determine the thermal efficiency and moisture content leaving the turbine for the following temperatures entering the turbine: saturated vapor at 400 lbf/in.², 600 F, 1000 F, 1400 F. Plot thermal efficiency vs. turbine inlet temperature for the given turbine inlet and exhaust pressures.

9.4 Consider the reheat cycle. Steam enters the turbine at 400 lbf/in.², 600 F and expands to 90 lbf/in.² It is then reheated to 600 F, after which it expands to 2 lbf/in.² Determine the thermal efficiency and the moisture content leaving the low-pressure turbine.

9.5 Consider the ideal regenerative cycle. Steam enters the turbine at 400 lbf/in.², 600 F. Condenser pressure is 2 lbf/in.² Steam is extracted at 90 lbf/in.² and 16 lbf/in.² for purposes of heating the feedwater. The feedwater heaters are open heaters, and the feedwater leaves at the temperature of the condensing steam. The appropriate pumps are used for the water leaving the condenser and the two feedwater heaters. Determine the thermal efficiency and the net work per lbm of steam.

9.6 Repeat Problem 9.5 assuming closed feedwater heaters. A single pump is used which pumps the water leaving the condenser to 400 lbf/in.² The condensate from the high-pressure heater is drained through a trap to the low-pressure heater, and the low-pressure heater is drained through a trap to the main condenser.

9.7 An ideal cycle combines the reheat and regenerative cycles. Steam enters the turbine at 400 lbf/in.², 600 F. Steam is extracted at 90 lbf/in.² for purposes of feedwater heating. The steam not extracted is reheated to 600 F. As this reheated steam expands through the turbine, steam is extracted at 16 lbf/in.² for feedwater heating. The condenser pressure is 2 lbf/in.² Both the feedwater heaters are open heaters. Determine the thermal efficiency and the net work per pound.

9.8 Steam leaves the boiler of a steam power plant at 400 lbf/in.², 600 F and when it enters the turbine it is at 370 lbf/in.², 560 F. The turbine has an efficiency of 80% and the condenser pressure is 2 lbf/in.² The condensate leaves the condenser at 2 lbf/in.². 100 F. The pump has an efficiency of 70% and the pressure of the water leaving the pump is 500 lbf/in.² Water enters the boiler at 460 lbf/in.², 96 F. Determine:

(*a*) The irreversibility for the process between the boiler and turbine. (Assume ambient temperature = 77 F.)

(*b*) The thermal efficiency of the cycle.

9.9 Consider an ideal steam cycle that combines the reheat cycle and the regenerative cycle. The net power output of the turbine is 100,000 kw. Steam enters the high-pressure turbine at 1200 lbf/in.², 1000 F. After expansion to 90 lbf/in.², some of the steam goes to an open feedwater heater and the balance is reheated to 700 F, after which it expands to 1 lbf/in.²

(a) Draw a line diagram of the unit and show the state points on a T-s diagram.

(b) What is the steam flow rate to the high-pressure turbine?

(c) What hp motor is required to drive each of the pumps?

(d) If there is a 20 F rise in the temperature of the cooling water, what is the rate of flow of cooling water through the condenser?

(e) The velocity of the steam flowing from the turbine to the condenser is limited to a maximum of 400 ft/sec. What is the diameter of this connecting pipe?

9.10 Consider the following reheat-cycle power plant. Steam enters the high-pressure turbine at 500 lbf/in.², 700 F, and expands to 70 lbf/in.², after which it is reheated to 700 F. The steam is then expanded through the low-pressure turbines to 1 lbf/in.² Liquid leaves the condenser at 90 F, is pumped to 500 lbf/in.², and returned to the boiler. Each turbine is adiabatic, with an efficiency of 85%, and the pump efficiency is 80%. If the total power output of the turbines is 1000 hp, determine

(a) mass flow rate of steam

(b) pump horsepower

(c) thermal efficiency of the unit.

9.11 It is desired to study the influence of the number of feedwater heaters on thermal efficiency for a cycle in which the steam leaves the steam generator at 2400 lbf/in.², 1000 F, and which has a condenser pressure of 1 lbf/in.². Assume that open feedwater heaters are used. Determine the thermal efficiency for each of the following cycles.

(a) No feedwater heater.

(b) One feedwater heater which operates at 140 lbf/in.²

(c) Two feedwater heaters, one operating at 450 lbf/in.² and the other at 35 lbf/in.²

9.12 Repeat Problem 9.11 assuming a turbine efficiency of 85%.

9.13 In a nuclear power plant heat is transferred in the reactor to liquid sodium. The liquid sodium is then pumped to a heat exchanger where heat is transferred to steam. The steam leaves this heat exchanger as saturated vapor at 800 lbf/in.², and is then superheated in an external gas fired superheater to 1100 F. The steam then enters the turbine, which has one extraction point at 60 lbf/in.², where steam flows to an open feedwater heater. The turbine efficiency is 70% and the condenser pressure is 1 lbf/in.²

Determine the heat transfer in the reactor and in the superheater to produce a power output of 60,000 kw.

9.14 A nuclear reactor to produce power is so designed that the maximum temperature in the steam cycle is 800 F. The minimum temperature of the steam cycle is 100 F. It is planned to build a steam power plant which has one open feedwater heater.

Select what you consider to be a reasonable cycle within these specifications, determine the ideal cycle efficiency, and explain why the particular pressures involved were selected.

9.15 Consider the preliminary design for a supercritical steam power plant cycle. The maximum pressure will be 4000 lbf/in.^{2}, and the maximum temperature will be 1100 F. The cooling water temperature is such that 1 lbf/in.^{2} pressure can be maintained in the condensers. Turbine efficiencies of at least 85% can be expected.

(a) Do you recommend any reheat for this cycle? If so, how many stages of reheat and at what pressures? Give reasons for your decisions.

(b) Do you recommend feedwater heaters? If so, how many and at what pressures would they operate? Would they be open or closed feedwater heaters?

(c) Estimate the thermal efficiency of the cycle which you recommend.

9.16 In both power and refrigeration cycles that operate over a wide temperature range it is frequently advantageous to use more than one working fluid. In refrigeration cycles this frequently is referred to as a cascade system.

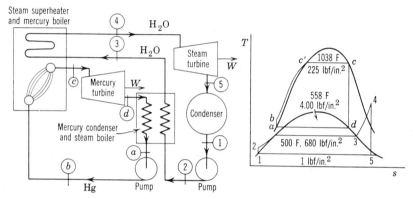

Fig. 9.38   Sketch for Problem 9.16.

In power plants the two fluids that have been used in combination are mercury and water, and this is referred to as a binary system. The advantage of this system is that mercury has a much lower vapor pressure than water, and it is possible to have an isothermal evaporation process in the mercury take place at a high temperature (much higher than the critical temperature of water) at a moderate pressure.

Such a binary system is shown in Fig. 9.38, with the temperatures and pressures for an ideal cycle shown on the corresponding T-s diagram.

(a) Determine the pounds of mercury condensed in the mercury condenser per pound of water evaporated.

(b) Determine the thermal efficiency of this cycle.

9.17 In an ideal refrigeration cycle the temperature of the condensing vapor is 100 F and the temperature during evaporation is 0 F. Determine the coefficient of performance of this cycle for the working fluids Freon-12 and ammonia.

9.18 In an actual refrigeration cycle using Freon-12 as a working fluid the rate of flow of refrigerant is 300 lbm/hr. The refrigerant enters the compressor at 25 lbf/in.^{2}, 20 F and leaves at 175 lbf/in.^{2}, 170 F. The power input to the compressor is 2.5 hp. The refrigerant enters the expansion valve at 165 lbf/in.^{2}, 100 F and leaves the evaporator at 27 lbf/in.^{2}, 10 F. Determine:

(a) The irreversibility during the compression process.

(b) The refrigeration capacity in tons.

(c) The coefficient of performance for this cycle.

9.19 A study is to be made of the influence on power requirements of the difference between the temperature of the refrigerant in the condenser and the temperature of the surroundings. For this purpose consider the ideal cycle of Fig. 9.15 with Freon-12 as the refrigerant. The temperature of the surroundings is 100 F and the temperature of the refrigerant in the evaporator is 10 F. Plot a curve of hp per ton of refrigeration for temperature differences of 0 to 100 F between the refrigerant in the condenser and the surroundings.

9.20 A study is to be made of the influence on power requirements of the temperature difference between the cold box and the refrigerant in the evaporator. For this purpose consider the ideal cycle of Fig. 9.15 with Freon-12 as the refrigerant. The temperature of the cold box is 10 F and the temperature of the refrigerant in the condenser is 160 F. Plot a curve of hp per ton of refrigeration for temperature differences of 0 to 60 F between the cold box and the refrigerant in the evaporator.

9.21 In a conventional refrigeration cycle which uses Freon-12 as the refrigerant, the temperature of the evaporating fluid is −10 F. It leaves the evaporator as saturated vapor at −10 F and enters the compressor. The pressure in the condenser is 200 lbf/in.² The liquid leaves the condenser and enters the expansion valve at a temperature of 100 F.

It is proposed to modify this cycle as shown in Fig. 9.39. In this case an additional exchanger is supplied in which the cold vapor leaving the evaporator cools the liquid which enters the expansion valve.

Compare the coefficient of performance of these two cycles.

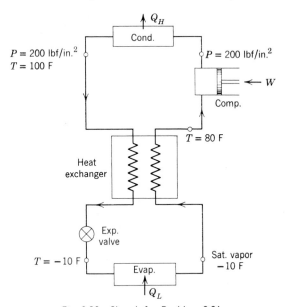

Fig. 9.39   Sketch for Problem 9.21.

9.22 An ammonia-absorption system has an evaporator temperature of 10 F and a condenser temperature of 120 F. The generator temperature is 302 F. In this cycle, 0.42 Btu is transferred to the ammonia in the evaporator for each Btu transferred to the ammonia solution in the generator from the high-temperature source.

We wish to compare the performance of this cycle with the performance of a similar vapor-compression cycle. To do this, assume that a reservoir is available at 302 F, and that heat is transferred from this reservoir to a reversible engine which rejects heat to the surroundings at 77 F. This work is then used to drive an ideal vapor-compression system with ammonia as the refrigerant. Compare the amount of refrigeration that can be achieved per Btu from the high-temperature source in this case with the 0.42 Btu that can be achieved in the adsorption system.

9.23 A stoichiometric mixture of fuel and air has an enthalpy of combustion of approximately -1200 Btu/lbm of mixture. In order to approximate an actual spark-ignition engine using such a mixture, consider an air-standard Otto cycle that has a heat addition of 1200 Btu per lbm of air, a compression ratio of 8, and a pressure and temperature at the beginning of the compression process of 14.7 lbf/in.², 60 F. Determine the following:
The maximum pressure and temperature for this cycle.
The thermal efficiency.
The mean effective pressure.
Assume:
(a) Constant specific heat as given in Table A.8.
(b) Variable specific heat. The Gas Tables are recommended for this calculation.

9.24 An air-standard Diesel cycle has a compression ratio of 14. The pressure at the beginning of the compression stroke is 14.7 lbf/in.², and the temperature is 60 F. The maximum temperature is 4500 R. Determine the thermal efficiency and the mean effective pressure for this cycle.

9.25 Consider an air-standard Ericsson cycle with an ideal regenerator incorporated. The temperature at which heat is supplied is 2000 R. Heat is rejected at 520 R. The pressure at the beginning of the isothermal compression process is 14.7 lbf/in.² Determine the compressor and turbine work per lbm of air and the thermal efficiency of the cycle. $Q_H = 200$ Btu/lbm.

9.26 The pressure ratio across the compressor of an air-standard Brayton cycle is 4 to 1. The pressure of the air entering the compressor is 14.7 lbf/in.², and the temperature is 60 F. The maximum temperature in the cycle is 1500 F. The rate of air flow is 20 lbm/sec. Determine the following, assuming both constant and variable specific heat:
(a) The compressor work, turbine work, and thermal efficiency of the cycle.
(b) If this cycle were utilized for a reciprocating machine, what would be the mean effective pressure? Would you recommend this cycle for a reciprocating machine?

9.27 An ideal regenerator is incorporated into the air-standard Brayton cycle of Problem 9.26. Determine the thermal efficiency of the cycle with this modification.

9.28 Consider a gas-turbine cycle with two stages of compression and two stages of expansion. The pressure ratio across each turbine and each compressor is 2. The temperature entering each compressor is 60 F and the temperature entering each turbine is 1500 F. An ideal regenerator is incorporated into the cycle. Determine the compressor work, turbine work, and thermal efficiency. $P_1 = 14.7$ lbf/in.^{2}

9.29 Repeat Problem 9.28 assuming that each compressor has an efficiency of 80%, each turbine has an efficiency of 85%, and the regenerator has an efficiency of 60%.

9.30 Consider the air-standard cycle for a gas turbine-jet propulsion unit shown in Fig. 9.34. The pressure and temperature entering the compressor are 14.7 lbf/in.^{2}, 60 F respectively. The pressure ratio across the compressor is 5 to 1 and the temperature at the turbine inlet is 1900 F. On leaving the turbine the air enters the nozzle and expands to 14.7 lbf/in.^{2} Determine the pressure at the nozzle inlet and the velocity of the air leaving the nozzle.

9.31 Repeat Problem 9.30, assuming that the efficiency of the compressor and turbine are both 85%, and that the nozzle efficiency is 95%.

9.32 A stationary gas-turbine power plant operates on the Brayton cycle and delivers 20,000 hp to an electric generator. The maximum temperature is 1540 F and the minimum temperature is 60 F. The minimum pressure is 14.0 lbf/in.^{2} and the maximum pressure is 60 lbf/in.^{2}

(a) What is the power output of the turbine?

(b) What fraction of the output of the turbine is used to drive the compressor?

(c) What is the mass rate of air flow to the compressor per min? What is the volume rate of air flow to the compressor per min?

9.33 Repeat Problem 9.32 assuming that a regenerator of 75% efficiency is added to the cycle, and the efficiency of the compressor is 80% and the efficiency of the turbine is 85%.

9.34 (a) A Brayton cycle has a minimum pressure of 15 lbf/in.^{2} and a minimum temperature of 40 F. The maximum pressure is 60 lbf/in.^{2} Plot a curve of thermal efficiency as a function of maximum cycle temperature.

(b) Repeat (a) assuming a compressor efficiency of 80%, a turbine efficiency of 85%, and a 2 lbf/in.^{2} pressure drop between the compressor and turbine. (A digital computer might well be used in solving this problem.)

9.35 A jet aircraft is flying at an altitude of 16,000 ft, where the ambient pressure is approximately 8 lbf/in.^{2} and the ambient temperature is 0 F. The velocity of the aircraft is 500 ft/sec, and the pressure ratio across the compressor is 4.

Devise an air-standard cycle that approximates this cycle, and determine the velocity (relative to the aircraft) of the air leaving the engine, assuming that it has been expanded to the ambient pressure. Assume a maximum gas temperature of 1600 F.

9.36 A Brayton cycle and Rankine cycle are to be combined in a power plant in such a way that heat transferred from the gas leaving the turbine is used to evaporate the water. The Brayton cycle, which utilizes air, has a minimum pressure of 15 lbf/in.^{2} and a maximum pressure of 70 lbf/in.^{2}, and a minimum temperature of 60 F and a maximum temperature of 1540 F. The Rankine cycle, which utilizes steam, has a maximum pressure of 400 lbf/in.^{2}, a maximum temperature of 600 F, and a minimum pressure of 1 lbf/in.^{2} All the heat transferred to the steam comes from the air leaving the turbine of the Brayton cycle, and after this heat-transfer process the air temperature is 600 F.

(a) Draw a line diagram of this power plant.

(b) Determine the thermal efficiency of this cycle.

9.37 A gas turbine cycle for use as an automotive powerplant is shown in Figure 9.40. In the first turbine, the gas expands to just a low enough pressure

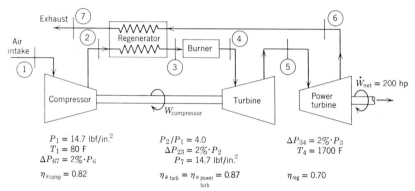

$P_1 = 14.7$ lbf/in.^{2} $P_2/P_1 = 4.0$ $\Delta P_{34} = 2\% \cdot P_3$
$T_1 = 80$ F $\Delta P_{23} = 2\% \cdot P_2$ $T_4 = 1700$ F
$\Delta P_{67} = 2\% \cdot P_6$ $P_7 = 14.7$ lbf/in.^{2}

$\eta_{s\,comp} = 0.82$ $\eta_{s\,turb} = \eta_{s\,power\,turb} = 0.87$ $\eta_{reg} = 0.70$

Fig. 9.40   Sketch for Problem 9.37.

P_5 for that turbine to drive the compressor. The gas is then expanded through a second turbine connected to the drive wheels. The data for this engine are as shown in the figure. Consider the working fluid to be air throughout the entire cycle. Determine

(a) Pressure P_5.

(b) Net work per lbm and mass flow rate.

(c) Temperature T_3 and thermal efficiency of the cycle.

(d) The T-s diagram for the cycle, showing all pressures and temperatures.

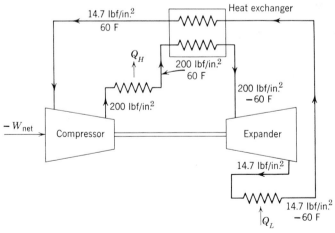

Fig. 9.41   Schematic arrangement of Problem 9.39.

9.38 A gas turbine is to be used for pumping natural gas through a cross country pipeline. The required power input to the natural gas compressor is 1000 hp. It has been decided to use a gas turbine to provide the necessary power input. A simple open cycle will be used with a regenerator of 50% efficiency. Since a supply of fuel is readily available, and since some of these units may be located in relatively isolated places, low maintenance costs are more important than a high efficiency.

Select a cycle which you would recommend, making appropriate assumptions for compressor and turbine efficiencies, and determine (for the gas turbine unit) the power output of the turbine, the power input to the compressor, and the efficiency.

9.39 A heat exchanger is incorporated into an air-standard refrigeration cycle as shown in Fig. 9.41. Assume that both the compression and expansion are reversible adiabatic processes. Determine the coefficient of performance for this cycle.

9.40 Repeat Problem 9.39 assuming an isentropic efficiency for the compressor and expander of 75%.

10 Thermodynamic Relations

We have already defined and used several thermodynamic properties. Among these are pressure, specific volume, density, temperature, mass, internal energy, enthalpy, entropy, constant-pressure and constant-volume specific heats, and Joule-Thomson coefficient. Two other properties, the Helmholtz function and the Gibbs function have been introduced and will be used more extensively in the following chapters. We have also had occasion to use tables of thermodynamic properties for a number of different substances.

One important question is now raised, namely, which of the thermodynamic properties can be experimentally measured? We can answer this question by considering the measurements we can make in the laboratory. Some of the properties such as internal energy and entropy, cannot be measured directly, and must be calculated from other experimental data. If we carefully consider all these thermodynamic properties, we conclude that there are only four that can be directly measured; pressure, temperature, volume, and mass.

This leads to a second question, namely, how can values of the thermodynamic properties that cannot be measured be determined from experimental data on those properties which can be measured? In answering this question we will develop certain general thermodynamic relations. In view of the fact that there are millions of such equations that can be written, our study will be limited to certain basic considerations, with particular reference to the determination of thermodynamic properties from experimental data. We shall also consider such related matters as generalized charts and equations of state.

10.1 Two Important Relations

This chapter involves partial derivatives, and two important relations are reviewed here. Consider a variable z which is a continuous function of

325

x and y.

$$z = f(x, y)$$

$$dz = \left(\frac{\partial z}{\partial x}\right)_y dx + \left(\frac{\partial z}{\partial y}\right)_x dy$$

It is convenient to write this in the form:

$$dz = M\, dx + N\, dy \tag{10.1}$$

$M = \left(\dfrac{\partial z}{\partial x}\right)_y$ = partial derivative of z with respect to x (the variable y being held constant)

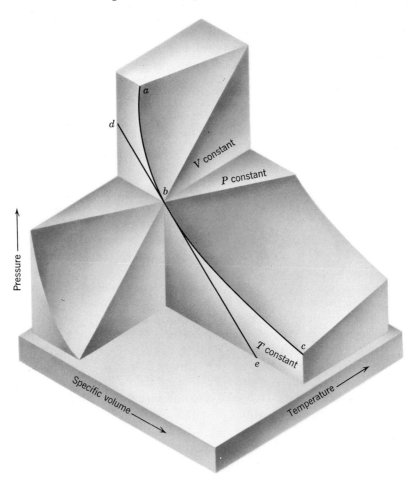

Fig. 10.1   Schematic representation of partial derivatives.

$N = \left(\dfrac{\partial z}{\partial y}\right)_x$ = partial derivative of z with respect to y (the variable x being held constant)

The physical significance of partial derivatives as they relate to the properties of a pure substance can be explained by referring to Fig. 10.1, which shows a P-v-T surface of the superheated vapor region of a pure substance. It shows a constant-temperature, constant-pressure, and a constant-specific volume plane which intersect at point b on the surface. Thus, the partial derivative $(\partial P/\partial v)_T$ is the slope of curve abc at point b. Line de represents the tangent to curve abc at point b. A similar interpretation can be made of the partial derivatives $(\partial P/\partial T)_v$ and $(\partial v/\partial T)_P$.

It should also be noted that if we wish to evaluate the partial derivative along a constant-temperature line the rules for ordinary derivatives can be applied. Thus, we can write for a constant-temperature process:

$$\left(\frac{\partial P}{\partial v}\right)_T = \frac{dP_T}{dv_T}$$

and the integration can be performed as usual. This point will be demonstrated later in a number of examples.

Let us return to the consideration of the relation

$$dz = M\,dx + N\,dy$$

If x, y, and z are all point functions (that is, quantities that depend only on the state and are independent of the path), the differentials are exact differentials. If this is the case, the following important relation holds:

$$\left(\frac{\partial M}{\partial y}\right)_x = \left(\frac{\partial N}{\partial x}\right)_y$$

The proof of this is as follows:

$$\left(\frac{\partial M}{\partial y}\right)_x = \frac{\partial^2 z}{\partial x\,\partial y}$$

$$\left(\frac{\partial N}{\partial x}\right)_y = \frac{\partial^2 z}{\partial y\,\partial x}$$

Since the order of differentiation makes no difference when point functions are involved, it follows that

$$\frac{\partial^2 z}{\partial x\,\partial y} = \frac{\partial^2 z}{\partial y\,\partial x}$$

$$\left(\frac{\partial M}{\partial y}\right)_x = \left(\frac{\partial N}{\partial x}\right)_y$$

The second important mathematical relation is

$$\left(\frac{\partial x}{\partial y}\right)_z \left(\frac{\partial y}{\partial z}\right)_x \left(\frac{\partial z}{\partial x}\right)_y = -1 \tag{10.2}$$

The proof of this relation is as follows. Consider three variables x, y, and z. Suppose there exists a relation between the variables of the form

$$x = f(y, z)$$

then
$$dx = \left(\frac{\partial x}{\partial y}\right)_z dy + \left(\frac{\partial x}{\partial z}\right)_y dz \tag{10.3}$$

If this relationship between the three variables is written in the form

$$y = f(x, z)$$

it follows that
$$dy = \left(\frac{\partial y}{\partial x}\right)_z dx + \left(\frac{\partial y}{\partial z}\right)_x dz \tag{10.4}$$

Substituting Eq. 10.4 into Eq. 10.3 we have

$$dx = \left(\frac{\partial x}{\partial y}\right)_z \left[\left(\frac{\partial y}{\partial x}\right)_z dx + \left(\frac{\partial y}{\partial z}\right)_x dz\right] + \left(\frac{\partial x}{\partial z}\right)_y dz$$

$$= \left(\frac{\partial x}{\partial y}\right)_z \left(\frac{\partial y}{\partial x}\right)_z dx + \left[\left(\frac{\partial x}{\partial y}\right)_z \left(\frac{\partial y}{\partial z}\right)_x + \left(\frac{\partial x}{\partial z}\right)_y\right] dz$$

Since there are only two independent variables, we may select x and z. Suppose that $dz = 0$ and $dx \neq 0$. It then follows that

$$\left(\frac{\partial x}{\partial y}\right)_z \left(\frac{\partial y}{\partial x}\right)_z = 1 \tag{10.5}$$

Similarly, suppose that $dx = 0$ and $dz \neq 0$. It then follows that

$$\left(\frac{\partial x}{\partial y}\right)_z \left(\frac{\partial y}{\partial z}\right)_x + \left(\frac{\partial x}{\partial z}\right)_y = 0$$

$$\left(\frac{\partial x}{\partial y}\right)_z \left(\frac{\partial y}{\partial z}\right)_x = -\left(\frac{\partial x}{\partial z}\right)_y$$

$$\left(\frac{\partial x}{\partial y}\right)_z \left(\frac{\partial y}{\partial z}\right)_x \left(\frac{\partial z}{\partial x}\right)_y = -1$$

This is Eq. 10.2 which we set out to derive.

10.2 The Maxwell Relations

Consider a simple compressible system of fixed chemical composition. The Maxwell relations, which can be written for such a system, are four equations relating the properties P, v, T, and s.

The Maxwell relations are most easily derived by considering four relations involving thermodynamic properties. Two of these relations have already been derived and are:

$$du = T\,ds - P\,dv \tag{10.6}$$

$$dh = T\,ds + v\,dP \tag{10.7}$$

The other two are derived from the definition of the Helmholtz function, a, and the Gibbs function, g.

$$a = u - Ts$$

$$da = du - T\,ds - s\,dT$$

Substituting Eq. 10.6 into this relation gives the third relation.

$$da = -P\,dv - s\,dT \tag{10.8}$$

Similarly,

$$g = h - Ts$$

$$dg = dh - T\,ds - s\,dT$$

Substituting Eq. 10.7 yields the fourth relation.

$$dg = v\,dP - s\,dT \tag{10.9}$$

Since Eqs. 10.6, 10.7, 10.8, and 10.9 are relations involving properties, we conclude that these are exact differentials, and, therefore, are of the general form

$$dz = M\,dx + N\,dy$$

Since

$$\left(\frac{\partial M}{\partial y}\right)_x = \left(\frac{\partial N}{\partial x}\right)_y \tag{10.10}$$

it follows from Eq. 10.6 that

$$\left(\frac{\partial T}{\partial v}\right)_s = -\left(\frac{\partial P}{\partial s}\right)_v \tag{10.11}$$

Similarly, from Eqs. 10.7, 10.8, and 10.9 we can write

$$\left(\frac{\partial T}{\partial P}\right)_s = \left(\frac{\partial v}{\partial s}\right)_P \tag{10.12}$$

$$\left(\frac{\partial P}{\partial T}\right)_v = \left(\frac{\partial s}{\partial v}\right)_T \tag{10.13}$$

$$\left(\frac{\partial v}{\partial T}\right)_P = -\left(\frac{\partial s}{\partial P}\right)_T \tag{10.14}$$

These four equations are known as the Maxwell relations for a simple compressible system, and the great utility of these equations will be demonstrated in later sections of this chapter. In particular, it should be noted that pressure, temperature, and specific volume can be measured by experimental methods, whereas entropy cannot be determined experimentally. By using the Maxwell relations changes in entropy can be determined from quantities that can be measured, i.e., pressure, temperature, and specific volume.

There are a number of other very useful relations that can be derived from Eqs 10.6 through 10.9. For example, from Eq. 10.6 we can write the relations

$$\left(\frac{\partial u}{\partial s}\right)_v = T \qquad \left(\frac{\partial u}{\partial v}\right)_s = -P \qquad (10.15)$$

Similarly, from the other equations we have the following:

$$\left(\frac{\partial h}{\partial s}\right)_P = T \qquad \left(\frac{\partial h}{\partial P}\right)_s = v$$

$$\left(\frac{\partial a}{\partial v}\right)_T = -P \qquad \left(\frac{\partial a}{\partial T}\right)_v = -s \qquad (10.16)$$

$$\left(\frac{\partial g}{\partial P}\right)_T = v \qquad \left(\frac{\partial g}{\partial T}\right)_P = -s$$

As already noted, the Maxwell relations just presented are written for a simple compressible substance. It is readily evident, however, that similar Maxwell relations can be written for substances involving other effects, such as electrical and magnetic effects. For example, Eq. 7.9 can be written in the form

$$dU = T\,dS - P\,dV + \mathcal{T}\,dL + \mathcal{S}\,dA + \mu_0 V \mathcal{H}\,d\mathcal{M} + \mathcal{E}\,dZ + \cdots \qquad (10.17)$$

Thus for a substance involving only magnetic effects we can write

$$dU = T\,dS + \mu_0 V \mathcal{H}\,d\mathcal{M}$$

and it follows that for such a substance

$$\left(\frac{\partial T}{\partial \mathcal{M}}\right)_S = \mu_0 V \left(\frac{\partial \mathcal{H}}{\partial S}\right)_{\mathcal{M}}$$

Other Maxwell relations similar to Eqs. 10.12 through 10.14 could be written for such a substance. The extension of this approach to other systems, as well as to the interrelation between the various effects that may occur in a given system, is readily evident. For example, suppose a system

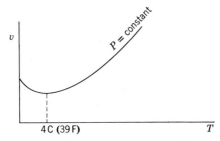

Fig. 10.2   Sketch for Example 10.1.

involved both magnetic and surface effects. For such a system we could consider a constant entropy process and write

$$\left(\frac{\partial \mathscr{S}}{\partial \mathscr{M}}\right)_{S,A} = \mu_0 V \left(\frac{\partial \mathscr{H}}{\partial A}\right)_{S,\mathscr{M}}$$

Example 10.1

Explain why the entropy correction $(s - s_f)$ in Table 4 of Keenan and Keyes' steam tables (Table A.1.4 in the Appendix) is positive at 32 F and negative at all the other temperatures listed.

Table 4 gives the changes in volume, enthalpy, and entropy of liquid water as the pressure increases while the temperature remains constant. Thus, the entropy correction in Table 4 is really $(\partial s/\partial P)_T$. From Eq. 10.14

$$\left(\frac{\partial s}{\partial P}\right)_T = -\left(\frac{\partial v}{\partial T}\right)_P$$

Therefore, the sign of the entropy correction in Table 4 depends on the sign of the term $(\partial v/\partial T)_P$. The physical significance of this term is that it involves the change in specific volume of water as the temperature changes while the pressure remains constant. Now, as water at moderate pressures and 32 F is heated in a constant-pressure process, the specific volume decreases until the point of maximum density is reached at approximately 39 F, after which it increases. This is shown on a v-T diagram in Fig. 10.2. Thus, the quantity $(\partial v/\partial T)_P$ is the slope of the curve in Fig. 10.2. Since this slope is negative at 32 F, the quantity $(\partial s/\partial P)_T$ is positive at 32 F. At the point of maximum density the slope is zero, and, therefore, the constant-pressure line shown in Fig. 7.7 crosses the saturated-liquid line at the point of maximum density.

10.3   Clapeyron Equation

The Clapeyron equation is an important relation involving the saturation pressure and temperature, the change of enthalpy associated with a change of phase, and the specific volumes of the two phases. In particular it is an example of how a change in a property that cannot be measured directly, the enthalpy in this case, can be determined from measurements of pressure, temperature, and specific volume. It can be derived in a number of ways. Here we proceed by considering one of the Maxwell relations, Eq. 10.13.

$$\left(\frac{\partial P}{\partial T}\right)_v = \left(\frac{\partial s}{\partial v}\right)_T$$

Consider, for example, the change of state from saturated liquid to saturated vapor of a pure substance. This is a constant-temperature process, and, therefore, Eq. 10.13 can be integrated between the saturated-liquid and saturated-vapor state. We also note that when saturated states are involved, pressure and temperature are independent of volume. Therefore,

$$\left(\frac{dP}{dT}\right)_{sat} = \frac{s_g - s_f}{v_g - v_f} = \frac{s_{fg}}{v_{fg}} = \frac{h_{fg}}{Tv_{fg}} \qquad (10.18)$$

The significance of this equation is that $(dP/dT)_{sat}$ is the slope of the vapor-pressure curve. Thus, h_{fg} at a given temperature can be determined from the slope of the vapor-pressure curve and the specific volume of saturated liquid and saturated vapor at the given temperature.

There are several different changes of phase that can occur at constant temperature and constant pressure. If we designate the two phases with superscripts " and ', we can write the Clapeyron equation for the general case.

$$\left(\frac{dP}{dT}\right)_{sat} = \frac{s'' - s'}{v'' - v'}$$

We also note that $T(s'' - s') = h'' - h'$. Therefore

$$\left(\frac{dP}{dT}\right)_{sat} = \frac{h'' - h'}{T(v'' - v')} \qquad (10.19)$$

If the phase designated " is vapor, then at low pressure the equation is usually simplified by assuming that $v'' \gg v'$ and assuming also that $v'' = RT/P$. The relation then becomes

$$\left(\frac{dP}{dT}\right)_{sat} = \frac{h_g - h'}{T(RT/P)}$$

$$\left(\frac{dP}{P}\right)_{sat} = \frac{(h_g - h')}{R}\left(\frac{dT}{T^2}\right)_{sat} \qquad (10.20)$$

Example 10.2

Determine the saturation pressure of water vapor at -100 F using data available in the steam tables. Table 5 of the steam tables (Appendix Table A.1.5) does not give saturation pressures for temperatures less than -40 F. However, we do notice that h_{ig} is relatively constant in this range, and, therefore, we proceed to use Eq. 10.20 and integrate between the limits -40 F and -100 F.

$$\int_1^2 \frac{dP}{P} = \int_1^2 \frac{h_{ig}}{R} \frac{dT}{T^2} = \frac{h_{ig}}{R} \int_1^2 \frac{dT}{T^2}$$

$$\ln \frac{P_2}{P_1} = \frac{h_{ig}}{R}\left(\frac{T_2 - T_1}{T_1 T_2}\right)$$

Let

$$P_2 = 0.0019 \text{ lbf/in.}^2 \qquad T_2 = 420 \text{ R}$$
$$P_1 = ? \qquad\qquad\qquad T_1 = 360 \text{ R}$$

Then

$$\ln \frac{P_2}{P_1} = \frac{1221 \times 778}{85.7}\left(\frac{420 - 360}{420 \times 360}\right)$$

$$\ln \frac{P_2}{P_1} = 4.40; \qquad \frac{P_2}{P_1} = 81.5; \qquad P_1 = \frac{0.0019}{81.5} = 2.33 \times 10^{-5} \text{ lbf/in.}^2$$

10.4 Some Thermodynamic Relations Involving Enthalpy, Internal Energy, and Entropy

Let us first derive two equations, one involving C_p and the other involving C_v.

We have defined C_p as

$$C_p \equiv \left(\frac{\partial h}{\partial T}\right)_P$$

We have also noted that for a pure substance

$$T \, ds = dh - v \, dP$$

Therefore,

$$C_p = \left(\frac{\partial h}{\partial T}\right)_P = T\left(\frac{\partial s}{\partial T}\right)_P \tag{10.21}$$

Similarly, from the definition of C_v,

$$C_v \equiv \left(\frac{\partial u}{\partial T}\right)_v$$

and the relation

$$T \, ds = du + P \, dv,$$

it follows that

$$C_v = \left(\frac{\partial u}{\partial T}\right)_v = T\left(\frac{\partial s}{\partial T}\right)_v \tag{10.22}$$

We will now derive a general relation for the change of enthalpy of a pure substance. We first note that for a pure substance

$$h = h(T, P)$$

Therefore,

$$dh = \left(\frac{\partial h}{\partial T}\right)_P dT + \left(\frac{\partial h}{\partial P}\right)_T dP$$

From the relation

$$T \, ds = dh - v \, dP$$

it follows that

$$\left(\frac{\partial h}{\partial P}\right)_T = v + T\left(\frac{\partial s}{\partial P}\right)_T$$

Substituting the Maxwell relation, Eq. 10.14, we have

$$\left(\frac{\partial h}{\partial P}\right)_T = v - T\left(\frac{\partial v}{\partial T}\right)_P \tag{10.23}$$

On substituting this equation and Eq. 10.21 we have

$$dh = C_p \, dT + \left[v - T\left(\frac{\partial v}{\partial T}\right)_P\right] dP \tag{10.24}$$

Along an isobar we have

$$dh_P = C_p \, dT_P$$

and along an isotherm,

$$dh_T = \left[v - T\left(\frac{\partial v}{\partial T}\right)_P\right] dP_T \tag{10.25}$$

The significance of Eq. 10.24 is that this equation can be integrated to give the change in enthalpy associated with a change of state.

$$h_2 - h_1 = \int_1^2 C_p \, dT + \int_1^2 \left[v - T\left(\frac{\partial v}{\partial T}\right)_P\right] dP \tag{10.26}$$

The information needed to integrate the first term is a constant pressure specific heat along one (and only one) isobar. The integration of the second integral requires that an equation of state giving the relation between P, v, and T be known. Furthermore, it is advantageous to have this equation of state explicit in v, for then the derivative $(\partial v/\partial T)_P$ is readily evaluated.

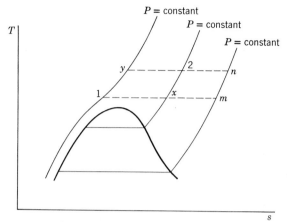

Fig. 10.3   Sketch showing various paths by which a given change of state can take place.

This can be further illustrated by reference to Fig. 10.3. Suppose we wished to know the change of enthalpy between states 1 and 2. We might do so along path 1–x–2, which consists of one isotherm (1–x) and one isobar (x–2). Thus we could integrate Eq. 10.26

$$h_2 - h_1 = \int_{T_1}^{T_2} C_p \, dT + \int_{P_1}^{P_2} \left[v - T \left(\frac{\partial v}{\partial T} \right)_P \right] dP$$

Since $T_1 = T_x$ and $P_2 = P_x$ this can be written

$$h_2 - h_1 = \int_{T_x}^{T_2} C_p \, dT + \int_{P_1}^{P_x} \left[v - T \left(\frac{\partial v}{\partial T} \right)_P \right] dP$$

The second term in this equation gives the change in enthalpy along the isotherm 1–x and the first term the change in enthalpy along the isobar x–2. When these are added together, the result is the net change in enthalpy between 1 and 2. It should be noted that in this case the constant-pressure specific heat must be known along the isobar passing through 2 and x. One could also find the change in enthalpy by following path 1–y–2, in which case the constant-pressure specific heat must be known along the 1–y isobar. If the constant-pressure specific heat is known at another pressure, say the isobar passing through m–n, the change in enthalpy could be found by following path 1–m–n–2. This would involve calculating the change of enthalpy along two isotherms, namely, 1–m and n–2.

Let us now derive a similar relation for the change of internal energy. All the steps in this derivation are given, but without detailed comment. Note that the starting point is to write $u = u(T, v)$ whereas in the case of enthalpy the starting point was $h = h(T, P)$.

$$u = f(T, v)$$

$$du = \left(\frac{\partial u}{\partial T}\right)_v dT + \left(\frac{\partial u}{\partial v}\right)_T dv$$

$$T\,ds = du + P\,dv$$

Therefore,

$$\left(\frac{\partial u}{\partial v}\right)_T = T\left(\frac{\partial s}{\partial v}\right)_T - P \tag{10.27}$$

Substituting the Maxwell relation, Eq. 10.13,

$$\left(\frac{\partial u}{\partial v}\right)_T = T\left(\frac{\partial P}{\partial T}\right)_v - P$$

Therefore,

$$du = C_v\,dT + \left[T\left(\frac{\partial P}{\partial T}\right)_v - P\right] dv \tag{10.28}$$

Along an isometric this reduces to

$$du_v = C_v\,dT_v,$$

and along an isotherm we have

$$du_T = \left[T\left(\frac{\partial P}{\partial T}\right)_v - P\right] dv_T \tag{10.29}$$

In a manner similar to that outlined above for changes in enthalpy, the change of internal energy for a given change of state for a pure substance can be determined from Eq. 10.28 if the constant-volume specific heat is known along one isometric and an equation of state explicit in P (to obtain the derivative $(\partial P/\partial T)_v$) is available in the region involved. A diagram similar to Fig. 10.3 could be drawn, with the isobars replaced with isometrics, and the same general conclusions would be reached.

To summarize, we have derived Eqs. 10.24 and 10.28,

$$dh = C_p\,dT + \left[v - T\left(\frac{\partial v}{\partial T}\right)_P\right] dP$$

$$du = C_v\,dT + \left[T\left(\frac{\partial P}{\partial T}\right)_v - P\right] dv$$

The first of these involves the change of enthalpy, the constant-pressure specific heat, and is particularly suited to an equation of state explicit in v. The second involves the change of internal energy, the constant-volume specific heat, and is particularly suited to an equation of state explicit in P. If the first of these equations is used to determine the change of enthalpy, the internal energy is readily found by noting that

$$u_2 - u_1 = h_2 - h_1 - (P_2 v_2 - P_1 v_1)$$

If the second equation is used to find changes of internal energy, the change of enthalpy is readily found from this same relation. Which of these two equations is used to determine changes in internal energy and enthalpy will depend on the information available for specific heat and an equation of state (or other P–v–T data).

Two parallel expressions can be found for the change of entropy.

$$s = s(T, P)$$

$$ds = \left(\frac{\partial s}{\partial T}\right)_P dT + \left(\frac{\partial s}{\partial P}\right)_T dP$$

Substituting Eqs. 10.21 and 10.14 we have

$$ds = C_p \frac{dT}{T} - \left(\frac{\partial v}{\partial T}\right)_P dP \tag{10.30}$$

$$s_2 - s_1 = \int_1^2 C_p \frac{dT}{T} - \int_1^2 \left(\frac{\partial v}{\partial T}\right)_P dP \tag{10.31}$$

Along an isobar we have

$$(s_2 - s_1)_P = \int_1^2 C_p \frac{dT_P}{T}$$

and along an isotherm,

$$(s_2 - s_1)_T = - \int_1^2 \left(\frac{\partial v}{\partial T}\right)_P dP$$

Note from Eq. 10.31 that if a constant-pressure specific heat is known along one isobar and an equation of state explicit in v is available, the change of entropy can be evaluated. This is analogous to the expression for the change of enthalpy given in Eq. 10.24.

The second equation for the change of entropy can be found as follows.

$$s = s(T, v)$$

$$ds = \left(\frac{\partial s}{\partial T}\right)_v dT + \left(\frac{\partial s}{\partial v}\right)_T dv$$

Substituting Eqs. 10.22 and 10.13,

$$ds = C_v \frac{dT}{T} + \left(\frac{\partial P}{\partial T}\right)_v dv \tag{10.32}$$

$$s_2 - s_1 = \int_1^2 C_v \frac{dT}{T} + \int_1^2 \left(\frac{\partial P}{\partial T}\right)_v dv \tag{10.33}$$

This expression for change of entropy involves the change of entropy along an isometric where the constant-volume specific heat is known and along an isotherm where an equation of state explicit in P is known, and thus it is analogous to the expression for change of internal energy given in Eq. 10.28.

Example 10.3

Over a certain range of pressures and temperatures the equation of state of a certain substance is given with considerable accuracy by the relation

$$\frac{Pv}{RT} = 1 - C' \frac{P}{T^4}$$

or

$$v = \frac{RT}{P} - \frac{C}{T^3}$$

where C and C' are constants.

Derive an expression for the change of enthalpy and entropy of this substance in an isothermal process.

Since the equation of state is explicit in v, Eq. 10.25 would be particularly relevant to this problem. On integrating this equation we have,

$$(h_2 - h_1)_T = \int_1^2 \left[v - T \left(\frac{\partial v}{\partial T} \right)_P \right] dP_T$$

From the equation of state,

$$\left(\frac{\partial v}{\partial T} \right)_P = \frac{R}{P} + \frac{3C}{T^4}$$

Therefore,

$$(h_2 - h_1)_T = \int_1^2 \left[v - T \left(\frac{R}{P} + \frac{3C}{T^4} \right) \right] dP_T$$

$$= \int_1^2 \left[\frac{RT}{P} - \frac{C}{T^3} - \frac{RT}{P} - \frac{3C}{T^3} \right] dP_T$$

$$(h_2 - h_1)_T = \int_1^2 - \frac{4C}{T^3} dP_T = - \frac{4C}{T^3} (P_2 - P_1)_T$$

For entropy we use Eq. 10.31, which is particularly relevant for an equation of state explicit in v.

$$(s_2 - s_1)_T = - \int_1^2 \left(\frac{\partial v}{\partial T} \right)_P dP_T = - \int_1^2 \left(\frac{R}{P} + \frac{3C}{T^4} \right) dP_T$$

$$(s_2 - s_1)_T = -R \ln \left(\frac{P_2}{P_1} \right)_T - \frac{3C}{T^4} (P_2 - P_1)_T$$

Example 10.4

The substance referred to in Example 10.3, having the equation of state

$$v = \frac{RT}{P} - \frac{C}{T^3}$$

has a constant-pressure specific heat along isobar P_x (which lies within the region covered by the equation of state) given by the relation

$$C_p = A + BT$$

Derive a general expression for the change of enthalpy, internal energy, and entropy of this substance.

In solving this problem it may be helpful to refer to Fig. 10.4, where points 1 and 2 and the constant pressure line P_x are arbitrarily selected.

The change in enthalpy between 1 and 2 is equal to the change in enthalpy along path 1–x–y–2.

$$h_2 - h_1 = (h_2 - h_y) + (h_y - h_x) + (h_x - h_1)$$

$$h_2 - h_1 = \int_{P_y=P_x}^{P_2} \left[v - T \left(\frac{\partial v}{\partial T} \right)_P \right] dP_T + \int_{T_x=T_1}^{T_y=T_2} C_p \, dT_P$$

$$+ \int_{P_1}^{P_x=P_y} \left[v - T \left(\frac{\partial v}{\partial T} \right)_P \right] dP_T$$

The first and last integrals have already been evaluated in Example 10.3.

$$h_2 - h_y = -\frac{4C}{T_2^3} (P_2 - P_x)$$

$$h_x - h_1 = -\frac{4C}{T_1^3} (P_x - P_1)$$

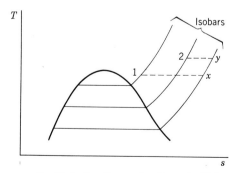

Fig. 10.4   *T-s* diagram for Example 10.4.

The second integral is readily evaluated since C_p is known along P_x

$$h_y - h_x = \int_{T_x=T_1}^{T_y=T_2} C_p \, dT = \int_{T_x=T_1}^{T_y=T_2} (A + BT) \, dT$$

$$= A(T_2 - T_1) + \frac{B}{2}(T_2^2 - T_1^2)$$

Therefore,

$$h_2 - h_1 = -\frac{4C}{T_2^3}(P_2 - P_x) + A(T_2 - T_1)$$

$$+ \frac{B}{2}(T_2^2 - T_1^2) - \frac{4C}{T_1^3}(P_x - P_1)$$

$$h_2 - h_1 = A(T_2 - T_1) + \frac{B}{2}(T_2^2 - T_1^2) - 4C\left[\frac{(P_2 - P_x)}{T_2^3} - \frac{(P_1 - P_x)}{T_1^3}\right]$$

$$u_2 - u_1 = h_2 - h_1 - (P_2 v_2 - P_1 v_1)$$

$$\therefore \; u_2 - u_1 = (A + R)(T_2 - T_1) + \frac{B}{2}(T_2^2 - T_1^2)$$

$$- 5C\left(\frac{P_2}{T_2^3} - \frac{P_1}{T_1^3}\right) + 4CP_x\left(\frac{1}{T_2^3} - \frac{1}{T_1^3}\right)$$

$$s_2 - s_1 = (s_2 - s_y) + (s_y - s_x) + (s_x - s_1)$$

From Eq. 10.30

$$s_2 - s_1 = -\int_{P_y=P_x}^{P_2}\left(\frac{\partial v}{\partial T}\right)_P dP_T + \int_{T_x=T_1}^{T_y=T_2} C_p\frac{dT_P}{T} - \int_{P_1}^{P_x}\left(\frac{\partial v}{\partial T}\right)_P dP_T$$

From the results of Example 10.3

$$s_2 - s_y = -R\ln\frac{P_2}{P_y} - \frac{3C}{T_2^4}(P_2 - P_y) = -R\ln\frac{P_2}{P_x} - \frac{3C}{T_2^4}(P_2 - P_x)$$

$$s_x - s_1 = -R\ln\frac{P_x}{P_1} - \frac{3C}{T_1^4}(P_x - P_1)$$

$$s_y - s_x = \int_{T_x=T_1}^{T_y=T_2} C_p\frac{dT}{T} = \int_{T_x=T_1}^{T_y=T_2}(A + BT)\frac{dT}{T} = A\ln\frac{T_2}{T_1} + B(T_2 - T_1)$$

Therefore,

$$s_2 - s_1 = -R\ln\frac{P_2}{P_x} - \frac{3C}{T_2^4}(P_2 - P_x) + A\ln\frac{T_2}{T_1} + B(T_2 - T_1)$$

$$- R\ln\frac{P_x}{P_1} - \frac{3C}{T_1^4}(P_x - P_1)$$

$$s_2 - s_1 = -R\ln\frac{P_2}{P_1} - 3C\left[\frac{(P_2 - P_x)}{T_2^4} - \frac{(P_1 - P_x)}{T_1^4}\right]$$

$$+ A\ln\frac{T_2}{T_1} + B(T_2 - T_1)$$

In this example we have selected relatively simple equations for the equation of state and the constant-pressure specific heat, and thus they would be accurate only over a limited range. When more complicated equations are used a digital computer can be utilized to excellent advantage in problems such as these.

10.5 Some Thermodynamic Relations Involving Specific Heat

Some important relations involving specific heats can also be developed. We have noted that the specific heat of an ideal gas is a function of the temperature only. For real gases the specific heat varies with pressure as well as temperature, and frequently we are interested in the variation of specific heat with pressure or volume. These relations can be derived as follows. Consider Eq. 10.30,

$$ds = \left(\frac{C_p}{T}\right) dT - \left(\frac{\partial v}{\partial T}\right)_P dP$$

Since this equation is of the general form $dz = M\, dx + N\, dy$, we can proceed as follows to find a relation that gives the variation of the constant-pressure specific heat with pressure at constant temperature.

$$\left(\frac{\partial(C_p/T)}{\partial P}\right)_T = -\left[\frac{\partial}{\partial T}\left(\frac{\partial v}{\partial T}\right)_P\right]_P$$

$$\left(\frac{\partial C_p}{\partial P}\right)_T = -T\left(\frac{\partial^2 v}{\partial T^2}\right)_P \tag{10.34}$$

The variation of the constant-volume specific heat with volume as the temperature remains constant can be found in a similar manner. Consider Eq. 10.32,

$$ds = \left(\frac{C_v}{T}\right) dT + \left(\frac{\partial P}{\partial T}\right)_v dv$$

Since this is of the form $dz = M\, dx + N\, dy$,

$$\left(\frac{\partial(C_v/T)}{\partial v}\right)_T = \left[\frac{\partial}{\partial T}\left(\frac{\partial P}{\partial T}\right)_v\right]_v$$

$$\left(\frac{\partial C_v}{\partial v}\right)_T = T\left(\frac{\partial^2 P}{\partial T^2}\right)_v \tag{10.35}$$

The important thing to note about Eqs. 10.34 and 10.35 is that the variation of the constant-volume and constant-pressure specific heats in a constant-temperature process can be found from the equation of state.

Example 10.5

Determine the variation of C_p with pressure at constant temperature for a substance such as the one in Example 10.3 over the range where the equation of state is given by the relation

$$v = \frac{RT}{P} - \frac{C}{T^3}$$

Using Eq. 10.34

$$\left(\frac{\partial C_p}{\partial P}\right)_T = -T\left(\frac{\partial^2 v}{\partial T^2}\right)_P$$

$$\left(\frac{\partial v}{\partial T}\right)_P = \frac{R}{P} + \frac{3C}{T^4}$$

$$\left(\frac{\partial^2 v}{\partial T^2}\right)_P = -\frac{12C}{T^5}$$

$$\left(\frac{\partial C_p}{\partial P}\right)_T = -T\left(-\frac{12C}{T^5}\right) = \frac{12C}{T^4}$$

A final interesting and useful relation involving the difference between C_p and C_v can be derived by equating Eqs. 10.30 and 10.32.

$$C_p \frac{dT}{T} - \left(\frac{\partial v}{\partial T}\right)_P dP = C_v \frac{dT}{T} + \left(\frac{\partial P}{\partial T}\right)_v dv$$

$$dT = \frac{T(\partial P/\partial T)_v}{C_p - C_v} dv + \frac{T(\partial v/\partial T)_P}{C_p - C_v} dP$$

But

$$T = f(v, P)$$

$$dT = \left(\frac{\partial T}{\partial v}\right)_P dv + \left(\frac{\partial T}{\partial P}\right)_v dP$$

Therefore,

$$\left(\frac{\partial T}{\partial v}\right)_P = \frac{T(\partial P/\partial T)_v}{C_p - C_v}$$

and

$$\left(\frac{\partial T}{\partial P}\right)_v = \frac{T(\partial v/\partial T)_P}{C_p - C_v}$$

When these equations are solved for $C_p - C_v$, they yield the same result.

$$C_p - C_v = T\left(\frac{\partial v}{\partial T}\right)_P\left(\frac{\partial P}{\partial T}\right)_v \qquad (10.36)$$

But from Eq. 10.2,

$$\left(\frac{\partial P}{\partial T}\right)_v = -\left(\frac{\partial v}{\partial T}\right)_P\left(\frac{\partial P}{\partial v}\right)_T$$

Therefore,

$$C_p - C_v = -T\left(\frac{\partial v}{\partial T}\right)_P^2 \left(\frac{\partial P}{\partial v}\right)_T \tag{10.37}$$

From this equation we draw several conclusions:

1. For a liquid and solid $(\partial v/\partial T)_P$ is usually relatively small, and, therefore, the difference between the constant-pressure and constant-volume specific heats of a liquid is small. For this reason many tables simply give the specific heat of a solid or a liquid without designating that it is at constant volume or pressure. Further, $C_p = C_v$ exactly when $(\partial v/\partial T)_P = 0$, as is true at the point of maximum density of water.

2. $C_p \to C_v$ as $T \to 0$, and, therefore, we conclude that the constant-pressure and constant-volume specific heats are equal at absolute zero.

3. The difference between C_p and C_v is always positive because $(\partial v/\partial T)_P^2$ is always positive and $(\partial P/\partial v)_T$ is negative for all known substances.

10.6 Volume Expansivity and Isothermal and Adiabatic Compressibility

The student has most likely encountered the coefficient of linear expansion in his studies of strength of materials. This coefficient indicates how the length of a solid body is influenced by a change in temperature while the pressure remains constant. In terms of the notation of partial derivatives the *coefficient of linear expansion*, δ_t, is defined as follows:

$$\delta_t = \frac{1}{L}\left(\frac{\partial L}{\partial T}\right)_P \tag{10.38}$$

A similar coefficient can be defined for changes in volume, and such a coefficient is applicable to liquids and gases as well as to solids. This coefficient of volume expansion α, also called the volume expansivity, is an indication of the change in volume that results from a change in temperature while the pressure remains constant. The definition of *volume expansivity* is

$$\alpha \equiv \frac{1}{V}\left(\frac{\partial V}{\partial T}\right)_P = \frac{1}{v}\left(\frac{\partial v}{\partial T}\right)_P \tag{10.39}$$

The isothermal compressibility β_T is an indication of the change in volume that results from a change in pressure while the temperature remains constant. The definition of the *isothermal compressibility* is

$$\beta_T \equiv -\frac{1}{V}\left(\frac{\partial V}{\partial P}\right)_T = -\frac{1}{v}\left(\frac{\partial v}{\partial P}\right)_T \tag{10.40}$$

The reciprocal of the isothermal compressibility is called the *isothermal bulk modulus* B_T.

$$B_T \equiv -v\left(\frac{\partial P}{\partial v}\right)_T \tag{10.41}$$

The *adiabatic compressibility* β_s is an indication of the change in volume that results from a change in pressure while the entropy remains constant, and is defined as follows:

$$\beta_s \equiv -\frac{1}{v}\left(\frac{\partial v}{\partial P}\right)_s \tag{10.42}$$

The *adiabatic bulk modulus* B_s is the reciprocal of the adiabatic compressibility.

$$B_s \equiv -v\left(\frac{\partial P}{\partial v}\right)_s \tag{10.43}$$

Both the volume expansivity and isothermal compressibility are thermodynamic properties of a substance, and for a simple compressible substance are functions of two independent properties. Values of these properties are found in the standard handbooks of physical properties. The following example gives an indication of the use and significance of the volume expansivity and isothermal compressibility.

Example 10.6

Show that $C_p - C_v$ can be expressed in terms of the volume expansivity α, the specific volume v, the temperature T, and the isothermal compressibility β_T, by the relation

$$C_p - C_v = \frac{\alpha^2 v T}{\beta_T}$$

From Eq. 10.37

$$C_p - C_v = -T\left(\frac{\partial v}{\partial T}\right)_P^2 \left(\frac{\partial P}{\partial v}\right)_T$$

$$\alpha \equiv \frac{1}{v}\left(\frac{\partial v}{\partial T}\right)_P; \qquad \left(\frac{\partial v}{\partial T}\right)^2 = \alpha^2 v^2$$

$$\beta_T \equiv -\frac{1}{v}\left(\frac{\partial v}{\partial P}\right)_T; \qquad \left(\frac{\partial P}{\partial v}\right)_T = -\frac{1}{\beta_T v}$$

Therefore

$$C_p - C_v = -T(\alpha^2 v^2)\left(-\frac{1}{\beta_T v}\right) = \frac{\alpha^2 v T}{\beta_T}$$

Example 10.7

The pressure on a block of copper having a mass of 1 lbm is increased in a reversible process from 1 atm to 1000 atm while the temperature is held constant at 60 F. Determine the work done on the copper during this process, the change in entropy per pound of copper, the heat transfer, the change of internal energy per pound, and $C_p - C_v$ for this change of state.

Over the range of pressures and temperatures involved in this problem the following data can be used:

$$\text{Volume expansivity} = \alpha = 2.8 \times 10^{-5} R^{-1}$$
$$\text{Isothermal compressibility} = \beta_T = 5.9 \times 10^{-8} \text{ in.}^2/\text{lbf}$$
$$\text{Specific volume} = 1.82 \times 10^{-3} \text{ ft}^3/\text{lbm}$$

The work done during the isothermal expansion is

$$w = \int P \, dv_T$$

The isothermal compressibility has been defined:

$$\beta_T = -\frac{1}{v}\left(\frac{\partial v}{\partial P}\right)_T$$
$$v\beta_T \, dP_T = -dv_T$$

Therefore, for this isothermal process

$$w = -\int_1^2 v\beta_T P \, dP_T$$

Since v and β_T remain essentially constant, this is readily integrated:

$$w = -\frac{v\beta_T}{2}(P_2{}^2 - P_1{}^2)$$
$$= -1.82 \times 10^{-3} \text{ ft}^3/\text{lbm} \times 5.9 \times 10^{-8} \text{ in.}^2/\text{lbf} \times \frac{1000^2 - 1^2}{2}$$
$$\times (14.7)^2 \text{ lbf}^2/\text{in.}^4 \times 144 \text{ in.}^2/\text{ft}^2 = -1.68 \text{ ft-lbf}$$

The change of entropy can be found by considering the Maxwell relation, Eq. 10.14, and the definition of volume expansivity.

$$\left(\frac{\partial s}{\partial P}\right)_T = -\left(\frac{\partial v}{\partial T}\right)_P = -\frac{v}{v}\left(\frac{\partial v}{\partial T}\right)_P = -v\alpha$$
$$ds_T = -v\alpha \, dP_T$$

This can be readily integrated as follows if we assume that v and α remain constant:

$$(s_2 - s_1)_T = -v\alpha(P_2 - P_1)_T$$

$$= -1.82 \times 10^{-3} \text{ ft}^3/\text{lbm} \times \frac{2.8 \times 10^{-5}}{R} \times (1000 - 1)$$

$$\times 14.7 \times 144 \text{ lbf/ft}^2 = -0.108 \text{ ft-lbf/lbm-R}$$

The heat transfer for this reversible isothermal process is $T(s_2 - s_1)$.

$$q = T(s_2 - s_1) = 520(-0.108) = -56.1 \text{ ft-lbf}$$

The change in internal energy follows directly from the first law.

$$(u_2 - u_1) = q - w = -56.1 - (-1.7) = -54.4 \text{ ft-lbf}$$

From Example 10.6,

$$C_p - C_v = \frac{\alpha^2 v T}{\beta_T}$$

Substituting the data for copper as given above,

$$C_p - C_v = \left(\frac{2.8}{10^5}\right)^2 \times \frac{1.82}{10^3} \times \frac{10^8}{5.9} \times 520 \times \frac{144}{778} = 0.0023 \frac{\text{Btu}}{\text{lbm-R}}$$

This is consistent with the earlier observation that $C_p - C_v$ is relatively small for solids.

10.7 Developing Tables of Thermodynamic Properties from Experimental Data

There are many ways in which tables of thermodynamic properties can be developed from experimental data. The purpose of this section is to convey some general principles and concepts by considering only the liquid and vapor phases.

Let us assume that the following data for a pure substance have been obtained in the laboratory.

a. Vapor-pressure data. That is, saturation pressures and temperatures have been measured over a wide range.

b. Pressure, specific volume, temperature data in the vapor region. These data are usually obtained by determining the mass of the substance in a closed vessel (which means a fixed specific volume) and then measuring the pressure as the temperature is varied. This is done for a large number of specific volumes.

c. Density of the saturated liquid and the critical pressure and temperature.

d. Zero-pressure specific heat for the vapor. This might be obtained either calorimetrically or from spectroscopic data.

From these data a complete set of thermodynamic tables for the saturated liquid, saturated vapor, and superheated vapor can be calculated. The first step is to determine an equation for the vapor-pressure curve that accurately fits the data. It may be necessary to use one equation for one portion of the vapor-pressure curve and a different equation for another portion of the curve.

One form of equation that has been used is

$$\ln P_{\text{sat}} = A + \frac{B}{T} + C \ln T + DT$$

Once an equation has been found that accurately represents the data, the saturation pressure for any given temperature can be found by solving this equation. Thus, the saturation pressures in Table 1 of *Thermodynamic Properties of Steam* would be determined for the given temperatures. The second step is to determine an equation of state for the vapor region that accurately represents the P-v-T data. There are many possible forms of the equation of state which may be selected. The important considerations are that the equation of state accurately represents the data, and that it be of such a form that the differentiations required can be performed (i.e., in some cases it may be desirable to have an equation of state explicit in v, whereas on other occasions an equation of state that is explicit in P may be more desirable).

Once an equation of state has been determined, the specific volume of superheated vapor at given pressures and temperatures can be determined by solving the equation and tabulating the results as in the superheat tables for steam, ammonia, and Freon-12. The specific volume of saturated vapor at a given temperature may be found by finding the saturation pressure from the vapor-pressure curve and substituting this saturation pressure and temperature into the equation of state.

The procedure followed in determining enthalpy and entropy is best explained with the aid of Fig. 10.5. Let us assume that the enthalpy and entropy of saturated liquid in state 1 are zero. The enthalpy of saturated vapor in state 2 can be found from the Clapeyron equation.

$$\left(\frac{dP}{dT}\right)_{\text{sat}} = \frac{h_{fg}}{T(v_g - v_f)}$$

The left side of this equation is found by differentiating the vapor-pressure curve. The specific volume of the saturated vapor is found by the procedure outlined in the last paragraph, and it is assumed the specific volume

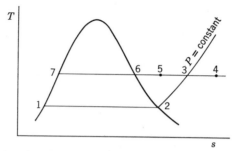

Fig. 10.5   Sketch showing procedure for developing a table of thermodynamic properties from experimental data.

of the saturated liquid has been measured. Thus, the enthalpy of evaporation, h_{fg}, can be found for this particular temperature, and the enthalpy at state 2 is equal to the enthalpy of evaporation (since the enthalpy in state 1 is assumed to be zero). The entropy at state 2 is readily found, since

$$s_{fg} = \frac{h_{fg}}{T}$$

The change in enthalpy between states 2 and 3 is readily found if the specific heat at this pressure is known. We have assumed that the zero-pressure specific heat, C_{po}, is known. Therefore, at a given pressure the specific heat, C_p, can be found by using Eq. 10.34.

$$\left(\frac{\partial C_p}{\partial P}\right)_T = -T\left(\frac{\partial^2 v}{\partial T^2}\right)_P$$

$$(dC_p)_T = -T\left(\frac{\partial^2 v}{\partial T^2}\right)_P dP_T$$

$$C_p - C_{po} = -\int_{P=0}^{P} T\left(\frac{\partial^2 v}{\partial T^2}\right)_P dP_T$$

The quantity $(\partial^2 v/\partial T^2)_P$ is found from the equation of state. If this equation of state is of the form $v = f(P, T)$ this differentiation can be readily obtained, and this is the reason for the previous statement regarding the form of the equation of state.

With the specific-heat equation for the given pressure, the change of enthalpy and entropy along the constant-pressure line is readily found.

$$(h_3 - h_2)_P = \int_5^3 C_p \, dT_P$$

$$(s_3 - s_2)_P = \int_5^3 C_p \, \frac{dT_P}{T}$$

From state 3 changes in enthalpy and entropy at constant temperature are readily found by using Eqs. 10.25 and 10.31 which were developed in the last section. For example:

$$h_3 - h_5 = \int_5^3 \left[v - T\left(\frac{\partial v}{\partial T}\right)_P \right] dP_T$$

$$s_3 - s_5 = \int_5^3 -\left(\frac{\partial v}{\partial T}\right)_P dP_T$$

The enthalpy and entropy of the saturated vapor in state 6 is found by this same procedure. Finally, the enthalpy and entropy of the saturated liquid in state 7 is found by applying the Clapeyron equation between states 6 and 7.

Thus, values for the pressure, temperature, specific volume, enthalpy, entropy, and internal energy of saturated liquid, saturated vapor, and superheated vapor can be tabulated for the entire region for which experimental data were obtained. It is evident that the accuracy of such a table depends both on the accuracy of the experimental data and the degree to which the equation for the vapor pressure and the equation of state represent the experimental data.

10.8   Ideal Gases

The properties of an ideal gas have been introduced at various relevant points in prior chapters. However, since an understanding of the properties of an ideal gas is essential to a study of the development of tables of thermodynamic properties, equations of state, and generalized charts, a brief summary of the properties of ideal gases is presented here. Two new parameters, the compressibility factor Z and the residual volume α are also introduced.

An ideal gas has the equation of state

$$P\bar{v} = \bar{R}T \tag{10.44}$$

where $\bar{R}$ is the universal gas constant. The numerical value of $\bar{R}$ depends on the units used for pressure, specific volume, and temperature. The value of $\bar{R}$ for some commonly used systems of units is as follows:

$$\bar{R} = 1545 \text{ ft-lbf/lb mole-R}$$
$$\bar{R} = 1.986 \text{ Btu/lb mole-R}$$
$$\bar{R} = 1.986 \text{ cal/gm mole-K}$$
$$\bar{R} = 0.08206 \text{ atm-lit/gm mole-K}$$
$$\bar{R} = 8.315 \text{ joules/gm mole-K}$$

The ideal gas equation of state on a mass basis is

$$Pv = RT \tag{10.45}$$

where $R = \bar{R}/M$. The value of R for a number of substances is given in Table A.8.

We can also write

$$PV = mRT = n\bar{R}T \tag{10.46}$$

As we consider the relationship of an ideal gas to actual gases it is helpful to define two additional parameters. The first is the compressibility factor Z, which is defined as,

$$Z \equiv \frac{Pv}{RT} \tag{10.47}$$

The compressibility factor has the value of unity for an ideal gas.

The second quantity is the residual volume α, which is defined as,

$$\alpha = \frac{\bar{R}T}{P} - \bar{v} \tag{10.48}$$

The residual volume is equal to zero for an ideal gas.

From numerous experimental observations on real gases it has been found that as the pressure is reduced toward zero, the specific volume becomes very large, and in the limit,

$$P\bar{v} \to \bar{R}T \quad \text{as} \quad P \to 0 \tag{10.49}$$

Or, to put this another way, as $P \to 0$, $Z \to 1$.

It is important to realize that even at low pressures, $P\bar{v}$ is not necessarily exactly equal to $\bar{R}T$, but only that Eq. 10.44 is very nearly satisfied at low pressures. An additional difference between ideal gases and actual gases is that the P-v-T relation of an actual gas might closely approach Eq. 10.44, the ideal gas equation of state, while the actual derivatives deviate significantly from those obtained from the ideal gas equation of state.

This point can be further amplified by considering the relation

$$\alpha = \frac{\bar{R}T}{P} - \bar{v}$$

Multiplying through by P we have

$$\alpha P = \bar{R}T - P\bar{v} \tag{10.50}$$

Thus the quantity αP is the difference between $\bar{R}T$ and $P\bar{v}$. Now as $P \to 0$, $RT \to Pv$. However, it does not necessarily follow that $\alpha \to 0$ as $P \to 0$. In fact it is only required that α remain finite, and experimental

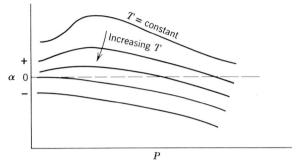

Fig. 10.6 Plot of isotherms on a residual volume—pressure diagram for a typical pure substance.

observations at low pressure show that α does approach a finite limiting value as $P \rightarrow 0$, the value being a function of the temperature as shown in Fig. 10.6.

The temperature at which $\alpha \rightarrow 0$ as $P \rightarrow 0$ is referred to as the Boyle Temperature.

The enthalpy of an ideal gas is a function of temperature only. This may be demonstrated as follows. For an ideal gas

$$Pv = RT$$

and

$$\left(\frac{\partial v}{\partial T}\right)_P = \frac{R}{P}$$

Therefore, for an ideal gas, we conclude from Eq. 10.23 that

$$\left(\frac{\partial h}{\partial P}\right)_T = v - \frac{TR}{P} = v - v = 0$$

In words, when the temperature of an ideal gas is held constant while the pressure varies, there is no change in enthalpy. We then conclude that the enthalpy of an ideal gas is a function of the temperature only.

Enthalpy is defined as

$$h = u + Pv$$

It follows that for an ideal gas

$$h = u + RT \tag{10.51}$$

Therefore the internal energy as well as the enthalpy of an ideal gas is a function of only the temperature.

The constant pressure specific heat is defined as

$$C_p = \left(\frac{\partial h}{\partial T}\right)_P$$

Since the enthalpy of an ideal gas is not a function of the pressure, it follows that for an ideal gas

$$dh = C_{po} \, dT \tag{10.52}$$

The subscript o is used to denote the specific heat of an ideal gas.

The constant volume specific heat is defined as

$$C_v = \left(\frac{\partial u}{\partial T} \right)_v$$

Since the internal energy of an ideal gas is not a function of volume, we can write

$$du = C_{vo} \, dT \tag{10.53}$$

where the subscript o denotes the ideal gas specific heat.

Equations for $\bar{C}_{po}$ as a function of temperature for a number of different substances are given in the Appendix, Table A.9. Changes in internal energy and enthalpy are readily found from Eqs. 10.53 and 10.52 if the specific heat is known as a function of temperature.

$$u_2 - u_1 = \int_1^2 C_{vo} \, dT \tag{10.54}$$

$$h_2 - h_1 = \int_1^2 C_{po} \, dT \tag{10.55}$$

The difference between C_{po} and C_{vo} is found as follows:

$$h = u + RT$$
$$dh = du + R \, dT$$
$$C_{po} \, dT = C_{vo} \, dT + R \, dT$$
$$\therefore \ C_{po} - C_{vo} = R \tag{10.56}$$

The change of entropy of an ideal gas can be found as follows:

$$T \, ds = dh - v \, dP$$

$$T \, ds = C_{po} \, dT - RT \frac{dP}{P}$$

$$ds = C_{po} \frac{dT}{T} - \frac{R \, dP}{P}$$

$$s_2 - s_1 = \int_1^2 C_{po} \frac{dT}{T} - R \ln \frac{P_2}{P_1} \tag{10.57}$$

Similarly, from the relation

$$T \, ds = du + P \, dv$$

one can derive the equation

$$s_2 - s_1 = \int_1^2 C_{vo} \frac{dT}{T} + R \ln \frac{v_2}{v_1} \tag{10.58}$$

10.9 *P-v-T* Behavior of Real Gases

A plot of lines of constant temperature on a *Z-P* diagram it one effective way of showing *P-v-T* behavior for a real gas. Figure 10.7 shows such a diagram for nitrogen. Note that as the pressure approaches zero, *Z* approaches unity for all isotherms, which is consistent with our observations made regarding ideal gases. However, the slope of the isotherm as the pressure approaches zero is zero for only one isotherm, namely the Boyle temperature. We noted before that, as the pressure is reduced, the residual volume α $\left(\alpha = \dfrac{\bar{R}T}{P} - \bar{v} \right)$ tends to zero only for the Boyle temperature. At pressures less than the critical pressure both saturated liquid and saturated vapor states can be shown on a *Z-P* diagram.

The behavior of the critical isotherm on a *P-v* diagram in the vicinity of the critical point is particularly important in a study of real gases. Consider the *P-v* plot for a pure substance shown in Fig. 10.8.

From a careful study of experimental data it is evident that at least the first two derivatives are zero at the critical point. This means that the critical isotherm goes through a point of inflection at the critical point.

$$\left(\frac{\partial P}{\partial v} \right)_T = 0 \tag{10.59}$$

$$\left(\frac{\partial^2 P}{\partial v^2} \right)_T = 0 \tag{10.60}$$

One of the most important characteristics of the *P-v-T* behavior of real gases involves the concept of reduced pressure, reduced temperature, and reduced specific volume. These are defined as follows:

Reduced pressure $= P_r = \dfrac{P}{P_c}$ $P_c =$ Critical pressure

Reduced temperature $= T_r = \dfrac{T}{T_c}$ $T_c =$ Critical temperature

Reduced specific volume $= v_r = \dfrac{v}{v_c}$ $v_c =$ Critical specific volume

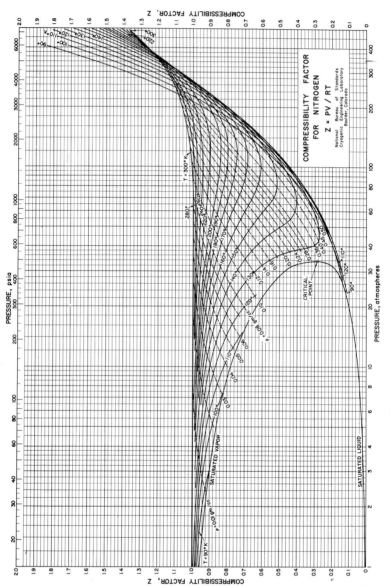

Fig. 10.7 Compressibility diagram for nitrogen.

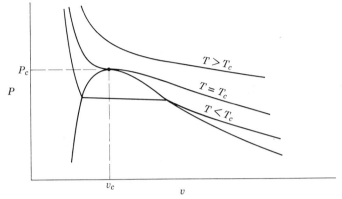

Fig. 10.8 Plot of isotherms in the region of the critical point on pressure-volume coordinates for a typical pure substance.

These equations state that the reduced property for a given state is the value of that property in this state divided by the value of that same property at the critical point.

If lines of constant T_r are plotted on a Z vs. P_r diagram, a plot such as Fig. A.1 is obtained. The striking fact is that when such Z vs. P_r diagrams are prepared for a large number of different substances, these diagrams very nearly coincide. This leads to the development of a generalized compressibility chart. Figure A.1 is actually a generalized diagram, which means that it represents the average diagram for a number of different substances. It should be noted that when such a diagram is used for a particular substance, the results might be slightly in error. On the other hand, if *P-v-T* information is required for a substance in a region where no experimental measurements have been made, the generalized compressibility diagram will in all probability give relatively accurate results. It is only necessary to know the critical pressure and the critical temperature in order to use the generalized chart. It should be emphasized that whenever one has accurate thermodynamic data for a given substance, these should be used rather than the generalized charts.

This behavior of pure substances that leads to the generalized compressibility chart is sometimes referred to as the rule of corresponding states, which may be expressed as

$$v_r = f(P_r, T_r)$$

That is, if the rule of corresponding states held exactly, there would be a single functional relation between v_r, P_r, and T_r which would apply to all substances. The generalized chart is one way of expressing this relationship, and the fact that this is only an approximate relation indicates the approximate nature of the rule of corresponding states.

The compressibility factor at the critical point varies considerably from one substance to another, generally in the range from 0.23–0.33, and therefore the generalized chart is usually not accurate in the immediate vicinity of the critical point. Also, since liquid compressibilities do not generalize well as functions of only T_r and P_r, the liquid region is often not included on a generalized chart.

Example 10.8

a. Volume unknown. Calculate the specific volume of propane at a pressure of 1000 lbf/in.² and a temperature of 300 F, and compare this with the specific volume given by the ideal-gas equation of state.

For propane

$$T_c = 666 \text{ R}$$
$$P_c = 617 \text{ lbf/in.}^2$$
$$R = 35.1 \text{ ft-lbf/lbm-R}$$
$$T_r = \tfrac{760}{666} = 1.141 \qquad P_r = \tfrac{1000}{617} = 1.62$$

From the compressibility chart

$$Z = 0.54$$
$$Pv = ZRT$$
$$v = \frac{0.54 \times 35.1 \times 760}{1000 \times 144} = 0.100 \text{ ft}^3/\text{lbm}$$

The ideal-gas equation would give the value

$$v = \frac{35.1 \times 760}{1000 \times 144} = 0.185 \text{ ft}^3/\text{lbm}$$

b. Pressure unknown. What pressure is required in order that propane have a specific volume of 0.100 ft³/lbm at a temperature of 300 F?

$$Pv = ZRT \qquad T_r = \tfrac{760}{666} = 1.141$$
$$P = P_c P_r$$

Therefore,

$$P_r = \frac{ZRT}{vP_c} = \frac{Z \times 35.1 \times 760}{0.100 \times 617 \times 144} = 3.00Z$$

$$Z = \frac{P_r}{3.00} = 0.33P_r$$

By a trial and error procedure, or by plotting a few points and drawing the curve representing this equation, P_r is found to be 1.62 at the point where $T_r = 1.141$. Therefore,

$$P = P_r P_c = 1.62(617) = 1000 \text{ lbf/in.}^2$$

c. Temperature unknown. What will be the temperature of propane when it has a specific volume of 0.100 ft³/lbm and a pressure of 1000 lbf/in.²?

$$Pv = ZRT \qquad T = T_c T_r$$
$$Pv = ZRT_c T_r$$
$$T_r = \frac{Pv}{ZRT_c} = \frac{1000 \times 144 \times 0.100}{Z \times 35.1 \times 666} = \frac{0.615}{Z}$$

When this line is plotted on the compressibility chart, the state point is given by the intersection of this line with the known reduced-pressure line ($P_r = 1.62$ in this case).

The reduced temperature is thus found to be

$$T_r = 1.14$$
$$T = T_r \times T_c = 1.14 \times 666 = 760 \text{ R}$$

10.10 Equations of State

An accurate equation of state, which is an analytical representation of P-v-T behavior, is often desirable from a computational standpoint. Many different equations of state have been developed. Most of these are accurate only to some density less than the critical density, though a few are reasonably accurate to approximately 2.5 times the critical density. All equations of state fail badly when the density exceeds the maximum density for which the equation was developed.

Three broad classifications of equations of state can be identified, namely, generalized, empirical, and theoretical.

The best known of the generalized equations of state is also the oldest, namely, the van der Waals equation, which was presented in 1873 as a semi-theoretical improvement over the ideal gas equation. The van der Waals equation of state is:

$$P = \frac{RT}{v - b} - \frac{a}{v^2} \tag{10.61}$$

The constant b is intended to correct for the volume occupied by the molecules, and the term a/v^2 is a correction that accounts for the inter-molecular forces of attraction. As might be expected in the case of a generalized equation, the constants a and b are evaluated from the general behavior of gases. In particular these constants are evaluated by noting that the critical isotherm passes through a point of inflection at the critical point, and that the slope is zero at this point. Thus, for the van der Waals equation of state we have

$$\left(\frac{\partial P}{\partial v}\right)_T = -\frac{RT}{(v-b)^2} + \frac{2a}{v^3} \tag{10.62}$$

$$\left(\frac{\partial^2 P}{\partial v^2}\right)_T = \frac{2RT}{(v-b)^3} - \frac{6a}{v^4} \tag{10.63}$$

Since both of these derivatives are equal to zero at the critical point we can write

$$-\frac{RT_c}{(v_c-b)^2} + \frac{2a}{v_c^3} = 0$$

$$\frac{2RT_c}{(v_c-b)^3} - \frac{6a}{v_c^4} = 0 \tag{10.64}$$

$$P_c = \frac{RT_c}{(v_c-b)} - \frac{a}{v_c^2}$$

Solving these three equations we find

$$v_c = 3b$$

$$a = \frac{27}{64}\frac{R^2 T_c^2}{P_c} \tag{10.65}$$

$$b = \frac{RT_c}{8P_c}$$

The compressibility factor at the critical point for the van der Waals equation is

$$Z_c = \frac{P_c v_c}{RT_c} = \frac{3}{8}$$

which is higher than the actual value for essentially all substances.

Van der Waals' equation can be written in terms of the compressibility factor and the reduced pressure and reduced temperature as follows:

$$Z^3 - \left(\frac{P_r}{8T_r} + 1\right)Z^2 + \left(\frac{27P_r}{64T_r^2}\right)Z - \frac{27P_r^2}{512T_r^3} = 0 \tag{10.66}$$

It is significant to note that this is of the same form as the generalized compressibility chart, namely, $Z = f(P_r, T_r)$, though the functional relation may be quite different from the generalized chart. This concept that different substances will have the same compressibility factor at the same reduced pressure and reduced temperature is another way of expressing the rule of corresponding states.

One of the best known empirical equations of state is the Beattie-Bridgeman equation, which is a pressure-explicit equation with five constants that are determined by a graphical procedure from experimental data for each substance. This equation was introduced in Chapter 3 in the form

$$P = \frac{RT(1 - \epsilon)}{v^2}(v + B) - \frac{A}{v^2} \qquad (10.67)$$

where
$$A = A_0(1 - a/v)$$
$$B = B_0(1 - b/v)$$
$$\epsilon = c/vT^3$$

This equation may also be written in the form

$$P = \frac{RT}{v} + \frac{\beta}{v^2} + \frac{\gamma}{v^3} + \frac{\delta}{v^4}$$

where
$$\beta = B_0 RT - A_0 - cR/T^2$$
$$\gamma = -B_0 bRT + A_0 a - B_0 cR/T^2$$
$$\delta = B_0 bcR/T^2$$

Table 10.1 gives the values of the five constants for a number of different substances.

The Beattie-Bridgeman equation of state is quite accurate for densities less than about 0.8 times the critical density. A more complex equation of state suitable for use at higher densities is that of Benedict, Webb, and Rubin,

$$P = \frac{RT}{v} + \frac{RTB_0 - A_0 - C_0/T^2}{v^2} + \frac{RTb - a}{v^3}$$
$$+ \frac{a\alpha}{v^6} + \frac{c}{v^3 T^2}\left(1 + \frac{\gamma}{v^2}\right)e^{-\gamma/v^2} \qquad (10.68)$$

which contains 8 empirical constants and is accurate to about twice the critical density. The Benedict-Webb-Rubin constants for a number of substances are given in Table 10.2. Many investigators have determined constants for other substances, and others have made certain changes in the form of the Benedict-Webb-Rubin equation in order to improve the accuracy of the equation for certain substances.

TABLE 10.1

Constants of the Beattie-Bridgeman Equation of State *

Pressure in atmospheres, volume in liters/gm mole, temperature in deg K

$R = 0.08206$ atm-liters/gm mole-K

Gas	A_0	a	B_0	b	$10^{-4} c$
Helium	0.0216	0.05984	0.01400	0.0	0.0040
Neon	0.2125	0.02196	0.02060	0.0	0.101
Argon	1.2907	0.02328	0.03931	0.0	5.99
Hydrogen	0.1975	−0.00506	0.02096	−0.04359	0.0504
Nitrogen	1.3445	0.02617	0.05046	−0.00691	4.20
Oxygen	1.4911	0.02562	0.04624	0.004208	4.80
Air	1.3012	0.01931	0.04611	−0.001101	4.34
CO_2	5.0065	0.07132	0.10476	0.07235	66.00
$(C_2H_5)_2O$	31.278	0.12426	0.45446	0.11954	33.33
C_2H_4	6.152	0.04964	0.12156	0.03597	22.68
Ammonia	2.3930	0.17031	0.03415	0.19112	476.87
CO	1.3445	0.02617	0.05046	−0.00691	4.20
N_2O	5.0065	0.07132	0.10476	0.07235	66.0
CH_4	2.2769	0.01855	0.05587	−0.01587	12.83
C_2H_6	5.8800	0.05861	0.09400	0.01915	90.00
C_3H_8	11.9200	0.07321	0.18100	0.04293	120
n-C_4H_{10}	17.794	0.12161	0.24620	0.09423	350
n-C_7H_{16}	54.520	0.20066	0.70816	0.19179	400

* *Proc. Am. Acad. Arts Sci.*, **63** (1928), pp. 229–308; *Z. Physik*, **62** (1930), pp. 95–101; *J. Chem. Phys.*, **3** (1935), pp. 93–96; *J. Am. Chem. Soc.*, **59** (1937), pp. 1587–1589, 1589-1590; **61** (1939), pp. 26–27.

Many other empirical equations of state, some even more complex in form than the Benedict-Webb-Rubin expression, have been developed and used to represent the *P-v-T* behavior of various substances.

A different approach to this problem is from the theoretical point of view. The theoretical equation of state, which is derived from kinetic theory or statistical thermodynamics, is written here in the form of a power series in reciprocal volume:

$$Z = \frac{Pv}{RT} = 1 + \frac{B}{v} + \frac{C}{v^2} + \frac{D}{v^3} + \cdots \qquad (10.69)$$

where B, C, D, $\cdots$ are temperature dependent, and are called virial coefficients. B is termed the second virial coefficient and is due to binary interactions on the molecular level. The virial coefficients can be expressed in terms of intermolecular forces from statistical mechanics, and evaluated

TABLE 10.2

Empirical Constants for Benedict-Webb-Rubin Equation*

Units:: Atmospheres, liters, moles, °K. *Gas Constants*: $R = 0.08206$; $T = 273.15 + T(°C)$

Gas	A_0	B_0	$C_0 \cdot 10^{-6}$	a	b	$c \cdot 10^{-6}$	$\alpha \cdot 10^3$	$\gamma \cdot 10^2$
Methane	1.85500	0.0426000	0.0225700	0.494000	0.00338004	0.00254500	0.124359	0.60000
Ethylene	3.33958	0.0556833	0.131140	0.259000	0.0086000	0.021120	0.178000	0.923000
Ethane	4.15556	0.0627724	0.179592	0.345160	0.0111220	0.0327670	0.243389	1.18000
Propylene	6.11220	0.0850647	0.439182	0.774056	0.0187059	0.102611	0.455696	1.82900
Propane	6.87225	0.0973130	0.508256	0.947700	0.0225000	0.129000	0.607175	2.20000
i-Butane	10.23264	0.137544	0.849943	1.93763	0.0424352	0.286010	1.07408	3.40000
i-Butylene	8.95325	0.116025	0.927280	1.69270	0.0348156	0.274920	0.910889	2.95945
n-Butane	10.0847	0.124361	0.992830	1.88231	0.0399983	0.316400	1.10132	3.40000
i-Pentane	12.7959	0.160053	1.74632	3.75620	0.0668120	0.695000	1.70000	4.63000
n-Pentane	12.1794	0.156751	2.12121	4.07480	0.0668120	0.824170	1.81000	4.75000
n-Hexane	14.4373	0.177813	3.31935	7.11671	0.109131	1.51276	2.81086	6.66849
n-Heptane	17.5206	0.199005	4.74574	10.36475	0.151954	2.47000	4.35611	9.00000

* M. Benedict, G. B. Webb, and L. C. Rubin, *Chem. Eng. Progress*, **47**, 419 (1951).

upon selection of an empirical potential function model. For all but the simplest functions the mathematical expressions become so complex that very little has been accomplished beyond the third virial coefficient. With this equation, including the third virial coefficient, it is possible to achieve accurate P-v-T representation at densities below approximately 0.7 times the critical density.

10.11   The Generalized Chart for Changes of Enthalpy at Constant Temperature

In Section 10.4, Eq. 10.25 was derived for the change of enthalpy at constant temperature.

$$(h_2 - h_1)_T = \int_1^2 \left[v - T\left(\frac{\partial v}{\partial T}\right)_P \right] dP_T$$

A similar equation for the change of enthalpy in an isothermal process can be developed as follows:

$$dh = T\,ds + v\,dP$$

$$\left(\frac{\partial h}{\partial v}\right)_T = T\left(\frac{\partial s}{\partial v}\right)_T + v\left(\frac{\partial P}{\partial v}\right)_T$$

Substituting one of the Maxwell relations, Eq. 10.13, we have

$$\left(\frac{\partial h}{\partial v}\right)_T = T\left(\frac{\partial P}{\partial T}\right)_v + v\left(\frac{\partial P}{\partial v}\right)_T$$

Therefore,

$$(h_2 - h_1)_T = \int_1^2 \left[T\left(\frac{\partial P}{\partial T}\right)_v + v\left(\frac{\partial P}{\partial v}\right)_T \right] dv_T$$

One essential point about these two equations for $(h_2 - h_1)_T$ is that the change of enthalpy at constant temperature is a function of the P-v-T behavior of the gas. This means that if the equation of state is known for a substance, the change in enthalpy at constant temperature can be determined by the appropriate differentiation and integration. It also follows that since the generalized chart is a representation of the P-v-T behavior of the gas, this chart can be used to prepare a generalized chart for the change of enthalpy in an isothermal process.

The procedure for the development of such a chart is as follows: It has been shown that

$$\left(\frac{\partial h}{\partial P}\right)_T = v - T\left(\frac{\partial v}{\partial T}\right)_P$$

But

$$v = \frac{ZRT}{P}$$

and

$$\left(\frac{\partial v}{\partial T}\right)_P = \frac{ZR}{P} + \frac{RT}{P}\left(\frac{\partial Z}{\partial T}\right)_P$$

Therefore

$$\left(\frac{\partial h}{\partial P}\right)_T = \frac{ZRT}{P} - \frac{ZRT}{P} - \frac{RT^2}{P}\left(\frac{\partial Z}{\partial T}\right)_P = -\frac{RT^2}{P}\left(\frac{\partial Z}{\partial T}\right)_P$$

$$dh_T = -\frac{RT^2}{P}\left(\frac{\partial Z}{\partial T}\right)_P dP_T$$

But $T = T_c T_r$ and $P = P_c P_r$. Therefore,

$$\frac{dT}{T} = \frac{dT_r}{T_r} \; ; \qquad \frac{dP}{P} = \frac{dP_r}{P_r}$$

$$dT = T_c \, dT_r; \qquad dP = P_c \, dP_r$$

Substituting these values we have

$$dh_T = -\frac{RT_c^2 T_r^2}{P_c P_r}\left(\frac{\partial Z}{T_c \, \partial T_r}\right)_{P_r} P_c (dP_r)_{T_r}$$

$$= -RT_c T_r^2 \left(\frac{\partial Z}{\partial T_r}\right)_{P_r} (d \ln P_r)_{T_r}$$

Integrating at constant temperature we have

$$\frac{\Delta \bar{h}_T}{T_c} = -\bar{R}\int_1^2 T_r^2 \left(\frac{\partial Z}{\partial T_r}\right)_{P_r} d \ln P_r \tag{10.70}$$

Let us designate by an asterisk, $\bar{h}^*$, the enthalpy per mole at a given temperature and a very low pressure, so that $P_r \to 0$, and let us designate without superscript the enthalpy at any state at the same temperature and a given pressure P_r. Then the integration is as follows:

$$\frac{\bar{h}^* - \bar{h}}{T_c} = \bar{R}\int_{P_r=0}^{P_r} T_r^2 \left(\frac{\partial Z}{\partial T_r}\right)_{P_r} d \ln P_r \tag{10.71}$$

The right side of this equation can be obtained by graphical integration of the compressibility chart, and is a function of only the reduced pressure and temperature. The left side represents the change in enthalpy as the pressure is increased from zero to the given pressure while the temperature is held constant. Sometimes this quantity is called the enthalpy departure. Figure A.3 shows a plot of this quantity, $(\bar{h}^* - \bar{h})/T_c$, as a function of P_r for various lines of constant T_r.

In many cases the specific heat of a substance is known at low pressure. This information, along with the generalized residual enthalpy chart, enables one to find the change of enthalpy for any given change of state.

Example 10.9

Nitrogen is throttled from 3000 lbf/in.², −100 F, to 200 lbf/in.² in an adiabatic, steady-state, steady-flow process. Determine the final temperature of the nitrogen. The zero-pressure specific heat of nitrogen in this temperature range is 0.248 Btu/lbm-R. This is a constant-enthalpy process, and in solving such a problem it is usually helpful to use a temperature-entropy diagram such as the one shown in Fig. 10.9.

$$P_1 = 3000 \text{ lbf/in.}^2 \qquad P_2 = 200 \text{ lbf/in.}^2$$
$$P_{r1} = \tfrac{3000}{492} = 6.1 \qquad P_{r2} = \tfrac{200}{492} = 0.406$$
$$T_1 = 360 \text{ R}$$
$$T_{r1} = \tfrac{360}{227} = 1.586$$

From the generalized chart for enthalpy change at constant temperature,

$$\frac{h_1^* - h_1}{T_c} = 3.6 \text{ Btu/lb mole-R}$$

$$h_1^* - h_1 = \frac{3.6 \times 227}{28} = 29.2 \text{ Btu/lbm}$$

It is now necessary to assume a final temperature and check to see if the net change in enthalpy for the process is zero. Let us assume that $T_2 = 265$ R. Then the change in enthalpy between 1* and 2* can be found

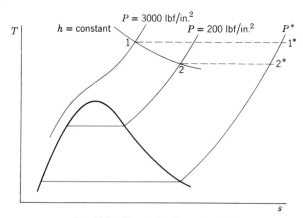

Fig. 10.9   Sketch for Example 10.9.

from the zero-pressure specific-heat data.

$$h_1{}^* - h_2{}^* = C_{po}(T_1{}^* - T_2{}^*) = 0.248(360 - 265) = 23.6 \text{ Btu/lbm}$$

(The variation in C_{po} with temperature can be taken into account when necessary.)

We now find the enthalpy change between 2* and 2.

$$T_{r2} = \tfrac{265}{227} = 1.17 \qquad P_{r2} = 0.406$$

Therefore, from the enthalpy departure chart, Fig. A.3,

$$\frac{\bar{h}_2{}^* - \bar{h}_2}{T_c} = 0.7 \text{ Btu/lb mole-R}$$

$$h_2{}^* - h_2 = \frac{0.7(227)}{28} = 5.7 \text{ Btu/lbm}$$

We now check to see if the net change in enthalpy for the process is zero.

$$h_1 - h_2 = 0 = -(h_1{}^* - h_1) + (h_1{}^* - h_2{}^*) + (h_2{}^* - h_2)$$
$$= -29.2 + 23.6 + 5.7 = 0.1 \text{ Btu/lbm}$$

This essentially checks, and we conclude that the final temperature is approximately 265 R.

10.12 Fugacity and the Generalized Fugacity Chart

At this point a new thermodynamic property, the fugacity, f, is introduced. The fugacity is particularly important when considering mixtures and equilibrium, which are discussed in two later chapters. However, in view of the fact that a generalized fugacity chart can be developed, the fugacity is introduced here.

The fugacity is essentially a pseudo-pressure. When the fugacity is substituted for pressure, one can, in effect, use the same equations for real gases that one normally uses for ideal gases. The concept of fugacity can be introduced as follows:

Consider the relation

$$dg = -s\, dT + v\, dP$$

At constant temperature

$$dg_T = v\, dP_T \qquad (10.72)$$

For an ideal gas this last equation may be written

$$dg_T = \frac{RT}{P}\, dP_T = RT\, d(\ln P)_T \qquad (10.73)$$

and for a real gas, with the equation of state $Pv = ZRT$, this equation becomes

$$dg_T = ZRT\frac{dP_T}{P} = ZRT\,d(\ln P)_T \tag{10.74}$$

Fugacity, f, is defined as

$$dg_T \equiv RT\,d(\ln f)_T \tag{10.75}$$

It follows from these last two equations that

$$\left(\frac{\partial \ln f}{\partial \ln P}\right)_T = Z \tag{10.76}$$

Since $Z \to 1$ as $P \to 0$, it follows that

$$\lim_{P \to 0} (f/p) = 1$$

Therefore, as $P \to 0$, $f \to 0$.

Let us consider the change in the Gibbs function of a real gas during an isothermal process at temperature T that involves a change in pressure from a very low pressure, $P*$ (where ideal gas behavior can be assumed) to a higher pressure P. Let the Gibbs function at this low pressure be designated $g*$. The value of the Gibbs function at this temperature T and at the pressure P can be found in terms of the fugacity at P and T and $g*$. This is evident if one integrates Eq. 10.75 from the very low pressure $P*$ to the pressure P.

$$\int_{g*}^{g} dg_T = \int_{f*=P*}^{f} RT(d \ln f)_T$$
$$g = g* + RT \ln (f/P*) \tag{10.77}$$

A generalized fugacity coefficient chart based on the generalized compressibility chart, Fig. A.4, can be developed by the following procedure. From Eqs. 10.72 and 10.75,

$$dg_T = v\,dP_T = \frac{ZRT\,dP_T}{P} = RT\,d(\ln f)_T$$

Therefore,

$$Z\,d(\ln P)_T = d(\ln f)_T$$

But

$$\frac{dP}{P} = \frac{dP_r}{P_r}; \qquad d \ln P = d \ln P_r$$

Therefore,

$$Z(d \ln P_r)_T = d(\ln f)_T$$
$$Z(d \ln P_r)_T - d(\ln P_r)_T = d(\ln f)_T - d(\ln P_r)_T \tag{10.78}$$
$$(Z - 1)(d \ln P_r)_T = d(\ln f/P)_T$$

Integrating at constant temperature from $P = 0$ to a finite pressure we have

$$\int_{f/P=1}^{f/P} d(\ln f/P)_T = \int_0^{P_r} (Z - 1)\, d \ln P_{rT}$$

$$\ln (f/P) = \int_0^{P_r} (Z - 1)\, d \ln P_{rT} \tag{10.79}$$

At any temperature the right hand side of this equation can be integrated graphically using the generalized compressibility chart to find Z at each P_r. The result is the generalized chart shown in Fig. A.4.

The reversible isothermal process is one type of problem in which the fugacity can be used to advantage.

Example 10.10

Calculate the work of compression and the heat transfer per pound when ethane is compressed reversibly and isothermally from 14.7 lbf/in.² to 1000 lbf/in.² at a temperature of 110 F in a steady-state, steady-flow process.

The first law for this process is,

$$q + h_1 + KE_1 + PE_1 = h_2 + KE_2 + PE_2 + w$$

Since the process is reversible and isothermal,

$$q = T(s_2 - s_1) = T_2 s_2 - T_1 s_1$$

Therefore,

$$-w = h_2 - h_1 - (T_2 s_2 - T_1 s_1) + \Delta KE + \Delta PE$$
$$-w = g_2 - g_1 + \Delta KE + \Delta PE$$

We assume that the changes in kinetic and potential energy are negligible.

$$-w = g_2 - g_1 = RT \ln (f_2/f_1)$$

The fugacity in state 1 and state 2 can be found from the generalized fugacity chart in the Appendix, Fig. A.4.

For ethane,

$$P_c = 708 \text{ lbf/in.}^2 \qquad T_c = 549.8 \text{ R}$$

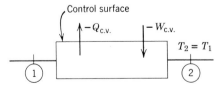

Fig. 10.10   Sketch for Example 10.10.

Therefore,

$$P_{r1} = \frac{14.7}{708} = 0.021 \qquad T_{r1} = T_{r2} = \frac{570}{549.8} = 1.037$$

$$P_{r2} = \frac{1000}{708} = 1.412$$

From the generalized enthalpy departure chart, Fig. A.3,

$$\frac{\bar{h}_2{}^* - \bar{h}_2}{T_c} = 6.8 \qquad \frac{\bar{h}_1{}^* - \bar{h}_1}{T_c} < 0.1$$

Since $h_1{}^* = h_2{}^* = h_1$

$$h_2{}^* - h_2 = h_1 - h_2 = \frac{6.8(549.8)}{30} = 124.8 \text{ Btu/lbm}$$

From the generalized fugacity chart, Fig. A.4,

$$f_2/P_2 = 0.58 \qquad f_2 = 1000(0.58) = 580 \text{ lbf/in.}^2$$
$$f_1/P_1 = 1.0 \qquad f_1 = 14.7(1.0) = 14.7 \text{ lbf/in.}^2$$

Therefore,

$$-w = g_2 - g_1 = RT \ln f_2/f_1 = \frac{1.986}{30} \times 570 \ln \frac{580}{14.7}$$

$$= 138.8 \text{ Btu/lbm}$$

$$g_2 - g_1 = (h_2 - h_1) - T(s_2 - s_1) = (h_2 - h_1) - q$$

$$138.8 \text{ Btu/lbm} = -124.8 - T(s_2 - s_1) = -124.8 - q$$

$$q = T_2(s_2 - s_1) = -124.8 - 138.8 = -263.6 \text{ Btu/lbm}$$

$$s_2 - s_1 = \frac{-263.6}{570} = -0.462 \text{ Btu/lbm-R}$$

10.13 The Generalized Chart for Changes of Entropy at Constant Temperature

A generalized chart for entropy can be developed that gives the difference between the entropy of an ideal gas and an actual gas as the pressure is increased from zero pressure along an isotherm. The thermodynamic analysis for the development of such a chart is as follows.

From Eq. 10.30

$$ds_T = -\left(\frac{\partial v}{\partial T}\right)_P dP_T$$

Integrating at constant temperature, T, from $P = 0$ to P we have

$$(s_P - s_0{}^*)_T = -\left[\int_{P=0}^{P} \left(\frac{\partial v}{\partial T}\right)_P dP_T\right] \qquad (10.80)$$

The entropy at zero pressure can be designated with an * (which we use to refer to ideal gas behavior) since ideal gas behavior is approached as $P \to 0$. However, $s \to \infty$ as $P \to 0$, and therefore this equation is not particularly useful in this form.

If we repeat this integration for an ideal gas we have

$$(s_P{}^* - s_0{}^*)_T = -\left[\int_{P=0}^{P}\left(\frac{\partial v}{\partial T}\right)_P dP_T\right] = -\left[\int_{P=0}^{P} R\frac{dP_T}{P}\right] \quad (10.81)$$

Subtracting Eq. 10.80 from Eq. 10.81,

$$(s_P{}^* - s_P) = -\int_{P=0}^{P}\left[\frac{R}{P} - \left(\frac{\partial v}{\partial T}\right)_P\right] dP_T$$

Therefore, with the equation of state $Pv = ZRT$,

$$(s_P{}^* - s_P) = -\int_{P=0}^{P}\left[\frac{R}{P} - \frac{ZR}{P} - \frac{RT}{P}\left(\frac{\partial Z}{\partial T}\right)_P\right] dP_T$$

or,

$$(\bar{s}_P{}^* - \bar{s}_P) = \bar{R}\int_0^{P_r}(Z-1)\frac{dP_r}{P_r} + \bar{R}T_r\int_0^{P_r}\left(\frac{\partial Z}{\partial T_r}\right)_{P_r}\frac{dP_r}{P_r}$$

But, from Eq. 10.79

$$\bar{R}\int_0^{P_r}(Z-1)\frac{dP_r}{P_r} = \bar{R}\ln(f/P)$$

and from Eq. 10.71,

$$\bar{R}T_r\int_0^{P_r}\left(\frac{\partial Z}{\partial T_r}\right)_{P_r}\frac{dP_r}{P_r} = \frac{\bar{h}^* - \bar{h}}{T_c T_r}$$

Therefore,

$$(\bar{s}_P{}^* - \bar{s}_P) = \bar{R}\ln f/P + \frac{\bar{h}^* - \bar{h}}{T_c T_r}$$

Thus, for the equation of state $Pv = ZRT$, the quantity $(s_P{}^* - s_P)$ can be obtained from the generalized enthalpy departure and the generalized fugacity coefficient charts. Figure A.5 shows such a chart.

Example 10.11

Nitrogen at 1000 lbf/in.², −200 F is throttled to 100 lbf/ie.². After passing through a short length of pipe the temperature is measured and found to be −260 F. Determine the heat transfer and the change of entropy using the generalized charts and compare these results with those

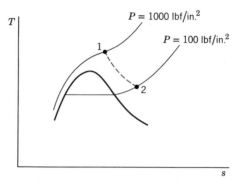

Fig. 10.11   Sketch for Example 10.11.

obtained by using the nitrogen tables.

$$P_{r1} = \frac{1000}{492} = 2.03 \qquad T_{r1} = \frac{260}{227.1} = 1.146$$

$$P_{r2} = \frac{100}{492} = 0.203 \qquad T_{r2} = \frac{200}{227.1} = 0.882$$

From the first law

$$q = h_2 - h_1 = -(h_2{}^* - h_2) + (h_2{}^* - h_1{}^*) + (h_1{}^* - h_1)$$

From Fig. A.3 in the Appendix,

$$\frac{\bar{h}_1{}^* - \bar{h}_1}{T_c} = 4.85 \text{ Btu/lb mole}; \qquad h_1{}^* - h_1 = \frac{227.1(4.85)}{28.0} = 41.0 \text{ Btu/lbm}$$

$$\frac{\bar{h}_2{}^* - \bar{h}_2}{T_c} = 0.7 \text{ Btu/lb mole}; \qquad h_2{}^* - h_2 = \frac{227.1(0.7)}{28.0} = 5.7 \text{ Btu/lbm}$$

Assuming a constant specific heat for the ideal gas,

$$h_2{}^* - h_1{}^* = C_{p0}(T_2 - T_1) = 0.248(200 - 260) = -14.9 \text{ Btu/lbm}$$
$$q = -5.7 - 14.9 + 41.0 = 20.4 \text{ Btu/lbm}$$

From the nitrogen tables, Table A.5, we can find the change of enthalpy directly.
$$q = h_2 - h_1 = 109.93 - 85.54 = 24.39 \text{ Btu/lbm}$$

To calculate the change of entropy using the generalized charts we proceed as follows:

$$\bar{s}_2 - \bar{s}_1 = -(\bar{s}_{P_2,T_2}^* - \bar{s}_2) + (\bar{s}_{P_2,T_2}^* - \bar{s}_{P_1,T_1}^*) + (\bar{s}_{P_1,T_1}^* - \bar{s}_1)$$

From Fig. A.5 in the Appendix,

$$\bar{s}_{P_1,T_1}^* - \bar{s}_1 = 3.35 \text{ Btu/lb mole-R}$$
$$\bar{s}_{P_2,T_2}^* - \bar{s}_2 = 0.65 \text{ Btu/lb mole-R}$$

Assuming a constant specific heat for the ideal gas,

$$\bar{s}^*_{P_2, T_2} - \bar{s}^*_{P_1, T_1} = \bar{C}_{p_0} \ln \frac{T_2}{T_1} - \bar{R} \ln \frac{P_2}{P_1}$$

$$= 6.95 \times \ln \tfrac{200}{260} - 1.986 \times \ln \tfrac{100}{1000} = 2.76 \text{ Btu/lb mole-R}$$

$$\bar{s}_2 - \bar{s}_1 = -0.65 + 2.76 + 3.35 = 5.46 \text{ Btu/lb mole-R}$$

$$s_2 - s_1 = \frac{5.46}{28.0} = 0.195 \text{ Btu/lbm-R}$$

From Table A.5

$$s_2 - s_1 = 0.6585 - 0.4419 = 0.2166 \text{ Btu/lbm-R.}$$

PROBLEMS

10.1 Show that on a Mollier diagram (h-s diagram) the slope of a constant-pressure line increases with temperature in the superheat region and that the constant-pressure line is straight in the two-phase region.

10.2 From the first Maxwell relation derived and the relation

$$\left(\frac{\partial x}{\partial y}\right)_z \left(\frac{\partial y}{\partial z}\right)_x \left(\frac{\partial z}{\partial x}\right)_y = -1$$

derive the other three Maxwell relations.

10.3 The following data are available at the triple point of water:

Pressure:	0.0885 lbf/in.^{2}
Temperature:	32.02 F
Enthalpy:	Liquid: 0.02 Btu/lbm
	Solid: -143.3 Btu/lbm
Specific Volume:	Liquid: 0.01603 ft^3/lbm
	Solid: 0.01747 ft^3/lbm

A man weighing 200 lbm is ice skating on "hollow ground" blades which have a total area in contact with the ice of 0.033 in.^{2} The temperature of the ice is 28 F. Will the ice melt under the blades?

10.4 At 1 atm pressure helium boils at 4.22 K, and the latent heat of vaporization is 19.9 cal/gm mole. Suppose one wishes to determine how low a temperature could be obtained by producing a vacuum over liquid helium, thus causing it to boil at a lower pressure and temperature. Determine what pressure would be necessary to produce a temperature of 1 K and 0.1 K.

What do you think is the lowest temperature that could be obtained by pumping a vacuum over liquid helium?

10.5 A transfer line for liquid nitrogen is so designed that it has a double walled pipe as indicated in Fig. 10.12. The annular space is so constructed that when the pipeline is at ambient temperature it contains carbon dioxide at 1 atm pressure. When liquid nitrogen at 1 atm pressure flows through the pipe the

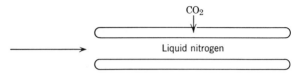

Fig. 10.12   Sketch for Problem 10.5.

carbon dioxide will freeze on the inner walls. The pressure of the carbon dioxide in the annular space will essentially be equal to the vapor pressure of carbon dioxide at the saturation temperature of nitrogen at 1 atm pressure. Suppose that the tables of thermodynamic properties which are available do not go down to this temperature. However, at 5 lbf/in.² pressure the saturation temperature is -132 F and the enthalpy of sublimation is 247 Btu/lbm. Estimate the pressure of the carbon dioxide in the annular space when liquid nitrogen is flowing through the tube.

10.6 Consider Fig. 3.4, and prove that for water the slope of the sublimation line is greater than the slope of the vaporization line at the triple point.

10.7 The equation for the vapor-pressure curve used in the Ammonia Tables (a summary of which appears in the Appendix) is as follows:

$$\log_{10} P = A - \frac{B}{T} - C \log_{10} T - DT + ET^2$$

where $A = 25.5743247$
$B = 3.2951254 \times 10^3$
$C = 6.4012471$
$D = 4.148279 \times 10^{-4}$
$E = 1.4759945 \times 10^{-6}$
$P = $ pressure in lbf/in.²
$T = $ absolute temperature in °R

(a) Derive an expression for h_{fg} in terms of the constants in the vapor-pressure curve, the absolute temperature, and the specific volume of the saturated liquid and saturated vapor.

(b) Calculate the enthalpy of evaporation at 40 F and compare the value thus calculated with the value given in the Ammonia Tables.

10.8 Derive expressions for $\left(\frac{\partial u}{\partial P}\right)_T$ and $\left(\frac{\partial u}{\partial T}\right)_P$ that do not contain the properties h, u, or s.

10.9 Derive expressions for $\left(\frac{\partial T}{\partial v}\right)_u$ and $\left(\frac{\partial h}{\partial s}\right)_v$ that do not contain the properties h, u, or s.

10.10 Show that for van der Waals' equation the following relations apply.

(a) $(h_2 - h_1)_T = (P_2 v_2 - P_1 v_1) + a\left(\frac{1}{v_1} - \frac{1}{v_2}\right)$

(b) $(s_2 - s_1)_T = R \ln\left(\frac{v_2 - b}{v_1 - b}\right)$

(c) $\left(\frac{\partial C_v}{\partial v}\right)_T = 0$

(d) $C_p - C_v = \dfrac{R}{1 - 2a(v - b)^2/RTv^3}$

10.11 Derive expressions for the changes in enthalpy and entropy at constant temperature for a substance that follows the Beattie-Bridgeman equation of state.

10.12 (a) Find the limiting values

$$\operatorname*{Lim}_{P\to 0} (Z)_T$$

$$\operatorname*{Lim}_{P\to 0} (\alpha)_T$$

(where Z is the compressibility factor and α the residual volume) as predicted by the van der Waals equation of state.

(b) Repeat part (a) for the virial equation of state.

(c) Compare these results with those for an ideal gas.

10.13 (a) The Boyle temperature is that temperature for which

$$\operatorname*{Lim}_{P\to 0} \left(\frac{\partial Z}{\partial P}\right)_T = 0$$

Using this relation, show that the residual volume α tends to zero at zero pressure only at the Boyle temperature.

(b) Use the results of part (a) and Problem 10.12 to find the Boyle temperature for the van der Waals and virial equations of state.

10.14 Show that the Joule-Thomson coefficient μ_J is given by the relation

$$\mu_J = \frac{1}{C_p}\left[T\left(\frac{\partial v}{\partial T}\right)_P - v\right]$$

10.15 Show that if the volume expansivity α is constant, the following relation is valid:

$$\left(\frac{\partial C_p}{\partial P}\right)_T = -vT\alpha^2$$

10.16 From the data given in Table A.1.4 of the Appendix determine the average value of the isothermal compressibility at 32 F, 100 F, and 400 F. Does the isothermal compressibility vary significantly with pressure at a given temperature?

10.17 In Chapter 14 it is shown that the velocity of sound, c, in a fluid is given by the relaton

$$\frac{c^2}{g_c} = \left(\frac{\partial P}{\partial \rho}\right)_s$$

(a) Show that the velocity of sound is given by the relation

$$c = \sqrt{\frac{g_c}{\beta_s \rho}}$$

where β_s is the adiabatic compressibility.

(b) At a temperature of 100 F the velocity of sound in water is 5040 ft/sec. Verify this by determining the adiabatic compressibility of water at 100 F by using Tables A.1.1 and A.1.4. (Note that the state of water after an isentropic process can be determined by using both Tables A.1.1 and A.1.4.)

10.18 The following data are available for ethyl alcohol at 20 C.

$$\rho = 49.2 \text{ lbm/ft}^3$$
$$\beta_s = 6.5 \times 10^{-6} \text{ in.}^2/\text{lbf}$$
$$\beta_T = 7.7 \times 10^{-6} \text{ in.}^2/\text{lbf}$$

(a) What is the velocity of sound (see Problem 10.17) in ethyl alcohol?

(b) The pressure on a cylinder having a volume of 1 ft³ containing ethyl alcohol at 20 C is increased from 1 atm to 200 atm while the temperature remains constant. Determine the work done on the ethyl alcohol during this process.

10.19 Suppose that the following data are available for a given pure substance:
A vapor-pressure curve.
An equation of state of the form $P = f(v, T)$.
Specific volume of saturated liquid.
Critical pressure and temperature.
Constant-volume specific heat of the vapor at one specific volume.
Outline the steps you would follow in order to develop a table of thermodynamic properties comparable to Tables 1, 2, and 3 of the steam tables.

10.20 Methane at a pressure of 1000 lbf/in.², 200 F is throttled in a steady-flow process to 100 lbf/in.² Determine the final temperature of the methane.

10.21 Ethane at 800 lbf/in.², 300 F is cooled in a heat exchanger to 120 F. The volume rate of flow entering the heat exchanger is 100 ft³/min, and the pressure drop through the heat exchanger is small. Determine the heat transfer per min.

10.22 Nitrogen at a pressure of 1500 lbf/in.², −100 F is contained in a tank of 10 ft³ volume. Heat is transferred to the nitrogen until the temperature is 200 F. Determine the heat transfer and the final pressure of the nitrogen using the generalized charts and compare these results with those obtained when using the nitrogen tables, Table A.5.

10.23 Saturated liquid nitrogen at −260 F is throttled to 100 lbf/in.² Calculate the quality at the outlet, using
(a) The generalized charts.
(b) The nitrogen tables.

10.24 Consider a 2 ft³ tank in which methane is stored at low temperature. The pressure is 14.7 lbf/in². and the tank contains 25% liquid, 75% vapor on a volume basis.

(a) If the tank is allowed to warm because of heat transfer with the ambient, what is the temperature of the methane when the pressure reaches 1500 lbf/in.²?

(b) Calculate the heat transfer during this process.

The following data may be used:
Saturation pressure

$$\ln P_{\text{sat}} = -\frac{1850}{T} + 11.88 \qquad \left(P_{\text{sat}} = \frac{\text{lbf}}{\text{in}^2}, T = R\right)$$

Liquid specific volume

$$v_f = 0.0378 \text{ ft}^3/\text{lbm at } 14.7 \text{ lbf/in.}^2$$

10.25 Propane flows through a pipe of constant cross-sectional area. At the inlet section of this pipe the velocity is 60 ft/sec, the pressure is 400 lbf/in.², and the temperature is 200 F. At the exit section the pressure is 100 lbf/in.^{2} There is no heat transfer to or from the gas as it flows in the pipe. Determine the temperature and velocity of the propane leaving the pipe.

10.26 A 2 ft^3 evacuated tank is to be filled from a supply line containing ethane at 100 F, 2000 lbf/in.^{2} Gas flows into the tank until the pressure reaches 2000 lbf/in.^{2}, at which time the valve is closed. The tank is well insulated so that heat transfer is negligible. Using the compressibility charts, determine the final temperature in the tank and the mass of ethane entering.

10.27 An insulated tank having a volume of 2 ft^3 contains carbon dioxide at 200 lbf/in.^{2}, 100 F. It is pressurized from a line in which carbon dioxide is flowing at 1200 lbf/in.^{2}, 100 F. The valve is closed when the pressure in the tank reaches 1200 lbf/in.^{2}

Using the generalized charts determine the amount of carbon dioxide which flows into the tank.

10.28 Carbon dioxide is to be liquefied in a steady-flow insulated condenser. CO_2 enters the condenser at 170 F, 900 lbf/in.^{2} at the rate of 1 ft^3/min, and leaves at 900 lbf/in.^{2} Cooling water enters at 40 F and leaves at 70 F. The flow rate of the cooling water is 1800 lbm/hr.

Determine the temperature of the CO_2 leaving the condenser and show the process for the CO_2 on a T-s diagram.

10.29 Find the change of enthalpy, internal energy, and entropy as propane undergoes a change of state from 60 F, 14.7 lbf/in.^{2} pressure to 300 F, 800 lbf/in.^{2} pressure.

10.30 Propane is compressed in a reversible isothermal steady-flow process from 1 atm pressure, 700 R to 40 atm pressure. Determine the work of compression and heat transfer per lbm of propane.

10.31 Propane is compressed in a reversible adiabatic steady-flow process from 1 atm pressure, 700 R to 40 atm pressure. Determine the work of compression per lbm of propane.

10.32 Freon-12 is compressed in a cylinder fitted with a piston in a reversible isothermal process from 100 lbf/in.^{2}, 300 F to 600 lbf/in.^{2} Determine the work of compression and the heat transfer by using the generalized charts, and compare these results with those obtained by using the Freon-12 tables in the Appendix.

10.33 Ethylene, C_2H_4, enters an uninsulated compressor at 60 F, 100 lbf/in.^{2} The flow rate is 45 lbm/hr, and the power input to the compressor is 1.5 hp. The outlet state is measured and found to be 150 F, 1000 lbf/in.^{2} Any heat transferred during the process is with the surrounding air at 60 F.

(a) Calculate the work and heat transfer per lbm of C_2H_4 compressed.

(b) Considering a control volume that includes the compressor, calculate the entropy changes of the control volume and the surroundings per lbm of C_2H_4, and show that the process does not violate the second law.

10.34 Methane at room temperature, 60 F, and 1200 lbf/in.^{2} is expanded irreversibly through an adiabatic nozzle, from which it exits at −55 F, 400 lbf/ in.^{2} Using the generalized charts, determine

(a) The velocity of the methane leaving the nozzle.

(b) The reversible work and irreversibility for the process.

10.35 Propane gas expands in a turbine from 400 lbf/in.², 300 F to 50 lbf/in.², 210 F. Assume the process to be adiabatic. Using the generalized charts determine:

(a) The work done per pound of propane entering the turbine.

(b) The increase of entropy per pound of propane as it flows through the turbine.

(c) The isentropic turbine efficiency.

10.36 Freon-12, which has a molecular weight of 121, expands in a cylinder from 300 lbf/in.², 180 F to 35 lbf/in.² in an isothermal process. During this process the heat transfer to the Freon-12 is 20 Btu/lbm. The process is not reversible.

Determine, for this process, the work per pound of Freon-12 using the following sources for thermodynamic data:

(a) The Freon-12 tables.

(b) The generalized charts.

(c) The relation

$$\left(\frac{\partial u}{\partial v}\right)_T = T\left(\frac{\partial P}{\partial T}\right)_v - P$$

and van der Waals' equation of state.

10.37 Using the generalized charts and the nitrogen tables, estimate the per cent correction (from saturated liquid values) in v, h, s for liquid nitrogen at -260 F, 1000 lbf/in.²

10.38 An uninsulated cylinder with a volume of 5 ft³ contains carbon dioxide as saturated liquid at a pressure of 900 lbf/in.² The cylinder valve is opened slightly until a pressure of 100 lbf/in.² is reached, at which time the valve is closed. During this process heat is transferred with the surroundings such that the temperature of the carbon dioxide remains constant. Assume that only vapor is withdrawn from the cylinder. Determine:

(a) The mass of carbon dioxide which escaped from the cylinder.

(b) The heat transferred during the process.

10.39 For a certain research project, it is necessary to have a supply of methane at 1500 lbf/in.², 80 F. The only supply available is at 200 lbf/in.², 80 F,

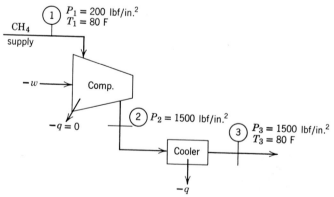

Fig. 10.13   Sketch for Problem 10.39.

so a compressor and cooler are used to obtain the desired state, as shown in Fig. 10.13.

The work input to the compressor is measured and found to be 200 Btu/lbm of methane.

Determine:

(a) The isentropic efficiency of the compressor.

(b) The compressor exit temperature, T_2.

(c) The heat transfer from the cooler per lbm of CH_4.

10.40 Propane is contained in a 1.5 ft^3 tank at 1000 R, 1350 lbf/in.^{2} The propane is then allowed to cool to 600 R.

Calculate

(a) The quality at the final state, and the heat transferred during the process.

(b) The irreversibility for the process, if the heat is rejected to the surroundings at 537 R.

10.41 An uninsulated cylinder with a volume of 2 ft^3 contains ethylene at 1000 lbf/in.^{2}, 80 F, the temperature of the surroundings. The cylinder valve leaks very slightly so that after a considerable length of time the cylinder pressure drops to 500 lbf/in.^{2} Determine:

(a) The mass of ethylene which escaped from the cylinder.

(b) The heat transferred during the process.

10.42 Carbon dioxide is flowing at low velocity in a line at 700 R, 1000 lbf/in.^{2} The velocity of the carbon dioxide is to be increased to 800 ft/sec by having it flow through an appropriate nozzle. Assuming the flow to be isentropic, determine the final pressure and temperature by use of the generalized charts.

11 Mixtures and Solutions

Up to this point in our development of thermodynamics we have limited our consideration primarily to pure substances. A large number of thermodynamic problems involve mixtures of different pure substances. Sometimes these mixtures are referred to as solutions—particularly in the liquid and solid phases.

In this chapter we shall turn our attention to various thermodynamic considerations of mixtures and solutions. We begin with a consideration of a rather simple problem, mixtures of ideal gases. This leads to a consideration of a simplified but very useful model of certain mixtures, such as air and water vapor, which may involve a condensed (solid or liquid) phase of one of the components. This is followed by certain considerations of mixtures and solutions in general.

An understanding of the material in this chapter is a necessary foundation for the consideration of chemical reactions and chemical and phase equilibrium. These topics are covered in subsequent chapters.

11.1 Mixtures of Ideal Gases

In any gaseous mixture, the mole fraction y_i of component i is defined as

$$y_i = \frac{n_i}{n} \tag{11.1}$$

where n_i is the number of moles of component i, and n the total number of moles in the mixture.

Similarly, in any gaseous mixture, the mass fraction mf_i is defined as

$$mf_i = \frac{m_i}{m} \tag{11.2}$$

where m_i is the mass of component i and m is the total mass of the mixture.

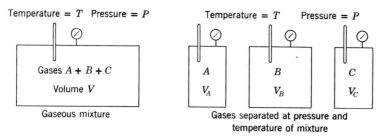

Fig. 11.1   Separation of a gaseous mixture into components at the pressure and temperature of the mixture.

Let us now consider a mixture of ideal gases and assume that the mixture itself can be considered an ideal gas. Let us further assume that the mixture consists of components A and B and that initially the components are separated and exist at the temperature and pressure of the mixture. We can then write the equation of state for the individual components and also for the mixture. It is convenient to write these equations on a molal basis as follows:

$$PV_A = n_A \bar{R} T$$
$$PV_B = n_B \bar{R} T \qquad (11.3)$$
$$PV = n \bar{R} T$$

The properties of the mixture are written without subscript. It follows that

$$\frac{V_A}{V} = \frac{n_A}{n} = y_A = vf_A \qquad (11.4)$$

In words, this equation states that the volume fraction V_A/V, is equal to the mole fraction. In general, the volume fraction vf_i of component i in a mixture is given by

$$vf_i = \frac{V_i}{V} \qquad (11.5)$$

where V_i is the volume occupied by n_i moles of pure i at the temperature and pressure of the mixture.

This leads us to a brief consideration of Amagat's rule of additive volumes, which states that the volume of a mixture is equal to the sum of the volumes of the individual constituents at the temperature and pressure of the mixture. For an ideal gas mixture Amagat's rule is exactly true. This may be demonstrated by referring to Fig. 11.1.

$$n = n_A + n_B$$

Substituting Eq. 11.3,

$$\frac{PV}{\bar{R}T} = \frac{PV_A}{\bar{R}T} + \frac{PV_B}{\bar{R}T}$$

Therefore,

$$V = V_A + V_B \tag{11.6}$$

Amagat's rule may also be stated in terms of the volume fractions as

$$\sum_{i=1}^{n} vf_i = 1 \tag{11.7}$$

An alternate approach in the analysis of ideal gas mixtures is to consider that each component occupies the entire volume. The pressure of the component under these conditions is referred to as the partial pressure. This is shown schematically in Fig. 11.2. As before, we can write the equation of state for each component and for the mixture.

$$P_A V = n_A \bar{R}T$$
$$P_B V = n_B \bar{R}T \tag{11.8}$$
$$PV = n\bar{R}T$$

From Eqs. 11.8 and 11.4 it is seen that

$$\frac{P_A}{P} = \frac{n_A}{n} = y_a = vf_A \tag{11.9}$$

Thus the ratio of the partial pressure to the pressure of the mixture is equal to the mole fraction and also to the volume fraction.

Dalton's rule of additive pressures states that the total pressure of the mixture is equal to the sum of the partial pressures of the individual constituents. This is readily demonstrated for a mixture of ideal gases.

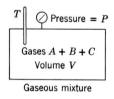

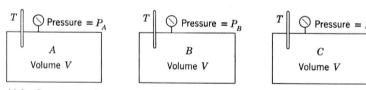

Fig. 11.2 Separation of a gaseous mixture into components at the volume and temperature of the mixture.

As in the previous analysis,

$$n = n_A + n_B$$

Substituting Eqs. 11.8,

$$\frac{PV}{RT} = \frac{P_A V}{RT} + \frac{P_B V}{RT}$$

or

$$P = P_A + P_B \tag{11.10}$$

where each partial pressure is evaluated at the temperature and volume of the mixture.

Dalton's rule in general states that

$$P = \sum_{i=1}^{n} P_i \tag{11.11}$$

We have noted that both Amagat's rule of additive volumes and Dalton's rule of additive pressures hold exactly for mixtures of ideal gases. In the next sections we will consider homogeneous mixtures in general, including certain cases for which such additive rules are valid for nonideal gas mixtures and solid and liquid solutions.

The internal energy, enthalpy, and entropy of an ideal gas mixture can be evaluated as the sum of the respective properties of the constituent gases at the condition at which the component exists in the mixture. Since for ideal gases the internal energy and enthalpy are functions only of temperature, it follows that

$$U = n\bar{u} = n_A \bar{u}_A + n_B \bar{u}_B$$
$$H = n\bar{h} = n_A \bar{h}_A + n_B \bar{h}_B$$

where $\bar{u}_A$ and $\bar{h}_A$ are the internal energy and enthalpy per mole for pure A and $\bar{u}_B$ and $\bar{h}_B$ are the same quantities for pure B, all at the temperature of the mixture.

The entropy of an ideal gas is a function of pressure as well as temperature. Since each component exists in the mixture at its partial pressure,

$$S = n\bar{s} = n_A \bar{s}_A + n_B \bar{s}_B$$

where $\bar{s}_A$ is the entropy per mole for pure A at T, P_A (the partial pressure of A), and $\bar{s}_B$ that for pure B at T and P_B.

Example 11.1

Let n_A moles of gas A at a given pressure and temperature be mixed with n_B moles of gas B at the same pressure and temperature in an adiabatic constant-volume process, shown in Fig. 11.3. Determine the increase in entropy for this process.

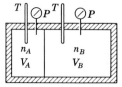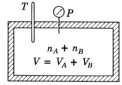

Fig. 11.3   Sketch for Example 11.1.

The final partial pressure of gas A is P_A and for gas B it is P_B. Since there is no change in temperature, Eq. 7.43 reduces to

$$(S_2 - S_1)_A = -n_A \bar{R} \ln \frac{P_A}{P} = -n_A \bar{R} \ln y_A$$

$$(S_2 - S_1)_B = -n_B \bar{R} \ln \frac{P_B}{P} = -n_B \bar{R} \ln y_B$$

The total change in entropy is the sum of the entropy changes for gases A and B.

$$S_2 - S_1 = -\bar{R}(n_A \ln y_A + n_B \ln y_B) \qquad (11.12)$$

This equation can be written for the general case of mixing any number of components at the same pressure and temperature as

$$S_2 - S_1 = -\bar{R} \sum_k n_k \ln y_k \qquad (11.13)$$

The interesting thing about this equation is that the increase in entropy depends only on the number of moles of component gases, and is independent of the composition of the gas. For example, when 1 mole of oxygen and 1 mole of nitrogen are mixed, the increase in entropy is the same as when 1 mole of hydrogen and 1 mole of nitrogen are mixed. But we also know that if 1 mole of nitrogen is "mixed" with another mole of nitrogen there is no increase in entropy. The question that arises is how dissimilar must the gases be in order to have an increase in entropy? The answer lies in our ability to distinguish between the two gases. The entropy increases whenever we can distinguish between the gases being mixed. When we cannot distinguish between the gases, there is no increase in entropy.

11.2   A Simplified Model of a Mixture Involving Gases and a Vapor

Before turning our attention to more complicated problems of mixtures, such as those involving nonideal gases, let us consider a simplification, which in many cases is a reasonable one, of the problem involving a mixture of ideal gases that is in contact with a solid or liquid phase of one of the components. The most familiar example is a mixture of air and water vapor in contact with liquid water or ice, such as the problems encountered in air conditioning or drying. We are all familiar with the condensation of water from the atmosphere when it is cooled on a summer day.

This problem, and a number of similar problems, can be analyzed quite simply and with considerable accuracy if the following assumptions are made:

1. The solid or liquid phase contains no dissolved gases.
2. The gaseous phase can be treated as a mixture of ideal gases.
3. When the mixture and the condensed phase are at a given pressure and temperature, the equilibrium between the condensed phase and its vapor is not influenced by the presence of the other component. This means that when equilibrium is achieved the partial pressure of the vapor will be equal to the saturation pressure corresponding to the temperature of the mixture.

Since this approach is used extensively and with considerable accuracy, let us give some attention to the terms that have been defined and the type of problems for which this approach is valid and relevant. In our discussion we will refer to this as a gas-vapor mixture.

The dew point of a gas-vapor mixture is the temperature at which the vapor condenses or solidifies when it is cooled at constant pressure. This is shown on the T-s diagram for the vapor shown in Fig. 11.4. Suppose that the temperature of the gaseous mixture and the partial pressure of the vapor in the mixture are such that the vapor is initially superheated at state 1. If the mixture is cooled at constant pressure the partial pressure of the vapor remains constant until point 2 is reached, and then condensation begins. The temperature at state 2 is the dew-point temperature. Line 1–3 on the diagram indicates that if the mixture is cooled at constant

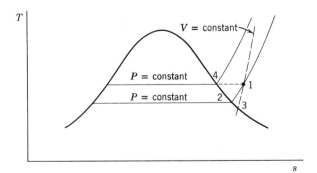

Fig. 11.4 Temperature-entropy diagram to show definition of the dew point.

volume the condensation begins at point 3, which is slightly lower than the dew-point temperature.

If the vapor is at the saturation pressure and temperature, the mixture is referred to as a saturated mixture, and for an air-water vapor mixture, the term "saturated air" is used.

The relative humidity ϕ is defined as the ratio of the mole fraction of the vapor in the mixture to the mole fraction of vapor in a saturated mixture at the same temperature and total pressure. Since the vapor is considered an ideal gas, the definition reduces to the ratio of the partial pressure of the vapor as it exists in the mixture P_v, to the saturation pressure of the vapor at the same temperature P_g.

$$\phi = \frac{P_v}{P_g}$$

In terms of the numbers on the T-s diagram of Fig. 11.4, the relative humidity ϕ would be

$$\phi = \frac{P_1}{P_4}$$

Since we are considering the vapor to be an ideal gas, the relative humidity can also be defined in terms of specific volume or density.

$$\phi = \frac{P_v}{P_g} = \frac{\rho_v}{\rho_g} = \frac{v_g}{v_v} \tag{11.14}$$

The humidity ratio ω of an air-water vapor mixture is defined as the ratio of the mass of water vapor m_v to the mass of dry air m_a. The term "dry air" is used to emphasize that this refers only to air and not to the water vapor. The term "specific humidity" is used synonymously with humidity ratio.

$$\omega = \frac{m_v}{m_a} \tag{11.15}$$

This definition is identical for any other gas-vapor mixture, and the subscript a refers to the gas, exclusive of the vapor. Since we are considering both the vapor and the mixture to be ideal gases, a very useful expression for humidity ratio in terms of partial pressures can be developed.

$$m_v = \frac{P_v V}{R_v T} = \frac{P_v V M_v}{\bar{R} T} \qquad m_a = \frac{P_a V}{R_a T} = \frac{P_a V M_a}{\bar{R} T}$$

Then

$$\omega = \frac{P_v V / R_v T}{P_a V / R_a T} = \frac{R_a P_v}{R_v P_a} = \frac{M_v P_v}{M_a P_a} \tag{11.16}$$

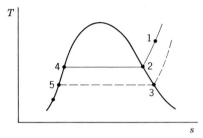

Fig. 11.5   Temperature-entropy diagram to show the cooling of a gas-vapor mixture at a constant pressure.

For an air-water vapor mixture this reduces to

$$\omega = 0.622 \frac{P_v}{P_a} \tag{11.17}$$

The degree of saturation is defined as the ratio of the actual humidity ratio to the humidity ratio of a saturated mixture at the same temperature and total pressure.

An expression for the relation between the relative humidity ϕ and the humidity ratio ω can be found by solving Eqs. 11.14 and 11.17 for P_v and equating them. The resulting relation for an air-water vapor mixture is

$$\phi = \frac{\omega P_a}{0.622 P_g}$$

A few words should also be said about the nature of the process that occurs when a gas-vapor mixture is cooled at constant pressure. Suppose that the vapor is initially superheated at state 1 in Fig. 11.5. As the mixture is cooled at constant pressure the partial pressure of the vapor remains constant until the dew point is reached at point 2, at which point the vapor in the mixture is saturated. The initial condensate is at state 4, and is in equilibrium with the vapor at state 2. As the temperature is lowered further, more of the vapor condenses, which lowers the partial pressure of the vapor in the mixture. The vapor that remains in the mixture is always saturated, and the liquid or solid is in equilibrium with it. For example, when the temperature is reduced to T_3, the vapor in the mixture is at state 3, and its partial pressure is the saturation pressure corresponding to T_3. The liquid in equilibrium with it is at state 5.

Example 11.2

Consider 2000 ft³ of an air-water vapor mixture at 14.70 lbf/in.², 90 F, 70 per cent relative humidity. Calculate the humidity ratio, dew point, mass of air, and mass of vapor.

From Eq. 11.14 and the steam tables,

$$\phi = 0.70 = \frac{P_v}{P_g}$$

$$P_v = 0.70(0.6982) = 0.4887 \text{ lbf/in.}^2$$

The dew point is the saturation temperature corresponding to this pressure, which is 78.9 F.

The partial pressure of the air is

$$P_a = P - P_v = 14.70 - 0.49 = 14.21 \text{ lbf/in.}^2$$

The humidity ratio can be calculated from Eq. 11.17.

$$\omega = 0.622 \times \frac{P_v}{P_a} = 0.622 \times \frac{0.4887}{14.21} = 0.02135$$

The mass of air is

$$m_a = \frac{P_a V}{R_a T} = \frac{14.21 \times 144 \times 2000}{53.34 \times 550} = 139.6 \text{ lbm}$$

The mass of the vapor can be calculated by using the humidity ratio or by using the ideal gas equation of state.

$$m_v = \omega m_a = 0.02135(139.6) = 2.98 \text{ lbm}$$

$$m_v = \frac{0.4887 \times 144 \times 2000}{85.7 \times 550} = 2.98 \text{ lbm}$$

Example 11.3

Calculate the amount of water vapor condensed if the mixture of Example 11.2 is cooled to 40 F in a constant-pressure process.

At 40 F the mixture is saturated, since this is below the dew-point temperature. Therefore

$$P_{v2} = P_{g2} = 0.1217 \text{ lbf/in.}^2$$

$$P_{a2} = 14.7 - 0.12 = 14.58 \text{ lbf/in.}^2$$

$$\omega_2 = 0.622 \times \frac{0.1217}{14.58} = 0.00520$$

The amount of water vapor condensed is equal to the difference between the initial and final mass of water vapor.

$$\text{mass of vapor condensed} = m_a(\omega_1 - \omega_2) = 139.6(0.02135 - 0.0052)$$

$$= 2.25 \text{ lbm}$$

11.3 The First Law Applied to Gas-Vapor Mixtures

In applying the first law of thermodynamics to gas-vapor mixtures it is helpful to realize that because of our assumption that ideal gases are involved, the various components can be treated separately when calculating changes of internal energy and enthalpy. Therefore, in dealing with air-water vapor mixtures the changes in enthalpy of the water vapor can be found from the steam tables and the ideal gas relations can be applied to the air. This is illustrated by the examples that follow.

Example 11.4

An air-conditioning unit is shown in Fig. 11.6, with pressure, temperature, and relative humidity data. Calculate the heat transfer per pound of dry air, assuming that changes in kinetic energy are negligible.

Let us consider a steady-state, steady-flow process for a control volume that excludes the cooling coils.

Since this is a steady-flow process, the continuity equation for the air and water vapor are

$$m_{a1} = m_{a2}$$
$$m_{v1} = m_{v2} + m_{l2}$$

The first law for this steady-state, steady-flow process is

$$Q_{\text{c.v.}} + \sum m_i h_i = \sum m_e h_e$$
$$Q_{\text{c.v.}} + m_a h_{a1} + m_{v1} h_{v1} = m_a h_{a2} + m_{v2} h_{v2} + m_{l2} h_{l2}$$

If we divide this equation by m_a, introduce the continuity equation for the H_2O, and note that $m_v = \omega m_a$, we can write the first law in the form

$$\frac{Q_{\text{c.v.}}}{m_a} + h_{a1} + \omega_1 h_{v1} = h_{a2} + \omega_2 h_{v2} + (\omega_1 - \omega_2)h_{l2}$$

The air can be considered an ideal gas with constant specific heat, and the values of enthalpy for the H_2O can be taken from the steam tables.

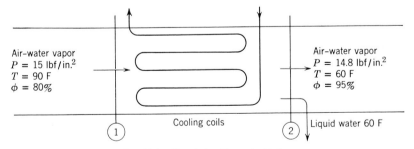

Air-water vapor
$P = 15 \text{ lbf/in.}^2$
$T = 90 \text{ F}$
$\phi = 80\%$

Air-water vapor
$P = 14.8 \text{ lbf/in.}^2$
$T = 60 \text{ F}$
$\phi = 95\%$

Cooling coils

Liquid water 60 F

1

2

Fig. 11.6   Sketch for Example 11.4.

(Since the water vapor at these low pressures is being considered an ideal gas, the enthalpy of the water vapor is a function of the temperature only. Therefore, the enthalpy of slightly superheated water vapor is equal to the enthalpy of saturated vapor at the same temperature.)

$$P_{v1} = \phi P_{g1} = 0.80(0.6982) = 0.5586 \text{ lbf/in.}^2$$

$$\omega_1 = \frac{R_a}{R_v} \frac{P_{v1}}{P_{a1}} = 0.622 \times \left(\frac{0.5586}{15.00 - 0.56}\right) = 0.0241$$

$$P_{v2} = \phi_2 P_{g2} = 0.95(0.2563) = 0.2435$$

$$\omega_2 = \frac{R_a}{R_v} \times \frac{P_{v2}}{P_{a2}} = 0.622 \times \left(\frac{0.2435}{14.80 - 0.24}\right) = 0.0104$$

$$Q_{c.v.}/m_a + h_{a1} + \omega_1 h_{v1} = h_{a2} + \omega_2 h_{v2} + (\omega_1 - \omega_2)h_{l2}$$

$$Q_{c.v.}/m_a = 0.240(60 - 90) + 0.0104(1088.0) - 0.0241(1100.9)$$
$$+ (0.0241 - 0.0104)28.06$$
$$= -7.20 + 11.32 - 26.53 + 0.38 = -22.03 \text{ Btu/lbm dry air}$$

Example 11.5

A tank has a volume of 10 ft³ and contains nitrogen and water vapor. The temperature of the mixture is 120 F and the total pressure is 30 lbf/in.². The partial pressure of the water vapor is 0.8 lbf/in.². Calculate the heat transfer when the contents of the tank are cooled to 50 F.

This is a constant-volume process, and since the work is zero the first law reduces to

$$Q = U_2 - U_1 = m_{N_2}C_{v_{(N_2)}}(T_2 - T_1) + (m_2 u_2)_v + (m_2 u_2)_l - (m_1 u_1)_v$$

This equation assumes that some of the vapor condensed. This must be checked, however, as shown below.

The mass of nitrogen and water vapor can be calculated using the ideal-gas equation of state.

$$m_{N_2} = \frac{P_{N_2}V}{R_{N_2}T} = \frac{29.2 \times 144 \times 10}{55.15 \times 580} = 1.314 \text{ lbm}$$

$$m_{v1} = \frac{P_{v1}V}{R_v T} = \frac{0.8 \times 144 \times 10}{85.76 \times 580} = 0.0232 \text{ lbm}$$

If condensation takes place the final state of the vapor will be saturated vapor at 50 F. In this case

$$m_{v2} = \frac{P_{v2}V}{R_v T} = \frac{0.1781 \times 144 \times 10}{85.76 \times 510} = 0.00586 \text{ lbm}$$

Since this is less than the original mass of vapor there must have been condensation.

The mass of liquid that is condensed, m_{l_2}, is

$$m_{l_2} = m_{v_1} = m_{v_2} = 0.0232 - 0.0059 = 0.0173 \text{ lbm}$$

The internal energy of the water vapor is equal to the internal energy of saturated water vapor at the same temperature. Therefore,

$$u_{v_1} = 1113.7 - \frac{1.6924 \times 144 \times 203.27}{778} = 1050.1 \text{ Btu/lbm}$$

$$u_{v_2} = 1083.7 - \frac{0.1781 \times 144 \times 1703.2}{778} = 1027.6 \text{ Btu/lbm}$$

$$\begin{aligned} Q_{\text{c.v.}} &= 1.314 \times 0.177(50 - 120) + 0.00586(1027.6) \\ &\quad + 0.0173(18.07) - 0.0232(1050.1) \\ &= -16.31 + 6.02 + 0.31 - 24.26 = -34.24 \text{ Btu} \end{aligned}$$

11.4 The Adiabatic Saturation Process

An important process involving an air-water vapor mixture is the adiabatic saturation process, in which an air-vapor mixture comes in contact with a body of water in a well-insulated duct (Fig. 11.7). If the initial relative humidity is less than 100 per cent some of the water will evaporate and the temperature of the air-vapor mixture will decrease. If the mixture leaving the duct is saturated and if the process is adiabatic, the temperature of the mixture on leaving is known as the adiabatic saturation temperature. In order for this to take place as a steady-flow process, make-up water at the adiabatic saturation temperature is added at the same rate at which water is evaporated. The pressure is assumed to be constant.

Considering the adiabatic saturation process to be a steady-state, steady-flow process, and neglecting changes in kinetic and potential energy, the first law reduces to

$$h_{a1} + \omega_1 h_{v1} + (\omega_2 - \omega_1)h_{l2} = h_{a2} + \omega_2 h_{v2}$$

$$\omega_1(h_{v1} - h_{l2}) = C_{pa}(T_2 - T_1) + \omega_2(h_{v2} - h_{l2}) \quad (11.18)$$

$$\omega_1(h_{v1} - h_{l2}) = C_{pa}(T_2 - T_1) + \omega_2 h_{fg2}$$

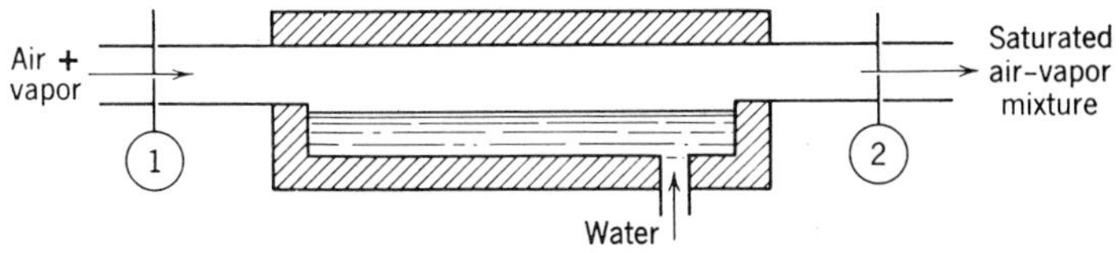

Fig. 11.7 The adiabatic saturation process.

The most significant point to be made about the adiabatic saturation process is that the adiabatic saturation temperature, the temperature of the mixture when it leaves the duct, is a function of the pressure, temperature, and relative humidity of the entering air-vapor mixture and of the exit pressure. Thus, the relative humidity and the humidity ratio of the entering air-vapor mixture can be determined from the measurements of the pressure and temperature of the air-vapor mixture entering and leaving the adiabatic saturator. Since these measurements are relatively easy to make, this is one means of determining the humidity of an air-vapor mixture.

Example 11.6

The pressure of the mixture entering and leaving the adiabatic saturator is 14.7 lbf/in.^{2}, the entering temperature is 84 F, and the temperature leaving is 70 F, which is the adiabatic saturation temperature. Calculate the humidity ratio and relative humidity of the air-water vapor mixture entering.

Since the water vapor leaving is saturated, $P_{v2} = P_{g2}$ and ω_2 can be calculated.

$$\omega_2 = 0.622 \times \frac{0.3631}{14.7 - 0.36} = 0.01573$$

ω_1 can be calculated using Eq. 11.18.

$$\omega_1 = \frac{C_{pa}(T_2 - T_1) + \omega_2 h_{fg2}}{(h_{v1} - h_{l2})}$$

$$\omega_1 = \frac{0.24(70 - 84) + 0.01573 \times 1054.3}{1098.4 - 38.0} = \frac{-3.36 + 16.60}{1060.4} = 0.0125$$

$$\omega_1 = 0.622 \times \left(\frac{P_{v1}}{14.7 - P_{v1}}\right) = 0.0125$$

$$P_{v1} = 0.289$$

$$\phi_1 = \frac{P_{v1}}{P_{g1}} = \frac{0.289}{0.577} = 0.501$$

11.5   Wet-Bulb and Dry-Bulb Temperatures

The humidity of an air-water vapor mixture is usually found from dry-bulb and wet-bulb data. These data are obtained by use of a psychrometer, which involves the flow of air past wet-bulb and dry-bulb thermometers. The bulb of the wet-bulb thermometer is covered with a cotton wick that is saturated with water. The dry-bulb thermometer is used simply to measure the temperature of the air. The flow of air may be maintained by a fan, as in the continuous-flow psychrometer shown in Fig. 11.8, or by moving the thermometer through the air, as in the sling psychrometer, which consists of wet-bulb and dry-bulb thermometers mounted so that they can be whirled.

The processes that take place at the wet-bulb thermometer are somewhat involved. First of all, if the air-water vapor mixture is not saturated, some of the water in the wick evaporates and diffuses into the surrounding air. A drop in the temperature of the water in the wick will be associated with this evaporation. However, as soon as the temperature of the water drops, heat is transferred to the water from both the air and the thermometer. Finally, a steady state, determined by heat and mass transfer rates, will be reached. In general, air velocities exceeding 700 ft per min are required in order that the convective heat transfer be large in comparison to the radiant heat transfer.

The psychrometric chart is the most convenient method of determining relative humidity and humidity ratio from wet-bulb and dry-bulb data, although equations that have been developed can also be used. A psychrometric chart is included in the Appendix, Fig. A.2.

The difference between the wet-bulb temperature and adiabatic saturation temperature should be carefully noted. The wet-bulb temperature is influenced by heat and mass transfer rates, whereas the adiabatic saturation temperature simply involves equilibrium between the entering air-vapor mixture and water at the adiabatic saturation temperature. However, it happens that the wet-bulb temperature and the adiabatic saturation temperature are approximately equal for air-water vapor mixtures at atmospheric temperature and pressure. This is not necessarily true at temperatures and pressures that deviate significantly from ordinary atmospheric conditions, or for other gas-vapor mixtures.

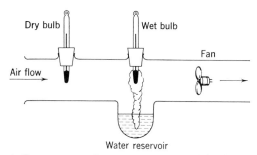

Fig. 11.8   Steady-flow apparatus for measuring wet- and dry-bulb temperature.

11.6 The Psychrometric Chart

Properties of air-water vapor mixtures are given in graphical form on psychrometric charts. These are available in a number of different forms, and only the main features are considered here.

The basic psychrometric chart consists of a plot of dry-bulb temperature (abscissa) and humidity ratio (ordinate). If we fix the total pressure for which the chart is to be constructed (which is usually one standard atmosphere), lines of constant relative humidity and wet-bulb temperature can be drawn on the chart, because for a given dry-bulb temperature, total pressure, and humidity ratio, the relative humidity and wet-bulb temperature are fixed. The partial pressure of the water vapor is fixed by the humidity ratio and total pressure, and therefore a second ordinate scale that indicates the partial pressure of the water vapor can be constructed.

Most psychrometric charts give the enthalpy of an air-vapor mixture per pound of dry air. The values given assume that the enthalpy of the dry air is zero at 0 F, and the enthalpy of the vapor is taken from the steam tables (which are based on the assumption that the enthalpy of saturated liquid is zero at 32 F). This procedure is satisfactory because we are usually concerned only with differences in enthalpy. The fact that lines of constant enthalpy are essentially parallel to lines of constant wet-bulb temperature is evident from the fact that the wet-bulb temperature is essentially equal to the adiabatic saturation temperature. Thus, in Fig. 11.7, if we neglect the enthalpy of the liquid entering the adiabatic saturator, the enthalpy of the air-vapor mixture entering is equal to the enthalpy of the saturated air-vapor mixture leaving, and a given adiabatic saturation temperature fixes the enthalpy of the mixture entering.

Some charts are available that give corrections for variation from standard atmospheric pressures. Before using a given chart one should fully understand the assumptions made in constructing it, and that it is applicable to the particular problem at hand.

11.7 Partial Molal Properties

We now turn our attention to some general considerations of mixtures and solutions. These considerations are not restricted to gaseous mixtures alone; they also are valid for solid, liquid, and gaseous solutions. In a later chapter the concepts introduced here will be extended to include equilibrium between phases, including mixtures that involve more than one phase. We begin by a consideration of partial molal properties.

Consider a function of two independent variables x, y. The function is said to be a homogeneous function of degree n if the relation

$$f(Kx, Ky) = K^n \cdot f(x, y) \qquad (11.19)$$

is satisfied, where K is arbitrary. For example, the function

$$z = 2x^2 + xy$$

is homogeneous in x, y, of degree 2, since Eq. 11.19 is satisfied. This can be demonstrated by replacing x and y with Kx and Ky respectively, or by substituting various values for x, y, K into the expression. On the other hand, the function

$$z = 2x^2 + xy^2$$

is not homogeneous in x, y, as can be seen by testing as before.

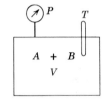

Euler's theorem on homogeneous functions states that for a homogeneous function of degree n,

$$n \cdot f(x, y) = x\left(\frac{\partial f}{\partial x}\right)_y + y\left(\frac{\partial f}{\partial y}\right)_x \qquad (11.20)$$

Fig. 11.9   Homogeneous mixture or solution of components A and B.

Euler's theorem can be shown to be valid by differentiating Eq. 11.19 and letting $K = 1$, which is permissible because the equation must be satisfied for any K. This demonstration is left as an exercise.

Consider a homogeneous mixture or solution of two components A and B, at temperature T and pressure P as shown in Fig. 11.9. We can express the volume in terms of the temperature, pressure, and number of moles of each substance.

$$V = V(T, P, n_A, n_B) \qquad (11.21)$$

Since Eq. 11.21 expresses a relation among properties (exact differentials),

$$dV = \left(\frac{\partial V}{\partial T}\right)_{P,n_A,n_B} dT + \left(\frac{\partial V}{\partial P}\right)_{T,n_A,n_B} dP$$

$$+ \left(\frac{\partial V}{\partial n_A}\right)_{T,P,n_B} dn_A + \left(\frac{\partial V}{\partial n_B}\right)_{T,P,n_A} dn_B \qquad (11.22)$$

At constant temperature and pressure, Eq. 11.22 becomes

$$dV_{T,P} = \left(\frac{\partial V}{\partial n_A}\right)_{T,P,n_B} dn_A + \left(\frac{\partial V}{\partial n_B}\right)_{T,P,n_A} dn_B \qquad (11.23)$$

From our physical experience, we realize that at a given T, P, the volume is a homogeneous function of first degree in n_A, n_B, as V is an extensive property. For example, if we double both n_A and n_B at constant T, P, the volume will be doubled. If we halve both n_A and n_B while holding T and P constant, the volume will also be halved. Therefore, by Euler's theorem, Eq. 11.20,

$$V_{T,P} = \left(\frac{\partial V}{\partial n_A}\right)_{T,P,n_B} \cdot n_A + \left(\frac{\partial V}{\partial n_B}\right)_{T,P,n_A} \cdot n_B \qquad (11.24)$$

This expression is also the result of integrating Eq. 11.23 at constant T, P. From Eq. 11.24, we note that

$$V = n_A \bar{V}_A + n_B \bar{V}_B \qquad (11.25)$$

where, by definition,

$$\bar{V}_A \equiv \left(\frac{\partial V}{\partial n_A}\right)_{T,P,n_B} \quad ; \quad \bar{V}_B \equiv \left(\frac{\partial V}{\partial n_B}\right)_{T,P,n_A} \qquad (11.26)$$

The quantity $\bar{V}_A$ is the "specific volume" of A as it exists in the mixture at T, P, and is called the partial molal volume of A. As an example, for the case of pure substance A,

$$\bar{V}_A = \left(\frac{\partial V}{\partial n_A}\right)_{T,P} = \bar{v}_A$$

and

$$V_A = \bar{v}_A \cdot n_A \qquad (11.27)$$

Thus the partial volume of A when no B is present reduces to the specific volume of pure A as would naturally be expected.

For a mixture of ideal gases A and B,

$$\bar{V}_A = \left(\frac{\partial V}{\partial n_A}\right)_{T,P,n_B} = \frac{\bar{R}T}{P} = \bar{v}$$

and

$$\bar{V}_B = \left(\frac{\partial V}{\partial n_B}\right)_{T,P,n_A} = \frac{\bar{R}T}{P} = \bar{v}$$

Since $\bar{v}$, $\bar{v}_A$, $\bar{v}_B$ are the same per mole,

$$\bar{V}_A = \bar{V}_B = \bar{v} = \bar{v}_A = \bar{v}_B \qquad (11.28)$$

Therefore, for a mixture of ideal gases we conclude from Eq. 11.25 that

$$V = n_A \bar{v}_A + n_B \bar{v}_B = V_A + V_B$$

which is Amagat's rule of additive volumes.

Consider now the general case in which partial molal volumes can be determined from experimental data by the method of intercepts, as shown in Fig. 11.10. Curve (DGI) represents the molal specific volume of a mixture, consisting of components A and B, as a function of y_A at constant T, P. It is desired to determine the partial volumes of A and B for a

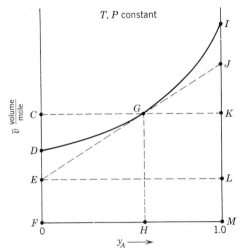

Fig. 11.10   Specific volume-composition diagram for a mixture of two components.

mixture at point G.   Note the following lengths in Fig. 11.10.

$$(CF) = (GH) = (KM) = \bar{v} \text{ (for the mixture)}$$
$$(DF) = \bar{v}_B \text{ (no } A \text{ present)}$$
$$(IM) = \bar{v}_A \text{ (no } B \text{ present)}$$
$$(CG) = (FH) = y_A \text{ (at the desired point } G\text{)}$$
$$(GK) = (HM) = y_B = (1 - y_A)$$

The partial volume of A at point G can be determined as follows:

$$V = n\bar{v} = (n_A + n_B)\bar{v}$$
$$\bar{V}_A = \left(\frac{\partial V}{\partial n_A}\right)_{T,P,n_B} = \bar{v} + (n_A + n_B)\left(\frac{\partial \bar{v}}{\partial n_A}\right)_{T,P,n_B}$$

But

$$y_A = \frac{n_A}{n_A + n_B}$$

and at constant, T, P, n_B,

$$\frac{dy_A}{dn_A} = \frac{n_B}{(n_A + n_B)^2}$$

or

$$\frac{n_A + n_B}{dn_A} = \left(\frac{n_B}{n_A + n_B}\right)\frac{1}{dy_A} = \frac{1 - y_A}{dy_A}$$

Therefore,

$$\bar{V}_A = \bar{v} + (1 - y_A)\left(\frac{\partial \bar{v}}{\partial y_A}\right)_{T,P,n_B}$$

or in terms of lengths in Fig. 11.10,

$$\bar{V}_A = (KM) + (GK) \times \frac{(JL)}{(EL)} = (KM) + (JK) = (JM)$$

That is, the partial molal volume of component A at point G is equal to the intercept at $y_A = 1.0$ of the tangent to the volume curve at point G.

Similarly, for the partial volume of B,

$$\bar{V}_B = \bar{v} + (n_A + n_B)\left(\frac{\partial \bar{v}}{\partial n_B}\right)_{T,P,n_A} = \bar{v} - y_A\left(\frac{\partial \bar{v}}{\partial y_A}\right)_{T,P,n_A}$$

In terms of lengths,

$$\bar{V}_B = (CF) - (CG) \times \frac{(JL)}{(EL)} = (CF) - (CE) = (EF)$$

Thus the partial molal volume of component B is equal to the intercept at $y_A = 0$ of the tangent to the volume curve at point G.

The physical significance of the partial molal volume may be visualized by considering a reasonably large volume of a mixture of components A and B. Let a very small amount of A be added while the temperature, pressure and moles of B remain constant. The composition of the mixture will be essentially unchanged. The volume of the mixture will be increased by an amount equal to the specific volume of component A in the mixture (the partial molal volume of A) multiplied by the number of moles of component A added. Thus, in this case,

$$dV = \left(\frac{\partial V}{\partial n_A}\right)_{T,P,n_B} dn_A = \bar{V}_A\, dn_A$$

Similar analyses can be performed for other extensive thermodynamic properties. Considering a mixture of components A and B, at constant T and P we can write

$$dH_{T,P} = \left(\frac{\partial H}{\partial n_A}\right)_{T,P,n_B} dn_A + \left(\frac{\partial H}{\partial n_B}\right)_{T,P,n_A} dn_B$$

In a manner similar to the definition of partial molal volume (Eq. 11.26) the partial molal enthalpy is defined as

$$\bar{H}_A \equiv \left(\frac{\partial H}{\partial n_A}\right)_{T,P,n_B} \quad ; \quad \bar{H}_B \equiv \left(\frac{\partial H}{\partial n_B}\right)_{T,P,n_A} \qquad (11.29)$$

From Euler's theorem we conclude that

$$H_{T,P} = \bar{H}_A \cdot n_A + \bar{H}_B \cdot n_B \qquad (11.30)$$

In a manner exactly the same as that previously discussed for determining partial molal volumes from experimental data, the partial molal

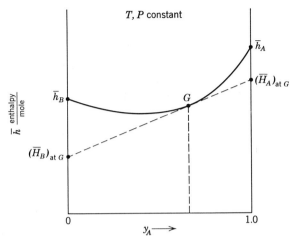

Fig. 11.11 Enthalpy-composition diagram for a mixture of two components.

enthalpies may also be found from the intercepts on an enthalpy-concentration plot. The results are shown in Fig. 11.11, in which the partial enthalpies of A and B in the mixture of composition G and at T, P, are given by the intercepts of the tangent at $y_A = 1.0$ and $y_A = 0$, respectively.

Another such relation of particular interest to equilibrium studies is that for the Gibbs function.

By the same procedure,

$$G_{T,P} = \bar{G}_A \cdot n_A + \bar{G}_B \cdot n_B \tag{11.31}$$

where

$$\bar{G}_A \equiv \left(\frac{\partial G}{\partial n_A}\right)_{T,P,n_B} \quad ; \quad \bar{G}_B \equiv \left(\frac{\partial G}{\partial n_B}\right)_{T,P,n_A} \tag{11.32}$$

Similar expressions involving the definition of partial molal properties can be written for other extensive properties of interest, such as S, U, and A.

For the general case we can define the partial molal property $\bar{X}$ of component i in a mixture as

$$\bar{X}_i = \left(\frac{\partial X}{\partial n_i}\right)_{T,P,\text{ all other } n\text{'s}} \tag{11.33}$$

Further, in accordance with Euler's Theorem, the property X for the mixture is given by the relation

$$X_{T,P} = \sum_{i=1}^{n} \bar{X} \cdot n_i$$

It can be shown that the thermodynamic relations that apply to a mixture as a whole also hold for relations between partial molal properties for a given component. For example, consider the relation

$$dG = dH - T \, dS - S \, dT$$

Let us again consider a mixture of components A and B, and let T, P, and n_B be held constant, and let n_A change by the amount dn_A. In this case, the preceding equation becomes,

$$\left(\frac{\partial G}{\partial n_A}\right)_{T,P,n_B} = \left(\frac{\partial H}{\partial n_A}\right)_{T,P,n_B} - T\left(\frac{\partial S}{\partial n_A}\right)_{T,P,n_B}$$

or

$$\bar{G}_A = \bar{H}_A - T\bar{S}_A \tag{11.34}$$

Similarly

$$\bar{H}_A = \bar{U}_A + P\bar{V}_A \tag{11.35}$$

$$\bar{A}_A = \bar{U}_A - T\bar{S}_A \tag{11.36}$$

11.8 Change in Properties upon Mixing

In this section, we will develop expressions for the changes in volume, enthalpy, and entropy upon mixing of two pure substances at constant temperature and pressure. We have previously seen that there is no volume change upon mixing of ideal gases at constant temperature and pressure. If two real gases each at T, P were mixed, however, the volume of the mixture would not necessarily equal the sum of the volumes of the constituents. The same is true for solutions involving liquids and solids. The change of volume on mixing, ΔV_{mix}, can be expressed as

$$\Delta V_{\text{mix}} = V_{\text{mixture}} - V_{\text{components}}$$

For a mixture of components A and B

$$\Delta V_{\text{mix}} = (\bar{V}_A n_A + \bar{V}_B n_B) - (\bar{v}_A n_A + \bar{v}_B n_B)$$
$$= (\bar{V}_A - \bar{v}_A)n_A + (\bar{V}_B - \bar{v}_B)n_B \tag{11.37}$$

The significance of this can be shown graphically by reference to Fig. 11.10. For this mixture the change in volume on mixing would be

$$\Delta V_{\text{mix}} = (IJ)n_A + (DE)n_B$$

Similarly the enthalpy change of mixing is given by

$$\Delta H_{\text{mix}} = (\bar{H}_A - \bar{h}_A)n_A + (\bar{H}_B - \bar{h}_B)n_B \tag{11.38}$$

and the entropy change of mixing by

$$\Delta S_{\text{mix}} = (\bar{S}_A - \bar{s}_A)n_A + (\bar{S}_B - \bar{s}_B)n_B \tag{11.39}$$

For a mixture of ideal gases, the special case previously discussed, we concluded (Eq. 11.28) that

$$(\bar{V}_A - \bar{v}_A) = 0$$
$$(\bar{V}_B - \bar{v}_B) = 0$$

Therefore,

$$\Delta V_{\text{mix}} = 0 \tag{11.40}$$

Also, for a mixture of ideal gases

$$(\bar{H}_A - \bar{h}_A) = 0$$
$$(\bar{H}_B - \bar{h}_B) = 0$$

and therefore

$$\Delta H_{\text{mix}} = 0 \tag{11.41}$$

But, the entropy of mixing for ideal gases is given by the relation

$$(\bar{S}_A - \bar{s}_A) = -\bar{R} \ln y_A$$
$$(\bar{S}_B - \bar{s}_B) = -\bar{R} \ln y_B \tag{11.42}$$
$$\Delta S_{\text{mix}} = -\bar{R}(n_A \ln y_A + n_B \ln y_B)$$

in which $\bar{S}_A$ is the partial entropy of A in the mixture at T, P, while $\bar{s}_A$ is that for pure A at the same temperature and pressure, and similarly for component B. This is the expression that was derived in Example 11.1.

11.9 The Thermodynamic Property Relation for Variable Composition

The thermodynamic property relation for a simple compressible substance of fixed composition was developed in Chapter 7 and extended in Chapter 10 to include magnetic, electrical, surface, and other effects. In order to remove the restriction of fixed composition, let us now consider a simple compressible substance comprised of a binary mixture of A and B. The Gibbs function for this substance is written as

$$G = f(T, P, n_A, n_B)$$

Therefore,

$$dG = \left(\frac{\partial G}{\partial T}\right)_{P,n} dT + \left(\frac{\partial G}{\partial P}\right)_{T,n} dP + \left(\frac{\partial G}{\partial n_A}\right)_{T,P,n_B} dn_A + \left(\frac{\partial G}{\partial n_B}\right)_{T,P,n_A} dn_B$$

Substituting Eqs. 10.16 and 11.32,

$$dG = -S\,dT + V\,dP + \bar{G}_A\,dn_A + \bar{G}_B\,dn_B \tag{11.43}$$

We find that the thermodynamic potential driving a composition or mass change of a component is its partial Gibbs function, which is also termed the chemical potential of the component.

Using the definition of the Gibbs function

$$G = U + PV - TS$$

$$dG = dU + P\,dV + V\,dP - T\,dS - S\,dT$$

and substituting into Eq. 11.43,

$$dU = T\,dS - P\,dV + \bar{G}_A\,dn_A + \bar{G}_B\,dn_B \tag{11.44}$$

which is the thermodynamic property relation for a simple compressible substance allowing for changes in composition. We realize that the surface, magnetic, and other terms considered in Chapter 10 may be added to this relation as necessary, thereby giving a completely general form for the property relation

$$dU = T\,dS - P\,dV + \sum_i \bar{G}_i\,dn_i + \mathscr{T}\,dL$$

$$+ \mathscr{S}\,dA + \mu_0 V \mathscr{H}\,d\mathscr{M} + \mathscr{E}\,dZ + \cdots \tag{11.45}$$

In terms of the enthalpy,

$$H = U + PV$$

Equation 11.44 becomes

$$dH = T\,dS + V\,dP + \bar{G}_A\,dn_A + \bar{G}_B\,dn_B \tag{11.46}$$

Finally in terms of the Helmholtz function,

$$A = U - TS$$

the property relation is

$$dA = -S\,dT - P\,dV + \bar{G}_A\,dn_A + \bar{G}_B\,dn_B \tag{11.47}$$

Equations 11.43, 11.46, and 11.47, the property relation in terms of G, H, and A, respectively, could also be written in the completely general form as was done for internal energy in Eq. 11.45.

11.10   Fugacity in a Mixture and Its Relation to Other Properties

Let us define the fugacity of component A in a mixture by a similar procedure to that for a pure substance in Section 10.12. At constant temperature we define $\bar{f}_A$ by

$$(d\bar{G}_A)_T = \bar{R}T\,d(\ln \bar{f}_A)_T \tag{11.48}$$

along with the requirement that

$$\lim_{P \to 0} \left(\frac{\bar{f}_A}{y_A P} \right) = 1 \tag{11.49}$$

so that as pressure approaches zero, the fugacity of component A approaches the ideal gas mixture partial pressure of component A. The fugacity of a component in a mixture as defined by these equations is not a true partial property according to the definitions of Eqs. 11.26, 11.29, and 11.32. Nevertheless, we include the bar above the symbol as a reminder that the substance involved is a component of a mixture. Note that in the sense that f is essentially a pseudopressure, $\bar{f}$ can be considered a pseudo-partial pressure. The fugacity of component B in the mixture is defined by a pair of equations analogous to Eqs. 11.48 and 11.49.

To determine the relation of fugacity of a component to other properties, consider first the property relation written in terms of the Gibbs function. For a mixture of components A and B, this relation is given by Eq. 11.43. At constant T and n_B this expression reduces to

$$dG_{T,n_B} = V\,dP_{T,n_B} + \bar{G}_A\,dn_{AT,n_B}$$

Taking a Maxwell cross-partial derivative we have

$$\left(\frac{\partial \bar{G}_A}{\partial P}\right)_{T,n_A,n_B} = \left(\frac{\partial V}{\partial n_A}\right)_{T,P,n_B} = \bar{V}_A \tag{11.50}$$

Therefore, from Eqs. 11.48 and 11.50, at constant temperature and composition,

$$(d\bar{G}_A)_{T,n_A,n_B} = \bar{R}T\,d(\ln \bar{f}_A)_{T,n_A,n_B} = \bar{V}_A\,dP_{T,n_A,n_B} \tag{11.51}$$

For pure substance A at the same constant temperature,

$$(d\bar{g}_A)_T = \bar{R}T\,d(\ln f_A)_T = \bar{v}_A\,dP_T \tag{11.52}$$

In order to derive an expression that permits us to evaluate the fugacity of component A in the mixture from measurable quantities, let us subtract Eq. 11.52 from Eq. 11.51, and integrate the resultant expression from P^* to P (where P^* is a very low pressure) at constant temperature and composition.

$$\int_{\ln \bar{f}_A*/f_A*}^{\ln \bar{f}_A/f_A} \bar{R}T\,d\left(\ln \frac{\bar{f}_A}{f_A}\right) = \int_{P^*\to 0}^{P}(\bar{V}_A - \bar{v}_A)\,dP \tag{11.53}$$

At this low pressure P^*, $\bar{f}_A{}^* = y_A P^*$ (Eq. 11.49) and $f_A{}^* = P^*$. Therefore as $P^* \to 0$,

$$\left(\ln \frac{\bar{f}_A{}^*}{f_A{}^*}\right) \to \ln\left(\frac{y_A P^*}{P^*}\right) = \ln y_A$$

Therefore we can write

$$\int_{\ln y_A}^{\ln \bar{f}_A/f_A} \bar{R}T\,d\left(\ln \frac{\bar{f}_A}{f_A}\right) = \int_{P^*\to 0}^{P}(\bar{V}_A - \bar{v}_A)\,dP$$

This integration results in the expression

$$\bar{R}T \ln\left(\frac{\tilde{f}_A}{y_A f_A}\right) = \int_0^P (\bar{V}_A - \bar{v}_A)\, dP \tag{11.54}$$

in which $\tilde{f}_A$ is the fugacity of component A in the mixture of given composition at the given temperature and pressure P, whereas f_A is the fugacity of pure A at the same temperature and pressure. Equation 11.54 expresses the relation between $\tilde{f}_A$ and f_A in terms of the difference between $\bar{V}_A$ and $\bar{v}_A$, a measurable quantity. It is also convenient to find a relation between $\tilde{f}_A$ and f_A in terms of the other quantities discussed in Section 11.7, namely $\bar{H}_A - \bar{h}_A$ and $\bar{S}_A - \bar{s}_A$, for such relations will permit evaluation of one or more of these quantities in terms of $\bar{V}_A - \bar{v}_A$.

First we shall determine the partial molal Gibbs function of component A in a mixture at T, P, with respect to a state at which the Gibbs function is known. Let us integrate Eq. 11.48 at constant T from P^* to P, where again P^* is sufficiently low to assume ideal gas behavior,

$$\int_{\bar{G}_A^*}^{\bar{G}_A} d\bar{G}_A = \int_{\tilde{f}_A^* \to y_A P^*}^{\tilde{f}_A} \bar{R}T\, d(\ln \tilde{f}_A)_T \tag{11.55}$$

This integration yields the result

$$\bar{G}_A = \bar{G}_A^* + \bar{R}T \ln \frac{\tilde{f}_A}{y_A P^*} = \bar{G}_A^* - \bar{R}T \ln y_A + \bar{R}T \ln \frac{\tilde{f}_A}{P^*}$$

We have noted, Eq. 11.34, that

$$\bar{G}_A = \bar{H}_A - T\bar{S}_A$$

Therefore,

$$\bar{G}_A = \bar{H}_A^* - T\bar{S}_A^* - \bar{R}T \ln y_A + \bar{R}T \ln \frac{\tilde{f}_A}{P^*} \tag{11.56}$$

But, at low pressures,

$$\bar{H}_A^* = \bar{h}_A^*$$

Also, from Eq. 11.42,

$$\bar{S}_A^* + \bar{R} \ln y_A = \bar{s}_A^*$$

Therefore,

$$\bar{G}_A = \bar{h}_A^* - T\bar{s}_A^* + \bar{R}T \ln \frac{\tilde{f}_A}{P^*}$$

$$\bar{G}_A = \bar{g}_A^* + \bar{R}T \ln \frac{\tilde{f}_A}{P^*} \tag{11.57}$$

To determine the change in $\bar{G}_A$ with respect to temperature, we take another Maxwell cross-partial derivative of Eq. 11.43,

$$\left(\frac{\partial \bar{G}_A}{\partial T}\right)_{P,n_A,n_B} = -\left(\frac{\partial S}{\partial n_A}\right)_{T,P,n_B} = -\bar{S}_A \qquad (11.58)$$

or, at constant pressure and composition,

$$d\bar{G}_A = -\bar{S}_A\, dT \qquad (11.59)$$

But, from Eq. 11.34,

$$\bar{S}_A = \frac{\bar{H}_A - \bar{G}_A}{T}$$

Substituting,

$$(d\bar{G}_A)_{P,n_A,n_B} = -\frac{\bar{H}_A - \bar{G}_A}{T}\, dT_{P,n_A,n_B}$$

which may be rearranged to the form

$$\frac{T\, d\bar{G}_A - \bar{G}_A\, dT}{T^2} = -\frac{\bar{H}_A}{T^2}\, dT \bigg|_{P,n_A,n_B} \qquad (11.60)$$

We note that Eq. 11.60 is, in effect,

$$d\left(\frac{\bar{G}_A}{T}\right)_{P,n_A,n_B} = -\frac{\bar{H}_A}{T^2}\, dT_{P,n_A,n_B} \qquad (11.61)$$

By the same procedure for pure A at constant pressure, we can write

$$d\left(\frac{\bar{g}_A}{T}\right)_P = -\frac{\bar{h}_A}{T^2}\, dT_P \qquad (11.62)$$

Now, let us divide Eq. 11.57 by T and differentiate at constant pressure and composition.

$$d\left(\frac{\bar{G}_A}{T}\right)_{P,n_A,n_B} = d\left(\frac{\bar{g}_A^*}{T}\right)_{P,n_A,n_B} + \bar{R}\, d(\ln f_A)_{P,n_A,n_B} \qquad (11.63)$$

Substituting Eqs. 11.61 and 11.62, we see that at constant pressure and composition,

$$(d \ln \bar{f}_A)_{P,n_A,n_B} = \frac{\bar{h}_A^* - \bar{H}_A}{\bar{R}T^2}\, dT_{P,n_A,n_B} \qquad (11.64)$$

Again, by the same procedure for pure A at constant pressure,

$$(d \ln f_A)_P = \frac{\bar{h}_A^* - \bar{h}_A}{\bar{R}T^2}\, dT_P \qquad (11.65)$$

Combining Eqs. 11.64 and 11.65,

$$d\left(\ln \frac{\bar{f}_A}{f_A}\right)_{P,n_A,n_B} = \frac{\bar{h}_A - \bar{H}_A}{\bar{R}T^2} dT_{P,n_A,n_B} \tag{11.66}$$

which gives another relation between $\bar{f}_A$ and f_A at a given T, P, in this case in terms of the difference between $(\bar{h}_A - \bar{H}_A)$.

Finally let us determine the relation between $\bar{f}_A$ and f_A in terms of the difference $(\bar{S}_A - \bar{s}_A)$. For pure component A,

$$\bar{g}_A = \bar{h}_A - T\bar{s}_A$$

Also,

$$\bar{G}_A = \bar{H}_A - T\bar{S}_A$$

Combining these equations,

$$(\bar{S}_A - \bar{s}_A) = \left(\frac{\bar{H}_A - \bar{h}_A}{T}\right) - \left(\frac{\bar{G}_A - \bar{g}_A}{T}\right) \tag{11.67}$$

Substituting Eqs. 10.77 and 11.57, we have

$$(\bar{S}_A - \bar{s}_A) = \left(\frac{\bar{H}_A - \bar{h}_A}{T}\right) - \bar{R}\ln\left(\frac{\bar{f}_A}{f_A}\right) \tag{11.68}$$

which can also be written in the form

$$(\bar{S}_A - \bar{s}_A) = \left(\frac{\bar{H}_A - \bar{h}_A}{T}\right) - \bar{R}\ln\left(\frac{\bar{f}_A}{y_A f_A}\right) - \bar{R}\ln y_A \tag{11.69}$$

so that the second term on the right side of the equation is similar to the first term of Eq. 11.54.

11.11   Ideal Solutions

There are many mixtures and solutions for which the change of volume on mixing is negligibly small. These are referred to as ideal solutions. By this definition a mixture of ideal gases is an ideal solution, and this is quite acceptable terminology. However, ideal solutions also include certain solid solutions and liquid solutions as well as mixtures of nonideal gases. A number of significant simplifications result from this assumption.

We have noted (Eq. 11.28) that for a mixture of ideal gases consisting of components A and B,

$$(\bar{V}_A - \bar{v}_A) = (\bar{V}_B - \bar{v}_B) = 0$$

Let us define an ideal solution as any solution or mixture for which

$$(\bar{V}_A - \bar{v}_A) = 0; \quad (\bar{V}_B - \bar{v}_B) = 0 \tag{11.70}$$

at the pressure of the mixture and for all lower pressures as well. This definition therefore requires that

$$\Delta V_{mix} = 0$$

as in the case of mixtures of ideal gases.

Since, in accordance with Eq. 11.25, the volume of a mixture of components A and B is

$$V = \bar{V}_A \cdot n_A + \bar{V}_B \cdot n_B$$

the assumption of an ideal solution, Eq. 11.70 is equivalent to assuming Amagat's rule of additive volumes,

$$V = \bar{v}_A n_A + \bar{v}_B n_B$$

where $\bar{v}_A$ and $\bar{v}_B$ are the molal specific volumes of pure A and pure B at T and P, the pressure and temperature of the mixture. It should be noted that in the case of an ideal solution, $\bar{v}_A$ and $\bar{v}_B$ are the actual specific volumes of these components, and no assumption of ideal gas behavior is made.

The fugacity of a component in an ideal solution is readily determined by reference to Eq. 11.54.

$$\bar{R}T \ln \left(\frac{\bar{f}_A}{y_A f_A} \right) = \int_0^P (\bar{V}_A - \bar{v}_A) \, dP$$

From the definition of an ideal solution, $(\bar{V}_A - \bar{v}_A) = 0$, it follows that

$$\bar{f}_A = y_A f_A \tag{11.71}$$

Similarly, for component B,

$$\bar{f}_B = y_B f_B \tag{11.72}$$

For the general case of an ideal solution we can write

$$\bar{f}_i = y_i f_i \tag{11.73}$$

Eq. 11.73 constitutes the Lewis-Randall rule, which holds for an ideal solution. Note the similar appearance of these equations and those for the partial pressures of ideal gas mixture components as discussed in Section 11.1. This is consistent with the concept that fugacity is a pseudo-pressure.

The enthalpy of mixing for a mixture of components A and B is given by Eq. 11.38.

$$\Delta H_{mix} = (\bar{H}_A - \bar{h}_A)n_A + (\bar{H}_B - \bar{h}_B)n_B$$

The fact that the enthalpy of mixing is zero for an ideal solution can be demonstrated by consideration of Eq. 11.66, which was written for constant composition.

$$d \left(\ln \frac{\bar{f}_A}{f_A} \right)_{P, n_A, n_B} = \left(\frac{\bar{h}_A - \bar{H}_A}{\bar{R}T^2} \right) dT_{P, n_A, n_B}$$

Substituting Eq. 11.54 it follows that for an ideal solution,

$$(\bar{h}_A - \bar{H}_A) = 0 \tag{11.74}$$

A similar expression can be written for component B, and therefore one concludes that the enthalpy of mixing for an ideal solution is equal to zero.

$$\Delta H_{\text{mix}} = 0$$

We had reached the same conclusion for a mixture of ideal gases, but for an ideal solution $\bar{h}_A$ and $\bar{h}_B$ are actual enthalpies, and no assumption of ideal gas behavior is made.

The entropy of mixing for an ideal solution can be found by consideration of Eq. 11.69.

$$\bar{S}_A - \bar{s}_A = \left(\frac{\bar{H}_A - \bar{h}_A}{T}\right) - \bar{R} \ln \left(\frac{\bar{f}_A}{y_A f_A}\right) - \bar{R} \ln y_A$$

Since $\bar{H}_A - \bar{h}_A = 0$ and $\bar{f}_A = y_A f_A$, it follows that for an ideal solution

$$(\bar{S}_A - \bar{s}_A) = -\bar{R} \ln y_A$$
$$(\bar{S}_B - \bar{s}_B) = -\bar{R} \ln y_B \tag{11.75}$$

in which $\bar{s}_A$ and $\bar{s}_B$ are for pure A and B at T, P, the pressure and temperature of the mixture

The entropy of mixing, Eq. 11.39, is

$$\Delta S_{\text{mix}} = (\bar{S}_A - \bar{s}_A)n_A + (\bar{S}_B - \bar{s}_B)n_B$$

Therefore, for an ideal solution the entropy of mixing is given by the relation

$$\Delta S_{\text{mix}} = -\bar{R}(n_A \ln y_A + n_B \ln y_B)$$

Note that the same expression for the entropy of mixing was obtained for a mixture of ideal gases, Eq. 11.12, although for an ideal solution $\bar{s}_A$ and $\bar{s}_B$ are actual entropies and not ideal gas entropies.

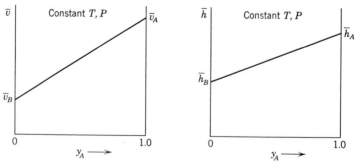

Fig. 11.12   Typical specific volume-composition and enthalpy-composition diagrams for an ideal solution.

It also follows that since $\bar{V}_A - \bar{v}_A = 0$ and $\bar{V}_B - \bar{v}_B = 0$ for an ideal solution, the specific volume-composition diagram is a straight line for an ideal solution. The same would be true for an enthalpy-composition diagram. These are shown in Fig. 11.12.

Example 11.7

A gas mixture consisting of 75% CH_4 and 25% C_2H_4 on a mole basis is stored at 77 F, 1200 lbf/in.^{2} in a cylinder having a volume of 10 ft^3. Determine the mass of gas in the tank assuming an ideal solution, and compare these results with those obtained from assuming a mixture of ideal gases.

From Eq. 11.25, which applies to all two component solutions,

$$V = n_A \bar{V}_A + n_B \bar{V}_B$$

Since we are assuming an ideal solution, we conclude from Eq. 11.70 that

$$\bar{V}_{CH_4} = \bar{v}_{CH_4}, \qquad \bar{V}_{C_2H_4} = \bar{v}_{C_2H_4}$$

and therefore

$$V = (n\bar{v})_{CH_4} + (n\bar{v})_{C_2H_4}$$

or

$$\bar{v} = (y\bar{v})_{CH_4} + (y\bar{v})_{C_2H_4}$$

which is Amagat's rule of additive volumes.

If we had a table of thermodynamic properties that gave the specific volume of CH_4 and C_2H_4 at 77 F and 1200 lbf/in.^{2}, we would simply find the molal specific volume $\bar{v}$ of each component at this temperature and pressure, and proceed with the solution. In the absence of these data we can use the generalized charts, which will yield fairly accurate results. For the CH_4 at 77 F and 1200 lbf/in.^{2},

$$T_r = \tfrac{537}{344} = 1.56; \qquad P_r = \tfrac{1200}{673} = 1.78$$

For the C_2H_4 at 77 F and 1200 lbf/in.^{2},

$$T_r = \tfrac{537}{508} = 1.06; \qquad P_r = \tfrac{1200}{742} = 1.61$$

From the generalized compressibility chart, Fig. A.1,

$$Z_{CH_4} = 0.88; \qquad Z_{C_2H_4} = 0.35$$

Therefore, at 77 F and 1200 lbf/in.^{2},

$$\bar{v}_{CH_4} = \frac{Z\bar{R}T}{P} = \frac{0.88 \times 1545 \times 537}{1200 \times 144} = 4.22 \text{ ft}^3/\text{lb mole}$$

$$\bar{v}_{C_2H_4} = \frac{Z\bar{R}T}{P} = \frac{0.35 \times 1545 \times 537}{1200 \times 144} = 1.68 \text{ ft}^3/\text{lb mole}$$

$$\bar{v} = 0.75(4.22) + 0.25(1.68) = 3.58 \text{ ft}^3/\text{lb mole}$$

$$M = (yM)_{CH_4} + (yM)_{C_2H_4} = 0.75(16) + 0.25(28.0) = 19.0$$

$$v = \frac{\bar{v}}{M} = \frac{3.58}{19} = 0.188 \text{ ft}^3/\text{lbm}$$

$$m = \frac{V}{v} = \frac{10}{0.188} = 53.2 \text{ lbm}.$$

Assuming this to be a mixture of ideal gases we can use either the partial pressure or additive volume approach. Let us use the former.

$$P_{CH_4} = y_{CH_4}P = 0.75(1200) = 900 \text{ lbf/in.}^2$$

$$m_{CH_4} = \frac{P_{CH_4}V}{RT} = \frac{900 \times 144 \times 10}{(1545/16) \times 537} = 25.0 \text{ lbm}$$

$$P_{C_2H_4} = y_{C_2H_4}P = 0.25(1200) = 300 \text{ lbf/in.}^2$$

$$m_{C_2H_4} = \frac{P_{C_2H_4}V}{RT} = \frac{300 \times 144 \times 10}{(1545/28) \times 537} = 14.6 \text{ lbm}$$

$$m = 25 + 14.6 = 39.6 \text{ lbm}$$

This compares with 53.2 lbm for the assumption of an ideal solution.

It is significant to note that if instead of assuming an ideal solution we assume that the mass of each component can be found at its partial pressure (where partial pressure is defined as $P_i = y_iP$) and the volume and temperature of the mixture, we obtain significantly different results from assuming an ideal solution. The reason is that at the given temperature Z may be quite different at the partial pressure than at the total pressure. For example, in this problem we would have the following results for this approach.

$$P = P_{CH_4} + P_{C_2H_4} = \left(\frac{nZ\bar{R}T}{V}\right)_{CH_4} + \left(\frac{nZ\bar{R}T}{V}\right)_{C_2H_4}$$

$$P = \frac{\bar{R}T}{V}[(nZ)_{CH_4} + (nZ)_{C_2H_4}] = \frac{P}{Z}[(yZ)_{CH_4} + (yZ)_{C_2H_4}]$$

Therefore,

$$Z = (yZ)_{CH_4} + (yZ)_{C_2H_4}$$

where the Z of the components is measured at the partial pressure of the component and the temperature of the mixture.

$(P_r)_{CH_4} = \frac{900}{673} = 1.34;$ $(T_r)_{CH_4} = \frac{537}{344} = 1.56;$ $Z_{CH_4} = 0.91$

$(P_r)_{C_2H_4} = \frac{300}{742} = 0.405;$ $(T_r)_{C_2H_4} = \frac{537}{508} = 1.06;$ $Z_{C_2H_4} = 0.88$

Therefore, for the mixture

$$Z = 0.75(0.91) + 0.25(0.88) = 0.90$$

$$m = \frac{PV}{ZRT} = \frac{1200 \times 144 \times 10}{0.90 \times (1545/19) \times 537} = 44.8 \text{ lbm}$$

In general the assumption of an ideal solution yields more accurate results than this assumption regarding partial pressures. Ultimately, however, the accuracy of even the assumption of an ideal solution can be judged only by comparison with actual experimental data.

11.12 Activity, Activity Coefficient, and the Gibbs-Duhem Equation

In our consideration of equilibrium in a following chapter we will find it convenient to make use of an additional property, the activity. It is appropriate, however, to introduce this property at this point.

We have noted that the partial molal Gibbs function for a component in a mixture can be expressed in terms of the low pressure ideal gas state, as was done in Eq. 11.57.

$$\bar{G}_A = \bar{g}_A{}^* + \bar{R}T \ln (\bar{f}_A/P^*)$$

A more general approach would be to express the partial Gibbs functions in terms of a state at which we consider the mixture to behave as an ideal solution instead of an ideal gas mixture. The temperature of this state is the same as that of the mixture, and the pressure is some value P° to be discussed later. It should be pointed out that this state may very well be a hypothetical one. That is, the mixture at T and P° may not actually behave as an ideal solution, but as long as we consistently calculate the mixture properties and develop the equations as though it did, the fact that it is a hypothetical reference state will introduce no difficulties. The significance of this statement will become evident as we proceed further.

The procedure for expressing $\bar{G}_A$ is similar to that followed in the development of Eq. 11.57. In this case Eq. 11.48 is integrated at constant temperature and composition from the pressure P° to the mixture pressure P,

$$\int_{\bar{G}_A{}^\circ}^{\bar{G}_A} (d\bar{G}_A)_T = \int_{f_A{}^\circ = y_A f_A{}^\circ}^{\bar{f}_A} \bar{R}T d(\ln \bar{f}_A)_T$$

in which $f_A{}^\circ$ is the fugacity of pure A at T, P°. Therefore,

$$
\begin{aligned}
\bar{G}_A &= \bar{G}_A{}^\circ + \bar{R}T \ln \left(\frac{\bar{f}_A}{y_A f_A{}^\circ}\right) \\
&= \bar{G}_A{}^\circ - \bar{R}T \ln y_A + \bar{R}T \ln \left(\frac{\bar{f}_A}{f_A{}^\circ}\right) \\
&= \bar{H}_A{}^\circ - T\bar{S}_A{}^\circ - \bar{R}T \ln y_A + \bar{R}T \ln \left(\frac{\bar{f}_A}{f_A{}^\circ}\right)
\end{aligned}
\qquad (11.76)
$$

Since we assume an ideal solution at $P°$, from Eq. 11.74,

$$\bar{H}_A° = \bar{h}_A°$$ (11.77)

and from Eq. 11.75

$$\bar{S}_A° + \bar{R} \ln y_A = \bar{s}_A°$$ (11.78)

Therefore,

$$\bar{G}_A = \bar{h}_A° - T\bar{s}_A° + \bar{R}T \ln \left(\frac{\bar{f}_A}{f_A°}\right)$$

$$= \bar{g}_A° + \bar{R}T \ln \left(\frac{\bar{f}_A}{f_A°}\right)$$ (11.79)

Thus we have an expression for the partial molal Gibbs function in terms of known values. It is from this important equation that the equilibrium constant is defined in Chapter 13. Consequently Eq. 11.79 is a very powerful relation. The values $f_A°$ and $\bar{g}_A°$ are for pure substance A at the temperature T and pressure $P°$, which is referred to as the standard state pressure. For gaseous mixtures, $P°$ is commonly taken as 1 atmosphere. For liquid and vapor phases in two-phase systems (discussed in Chapter 13), the standard state for each component is taken as the pure substance in that phase at the pressure of the mixture.

Examining Eq. 11.79, we find it convenient to define a quantity called activity. The activity a_A of component A in a mixture at T, P, is defined as

$$a_A = \frac{\bar{f}_A}{f_A°}$$ (11.80)

The activity of component B is, of course, similarly defined. Equation 11.79 may now be written in the convenient form

$$\bar{G}_A = \bar{g}_A° + \bar{R}T \ln a_A$$ (11.81)

Several special cases for evaluating $\bar{G}_A$ from this equation have already been considered. For example, in the case for which the mixture can be assumed an ideal gas mixture at the standard state pressure, the equation reduces to Eq. 11.57. If the mixture can be assumed an ideal solution at pressure P as well as at $P°$, then from Eq. 11.71,

$$a_A = \frac{y_A f_A}{f_A°}$$ (11.82)

If conditions are such that an ideal gas mixture can be assumed at both $P°$ and P, then from Eq. 11.49

$$a_A = \frac{y_A P}{P°}$$ (11.83)

Another parameter commonly used in the description of mixtures is the activity coefficient γ, which for any component A is defined in terms of its activity and mole fraction as

$$\gamma_A = \frac{a_A}{y_A} \qquad (11.84)$$

The activity coefficient is very useful for indicating the nonideality of a mixture and is particularly important for liquid or solid solutions. For example, if the standard state pressure P° is taken as the pressure of the mixture, and if the mixture behaves as an ideal solution, then from Eqs. 11.82 and 11.84 the activity coefficient is unity. Departures of γ from unity then indicate nonideal behavior of the mixture.

There is another powerful thermodynamic relation, the Gibbs-Duhem equation, which is useful for the correlation of mixture behavior. We develop this equation in the following manner. At a given temperature and pressure, from Eq. 11.31,

$$G_{T,P} = \sum_i \bar{G}_i n_i \qquad (11.85)$$

Differentiating at constant T, P,

$$dG_{T,P} = \sum_i \bar{G}_i \, dn_{i(T,P)} + \sum_i n_i \, d\bar{G}_{i(T,P)} \qquad (11.86)$$

Consider the thermodynamic property relation written in terms of the Gibbs function.

$$dG = -S \, dT + V \, dP + \sum_i \bar{G}_i \, dn_i \qquad (11.87)$$

At constant temperature and pressure, we note from Eqs. 11.86 and 11.87 that

$$\sum_i n_i \, d\bar{G}_{i_{T,P}} = 0 \qquad (11.88)$$

If we divide each term of Eq. 11.88 by the total number of moles n, this relation can also be expressed in terms of the mole fractions as

$$\sum_i y_i \, d\bar{G}_{i_{T,P}} = 0 \qquad (11.89)$$

Using an equation of the form of Eq. 11.81 for each partial Gibbs function,

$$\bar{G}_i = \bar{g}_i^\circ + \bar{R}T \ln a_i \qquad (11.90)$$

and substituting the definition of activity coefficient γ_i from Eq. 11.84 and differentiating at constant T, P, we have

$$d\bar{G}_{i(T,P)} = \bar{R}T \, d \ln \gamma_{i(T,P)} + \bar{R}T \, d \ln y_{i(T,P)} \qquad (11.91)$$

If we substitute this expression into Eq. 11.89 for each component, the result is

$$\bar{R}T \sum_i y_i \, d \ln \gamma_{i(T,P)} + \bar{R}T \sum_i y_i \, d \ln y_{i(T,P)} = 0$$

However, the second term of this expression is seen to be identically zero. Therefore,

$$\sum_i y_i \, d \ln \gamma_{i(T,P)} = 0 \tag{11.92}$$

which is the important Gibbs-Duhem equation, giving a relation among the activity coefficients for the components in a mixture.

For a binary mixture of A, B, the Gibbs-Duhem equation reduces to the form

$$y_A \, d \ln \gamma_{A(T,P)} + y_B \, d \ln \gamma_{B(T,P)} = 0 \tag{11.93}$$

Dividing this expression by dy_A and realizing that

$$dy_A + dy_B = 0$$

the equation becomes

$$y_A \left(\frac{\partial \ln \gamma_A}{\partial y_A} \right)_{T,P} = y_B \left(\frac{\partial \ln \gamma_B}{\partial y_B} \right)_{T,P} \tag{11.94}$$

We note that the Gibbs-Duhem equation in this form enables us to evaluate the activity coefficient of one component in the mixture in terms of that for the other component.

11.13 Equations of State and Pseudocritical State for Mixtures

Frequently it is desirable to have an equation of state for a mixture of gases. The question arises as to how an equation of state for a mixture can be developed from the equations of state for the pure components. For example, suppose the equations of state of the components are available in a given form, with given constants for each component. How should these constants be combined to provide an equation of state that accurately represents the P-v-T behavior of the mixture?

Various combining rules have been used. Three of the most common are:

$$\text{Linear combination: } k_m = \sum_i y_i k_i \tag{11.95}$$

where k represents a constant in the equation of state and y the mole fraction.

$$\text{Square root combination: } k_m = \left(\sum_i y_i k_i^{1/2} \right)^2 \tag{11.96}$$

$$\text{Cube root or Lorentz combination: } k_m = \frac{1}{8} \sum_i \sum_j y_i y_j (k_i^{1/3} + k_j^{1/3})^3$$

For two components this latter relation reduces to

$$k_m = y_1^2 k_1 + \tfrac{1}{4} y_1 y_2 (k_1^{1/3} + k_2^{1/3})^3 + y_2^2 k_2 \tag{11.97}$$

For van der Waals' equation the square root combination is usually used for "a" and the linear combination is used for "b,"

$$a_m = \left(\sum_i y_i a_i^{\frac{1}{2}} \right)^2$$

$$b_m = \sum_i y_i b_i$$

(11.98)

For a number of equations of state, considerable work has been done to determine the best combining rule for the various constants. For example, it appears that for the Beattie-Bridgeman equation of state considerable accuracy is achieved by using a square root combination for constants A and C, a Lorentz combination for B, and a linear combination for a and b.

As noted earlier, when limited P-v-T data are available, the generalized compressibility chart can often be used with considerable accuracy. In the case of a mixture there are two ways in which the generalized chart can be used. One is to determine the compressibility factor for the mixture from the compressibility factors for the pure components. A simple combining relation has been used.

$$Z_{\text{mix}} = \sum_i y_i Z_i$$

This relation is accurate for ideal solutions, but not for nonideal solutions.

An alternate approach is to define pseudocritical constants for the mixture so that the generalized chart gives with reasonable accuracy the compressibility factor for the mixture. W. B. Kay* in 1936 first suggested a simple linear combination.

$$(P_c)_{\text{mix}} = \sum_i y_i P_{ci}$$

$$(T_c)_{\text{mix}} = \sum_i y_i T_{ci}$$

(11.99)

These relations give results of reasonable accuracy for mixtures. A number of other procedures for defining pseudocritical constants for mixtures have also been proposed. These procedures are in general more complicated to use than Kay's rule, but may yield somewhat more accurate results.

Example 11.8

A mixture of 59.39% CO_2 and 40.61% CH_4 (mole basis) is maintained at 310.94 K, 85.06 atm., at which condition the specific volume has been measured as 0.2205 lit/mole. Calculate the per cent deviation if the

* W. B. Kay, *Ind. Eng. Chem.*, **28**, 1014 (1936).

specific volume had been calculated by (a) Kay's Rule, (b) Ideal Solution, and (c) van der Waals' equation of state.

a. For convenience, let

$$CO_2 = A, \qquad CH_4 = B.$$

Then

$$T_{c_A} = 304.2 \text{ K}, \qquad P_{c_A} = 72.9 \text{ atm}$$
$$T_{c_B} = 191.1 \text{ K}, \qquad P_{c_B} = 45.8 \text{ atm}$$

For Kay's Rule, Eq. 11.99

$$T_{c_m} = \sum_i y_i T_{c_i} = y_A T_{c_A} + y_B T_{c_B}$$
$$= 0.5939(304.2) + 0.4061(191.1)$$
$$= 258.0 \text{ K}$$

$$P_{c_m} = \sum_i y_i P_{c_i} = y_A P_{c_A} + y_B P_{c_B}$$
$$= 0.5939(72.9) + 0.4061(45.8)$$
$$= 62.0 \text{ atm.}$$

Therefore, the pseudo-reduced properties of the mixture are

$$T_{r_m} = \frac{T}{T_{c_m}} = \frac{310.94}{258.0} = 1.205$$

$$P_{r_m} = \frac{P}{P_{c_m}} = \frac{85.06}{62.0} = 1.372$$

From the generalized chart,

$$Z_m = 0.705$$

and

$$\bar{v} = \frac{Z_m \bar{R} T}{P} = \frac{0.705(0.08206)(310.94)}{85.06}$$

$$= 0.2115 \text{ lit/mole}$$

The per cent deviation from the experimental value is

$$\% \text{ Dev.} = \left(\frac{0.2205 - 0.2115}{0.2205}\right) \times 100 = 4.08\%$$

b. For an ideal solution, using the same procedure as in Example 11.7,

$$T_{r_A} = \frac{310.94}{304.2} = 1.022, \qquad P_{r_A} = \frac{85.06}{72.9} = 1.17$$

$$Z_A = 0.35$$

$$\bar{v}_A = \frac{Z_A \bar{R} T}{P} = \frac{0.35(0.08206)(310.94)}{85.06} = 0.105 \text{ lit/mole}$$

$$T_{r_B} = \frac{310.94}{191.1} = 1.63, \qquad P_{r_B} = \frac{85.06}{45.8} = 1.857$$

$$Z_B = 0.91$$

$$\bar{v}_B = \frac{Z_B \bar{R} T}{P} = \frac{0.91(0.08206)(310.94)}{85.06} = 0.273 \text{ lit/mole}$$

Therefore,

$$\bar{v} = y_A \bar{v}_A + y_B \bar{v}_B$$
$$= 0.5939(0.105) + 0.4061(0.273)$$
$$= 0.1733 \text{ lit/mole}$$

and

$$\% \text{ Dev.} = \left(\frac{0.2205 - 0.1733}{0.2205} \right) \times 100 = 22.4\%$$

c. For van der Waals' equation, the pure substance constants are

$$a_A = \frac{27 \bar{R}^2 T_{cA}{}^2}{64 P_{cA}} = 3.606 \frac{\text{atm-lit}^2}{\text{mole}^2}$$

$$b_A = \frac{\bar{R} T_{cA}}{8 P_{cA}} = 0.0428 \text{ lit/mole}$$

and

$$a_B = \frac{27 \bar{R}^2 T_{cB}{}^2}{64 P_{cB}} = 2.256 \frac{\text{atm-lit}^2}{\text{mole}^2}$$

$$b_B = \frac{\bar{R} T_{cB}}{8 P_{cB}} = 0.04271 \text{ lit/mole}$$

Therefore, for the mixture, from Eq. 11.98,

$$a_m = (y_A \sqrt{a_A} + y_B \sqrt{a_B})^2$$
$$= (0.5939 \sqrt{3.606} + 0.4061 \sqrt{2.256})^2$$
$$= 3.030 \frac{\text{atm-lit}^2}{\text{mole}^2}$$

$$b_m = y_A b_A + y_B b_B$$
$$= 0.5939(0.0428) + 0.4061(0.04271)$$
$$= 0.04276 \text{ lit/mole}$$

The equation of state for the mixture of this composition is

$$P = \frac{\bar{R} T}{\bar{v} - b_m} - \frac{a_m{}^2}{\bar{v}^2}$$

$$85.06 = \frac{0.08206(310.94)}{\bar{v} - 0.04276} - \frac{3.03}{\bar{v}^2}$$

Solving for $\bar{v}$ by trial and error,

$$\bar{v} = 0.2050 \text{ lit/mole}$$

$$\% \text{ Dev.} = \left(\frac{0.2205 - 0.2050}{0.2205}\right) \times 100 = 7.03\%$$

As a point of interest from the ideal gas law, $v = 0.30$ lit/mole, which is a deviation of 36 per cent from the measured value.

We must be careful not to draw too general a conclusion from the results of this example. We have calculated per cent deviation in v at only a single point for only one mixture. We do note, however, that the various methods used give quite different results. From a more general study of these models for a number of mixtures, we find that the results found here are fairly typical, at least qualitatively. Kay's rule is very useful because it is fairly accurate and yet relatively simple. The ideal solution model does not in general yield values as accurate for P-v-T behavior of mixtures, but it is of considerable value for use in phase equilibrium predictions, which we will discuss in Chapter 13. The van der Waals equation is too simplified an expression to accurately represent P-v-T behavior except at moderate densities, but it is useful to demonstrate the procedures followed in utilizing more complex analytical equations of state.

The more sophisticated generalized behavior models and empirical equations of state will represent mixture P-v-T behavior to within about one per cent over a wide range of density, but they are of course more difficult to use than the methods considered in Example 11.8. The generalized models have the advantage of being eaiser to use, and they are suitable for hand computations. Calculations with the complex empirical equations of state become very involved, but have the advantage of expressing the P-v-T-composition relations in analytical form, which is of great value in digital computer calculations.

PROBLEMS

11.1 Following is the volumetric analysis of a gaseous mixture:

Constituent	% by Volume
N_2	60
CO_2	22
CO	11
O_2	7

(a) Determine the analysis on a mass basis.

(*b*) What is the mass of 1000 ft³ of this gas when the pressure is 15.0 lbf/in.²
and the temperature 80 F?

(*c*) This mixture is heated in a steady-state, steady-flow process from an
initial temperature of 100 F to a final temperature of 500 F. Determine the
heat transfer.

11.2 A vessel contains one lb mole of nitrogen and one lb mole of helium,
each at 1 atm pressure and 77 F and separated by a membrane.

Determine the change of entropy which occurs when the membrane ruptures
and a homogeneous mixture fills the vessel. Assume no heat transfer during
the process.

11.3 The vacuum space in the dewar shown in Fig. 11.13 contained air at
ambient conditions when the dewar was empty. However, when the liquid
hydrogen was placed in the dewar, essentially all of the CO_2, O_2. N_2, and H_2O

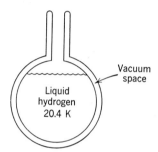

Fig. 11.13   Sketch for Problem 11.3.

froze out on the inner walls, leaving only hydrogen and helium in the vacuum
space. If the air initially contained 0.01% helium and 0.01% hydrogen by
volume, what would be the pressure in the vacuum space if the average temperature of the gas is considered to be 50 K?

11.4 Nitrogen and hydrogen are mixed in a steady-flow adiabatic process
in the ratio of 3 lbm of hydrogen per lbm of nitrogen. The hydrogen enters
at 20 lbf/in.², 100 F, and the nitrogen at 20 lbf/in.², 500 F. The pressure after
mixing is 18 lbf/in.² Determine the final temperature of the mixture and the
net entropy change per lbm of mixture.

11.5 A mixture of CO_2 and O_2 is expanded in a cylinder in a reversible
adiabatic process from 30 lbf/in.², 200 F, to 15 lbf/in.² The mole fraction of the
CO_2 is 0.2. Determine the work done per mole of mixture, the final temperature,
and the entropy change of the CO_2 and the O_2.

11.6 Consider the compression of a fuel-air mixture which takes place in an
internal combustion engine. Assume that the fuel is ethane and that the air-
fuel ratio on a mass basis is 15 to 1. The engine has a compression ratio of 9
to 1 and before the compression stroke begins the pressure in the cylinder is
13.0 lbf/in.² and the temperature is 100 F. Determine the pressure and temperature after compression and the work of compression per pound of mixture.

11.7 A tank having a volume of 10 ft³ contains oxygen at 50 lbf/in.², 80 F.
Nitrogen at a pressure of 100 lbf/in.², 300 F flows from a pipe into the tank

until the pressure reaches 90 lbf/in.² The entire process is adiabatic. Determine the final temperature of the mixture and the change in entropy for this process.

11.8 (a) 0.79 mole of nitrogen at 14.7 lbf/in.², 77 F are separated from 0.21 mole of oxygen at 14.7 lbf/in.², 77 F by a membrane. The membrane ruptures and the gases mix in an adiabatic process to form a uniform mixture. Determine the reversible work and irreversibility for this process.

(b) Determine the minimum work required to separate 1 mole of air (assume composition to be 79% nitrogen and 21% oxygen by volume) at 14.7 lbf/in.², 77 F into nitrogen and oxygen at 14.7 lbf/in.², 77 F.

(c) How would you evaluate the performance of an air separation plant regarding work input?

11.9 A room of dimensions 10 ft × 20 ft × 8 ft contains an air-water vapor mixture at a total pressure of 14.7 lbf/in.² and a temperature of 90 F. The partial pressure of the water vapor is 0.3 lbf/in.² Calculate:

(a) The humidity ratio.

(b) The dew point.

(c) The total mass of water vapor in the room.

11.10 A certain apparatus involves a precise knowledge of the amount of water vapor in an electrical conductivity test cell. This is obtained by charging the bomb with a mixture of nitrogen and water vapor at 1000 lbf/in.² pressure at a temperature of 80 F. The water vapor in the mixture is saturated. What is the humidity ratio of the mixture in the cell?

11.11 One method of removing moisture from atmospheric air is to cool the air so that the moisture condenses or freezes out. Suppose an experiment requires a humidity ratio of 0.0001. To what temperature must the air be cooled at a pressure of 1 atm in order to achieve this humidity? To what temperature must it be cooled if the pressure is 100 atm?

11.12 An air-water vapor mixture enters an air-conditioning unit at a pressure of 20 lbf/in.², a temperature of 90 F, and a relative humidity of 80 %. The mass of dry air entering per min is 100 lbm. The air-vapor mixture leaves the air-conditioning unit at 18 lbf/in.², 55 F, 100% relative humidity. The moisture condensed leaves at 55 F. Determine the heat transfer per min from the air.

11.13 Atmospheric air enters a two-stage compressor at 14.2 lbf/in.², 90 F, and 70% relative humidity. The volume rate of flow into the compressor is

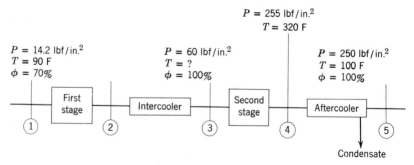

Fig. 11.14   Sketch for Problem 11.13.

500 ft³/min. On leaving the first stage the air enters the intercooler. The pressure at the exit of the intercooler is 60 lbf/in.² The air leaves the second stage at 255 lbf/in.², 320 F and then enters the aftercooler. The air leaves the aftercooler at 250 lbf/in.², 100 F. This is shown schematically in Fig. 11.14.

(a) What will be the temperature of the air leaving the intercooler if the relative humidity on leaving is 100%, but no moisture is condensed in the intercooler?

(b) How much moisture is condensed per hr in the aftercooler, assuming no condensation in the intercooler?

11.14 (a) Determine (by a first-law analysis) the humidity ratio and relative humidity of an air-water vapor mixture that has a dry-bulb temperature of 85 F, an adiabatic saturation temperature of 76 F, and a pressure of 14.7 lbf/in.²

(b) By use of the psychrometric chart determine the humidity ratio and relative humidity of an air-water vapor mixture that has a dry-bulb temperature of 85 F, a wet-bulb temperature of 76 F, and a pressure of 14.7 lbf/in.²

11.15 An air-water vapor mixture at 14.7 lbf/in.², 80 F, and 60% relative humidity is contained in a 10 ft³ closed tank. If the tank is cooled, find the temperature at which H_2O will begin to condense out of the mixture. If the tank is then cooled 10 degrees further, how much H_2O will be condensed?

11.16 A combination air cooler and dehumidifier unit receives outside air at 100 F, 14.7 lbf/in.², relative humidity of 90%. The air-water vapor mixture is first cooled to a low temperature to condense the proper amount of water, after which the air-vapor mixture is heated, leaving the unit at 70 F, 14.7 lbf/in.², relative humidity of 30%. The volume flow rate of the air-vapor mixture at the outlet is 10 ft³/min.

(a) Find the temperature to which the mixture is initially cooled, and the mass of water condensed per lbm of dry air. Show the process the H_2O undergoes on a T-s diagram.

(b) If all the liquid condensed leaves the unit at the minimum temperature, calculate the heat transfer rate in Btu/hr.

11.17 An uninsulated tank having a volume of 5 ft³ contains an air-water vapor mixture with a relative humidity of 80% at 100 F, 15 lbf/in.² Dry air at 100 F, 50 lbf/in.² flows from a pipe into the tank until the pressure reaches 50 lbf/in.² Heat is transferred during this process such that the temperature of the material within the tank remains constant at 100 F. Determine the amount of heat transferred, in Btu, as well as the relative humidity and humidity ratio existing at the completion of the process.

11.18 In areas where the temperature is high and the humidity is low, some measure of air conditioning can be achieved by evaporative cooling. This

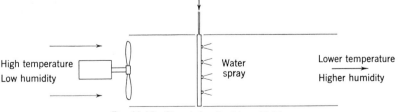

Fig. 11.15 Sketch for Problem 11.18.

involves spraying water into the air, which subsequently evaporates with a resulting decrease in the temperature of the mixture. Such a scheme is shown in Fig. 11.15.

Consider the case of atmospheric air at 100 F, 10% relative humidity, and 14.7 lbf/in.² Cooling water at 50 F is sprayed into the air. If the air-water vapor mixture is to be cooled to 80 F, what will be the relative humidity? What are the disadvantages of this approach to air conditioning?

11.19 When limited quantities of cooling water for a condenser are available, a cooling tower is often used (Fig. 11.16). Consider the case where 20,000 lbm/hr of water at 105 F enters the top of the cooling tower, and the cool water leaves

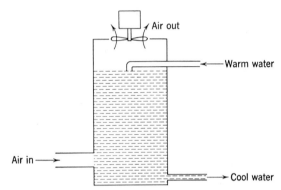

Fig. 11.16   Sketch for Problem 11.19.

the bottom at 65 F. The air-water vapor mixture enters the bottom of the cooling tower at 14.7 lbf/in.², and has a dry-bulb temperature of 72 F and a wet-bulb temperature of 60 F. The air-water vapor mixture leaving the tower has a pressure of 14.3 lbf/in.², a temperature of 90 F, and a relative humidity of 80%. Determine the lbm of dry air per min that must be used and the fraction of the incoming water that evaporates. Assume the process to be adiabatic.

11.20 An air-water vapor mixture is contained in a vertical cylinder fitted with a frictionless piston. The initial volume is 2 ft³, and the mixture is at 130 F, 20 lbf/in.², 40% relative humidity. The system is then allowed to cool to the temperature of the surroundings, 60 F.

Calculate:
(a) Heat transfer during the process.
(b) Entropy change of the system.
(c) Irreversibility of the process.

11.21 In an air liquefaction and separation plant, air is compressed from the ambient pressure to 3000 lbf/in.², after which the air enters a heat exchanger. The ambient conditions of the air are 14.7 lbf/in.², 85 F, 65% relative humidity. After compression and before entering the heat exchanger the air is cooled to 90 F. In the heat exchanger the air is cooled to −150 F, at which temperature the vapor pressure of the H₂O is very low, and it may be assumed that all of the water vapor which enters the heat exchanger freezes out on the tubes of the heat exchanger. If the compressor handles 3000 ft³/min of air, how much moisture will freeze out in the heat exchanger in 1 hr of operation? Would you recommend operating a plant in this manner?

11.22 The process of injection cooling may be demonstrated by the following problem: Consider a column of water 10 ft high which is insulated from the surroundings. Let dry air be bubbled through the water. During this process some of the water will evaporate and be carried away by the air and the temperature of the remaining liquid will decrease.

Assume that the water is initially at a temperature of 90 F, and that the dry air enters at 90 F and a pressure slightly above 1 atm. Assume that the air vapor mixture leaves the surface of the water at 1 atm pressure and the same temperature as the water and at a relative humidity of 100%.

(a) What is the heat transfer from the water for each pound of air entering under the initial conditions?

(b) What will be the ratio of the mass of air bubbled through the liquid to the mass of water cooled if the temperature of the water is decreased 10 F?

11.23 Consider the compressor and aftercooler shown in Fig. 11.17. Atmospheric air at a pressure of 14.7 lbf/in.^{2}, a temperature of 90 F, and a relative humidity of 75% enters the compressor. Under these conditions the volume

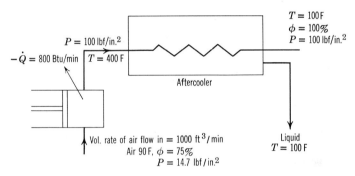

Fig. 11.17   Sketch for Problem 11.23.

flow into the compressor is 1000 ft^3/min. The rate of heat transfer from the compressor is 800 Btu/min, and the air-vapor mixture leaves the compressor at 100 lbf/in.^{2}, 400 F. It then enters the aftercooler, where it is cooled to 100 F in a constant pressure process. The air-vapor mixture leaving the aftercooler has a relative humidity of 100%, and the condensate leaves at 100 F.

(a) What is the power input to the compressor?

(b) Determine the amount of condensate per hour.

11.24 Frequently a source of dry air is needed for such purposes as pressurizing telephone cables and similar applications. One scheme for providing dry air is shown in Fig. 11.18. Atmospheric air is compressed to 165 lbf/in.^{2} It is cooled to 70 F in an aftercooler and a counterflow heat exchanger. Finally it is cooled to 35 F by heat transfer to the refrigerant in the evaporator of the refrigeration cycle. The water condensed in these processes is separated from the air and leaves through an automatic water ejector. The air-water vapor mixture remaining is used as the cooling medium in the heat exchanger and is then throttled to 25 lbf/in.^{2} and is used for the intended application.

If the volume to the compressor is 200 ft^3/hr, determine:

(a) The amount of moisture condensed per hour.

(b) The heat transfer to the refrigerant in the evaporator per hour.

(c) The relative humidity of the air-vapor mixture entering the apparatus which requires the dry air.

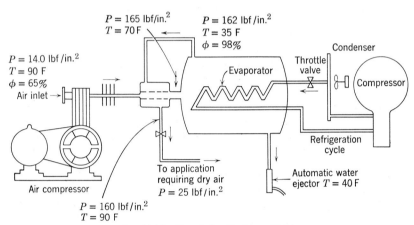

Fig. 11.18   Sketch for Problem 11.24.

11.25 Two streams of air, each saturated with water vapor, and at the pressure and temperature shown in Fig. 11.19 are mixed together in an adiabatic, steady-flow process. Determine the exit temperature, T_3.

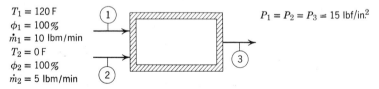

Fig. 11.19   Sketch for Problem 11.25.

11.26 An air-water vapor mixture enters a heater-humidifier unit at 50 F, 14.7 lbf/in.^{2}, with a relative humidity of 40%. Liquid water at 50 F, 14.7 lbf/in.^{2} is fed to the unit at the rate of 0.03 lbm/lbm of air-vapor mixture leaving the unit. The heat transfer to the unit is 50 Btu/lbm of mixture leaving.

(a) Determine the temperature and relative humidity of the mixture leaving the unit, assuming that the pressure is 14.7 lbf/in.^{2}.

(b) If the room temperature is 70 F and the heat transferred to the unit comes from a reservoir at 600 F, calculate the irreversibility of the process.

11.27 The following data have been measured for carbon dioxide, methane, and their mixtures at 1250 lbf/in.², 100 F:

y_{CO_2}	y_{CH_4}	Z
1.0000	0.0000	0.3117
0.7961	0.2039	0.6262
0.5939	0.4061	0.7350
0.3944	0.6056	0.8084
0.1528	0.8472	0.8634
0.0000	1.0000	0.8892

(*a*) Determine the partial volumes of the components for a mixture of 50% CO_2, 50% CH_4 at this pressure and temperature.

(*b*) Evaluate the assumption of ideal solution for this system at the given temperature and pressure.

11.28 A 1.4 ft³ tank containing air at 2200 lbf/in.², 537 R, is cooled to 350 R. Determine the final pressure in the tank and the heat transfer for the process, assuming the air to be

(*a*) An ideal gas.

(*b*) An ideal solution of 79% nitrogen and 21% oxygen on a mole basis.

(*c*) A pseudo-pure substance using Kay's rule.

(*d*) A pseudo-pure substance using the Beattie-Bridgeman equation of state.

11.29 A gas mixture of 75% ethylene and 25% ethane on a mole basis enters a compressor at 100 F, 5 atm. pressure, at the rate of 20 ft³/min. The power input to the compressor is 10 hp and the mixture leaves at 150 F, 20 atm. Assuming the mixture to behave as an ideal solution, calculate

(*a*) Mass flow rate, lbm/min.

(*b*) Heat transfer rate from the compressor, Btu/min.

11.30 A mixture of 50% N_2, 50% O_2 on a mole basis flows through a long pipe. At the pipe inlet, the mixture is at 500 lbf/in.², −150 F, with a velocity of 100 ft/sec. If the pressure drop in the pipe is estimated to be 100 lbf/in.², determine the exit temperature and velocity. Assume an ideal solution.

11.31 A mixture of 85% methane, 15% ethane on a mole basis is contained in an insulated 5 ft³ tank at 500 lbf/in.², 100 F. The valve is opened accidentally, and the pressure quickly drops to 300 lbf/in.² before the valve is closed.

(*a*) Using Kay's rule and assuming a homogeneous mixture, calculate the mass that escaped from the tank.

(*b*) Eventually the temperature inside the tank returns to that of the surroundings, 100 F. What is the tank pressure at this time?

11.32 It is frequently necessary to have a gas mixture of a certain composition and pressure. Such a mixture is prepared by initially charging one of the components into the tank at some pressure such that when the second component is charged until the final desired pressure is reached the composition will be of the proper proportions. It is desired to prepare a mixture of 80% C_2H_4, 20% CO_2 at 1500 lbf/in.², 80 F, in an uninsulated 1.5 ft³ tank. The tank is initially to contain CO_2 at 80 F, and some pressure P_1. The valve is then opened slightly and C_2H_4 flows slowly into the tank from the line at 80 F, 1500 lbf/in.² until the tank pressure reaches 1500 lbf/in.² Assume Kay's rule for the mixture.

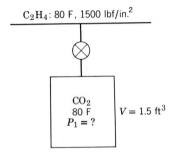

Fig. 11.20   Sketch for Problem 11.32.

(a) If the final composition is to be 80% C_2H_4, what must the initial pressure P_1 be?

(b) Determine the heat transfer and the net entropy change for the process of charging C_2H_4 into the tank.

12 *Chemical Reactions*

Many thermodynamic problems involve chemical reactions. Among the most familiar of these is the combustion of hydrocarbon fuels, for this process is utilized in most of our power generating devices. However, we can all think of a host of other processes involving chemical reactions, including those that occur in the human body.

It is our purpose in this chapter to consider a first and second law analysis of systems undergoing a chemical reaction. In many respects, this chapter is simply an extension of our previous consideration of the first and second laws. However, a number of new terms are introduced, and it will also be necessary to introduce the third law of thermodynamics.

In this chapter the combustion process is considered in detail. There are two reasons for this emphasis. The first is that the combustion process is of great significance in many problems and devices with which the engineer is concerned. The second is that the combustion process provides an excellent vehicle for teaching the basic principles of the thermodynamics of chemical reactions. The student should keep both of these objectives in mind as the study of this chapter progresses.

Chemical equilibrium will be considered in Chapter 13, and, therefore, the matter of dissociation will be deferred until then.

12.1 Fuels

A thermodynamics textbook is not the place for a detailed treatment of fuels. However, some knowledge of them is a prerequisite to consideration of combustion, and this section is therefore devoted to a brief discussion of some of the hydrocarbon fuels. Most fuels fall into one of the three categories coal, liquid hydrocarbons, or gaseous hydrocarbons.

Most liquid and gaseous hydrocarbon fuels are a mixture of many different hydrocarbons. For example, gasoline consists primarily of a mixture of about forty hydrocarbons, with many others present in very

TABLE 12.1

Characteristics of Some of the Hydrocarbon Families

Family	Formula	Structure	Saturated
Paraffin	C_nH_{2n+2}	Chain	Yes
Olefin	C_nH_{2n}	Chain	No
Diolefin	C_nH_{2n-2}	Chain	No
Naphthene	C_nH_{2n}	Ring	Yes
Aromatic			
Benzene	C_nH_{2n-6}	Ring	No
Naphthalene	C_nH_{2n-12}	Ring	No

small quantities. In discussing hydrocarbon fuels, therefore, brief consideration should be given to the most important families of hydrocarbons, which are summarized in Table 12.1.

Three terms should be defined. The first pertains to the structure of the molecule. The important types are the ring and chain structures; the difference between the two is illustrated in Fig. 12.1. The same figure illustrates the definition of saturated and unsaturated hydrocarbons. An unsaturated hydrocarbon has two or more adjacent carbon atoms joined by a double or triple bond, whereas in a saturated hydrocarbon all the carbon atoms are joined by a single bond. The third term to be defined is an isomer. Two hydrocarbons with the same number of carbon and hydrogen atoms and different structures are called isomers. Thus, there are several different octanes (C_8H_{18}) each having 8 carbon atoms and 18 hydrogen atoms, but each has a different structure.

The various hydrocarbon families are identified by a common suffix. The compounds comprising the paraffin family all end in "-ane" (as propane and octane). Similarly, the compounds comprising the olefin family end in "-ylene" or "-ene" (as propene and octene), and the diolefin family ends in "-diene" (as butadiene). The naphthene family has the same chemical formula as the olefin family, but has a ring rather than chain

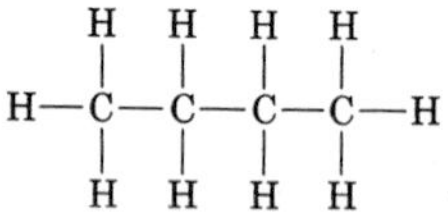

Chain structure,
saturated

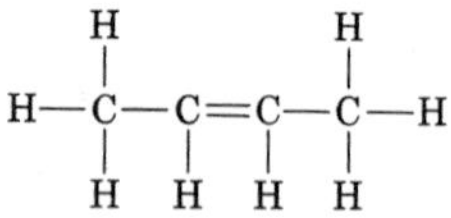

Chain structure,
unsaturated

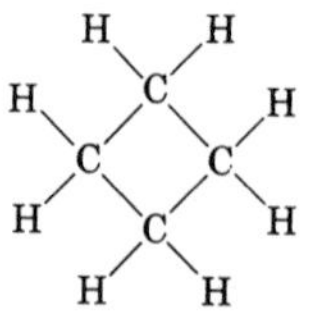

Ring structure,
saturated

Fig. 12.1   Molecular structure of some hydrocarbon fuels.

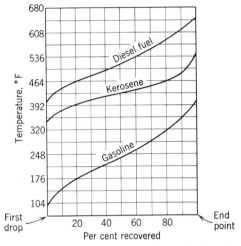

Fig. 12.2   Typical distillation curves of some hydrocarbon fuels.

structure. The hydrocarbons in the naphthene family are named by adding the prefix "cyclo-" (as cyclopentane).

The aromatic family includes the benzene series (C_nH_{2n-6}) and the naphthalene series (C_nH_{2n-12}). The benzene series has a ring structure and is unsaturated.

Alcohols are sometimes used as a fuel in internal combustion engines. The characteristic feature of the alcohol family is that one of the hydrogen atoms is replaced by an OH radical. Thus methyl alcohol, also called methanol, is CH_3OH.

Most liquid hydrocarbon fuels are mixtures of hydrocarbons that are derived from crude oil through distillation and cracking processes. Thus, from a given crude oil a variety of different fuels can be produced, some of the common ones being gasoline, kerosene, diesel fuel, and fuel oil. Within each of these classifications there is a wide variety of grades, and each is made up of a large number of different hydrocarbons. The important distinction between these fuels is the distillation curve, Fig. 12.2. The distillation curve is obtained by slowly heating a sample of fuel so that it vaporizes. The vapor is then condensed and the amount measured. The more volatile hydrocarbons are vaporized first, and thus the temperature of the nonvaporized fraction increases during the process. The distillation curve, which is a plot of the temperature of the nonvaporized fraction vs. the amount of vapor condensed, is an indication of the volatility of the fuel.

In dealing with combustion of liquid fuels it is convenient to express the composition in terms of a single hydrocarbon, even though it is a mixture of many hydrocarbons. Thus gasoline is usually considered to be octane, C_8H_{18}, and diesel fuel is considered to be dodecane, $C_{12}H_{26}$. The composition of a hydrocarbon fuel may also be given in terms of percentage of carbon and hydrogen.

The two primary sources of gaseous hydrocarbon fuels are natural gas wells and manufacturing processes. Table 12.2 gives the composition of

TABLE 12.2

Volumetric Analyses of Some Typical Gaseous Fuels

Constituent	Various Natural Gases				Producer Gas from Bituminous Coal	Carbureted Water Gas	Coke-Oven Gas
	A	B	C	D			
Methane	93.9	60.1	67.4	54.3	3.0	10.2	32.1
Ethane	3.6	14.8	16.8	16.3			
Propane	1.2	13.4	15.8	16.2			
Butanes plus*	1.3	4.2		7.4			
Ethene						6.1	3.5
Benzene						2.8	0.5
Hydrogen					14.0	40.5	46.5
Nitrogen		7.5		5.8	50.9	2.9	8.1
Oxygen					0.6	0.5	0.8
Carbon monoxide					27.0	34.0	6.3
Carbon dioxide					4.5	3.0	2.2

* This includes butane and all heavier hydrocarbons.

a number of gaseous fuels. The major constituent of natural gas is methane, which distinguishes it from manufactured gas.

12.2 The Combustion Process

The combustion process involves the oxidation of constituents in the fuel that are capable of being oxidized, and can therefore be represented by a chemical equation. During a combustion process the mass of each element remains the same. Thus, writing chemical equations and solving problems involving quantities of the various constituents basically involves the conservation of mass of each element.

Consider first the reaction of carbon with oxygen.

Reactants   Products

$$C + O_2 \rightarrow CO_2$$

This equation states that one mole of carbon reacts with one mole of oxygen to form one mole of carbon dioxide. This also means that 12 lbm of carbon react with 32 lbm of oxygen to form 44 lbm of carbon dioxide. All the initial substances that undergo the combustion process are called the reactants, and the substances that result from the combustion process are called the products.

When a hydrocarbon fuel is burned both the carbon and the hydrogen are oxidized. Consider the combustion of methane as an example.

$$CH_4 + 2O_2 \rightarrow CO_2 + 2H_2O \tag{12.1}$$

In this case the products of combustion include both carbon dioxide and water. The water may be in the vapor, liquid, or solid phases, depending on the temperature and pressure of the products of combustion.

It should be pointed out that in the combustion process there are many intermediate products formed during the chemical reaction. In this book we are concerned with the initial and final products and not with the intermediate products, but this aspect is very important in a detailed consideration of combustion.

In most combustion processes the oxygen is supplied as air rather than as pure oxygen. The composition of air on a molal basis is approximately 21 per cent oxygen, 78 per cent nitrogen, and 1 per cent argon. The nitrogen and the argon do not undergo chemical reaction (except for dissociation which will be considered in Chapter 13). They do leave at the same temperature as the other products, however, and therefore undergo a change of state if the products are at a temperature other than the original air temperature.

In combustion calculations involving air, the argon is usually neglected, and the air is considered to be composed of 21 per cent oxygen and 79 per cent nitrogen by volume. When this assumption is made, the nitrogen is sometimes referred to as "atmospheric nitrogen." Atmospheric nitrogen has a molecular weight of 28.16 (which takes the argon into account) as compared to 28.016 for pure nitrogen. This distinction will not be made in this text, and we will consider the 79 per cent nitrogen to be pure nitrogen.

The assumption that air is 21.0 per cent oxygen and 79.0 per cent nitrogen by volume leads to the conclusion that for each mole of oxygen, $79.0/21.0 = 3.76$ moles of nitrogen are involved. Therefore, when the oxygen for the combustion of methane is supplied as air, the reaction can be written

$$CH_4 + 2O_2 + 2(3.76)N_2 \rightarrow CO_2 + 2H_2O + 7.52N_2 \qquad (12.2)$$

The minimum amount of air that supplies sufficient oxygen for the complete combustion of all the carbon, hydrogen, and any other elements in the fuel that may oxidize is called the "theoretical air." When complete combustion is achieved with theoretical air, the products contain no oxygen. In practice, it is found that complete combustion is not likely to be achieved unless the amount of air supplied is somewhat greater than the theoretical amount. The amount of air actually supplied is expressed in terms of per cent theoretical air. Thus 150 per cent theoretical air means that the air actually supplied is 1.5 times the theoretical air. The complete combustion of methane with 150 per cent theoretical air is written

$$CH_4 + 2(1.5)O_2 + 2(3.76)(1.5)N_2 \rightarrow CO_2 + 2H_2O + O_2 + 11.28N_2$$
$$(12.3)$$

The amount of air actually supplied may also be expressed in terms of per cent excess air. The excess air is the amount of air supplied over and above the theoretical air. Thus 150 per cent theoretical air is equivalent to 50 per cent excess air. The terms theoretical air and excess air are both in current usage.

Two important parameters applied to combustion processes are the air-fuel ratio (designated AF) and its reciprocal, the fuel-air ratio (designated FA). The air-fuel ratio is usually expressed on a mass basis, but a mole basis is also used at times. The theoretical air-fuel ratio is the ratio of the mass (or moles) of theoretical air to the mass (or moles) of fuel.

When the amount of air supplied is less than the theoretical air required, the combustion is incomplete. If there is only a slight deficiency of air, the usual result is that some of the carbon unites with the oxygen to form carbon monoxide (CO) instead of carbon dioxide (CO_2). If the air supplied is considerably less than the theoretical air, there may also be some hydrocarbons in the products of combustion.

Even when some excess air is supplied there may be small amounts of carbon monoxide present, the exact amount depending on a number of factors including the mixing and turbulence during combustion. Thus, the combustion of methane with 110 per cent theoretical air might be as follows:

$$CH_4 + 2(1.1)O_2 + 2(1.1)3.76N_2 \rightarrow$$
$$+0.95CO_2 + 0.05CO + 2H_2O + 0.225O_2 + 8.27N_2 \quad (12.4)$$

The material covered so far in this section is illustrated by the following examples.

Example 12.1

Calculate the theoretical air-fuel ratio for the combustion of octane, C_8H_{18}.

The combustion equation is

$$C_8H_{18} + 12.5O_2 + 12.5(3.76)N_2 \rightarrow 8CO_2 + 9H_2O + 47.0N_2$$

The air-fuel ratio on a mole basis is

$$AF = \frac{12.5 + 47.0}{1} = 59.5 \text{ moles air/mole fuel}$$

The theoretical air-fuel ratio on a mass basis is found by introducing the molecular weight of the air and fuel.

$$AF = \frac{59.5(28.95)}{114.2} = 15.0 \text{ lbm air/lbm fuel}$$

Example 12.2

Determine the molal analysis of the products of combustion when octane, C_8H_{18}, is burned with 200 per cent theoretical air, and the dew point of the products if the pressure is 14.7 lbf/in.².

The equation for the combustion of octane with 200 per cent theoretical air is

$$C_8H_{18} + 12.5(2)O_2 + 12.5(2)(3.76)N_2 \rightarrow 8CO_2 + 9H_2O + 12.5O_2 + 94.0N_2$$

Total moles of product $= 8 + 9 + 12.5 + 94.0 = 123.5$

Molal analysis of products:

$$
\begin{array}{lll}
CO_2 = 8/123.5 & = & 6.47\% \\
H_2O = 9/123.5 & = & 7.29 \\
O_2 = 12.5/123.5 & = & 10.12 \\
N_2 = 94/123.5 & = & \underline{76.12} \\
& & 100.00
\end{array}
$$

The partial pressure of the H_2O is $14.7(0.0729) = 1.072$ lbf/in.².

The saturation temperature corresponding to this pressure is 104 F, which is also the dew-point temperature.

The water condensed from the products of combustion usually contains some dissolved gases and therefore may be quite corrosive. For this reason the products of combustion are often kept above the dew point until discharged to the atmosphere.

Example 12.3

Producer gas from bituminous coal (see Table 12.2) is burned with 20 per cent excess air. Calculate the air-fuel ratio on a volumetric basis and on a mass basis.

To calculate the theoretical air requirement, let us write the combustion equation for the combustible substances in 1 mole of fuel.

$$0.14H_2 \quad + 0.070O_2 \rightarrow 0.14H_2O$$
$$0.27CO \quad + 0.135O_2 \rightarrow 0.27CO_2$$
$$0.03CH_4 + 0.06O_2 \quad \rightarrow 0.03CO_2 + 0.06H_2O$$

$$
\begin{array}{ll}
\underline{0.265} & = \text{moles oxygen required/mole fuel} \\
\underline{-0.006} & = \text{oxygen in fuel/mole fuel} \\
0.259 & = \text{moles oxygen required from air/mole fuel}
\end{array}
$$

Therefore, the complete combustion equation for 1 mole of fuel is

fuel

$$0.14H_2 + 0.27CO + 0.03CH_4 + 0.006O_2 + 0.509N_2 + 0.045CO_2$$

air

$$+ 0.259O_2 + 0.259(3.76)N_2 \rightarrow 0.20H_2O + 0.345CO_2 + 1.482N_2$$

$$\left(\frac{\text{moles air}}{\text{mole fuel}}\right)_{\text{theo}} = 0.259 \times \frac{1}{0.21} = 1.233$$

If the air and fuel are at the same pressure and temperature, this also represents the ratio of the volume of air to the volume of fuel.

For 20 per cent excess air, $\dfrac{\text{moles air}}{\text{mole fuel}} = 1.233 \times 1.200 = 1.48$

The air-fuel ratio on a mass basis is

$$AF = \frac{1.48(28.95)}{0.14(2) + 0.27(28) + 0.03(16) + 0.006(32) + 0.509(28) + 0.045(44)}$$

$$= \frac{1.48(28.95)}{24.74} = 1.73 \text{ lbm air/lbm fuel}$$

12.3 Analysis of the Products of Combustion

An analysis of the products of combustion affords a very simple method for calculating the actual amount of air supplied in a combustion process. In some cases the analysis of the fuel may also be calculated from an analysis of the products. The Orsat apparatus, a schematic sketch of which is shown in Fig. 12.3, is one device that can be used to make an analysis of the products of combustion, though many more modern devices are now extensively used.

In this apparatus a measured volume of combustion gases is successively passed through a number of chemical solutions, each of which absorbs one of the components of the products of combustion. The volume is measured before and after the gas is passed through each solution, and the decrease in volume is the volume of that component absorbed by the given solution. From these data a volumetric analysis of the combustion gases can be determined. The gas is moved into and out of the apparatus by lowering or raising the leveling bottle, which contains water (occasionally brine or mercury are also used).

In detail the operation is as follows. The measuring burette is filled with the combustion products and the volume is accurately measured. The gas is then passed into pipette A, containing potassium hydroxide, which absorbs carbon dioxide. The remaining gas is brought back into the measuring burette and the volume measured. The difference between the original volume and this volume is the volume of carbon dioxide. In a similar manner the gas is successively passed into pipettes B and C. Pipette B contains a solution of pyrogallic acid which absorbs oxygen, and pipette C contains cuprous chloride, which absorbs carbon monoxide. When it is necessary to analyze products of combustion containing other constituents, the gas can be passed through additional solutions which absorb these constituents. The gas that is not absorbed is assumed to be nitrogen.

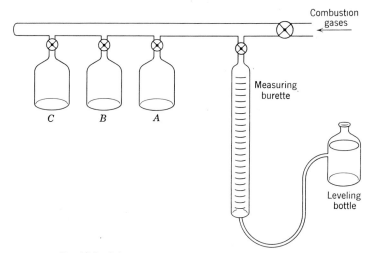

Fig. 12.3   Schematic arrangement of Orsat apparatus.

The volumetric analysis obtained when using the Orsat apparatus is on a dry basis; that is, the water formed during combustion does not appear in the analysis. This is true because the analysis is made at room temperature, which is considerably below the dew point of the products of combustion of most hydrocarbon fuels, because the gas remains saturated during the analysis, and because the analysis takes place at constant pressure and temperature.

In using the analysis of the products of combustion to obtain the actual fuel-air ratio, the basic principle is the conservation of the mass of each of the elements. Thus, in changing from reactants to products we can make a carbon balance, hydrogen balance, oxygen balance, and nitrogen balance (plus any other elements that may be involved). Further, we recognize that there is a definite ratio between the amounts of some of these elements. Thus, the ratio between the nitrogen and oxygen supplied in the air is fixed, as well as the ratio between carbon and hydrogen if the composition of a hydrocarbon fuel is known.

These principles involving the analysis of the products of combustion are illustrated in the following examples.

Example 12.4

Methane (CH_4) is burned with atmospheric air. The analysis of the products as determined by an Orsat apparatus is as follows:

CO_2	10.00%
O_2	2.37
CO	0.53
N_2	87.10
	100.00%

Calculate the air-fuel ratio, the per cent theoretical air, and determine the combustion equation.

The solution involves writing the combustion equation for 100 moles of dry products, introducing letter coefficients for the unknown quantities, and then solving for them.

From the Orsat analysis, the following equation can be written, keeping in mind that the Orsat analysis is on a dry basis.

$$aCH_4 + bO_2 + cN_2 \rightarrow 10.0CO_2 + 0.53CO + 2.37O_2 + dH_2O + 87.1N_2$$

A balance for each of the elements involved will enable us to solve for all the unknown coefficients:

Nitrogen balance: $c = 87.1$

Since all the nitrogen comes from the air,

$$\frac{c}{b} = 3.76 \qquad b = \frac{87.1}{3.76} = 23.16$$

Carbon balance: $a = 10.00 + 0.53 = 10.53$

Hydrogen balance: $d = 2a = 21.06$

Oxygen balance: All the unknown coefficients have been solved for, and in this case the oxygen balance provides a check on the accuracy. Thus, b can also be determined by an oxygen balance.

$$b = 10.00 + \frac{0.53}{2} + 2.37 + \frac{21.06}{2} = 23.16$$

Substituting these values for a, b, c, d, and e we have,

$$10.53CO_2 + 23.16O_2 + 87.1N_2 \rightarrow$$
$$10.0CO_2 + 0.53CO + 2.37O_2 + 21.06H_2O + 87.1N_2$$

Dividing through by 10.53 yields the combustion equation per mole of fuel.

$$CH_4 + 2.2O_2 + 8.27N_2 \rightarrow$$
$$0.95CO_2 + 0.05CO + 2H_2O + 0.225O_2 + 8.27N_2$$

The air-fuel ratio on a mole basis is

$$2.2 + 8.27 = 10.47 \text{ moles air/mole fuel}$$

The air-fuel ratio on a mass basis is found by introducing the molecular weights.

$$AF = \frac{10.47 \times 28.95}{16.0} = 18.97 \text{ lbm air/lbm fuel}$$

The theoretical air-fuel ratio is found by writing the combustion equation for theoretical air.

$$CH_4 + 2O_2 + 2(3.76)N_2 \rightarrow CO_2 + 2H_2O + 7.52N_2$$

$$AF_{theo} = \frac{(2 + 7.52)28.95}{16.0} = 17.23 \text{ lbm air/lbm fuel}$$

The per cent theoretical air is $\frac{18.97}{17.23} = 110\%$

Example 12.5

The products of combustion of a hydrocarbon fuel of unknown composition have the following composition as measured by an Orsat apparatus:

$$
\begin{array}{lr}
CO_2 & 8.0\% \\
CO & 0.9 \\
O_2 & 8.8 \\
N_2 & \underline{82.3} \\
& \overline{100.0\%}
\end{array}
$$

Calculate (a) The air-fuel ratio, (b) The composition of the fuel on a mass basis, and (c) The per cent theoretical air on a mass basis.

Let us first write the combustion equation for 100 moles of dry product.

$$C_aH_b + dO_2 + cN_2 \rightarrow 8.0CO_2 + 0.9CO + 8.8O_2 + eH_2O + 82.3N_2$$

Nitrogen balance: $c = 82.3$

From composition of air, $\dfrac{c}{d} = 3.76;$ $d = \dfrac{82.3}{3.76} = 21.9$

Oxygen balance: $21.9 = 8.0 + \dfrac{0.9}{2} + 8.8 + \dfrac{e}{2};$ $e = 9.3$

Carbon balance: $a = 8.0 + 0.9 = 8.9$

Hydrogen balance: $b = 2e = 2 \times 9.3 = 18.6$

Thus the composition of the fuel could be written $C_{8.9}H_{18.6}$
The air-fuel ratio can now be found, using the molecular weights.

$$AF = \frac{(21.9 + 82.3)28.95}{8.9(12) + 18.6(1)} = 24.1 \text{ lbm air/lbm fuel}$$

On a mass basis the composition of fuel is:

$$\text{Carbon} = \frac{8.9(12)}{8.9(12) + 18.6(1)} = 85.2\%$$

$$\text{Hydrogen} = \frac{18.6(1)}{8.9(12) + 18.6(1)} = 14.8\%$$

The theoretical air requirement can be found by writing the theoretical combustion equation.

$$C_{8.9}H_{18.6} + 13.5O_2 + 13.5(3.76)N_2 \rightarrow 8.9CO_2 + 9.3H_2O + 50.8N_2$$

$$AF_{theo} = \frac{(13.5 + 50.8)28.95}{8.9(12) + 18.6(1)} = 14.9 \text{ lbm air/lbm fuel}$$

$$\% \text{ theoretical air} = \frac{24.1}{14.9} = 162\%$$

Example 12.6

Producer gas from bituminous coal (Table 12.2) is burned with air. The composition of the products of combustion is analyzed with an Orsat apparatus and is as follows:

CO_2	11.9%
CO	1.8
O_2	6.5
N_2	79.8

Calculate the actual air-fuel ratio on a mole basis and the per cent theoretical air.

The combustion equation for 100 moles of dry product is first written, using letter coefficients for the unknown constituents.

$$a(0.14H_2 + 0.27CO + 0.03CH_4 + 0.006O_2 + 0.509N_2$$
$$+ 0.045CO_2) + bO_2 + 3.76(b)N_2 \rightarrow 11.9CO_2 + 1.8CO + 6.5O_2$$
$$+ cH_2O + 79.8N_2$$

Carbon balance: $a(0.27 + 0.03 + 0.045) = 11.9 + 1.8$

$$a = \frac{13.7}{0.345} = 39.7$$

Nitrogen balance: $0.509a + 3.76b = 79.8$

$$0.509(39.7) + 3.76b = 79.8$$
$$b = 15.85$$

Hydrogen balance: $a(0.14 + 0.06) = c$

$$c = 39.7(0.2) = 7.94$$

The oxygen balance provides a check on the accuracy of our work.

$$a(0.135 + 0.006 + 0.045) + b = 11.9 + \frac{1.8}{2} + 6.5 + \frac{c}{2}$$

$$39.7(0.186) + 15.85 = 11.9 + 0.9 + 6.5 + 3.97$$

$$23.24 = 23.27$$

$$AF_{actual} = \frac{b + 3.76(b)}{a} = \frac{15.85 + 3.76(15.85)}{39.7}$$

$$= 1.903 \text{ moles air/mole fuel}$$

AF_{theo} (From Example 12.3) $= 1.233$ moles air/mole fuel

$$\text{Per cent theoretical air} = \frac{1.903}{1.233} = 155\%$$

12.4 Enthalpy of Formation

In the first eleven chapters of this book the problems considered always involved a fixed chemical composition, and never involved a change of composition due to chemical reaction. Therefore, in dealing with a thermodynamic property we made use of tables of thermodynamic properties for the given substance, and in each of these tables the thermodynamic properties were given relative to some arbitrary base. In the steam tables, for example, the enthalpy of saturated liquid at 32 F is assumed to be zero. This procedure is quite adequate when no change in composition is involved, because we are concerned with the changes in the properties of a given substance. However, it is evident that this procedure is quite inadequate when dealing with a chemical reaction, because the composition changes during the process.

The technique used in applying the first law to chemical reactions is to assume that the enthalpy of all the elements is zero at the reference state of 25 C (77 F) and 1 atm pressure. The enthalpy of formation of a compound is its enthalpy at this same temperature and pressure (25 C, 1 atm pressure) with reference to this base in which the enthalpy of the elements is assumed to be zero. We will refer to this simply as the 25 C, 1 atm base.

Consider carbon dioxide as an example. Let 1 mole of carbon at 25 C and 1 atm pressure react with 1 mole of oxygen at 25 C and 1 atm pressure in a steady-state, steady-flow process, to form 1 mole of CO_2 at 1 atm pressure. Let sufficient heat be transferred so that the CO_2 formed exists at 25 C. If the heat transfer is carefully determined it is found to be $-169,297$ Btu. This reaction can be written

$$C + O_2 \rightarrow CO_2$$

Applying the first law to this process we have

$$Q_{\text{c.v.}} + H_R = H_P \tag{12.5}$$

where the subscripts R and P refer to the reactants and products respectively. We will find it convenient to also write the first law for such a process in the form

$$Q_{\text{c.v.}} + \sum_R n_i \bar{h}_i = \sum_P n_e \bar{h}_e \tag{12.6}$$

where the summations refer respectively to all the reactants or all the products.

In the process under consideration here, the reactants consist of carbon and oxygen, both of which are elements and both are at 25 C and 1 atm pressure. Therefore, the enthalpy of the reactants is zero, and it follows that

$$Q_{\text{c.v.}} = H_P = -169,297 \text{ Btu/mole fuel}$$

The enthalpy of CO_2 at 25 C and 1 atm pressure (with reference to this base at which the enthalpy of elements is assumed to be zero) is called the enthalpy of formation. We will designate this with the symbol $\bar{h}_f{}^\circ$. Thus,

$$(\bar{h}_f{}^\circ)_{CO_2} = -169,297 \text{ Btu/mole}$$

Frequently students are bothered by the minus sign when the enthalpy of formation is negative. The significance of this is simply that the enthalpy of the CO_2 is less than the enthalpy of the carbon and the oxygen. This is quite evident because the heat transfer was negative during the steady-flow chemical reaction, and the energy of the CO_2 must be less than the sum of energy of the carbon and oxygen initially. This is quite analogous to the situation we would have in the steam tables if we let the enthalpy of saturated vapor be zero at 1 atm pressure, for in this case the enthalpy of the liquid would be negative, and we would simply use the negative value for the enthalpy of the liquid when solving problems.

Table 12.3 gives values of the enthalpy of formation for a number of substances in both the units cal/gm mole and Btu/lb mole.

It will be noted from Table 12.3 that two values for H_2O at 14.7 lbf/in.^{2}, 77 F, are given; one is for liquid H_2O and the other for gaseous H_2O. We know from the thermodynamic properties of water that under equilibrium conditions water exists as a slightly compressed liquid at 14.7 lbf/in.^{2}, 77 F. However, in many cases, we find it convenient to consider a pseudo-equilibrium state, in which water is a vapor at 14.7 lbf/in.^{2}, 77 F. In doing so we assume that the substance behaves as an ideal gas between saturated vapor at 77 F and this pseudo-equilibrium state at 14.7 lbf/in.^{2}, 77 F. Thus, the enthalpy in the pseudo-equilibrium state is the same as that of saturated vapor at this same temperature, and the change in entropy between these two states would be found from the appropriate ideal gas relations. It also follows that the difference between the enthalpy of formation of $H_2O(l)$ and $H_2O(g)$ at 14.7 lbf/in.^{2}, 77 F is h_{fg}, the enthalpy of evaporation at 77 F. (The correction due to the fact that H_2O is a compressed liquid at 14.7 lbf/in.^{2}, 77 F, is very small and may be neglected.) This same procedure is used in the case of other substances which have a vapor pressure of less than one atmosphere at 77 F.

12.5   First Law Analysis of Reacting Systems

The significance of the enthalpy of formation is that it is most convenient in performing a first law analysis of a reacting system, for the enthalpies of different substances can be added or subtracted, since they are all given relative to the same base.

TABLE 12.3

Enthalpy of Formation, Gibbs Function of Formation and Absolute Entropy of Various Substances at 77 F (25 C) and 1 Atmosphere Pressure

Substance	Formula	M	State	$\bar{h}_f^{\,\circ}$		$\bar{g}_f^{\,\circ}$		$\bar{s}^{\,\circ}$
				Cal/gm mole	Btu/lb mole	Cal/gm mole	Btu/lb mole	Cal/gm mole-K Btu/lb mole-R
Carbon monoxide[a]	CO	28.011	gas	−26,417	−47,551	−32,783	−59,009	47.214
Carbon dioxide[a]	CO_2	44.011	gas	−94,054	−169,297	−94,265	−169,677	51.072
Water[a,b]	H_2O	18.016	gas	−57,798	−104,036	−54,636	−98,345	45.106
Water[b]	H_2O	18.016	liq.	−68,317	−122,971	−56,690	−102,042	16.716
Methane[a]	CH_4	16.043	gas	−17,895	−32,211	−12,145	−21,861	44.490
Acetylene[a]	C_2H_2	26.038	gas	54,190	97,542	49,993	89,987	48.004
Ethene[a]	C_2H_4	28.054	gas	12,496	22,493	16,281	29,306	52.447
Ethane[c]	C_2H_6	30.070	gas	−20,236	−36,425	−7,860	−14,148	54.85
Propane[c]	C_3H_8	44.097	gas	−24,820	−44,676	−5,614	−10,105	64.51
Butane[c]	C_4H_{10}	58.124	gas	−30,150	−54,270	−4,100	−7,380	74.12
Octane[c]	C_8H_{18}	114.23	gas	−49,820	−89,680	3,950	7,110	111.55
Octane[c]	C_8H_{18}	114.23	liq.	−59,740	−107,532	1,580	2,844	86.23
Carbon[a] (graphite)	C	12.011	solid	0	0	0	0	1.359

[a] From JANAF Thermochemical Data, The Dow Chemical Company, Thermal Laboratory, Midland, Mich.
[b] From Circular 500, National Bureau of Standards.
[c] From F. D. Rossini et al., API Research Project 44.

In such problems we will write the first law for a steady-state, steady-flow process in the form

$$Q_{c.v.} + H_R = W_{c.v.} + H_P \qquad (12.7)$$

or

$$Q_{c.v.} + \sum_R n_i \bar{h}_i = W_{c.v.} + \sum_P n_e \bar{h}_e$$

where R and P refer to the reactants and products respectively. In each problem it is necessary to choose one parameter as the basis of the solution. Usually this is taken as one mole of fuel.

Example 12.7

Consider the following reaction, which occurs in a steady-state, steady-flow process.

$$CH_4 + 2O_2 \rightarrow CO_2 + 2H_2O(l)$$

The reactants and products are each at a total pressure of 1 atm and 25 C. Determine the heat transfer per lb mole of fuel entering the combustion chamber.

Applying the first law,

$$Q_{c.v.} + \sum_R n_i \bar{h}_i = \sum_P n_e \bar{h}_e$$

From Table 12.3

$$\sum_R n_i \bar{h}_i = (\bar{h}_f^\circ)_{CH_4} = -32{,}211 \text{ Btu/lb mole fuel}$$

$$\sum_P n_e \bar{h}_e = (\bar{h}_f^\circ)_{CO_2} + 2(\bar{h}_f^\circ)_{H_2O(l)}$$

$$= -169{,}297 + 2(-122{,}971) = -415{,}239 \text{ Btu/lb mole fuel}$$

$$Q_{c.v.} = -415{,}239 - (-32{,}211) = -383{,}028 \text{ Btu/lb mole fuel}$$

In most cases however, the substances which comprise the reactants and products in a chemical reaction are not at a temperature of 77 F and a pressure of 1 atm (the state at which the enthalpy of formation is given). Therefore the change of internal energy (in the case of a reaction that takes place at constant volume), or the change of enthalpy (in the case of a constant pressure or steady-state, steady-flow process) between 77 F and one atm and the given state must be known. Let us first consider the change of enthalpy between 77 F and 1 atm and the given state. Three general approaches can be followed in finding this change.

1. Assume ideal gas behavior between 77 F, 1 atm, and the given state. In this case, the enthalpy is a function of the temperature only, and can be found by use of an equation for C_{po} or from tabulated values of enthalpy as a function of temperature (which assumes ideal gas behavior). Table A.9 gives an equation for $\bar{C}_{po}$ for a number of substances and Table A.11

gives values of $(\bar{h}° - \bar{h}°_{298})$, in cal/gm mole and $(\bar{h}° - \bar{h}°_{537})$ in Btu/lb mole ($\bar{h}°_{298}$ refers to 25 C or 298.15K, and $\bar{h}°_{537}$ refers to 77 F or 536.7 R. For simplicity these are designated $\bar{h}°_{298}$ and $\bar{h}°_{537}$ respectively). The superscript ° is used to designate that this is the enthalpy at one atmosphere pressure, based on ideal gas behavior.

2. If a table of thermodynamic properties is available, $\bar{h} - \bar{h}°_{298}$ can be found directly from these tables. This is necessary when the deviation from ideal gas behavior is significant.

3. If the deviation from ideal gas behavior is significant, but no tables of thermodynamic properties are available, the value for $\bar{h} - \bar{h}°_{298}$ can be found from the generalized charts and the values for $\bar{C}_{po}$ or $(\bar{h}° - \bar{h}°_{298})$ at one atmosphere pressure as indicated above.

Thus, in general, for applying the first law to a steady-state, steady-flow process involving a chemical reaction and negligible changes in kinetic and potential energy we can write

$$Q_{c.v.} + \sum_R n_i[\bar{h}_f° + (\bar{h} - \bar{h}°_{298})]_i$$
$$= W_{c.v.} + \sum_P n_e[\bar{h}_f° + (\bar{h} - \bar{h}°_{298})]_e \quad (12.8)$$

Example 12.8

Calculate the enthalpy of H_2O (on a lb mole basis) at 500 lbf/in², 600 F, relative to the 77 F and 1 atm base, using the following procedures.

a. Assume the steam to be an ideal gas with the value of $\bar{C}_{po}$ given in the Appendix, Table A.9.

b. Assume the steam to be an ideal gas with the value for $(\bar{h}° - \bar{h}°_{298})$ as given in the Appendix, Table A.11.

c. The steam tables.

d. The specific heat equations given in (a) above and the generalized charts.

For each of these procedures we can write,

$$\bar{h} = [\bar{h}_f° + (\bar{h}_T - \bar{h}°_{537})]$$

The only difference is in the procedure by which we calculate $(\bar{h}_T - \bar{h}°_{537})$. From Table 12.3 we note that

$$(h_f°)_{H_2O(g)} = -104{,}036 \text{ Btu/lb mole.}$$

(a) Using the specific heat equation for $H_2O(g)$ from Table A.9,

$$\bar{C}_{po} = 19.86 - \frac{597}{\sqrt{T}} + \frac{7500}{T}$$

Therefore,

$$(\bar{h}_T{}^\circ - \bar{h}_{537}^\circ) = \int_{537}^{1060} \left(19.86 + \frac{597}{\sqrt{T}} + \frac{7500}{T} \right) dT$$

$$= 4260 \text{ Btu/lb mole}$$

$$\bar{h} = -104{,}036 + 4260 = -99{,}776 \text{ Btu/lb mole.}$$

(b) Using Table A.11 for $H_2O(g)$,

$$(\bar{h}_{1060}^\circ - \bar{h}_{537}^\circ) = 4345 \text{ Btu/lb mole}$$

$$\bar{h} = -104{,}036 + 4345 = -99{,}691 \text{ Btu/lb mole}$$

(c) Using the steam tables,

$$(\bar{h}_{500 \text{ lbf/in}^2, \, 600 \text{ F}} - \bar{h}_{537}^\circ) = 18.016(1298.6 - 1095.4)$$

$$= 3661 \text{ Btu/lb mole.}$$

$$\bar{h} = -104{,}036 + 3661 = -100{,}375 \text{ Btu/lb mole}$$

(d) When using the generalized charts we use the notation introduced in Chapter 10.

$$\bar{h} = \bar{h}_f{}^\circ - (\bar{h}_2{}^* - \bar{h}_2) + (\bar{h}_2{}^* - \bar{h}_1{}^*) + (\bar{h}_1{}^* - \bar{h}_1)$$

where subscript 2 refers to the state at 500 lbf/in.^{2}, 600 F and state 1 refers to the state at 1 atm, 77 F.
From part (a) $\bar{h}_2{}^* - \bar{h}_1{}^* = 4260 \text{ Btu/lb mole.}$;

$$\bar{h}_1{}^* - \bar{h}_1 = 0$$

$$P_{r_2} = \tfrac{500}{3206} = 0.156; \qquad T_{r_2} = \tfrac{1060}{1165} = 0.91$$

From the generalized enthalpy chart,

$$\frac{\bar{h}_2{}^* - \bar{h}_2}{T_c} = 0.53; \quad \therefore \; \bar{h}_2{}^* - \bar{h}_2 = 0.53(1165) = 619 \text{ Btu/lb mole}$$

$$\bar{h} = -104{,}036 - 619 + 4260 = -100{,}395 \text{ Btu/lb mole}$$

The particular approach that is used in a given problem will depend on the data available for the given substance.

Example 12.9

A small gas turbine uses $C_8H_{18(l)}$ for fuel, and 400 per cent theoretical air. The air and fuel enter at 77 F, and the products of combustion leave at 1100 F. The output of the engine and the fuel consumption are measured and it is found that the specific fuel consumption is one pound of fuel per horsepower-hour. Determine the heat transfer from the engine per pound mole of fuel. Assume complete combustion.

The combustion equation is

$$C_8H_{18}(l) + 4(12.5)O_2 + 4(12.5)(3.76)N_2$$
$$\rightarrow 8CO_2 + 9H_2O + 37.5O_2 + 188.0N_2$$

We consider that we have a steady-state, steady-flow process involving ideal gases (except for the $C_8H_{18(l)}$). Therefore we can write:

First law:

$$Q_{c.v.} + \sum_R n_i[(\bar{h}_f^\circ + (\bar{h}^\circ - \bar{h}_{537}^\circ)]_i = W_{c.v.} + \sum_P n_e[\bar{h}_f^\circ + (\bar{h}^\circ - \bar{h}_{537}^\circ)]_e$$

Property relation: Table A.11 for ideal gases and Table 12.3 for $C_8H_{18}(l)$. Since the air is composed of elements at 77 F,

$$\sum_R n_i[\bar{h}_f^\circ + (\bar{h}^\circ - \bar{h}_{537}^\circ)]_i = (\bar{h}_f^\circ)_{C_8H_{18(l)}} = -107,532 \text{ Btu/lb mole.}$$

Considering the products

$$\sum_P n_e[\bar{h}_f^\circ + (\bar{h}_{1560}^\circ - \bar{h}_{537}^\circ)]_e$$
$$= n_{CO_2}[\bar{h}_f^\circ + (\bar{h}_{1560}^\circ - \bar{h}_{537}^\circ)]_{CO_2}$$
$$+ n_{H_2O}[\bar{h}_f^\circ + (\bar{h}_{1560}^\circ - \bar{h}_{537}^\circ)]_{H_2O} + n_{O_2}[\bar{h}_{1560}^\circ - \bar{h}_{537}^\circ]_{O_2}$$
$$+ n_{N_2}[\bar{h}_{1560}^\circ - \bar{h}_{537}^\circ]_{N_2}$$
$$= 8(-169,297 + 11,315) + 9(-104,036 + 8869)$$
$$+ 37.5(7792) + 188(7384)$$
$$= -439,969 \text{ Btu/lb mole fuel.}$$
$$W_{c.v.} = 2545 \times 114.23 = 290,715 \text{ Btu/lb mole fuel}$$

Therefore, from the first law,

$$Q_{c.v.} = -439,969 + 290,715 - (-107,532)$$
$$= -41,722 \text{ Btu/lb mole fuel.}$$

Example 12.10

A gasoline engine delivers 200 hp. The fuel used is $C_8H_{18}(l)$ and it enters the engine at 77 F; 150 per cent theoretical air is used and enters at 110 F. The products of combustion leave the engine at 920 F, and the heat transfer from the engine is 700,000 Btu/hr. Determine the fuel consumption per hour if complete combustion is achieved.

The chemical reaction is

$$C_8H_{18}(l) + 1.5(12.5)O_2 + 1.5(3.76)(12.5)N_2 \rightarrow$$
$$8CO_2 + 9H_2O(g) + 6.25O_2 + 70.5N_2$$

We consider a steady-state, steady-flow process for a control surface around the engine, and assume that all the reactants and products, except for the fuel, are ideal gases.

First law: $\dot{Q}_{c.v.} + \sum_R \dot{n}_i[\bar{h}_f^\circ + (\bar{h}^\circ - \bar{h}_{537}^\circ)]_i$

$$= \dot{W}_{c.v.} + \sum_P \dot{n}_e[\bar{h}_f^\circ + (\bar{h}^\circ - \bar{h}_{537}^\circ)]_e$$

Property relation: Table A.11 for the gaseous reactants and products and Table 12.3 for the fuel.

In solving this problem it is convenient to consider the mass rate of flow of fuel on a mole basis, $\dot{n}_f$, and rewrite the first law in the form

$$\frac{\dot{Q}_{c.v.}}{\dot{n}_f} + \sum_R \frac{\dot{n}_i}{\dot{n}_f}[\bar{h}_f^\circ + (\bar{h}^\circ - \bar{h}_{537}^\circ)]_i = \frac{\dot{W}_{c.v.}}{\dot{n}_f} + \sum_P \frac{\dot{n}_e}{\dot{n}_f}[\bar{h}_f^\circ + (\bar{h}^\circ - \bar{h}_{537}^\circ)]_e$$

$$\sum_R \frac{\dot{n}_i}{\dot{n}_f}[\bar{h}_f^\circ + (\bar{h}^\circ - \bar{h}_{537}^\circ)]_i$$

$$= (\bar{h}_f^\circ)_{C_8H_{18(l)}} + 18.75(\bar{h}_{570}^\circ - \bar{h}_{537}^\circ)_{O_2} + 70.5(\bar{h}_{570}^\circ - \bar{h}_{537}^\circ)_{N_2}$$
$$= -107,532 + 18.75(236) + 70.5(232)$$
$$= -86,748 \text{ Btu/lb mole fuel}$$

$$\sum_P \frac{\dot{n}_e}{\dot{n}_f}[\bar{h}_f^\circ + (\bar{h}^\circ - \bar{h}_{537}^\circ)] = 8(-169,297 + 9092)$$

$$+ 9(-104,036 + 6655) + 6.25(6336) + 70.5(6020)$$
$$= -1,692,054 \text{ Btu/lb mole fuel}$$
$$\dot{W}_{c.v.} = 200(2545) = 509,000 \text{ Btu/hr}$$

Substituting these values into the first law equation we have

$$-\frac{700,000}{\dot{n}_f} + (-86,748) = \frac{509,000}{\dot{n}_f} + (-1,692,054)$$

$$\dot{n}_f = \frac{1,209,000}{1,605,306} = 0.754 \text{ moles fuel/hr}$$

$$\dot{m}_f = 0.754(114.23) = 86.1 \text{ lbm fuel/hr}$$

Example 12.11

A mixture of one mole of gaseous ethene and three moles of oxygen at 298 K react in a constant volume bomb. Heat is transferred until the products are cooled to 600 K. Determine the amount of heat transfer in cal/gm mole from the reactants.

The chemical reaction is

$$C_2H_4 + 3O_2 \rightarrow 2CO_2 + 2H_2O(g)$$

First law: $Q + U_R = U_P$

$$Q + \sum_R n[\bar{h}_f^\circ + (\bar{h}^\circ - \bar{h}_{298}^\circ) - \bar{R}T]$$
$$= \sum_P n[\bar{h}_f^\circ + (\bar{h}^\circ - \bar{h}_{298}^\circ) - \bar{R}T]$$

$$\sum_R n[\bar{h}_f^\circ + (\bar{h}^\circ - \bar{h}_{298}^\circ) - \bar{R}T]$$
$$= [\bar{h}_f^\circ - \bar{R}T]_{C_2H_4} - n_{O_2}[\bar{R}T]_{O_2} = (\bar{h}_f^\circ)_{C_2H_4} - 4\bar{R}T$$
$$= 12{,}496 - 4 \times 1.986 \times 298 = 10{,}130 \text{ cal/gm mole fuel.}$$

$$\sum_P n[\bar{h}_f^\circ + (\bar{h}^\circ - \bar{h}_{298}^\circ) - \bar{R}T]$$
$$= 2[(\bar{h}_f^\circ)_{CO_2} + (\bar{h}_{600}^\circ - \bar{h}_{298}^\circ)_{CO_2}]$$
$$+ 2[(\bar{h}_f^\circ)_{H_2O(g)} + (\bar{h}_{600}^\circ - \bar{h}_{298}^\circ)_{H_2O(g)}] - 4\,\bar{R}T$$
$$= 2[-94{,}054 + 3087] + 2[-57{,}798 + 2509] - 4 \times 1.986 \times 600$$
$$= -181{,}934 - 110{,}578 - 4766 = -297{,}278 \text{ cal/gm mole fuel.}$$

Therefore,

$$Q = -297{,}278 - 10{,}130 = 307{,}408 \text{ cal/gm mole fuel}$$

12.6 Adiabatic Flame Temperature

Consider a given combustion process that takes place adiabatically and with no work or changes in kinetic or potential energy involved. For such a process the temperature of the products is referred to as the adiabatic flame temperature. With the assumptions of no work and no changes in kinetic or potential energy, this is the maximum temperature that can be achieved for the given reactants because any heat transfer from the reacting substances and any incomplete combustion would tend to lower the temperature of the products.

For a given fuel and given pressure and temperature of the reactants, the maximum adiabatic flame temperature that can be achieved is with a stoichiometric mixture. The adiabatic flame temperature can be controlled by the amount of excess air that is used. This is important, for example, in gas turbines, where the maximum permissible temperature is determined by metallurgical considerations in the turbine, and close control of the temperature of the products is essential.

Example 12.12 shows how the adiabatic flame temperature may be found. The dissociation that takes place in the combustion products, which has a significant effect on the adiabatic flame temperature, will be considered in the next chapter.

Example 12.12

Liquid octane at 77 F is burned with 400 per cent theoretical air at 77 F in a steady-flow process. Determine the adiabatic flame temperature. The reaction

$$C_8H_{18}(l) + 4(12.5)O_2 + 4(12.5)(3.76)N_2 \rightarrow$$
$$8CO_2 + 9H_2O(g) + 37.5O_2 + 188.0N_2$$

We assume ideal gas behavior for all the constituents except the liquid octane. In this case the first law reduces to

$$H_R = H_P$$
$$\sum_R n_i[\bar{h}_f{}^\circ + (\bar{h} - \bar{h}_{537}^\circ)]_i = \sum_P n_e[\bar{h}_f{}^\circ + (\bar{h}_T{}^\circ - \bar{h}_{537}^\circ)]_e$$

where h_T refers to the enthalpy of each constituent at the adiabatic flame temperature.

$$\sum_R n_i[\bar{h}_f{}^\circ + (\bar{h} - \bar{h}_{537}^\circ)]_i = (\bar{h}_f{}^\circ)_{C_8H_{18}(l)} = -107,532 \text{ Btu/mole fuel}$$

$$\sum_P n_e[\bar{h}_f{}^\circ + (\bar{h}_T - \bar{h}_{537}^\circ)]_e$$
$$= 8[-169,297 + (\bar{h}_T{}^\circ - \bar{h}_{537}^\circ)_{CO_2}] + 9[-104,036 + (\bar{h}_T{}^\circ - \bar{h}_{537}^\circ)_{H_2O}]$$
$$+ 37.5(\bar{h}_T{}^\circ - \bar{h}_{537}^\circ)_{O_2} + 188.0(\bar{h}_T{}^\circ - \bar{h}_{537}^\circ)_{N_2}$$

By trial-and-error solution, a temperature of the products is found that satisfies this equation. Assume

$$T_P = 1620 \text{ R}$$
$$H_P = \sum_P n_e[\bar{h}_f{}^\circ + (\bar{h}_T{}^\circ - \bar{h}_{537}^\circ)]_e$$
$$= 8(-169,297 + 12,063) + 9(-104,036 + 9432)$$
$$+ 37.5(8281) + 188.0(7839)$$
$$= -1,257,872 - 851,436 + 310,537 + 1,473,732$$
$$= -325,039$$

Assume

$$T_P = 1800 \text{ R}$$
$$H_P = \sum_P n_e[\bar{h}_f{}^\circ + (\bar{h}_T{}^\circ - \bar{h}_{537}^\circ)]_e$$
$$= 8(-169,297 + 14,371) + 9(-104,036 + 11,176)$$
$$+ 37.5(9769) + 188(9232)$$
$$= -1,239,408 - 835,740 + 366,337 + 1,735,616$$
$$= +26,807$$

Since $H_P = H_R = -107{,}032$, we find, by interpolation that the adiabatic flame temperature is 1733 R.

12.7 Enthalpy and Internal Energy of Combustion; Heat of Reaction

The enthalpy of combustion, h_{RP}, is defined as the difference between the enthalpy of the products and the enthalpy of the reactants when complete combustion occurs at a given temperature and pressure. That is,

$$\bar{h}_{RP} = H_P - H_R$$

$$\bar{h}_{RP} = \sum_P n_e[\bar{h}_f^\circ + (\bar{h}_T - \bar{h}_{298}^\circ)]_e - \sum_R n_i[\bar{h}_f^\circ + (\bar{h}_T - \bar{h}_{298}^\circ)]_i \quad (12.9)$$

The usual parameter for expressing the enthalpy of combustion is a unit mass of fuel, such as a lbm (h_{RP}) or a lb mole ($\bar{h}_{RP}$) of fuel.

The tabulated values of the enthalpy of combustion of fuels are usually given for a temperature of 25 C and a pressure of one atmosphere. The enthalpy of combustion for a number of hydrocarbon fuels at this temperature and pressure, which we designate h_{RP_0}, is given in Table 12.4.

The internal energy of combustion is defined in a similar manner.

$$\bar{u}_{RP} = U_P - U_R$$

$$= \sum_P n_e[\bar{h}_f^\circ + (\bar{h}_T - \bar{h}_{298}^\circ) - P\bar{v}]_e - \sum_R n_i[\bar{h}_f^\circ + (\bar{h}_T - \bar{h}_{298}^\circ) - P\bar{v}]_i$$
$$(12.10)$$

When all the gaseous constituents can be considered as ideal gases, and the volume of the liquid and solid constituents is negligible compared to the volume of the gaseous constituents, this relation for $\bar{u}_{RP}$ reduces to

$$\bar{u}_{RP} = \bar{h}_{RP} - \bar{R}T\,(n_{\text{gaseous products}} - n_{\text{gaseous reactants}}) \quad (12.11)$$

Frequently the term "heating value" or "heat of reaction" is used. This represents the heat transferred from the chamber during combustion or reaction at constant temperature. In the case of a constant pressure or steady-flow process, we conclude from the first law of thermodynamics that this is equal to the negative of the enthalpy of combustion. For this reason this heat transfer is sometimes designated the constant-pressure heating value for combustion processes.

In the case of a constant volume process the heat transfer is equal to the negative of the internal energy of combustion. This is sometimes designated the constant-volume heating value in the case of combustion.

When the term heating value is used the terms "higher" and "lower" heating value are used. The higher heating value is the heat transfer with

TABLE 12.4

Enthalpy of Combustion of Some Hydrocarbons at 25 C (77 F)

| Hydrocarbon | Formula | Liquid H_2O in Products (Negative of Higher Heating Value) | | Vapor H_2O in Products (Negative of Lower Heating Value) | |
		Liquid Hydrocarbon, Btu/lbm fuel	Gaseous Hydrocarbon, Btu/lbm fuel	Liquid Hydrocarbon, Btu/lbm fuel	Gaseous Hydrocarbon, Btu/lbm fuel
Paraffin Family:					
Methane	CH_4		−23,861		−21,502
Ethane	C_2H_6		−22,304		−20,416
Propane	C_3H_8	−21,490	−21,649	−19,773	−19,929
Butane	C_4H_{10}	−21,134	−21,293	−19,506	−19,665
Pentane	C_5H_{12}	−20,914	−21,072	−19,340	−19,499
Hexane	C_6H_{14}	−20,772	−20,930	−19,233	−19,391
Heptane	C_7H_{16}	−20,668	−20,825	−19,157	−19,314
Octane	C_8H_{18}	−20,591	−20,747	−19,100	−19,256
Decane	$C_{10}H_{22}$	−20,484	−20,638	−19,020	−19,175
Dodecane	$C_{12}H_{26}$	−20,410	−20,564	−18,964	−19,118
Olefin Family:					
Ethene	C_2H_4		−21,626		−20,276
Propene	C_3H_6		−21,033		−19,683
Butene	C_4H_8		−20,833		−19,483
Pentene	C_5H_{10}		−20,696		−19,346
Hexene	C_6H_{12}		−20,612		−19,262
Heptene	C_7H_{14}		−20,552		−19,202
Octene	C_8H_{16}		−20,507		−19,157
Nonene	C_9H_{18}		−20,472		−19,122
Decene	$C_{10}H_{20}$		−20,444		−19,094
Alkylbenzene Family:					
Benzene	C_6H_6	−17,985	−18,172	−17,259	−17,446
Methylbenzene	C_7H_8	−18,247	−18,423	−17,424	−17,601
Ethylbenzene	C_8H_{10}	−18,488	−18,659	−17,596	−17,767
Propylbenzene	C_9H_{12}	−18,667	−18,832	−17,722	−17,887
Butylbenzene	$C_{10}H_{14}$	−18,809	−18,970	−17,823	−17,984

liquid H_2O in the products, and the lower heating value is the heat transfer with vapor H_2O in the products.

Example 12.13

Calculate the enthalpy of combustion of propane at 77 F on both a lb mole and lbm basis under the following conditions.
(a) Liquid propane with liquid H_2O in the products.
(b) Liquid propane with gaseous H_2O in the products.
(c) Gaseous propane with liquid H_2O in the products.
(d) Gaseous propane with gaseous H_2O in the products.
The enthalpy of evaporation of propane is 159 Btu/lbm.
The basic combustion equation is:

$$C_3H_8 + 5O_2 \rightarrow 3CO_2 + 4H_2O$$

From Table 12.3, $(\bar{h}_f^\circ)_{C_3H_8(g)} = -44{,}676$ Btu/lb mole. Therefore,

$$(\bar{h}_f^\circ)_{C_3H_8(l)} = -44{,}676 - 44.10(159) = -51{,}688 \text{ Btu/lb mole.}$$

(a) Liquid propane $-$ liquid H_2O

$$\begin{aligned}
\bar{h}_{RP_0} &= 3(\bar{h}_f^\circ)_{CO_2} + 4(\bar{h}_f^\circ)_{H_2O(l)} - (\bar{h}_f^\circ)_{C_3H_8(l)} \\
&= 3(-169{,}297) + 4(-122{,}971) - (-51{,}688) \\
&= -948{,}087 \text{ Btu/lb mole} \\
&= \frac{-948{,}087}{44.10} = -21{,}490 \text{ Btu/lbm}
\end{aligned}$$

The higher heating value of liquid propane is therefore 21,490 Btu/lbm.
(b) Liquid propane $-$ gaseous H_2O

$$\begin{aligned}
\bar{h}_{RP_0} &= 3(\bar{h}_f^\circ)_{CO_2} + 4(\bar{h}_f^\circ)_{H_2O(g)} - (\bar{h}_f^\circ)_{C_3H_8(l)} \\
&= 3(-169{,}297) - 4(-104{,}036) - (-51{,}688) \\
&= -872{,}347 \text{ Btu/lb mole} \\
&= \frac{-872{,}347}{44.10} = -19{,}770 \text{ Btu/lbm.}
\end{aligned}$$

The lower heating value of liquid propane is 19,770 Btu/lbm.
(c) Gaseous propane $-$ liquid H_2O

$$\begin{aligned}
\bar{h}_{RP_0} &= 3(\bar{h}_f^\circ)_{CO_2} + 4(\bar{h}_f^\circ)_{H_2O(l)} - \bar{h}_{C_3H_8(g)}^\circ \\
&= 3(-169{,}297) + 4(-122{,}971) - (-44{,}676) \\
&= -955{,}099 \text{ Btu/lb mole} \\
&= \frac{-955{,}099}{44.10} = -21{,}650
\end{aligned}$$

The higher heating value of gaseous propane is 21,650 Btu/lbm.

(d) Gaseous propane − gaseous H_2O

$$\bar{h}_{RP_0} = 3(\bar{h}_f^\circ)_{CO_2} + 4(\bar{h}_f^\circ)_{H_2O(g)} - (\bar{h}_f^\circ)_{C_3H_8(g)}$$
$$= 3(-169,297) + 4(-104,036) - (-44,676) = -879,359 \text{ Btu/mole}$$
$$= -19,930 \text{ Btu/lbm.}$$

The lower heating value of gaseous propane is 19,930 Btu/lbm.

Example 12.14

Calculate the enthalpy of combustion of gaseous propane at 400 F. (At this temperature all the water formed during combustion will be in the vapor phase.) This example will demonstrate how the enthalpy of combustion of propane varies with temperature. The average constant-pressure specific heat of propane between 77 F and 400 F is 0.5 Btu/lbm-R.

$$(\bar{h}_{RP})_T = \sum_P n_e[\bar{h}_f^\circ + (\bar{h}_T^\circ - \bar{h}_{537}^\circ)]_e - \sum_R n_i[\bar{h}_f^\circ + (\bar{h}_T^\circ - \bar{h}_{537}^\circ)]_i$$

$$C_3H_8(g) + 5O_2 \rightarrow 3CO_2 + 4H_2O(g)$$

$$\bar{h}_{R_{400}} = [\bar{h}_f^\circ + \bar{C}_{pav}(400 - 77)]_{C_3H_8(g)} + n_{O_2}(\bar{h}_{860}^\circ - \bar{h}_{537}^\circ)_{O_2}$$
$$= -44,676 + 0.5 \times 44.10(400 - 77) + 5(2325)$$
$$= -44,676 + 7122 + 11,605 = -25,929 \text{ Btu/lb mole.}$$

$$\bar{h}_{P_{400}} = n_{CO_2}[\bar{h}_f^\circ + (\bar{h}_{860}^\circ - \bar{h}_{537}^\circ)]_{CO_2} + n_{H_2O}[\bar{h}_f^\circ + (\bar{h}_{860}^\circ - \bar{h}_{537}^\circ)]_{H_2O}$$
$$= 3(-169,297 + 3166) + 4[-104,036 + 2646]$$
$$= -498,393 - 405,560 = -903,953 \text{ Btu/lb mole.}$$

$$\bar{h}_{RP_{400}} = -903,953 - (-25,929) = -878,024 \text{ Btu/lb mole}$$

$$h_{RP_{400}} = \frac{-878,024}{44.10} = -19,901 \text{ Btu/lbm}$$

This compares with a value of −19,929 at 77 F.

This problem could also have been solved using the given value of the enthalpy of combustion at 77 F by noting that

$$(\bar{h}_{RP})_{400} = (H_P)_{400} - (H_R)_{400}$$
$$= n_{CO_2}[\bar{h}_f^\circ + (\bar{h}_{860}^\circ - \bar{h}_{537}^\circ)]_{CO_2} + n_{H_2O}[\bar{h}_f^\circ + (\bar{h}_{860}^\circ - \bar{h}_{537}^\circ)]_{H_2O}$$
$$- [\bar{h}_f^\circ + \bar{C}_{pav}(400 - 77)]_{C_3H_8(g)} - n_{O_2}(\bar{h}_{860}^\circ - \bar{h}_{537}^\circ)_{O_2}$$
$$= \bar{h}_{RP_0} + n_{CO_2}(\bar{h}_{860}^\circ - \bar{h}_{537}^\circ)_{CO_2} + n_{H_2O}(\bar{h}_{860}^\circ - \bar{h}_{537}^\circ)_{H_2O}$$
$$- \bar{C}_{pav}(400 - 77)_{C_3H_8(g)} - n_{O_2}(\bar{h}_{860}^\circ - \bar{h}_{537}^\circ)_{O_2}$$

$$(\bar{h}_{RP_0})_{400} = -19,929 \times 44.10 + 3(3166) + 4(2646)$$
$$- 0.5 \times 44.1(400 - 77) - 5(2325)$$

$$(h_{RP_0})_{400} = -19,929 + \frac{1235}{44.1} = -19,929 + 28 = -19,901 \text{ Btu/lbm.}$$

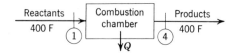

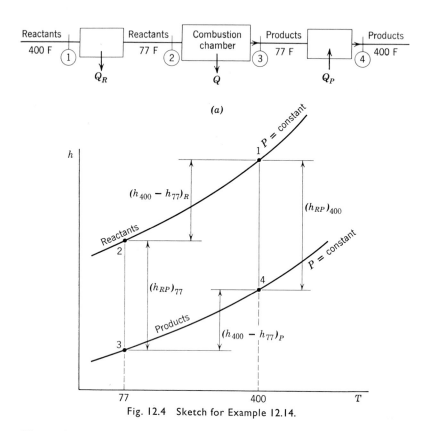

Fig. 12.4   Sketch for Example 12.14.

The various states and changes of enthalpy involved in this example are shown in Fig. 12.4. From this example it is evident that the enthalpy of combustion changes with temperature only because the changes of enthalpy with temperature of the products and reactants are not, in general, equal. The change in enthalpy of combustion with temperature is relatively small.

12.8   Second-Law Analysis of Reacting Systems

From our consideration of the second law we would conclude that since the combustion process proceeds so readily, it is probably an irreversible process. This can be verified by determining the entropy change during an adiabatic combustion process. However, to do this we must know the entropy of each of the reactants and products relative to the same base. This would be similar to our procedure in defining the enthalpy of formation.

This leads to a consideration of the third law of thermodynamics even though a detailed discussion of the third law is beyond the scope of this book. In essence the third law states that the entropy of all pure substances can be assigned the value of zero at absolute zero. Entropy measured relative to this base is called the absolute entropy. It may be determined from either calorimetric or spectroscopic data. Table 12.3 gives the absolute entropy of a number of substances at 77 F (25 C) and 1 atm pressure and Table A.11 gives the absolute entropy for a number of substances at various temperatures at one atmosphere pressure. The absolute entropy at one atmosphere pressure is designated $\bar{s}°$. The entropy of a reacting substance in any given state can be found by using appropriate thermodynamic relations, tables, or charts to determine the change of entropy between the given state and the entropy at this given temperature and one atmosphere pressure, and adding this to the value of $\bar{s}°$ given in Table A.11.

We therefore know the value of entropy of all substances relative to the same base, and the change of entropy for any process involving a chemical reaction can be found by the application of the second law as indicated in Chapter 7.

In Chapter 8 the concepts of reversible work, irreversibility and availability were introduced. These concepts involved both the first and second laws of thermodynamics. At the conclusion of Chapter 8 the Gibbs function was introduced, and the statement was made that this thermodynamic property would be particularly applicable in dealing with chemical reactions.

The reversible work, Eq. 8.9, for a steady-state, steady-flow process, in the absence of changes in kinetic and potential energy is,

$$W_{\text{rev}} = \sum m_i(h_i - T_0 s_i) - \sum m_e(h_e - T_0 s_e)$$

Applying this to a steady-state, steady-flow process involving a chemical reaction, and introducing the symbols we have been using in this chapter we have

$$W_{\text{rev}} = \sum_R n_i[\bar{h}_f° + (\bar{h} - \bar{h}_{298}°) - T_0\bar{s}]_i - \sum_P n_e[\bar{h}_f° + (\bar{h} - \bar{h}_{298}°) - T_0\bar{s}]_e$$

$$(12.12)$$

Similarly, the irreversibility for such a process, which was given in Eq. 8.14, becomes

$$I = \sum_P n_e T_0 \bar{s}_e - \sum_R n_i T_0 \bar{s}_i - Q_{\text{c.v.}} \qquad (12.13)$$

The availability, Ψ', in the absence of kinetic and potential energy changes, for a steady-state, steady flow process was defined, Eq. 8.16, as

$$\Psi' = (h - T_0 s) - (h_0 - T_0 s_0)$$

It was also indicated that when a steady-state, steady-flow chemical reaction takes place in such a manner that both the reactants and products are in temperature equilibrium with the surroundings, the Gibbs function $(g = h - Ts)$ becomes a significant variable, Eq. 8.28. For such a process, in the absence of changes in kinetic and potential energy, the reversible work is given by the relation

$$W_{\text{rev}} = \sum_R n_i \bar{g}_i - \sum_P n_e \bar{g}_e \qquad (12.14)$$

Since many chemical reactions do occur in such a manner, the change in Gibbs function is particularly relevant in combustion processes. For this reason, the Gibbs function of formation, $\bar{g}_f^\circ$, has been defined by a procedure similar to that used in defining the enthalpy of formation. That is, the Gibbs function of each of the elements at 25 C and 1 atm pressure is assumed to be zero, and the Gibbs function of each element is found relative to this base. Table 12.3 lists the Gibbs function of formation of a number of substances at 25 C (77 F) and 1 atm pressure. It is also evident that the Gibbs function can be found directly from data for $\bar{h}_f^\circ$ and $\bar{s}^\circ$ at the given temperature, as indicated in the following example.

Example 12.15

Determine the Gibbs function of formation of CO_2.
Consider the reaction

$$C + O_2 \rightarrow CO_2$$

Assume that the carbon and oxygen are each initially at 77 F and 1 atm pressure, and that the CO_2 is finally at 77 F and 1 atm pressure.
The change in Gibbs function for this reaction is found first.

$$G_P - G_R = (H_P - H_R) - T_0(S_P - S_R)$$
$$\sum_P n_e (\bar{g}_f^\circ)_e - \sum_R n_i (\bar{g}_f^\circ)_i$$
$$= \sum_P n_e (\bar{h}_f^\circ)_e - \sum_R n_i (\bar{h}_f^\circ)_i - T_0 \left[\sum_P n_e (\bar{s}_{537}^\circ)_e - \sum_R n_i (\bar{s}_{537}^\circ)_i \right]$$

This reduces to

$$G_P - G_R = (\bar{h}_f^\circ)_{CO_2} - 536.7[(\bar{s}_{537}^\circ)_{CO_2} - (\bar{s}_{537}^\circ)_C - (\bar{s}_{537}^\circ)_{O_2}]$$
$$= -169{,}297 - 536.7(51.072 - 1.359 - 49.004)$$
$$= -169{,}297 - 380 = -169{,}677 \text{ Btu/lb mole.}$$

Since the Gibbs function of the reactants, G_R, is zero (in accordance with the assumption that the Gibbs function of the elements is zero at 25 C and 1 atm pressure), it follows that

$$G_P = (\bar{g}_f°)_{CO_2} = -169,667 \text{ Btu/lb mole}$$

This is the value given in Table 12.3.

Consider one lb mole of hydrocarbon fuel and the necessary air for complete combustion, each at one atmosphere pressure and 77 F, the pressure and temperature of the surroundings. What is the maximum work that can be done as this fuel reacts with the air? From our considerations in Chapter 8 we conclude that the maximum work would be done if this chemical reaction took place reversibly and the products were finally in pressure and temperature equilibrium with the surroundings. From Eq. 12.14 we conclude this reversible work could be calculated from the relation

$$W_{\text{rev}} = \sum_R n_i \bar{g}_i - \sum_P n_e \bar{g}_e$$

However, since the final state is in equilibrium with the surroundings we could consider this amount of work to be the availability of the fuel and air.

Example 12.16

Ethene (g) at 77 F and 1 atm pressure is burned with 400 per cent theoretical air at 77 F and 1 atm pressure. Assume that this reaction takes place reversibly at 77 F and that the products leave at 77 F and 1 atm pressure. To further simplify this problem assume that the oxygen and nitrogen are separated before the reaction takes place (each at 1 atm, 77 F), that the constituents in the products are separated, and that each is at 77 F and 1 atm pressure. Thus, the reaction takes place as shown in Fig. 12.5. For purposes of comparison between this and the two subsequent examples, we consider all of the H_2O in the products to be a gas (a hypothetical situation in this example and Example 12.18).

Determine the reversible work for this process (i.e., the work that would be done if this chemical action took place reversibly and isothermally).

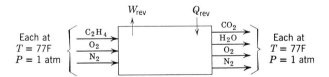

Fig. 12.5   Sketch for Example 12.16.

The equation for this chemical reaction is

$$C_2H_4(g) + 3(4)O_2 + 3(4)(3.76)N_2 \rightarrow 2CO_2 + 2H_2O(g) + 9O_2 + 45.1N_2$$

The reversible work for this process is equal to the decrease in Gibbs function during this reaction, Eq. 12.14. The values for the Gibbs function can be taken directly from Table 12.3, since each is at 77 F and 1 atm pressure. From Eq. 12.14

$$W_{\text{rev}} = \sum_R n_i \bar{g}_i - \sum_P n_e \bar{g}_e$$

Since each of the reactants and each of the products are at one atmosphere pressure and 77 F this reduces to

$$
\begin{aligned}
W_{\text{rev}} &= (\bar{g}_f{}^\circ)_{C_2H_4} - 2(\bar{g}_f{}^\circ)_{CO_2} - 2(\bar{g}_f{}^\circ)_{H_2O(g)} \\
&= 29{,}306 - 2(-169{,}677) - 2(-98{,}345) \\
&= 565{,}350 \text{ Btu/lb mole} = 20{,}140 \text{ Btu/lbm}
\end{aligned}
$$

Therefore we might say that when the one pound of ethene is at 77 F, one atm pressure, the temperature and pressure of the surroundings, it has an availability of 20,140 Btu.

Thus it would seem logical to rate the efficiency of a device designed to do work by utilization of a combustion process, such as an internal-combustion engine or a steam power plant, as the ratio of actual work to the decrease in Gibbs function for the given reaction, rather than to the heating value, as is current practice. However, as is evident from the preceding example, the difference between the decrease in Gibbs function and the heating value is small for hydrocarbon fuels and the efficiency defined in terms of heating value is essentially equal to that defined in terms of decrease in Gibbs function.

It is of particular interest to study the irreversibility that takes place during a combustion process. The following examples are presented to illustrate this matter, where we consider the same hydrocarbon fuel that was used in Example 12.16, namely Ethene (g) at 77 F and 1 atm. We determined the availability and found that it was 20,140 Btu/lbm. Now let us burn this fuel with 400 per cent theoretical air in a steady-state, steady-flow adiabatic process. We can determine the irreversibility of this process in two ways. The first is to calculate the increase in entropy for the process. Since the process is adiabatic, the increase in entropy is due entirely to the irreversibilities for the process and we can find the irreversibility from Eq. 12.13. We can also calculate the availability of the products of combustion at the adiabatic flame temperature, and note that they are less than the availability of the fuel and air before the combustion process, the difference being the irreversibility that occurs during the combustion process.

Example 12.17

Consider the same combustion process as in Example 12.16, but let it take place adiabatically, and assume that each constituent in the products is at 1 atmosphere pressure and at the adiabatic flame temperature. This combustion process is shown schematically in Fig. 12.6. The temperature of the surroundings is 77 F.

For this combustion process determine: (a) The increase in entropy during combustion. (b) The availability of the products of combustion.

The combustion equation is

$$C_2H_4 + 12O_2 + 12(3.76)N_2 \rightarrow 2CO_2 + 2H_2O(g) + 9O_2 + 45.1N_2$$

The adiabatic flame temperature is determined first.

$$H_R = H_P$$

$$\sum_R n_i(\bar{h}_f°)_i = \sum_P n_e[\bar{h}_f° + (\bar{h}_T° - \bar{h}_{537}°)]_e$$

$$22{,}493 = 2[-169{,}297 + (\bar{h}_T° - \bar{h}_{537}°)_{CO_2}]$$
$$+ 2[-104{,}036 + (\bar{h}_T° - \bar{h}_{537}°)_{H_2O(g)}]$$
$$+ 9(\bar{h}_T° - \bar{h}_{537}°)_{O_2} + 45.1(\bar{h}_T° - \bar{h}_{537}°)_{N_2}$$

By a trial and error solution we find the adiabatic flame temperature to be 1829 R.

We now proceed to find the change in entropy during this adiabatic combustion process.

$$S_R = \sum_R (n_i \bar{s}_i°)_{537} = (\bar{s}°_{C_2H_4} + 12\bar{s}°_{O_2} + 45.1\bar{s}°_{N_2})_{537}$$

$$= 52.447 + 12(49.004) + 45.1(45.770)$$

$$= 2704.72 \text{ Btu/lb mole fuel-R}$$

$$S_P = \sum_P (n_e \bar{s}_e°)_{1829} = (2\bar{s}°_{CO_2} + 2\bar{s}°_{H_2O(g)} + 9\bar{s}°_{O_2} + 45.1\bar{s}°_{N_2})_{1829}$$

$$= 2(64.546) + 2(55.752) + 9(53.321) + 45.1(54.628)$$

$$= 3229.21 \text{ Btu/lb mole fuel-R}$$

$$S_P - S_R = 524.49 \text{ Btu/lb mole fuel-R}.$$

Fig. 12.6   Sketch for Example 12.17.

Since this is an adiabatic process, the increase in entropy indicates the irreversibility of the adiabatic combustion process. This irreversibility can be found from Eq. 12.13.

$$I = T_0 \left[\sum_P n_e \bar{s}_e - \sum_R n_i \bar{s}_i \right]$$
$$= 536.7(524.49) = 281,494 \text{ Btu/lb mole fuel}$$
$$= 10,020 \text{ Btu/lbm fuel}$$

Therefore, the availability after the combustion process is
$$\Psi_P = 20,140 - 10,020 = 10,120 \text{ Btu/lbm fuel.}$$

The availability of the products can also be found from the relation
$$\Psi_P = \sum_P [(\bar{h}_e - T_0 \bar{s}_e) - (h_0 - T_0 \bar{s}_0)]$$

Since in this problem the products are separated and each is at one atmosphere pressure and the adiabatic flame temperature of 1829 R, this reduces to

$$\Psi_P = \sum_P n_e [(\bar{h}_e{}^\circ - \bar{h}_0{}^\circ) - T_0(\bar{s}_e{}^\circ - \bar{s}_0{}^\circ)]$$
$$= 2(14,751) + 2(11,466) + 9(10,012) + 45.1(9460)$$
$$- 536.7[2(64.546 - 51.072) + 2(55.752 - 45.106)$$
$$+ 9(58.321 - 49.004) + 45.1(54.628 - 45.770)]$$
$$= 569,182 - 285,283 = 283,899 \text{ Btu/lb mole fuel}$$
$$= 10,120 \text{ Btu/lbm fuel.}$$

That is, if every process after the adiabatic combustion process were reversible, the maximum amount of work that could be done is 10,120 Btu/lbm fuel. This compares to a value of 20,140 Btu/lbm for the reversible isothermal reaction. This means that if we had an engine that had the indicated adiabatic combustion process, and if all other processes were completely reversible, the efficiency would be about 50 per cent.

In the two prior examples we made the assumption, for purposes of simplifying the calculation, that the constituents in the reactants and products were separated, and each was at one atmosphere pressure. This of course is not a realistic problem, and in the following example, Example 12.16 is repeated with the assumption that the reactants and products each consist of a mixture at one atmosphere pressure.

Example 12.18

Consider the same combustion process of Example 12.16, but assume that the reactants consist of a mixture at 1 atm pressure and 77 F and that

Fig. 12.7   Sketch for Example 12.18.

the products also consist of a mixture at 1 atm and 77 F. Thus, the combustion process is as shown in Fig. 12.7. Assume each constituent to be an ideal gas.

Determine the work that would be done if this combustion process took place reversibly and in pressure and temperature equilibrium with the surroundings.

The combustion equation, as noted previously, is

$$C_2H_4(g) + 3(4)O_2 + 3(4)(3.76)N_2 \rightarrow 2CO_2 + 2H_2O(g) + 9O_2 + 45.1N_2$$

In this case we must find the entropy of each substance as it exists in the mixture; i.e., at its partial pressure and the given temperature of 77 F. Since the absolute entropies given in Tables 12.3 and A.11 are at 1 atm pressure and 77 F, the entropy of each constituent in the mixture can be found from the relation

$$\bar{s} - \bar{s}^\circ = -\bar{R} \ln y \, \frac{P}{P^\circ}$$

where $\bar{s}$ = entropy of the constituent in the mixture
   $\bar{s}^\circ$ = absolute entropy at the same temperature and 1 atm pressure
   P = pressure of the mixture
   P° = 1 atm pressure
   y = mole fraction of the constituent

Since P° and the pressure of the mixture are both 1 atm pressure, the entropy of each constituent can be found by the relation

$$\bar{s} = \bar{s}^\circ - \bar{R} \ln y = \bar{s}^\circ + \bar{R} \ln \frac{1}{y}$$

For the reactants:

	n	$1/y$	$\bar{R} \ln 1/y$	$\bar{s}^\circ$	$\bar{s}$
C_2H_4	1	58.100	8.060	52.447	60.507
O_2	12	4.850	3.135	49.004	52.139
N_2	45.1	1.285	0.498	45.770	46.268
	58.1				

For the products:

	n	$1/y$	$\bar{R} \ln 1/y$	$\bar{s}^{\circ}$	$\bar{s}$
CO_2	2	29.050	6.690	51.072	57.762
H_2O	2	29.050	6.690	45.106	51.796
O_2	9	6.460	3.700	49.004	52.704
N_2	45.1	1.285	0.498	45.770	46.268
	58.1				

With the assumption of ideal gas behavior, the enthalpy of each constituent is equal to the enthalpy of formation at 77 F. The values of entropy are as calculated above. Therefore, from Eq. 12.12

$$W_{\text{rev}} = \sum_R n_i(\bar{h}_f^{\circ})_i - \sum_P n_e(\bar{h}_f^{\circ})_e - T_0\left[\sum_R n_i\bar{s}_i - \sum_P n_e\bar{s}_e\right]$$

$$= (\bar{h}_f^{\circ})_{C_2H_4} - 2(\bar{h}_f^{\circ})_{CO_2} - 2(\bar{h}_f^{\circ})_{H_2O(g)}$$
$$- 536.7[\bar{s}_{C_2H_4} + 12\bar{s}_{O_2} + 45.1\bar{s}_{N_2} - 2\bar{s}_{CO_2}$$
$$- 2\bar{s}_{H_2O(g)} - 9\bar{s}_{O_2} - 45.1\bar{s}_{N_2}]$$

$$= 22{,}493 - 2(-169{,}297) - 2(-104{,}036)$$
$$- 536.7[(60.507) + 12(52.139) + 45.1(46.268)$$
$$- 2(57.762) - 2(51.796) - 9(52.704) - 45.1(46.268)]$$
$$= 569{,}159 - 536.7[2772.862 - 2779.139]$$
$$569{,}159 + 3369 = 572{,}528 \text{ Btu/lb mole fuel}$$

$$= \frac{572{,}528}{28.054} = 20{,}200 \text{ Btu/lbm fuel}$$

Note that this is essentially the same value that was obtained in Example 12.16, when the reactants and products were each separated and at one atmosphere pressure. These examples raise the question of the possibility of a reversible chemical reaction. Some reactions can be made to approach reversibility by having them take place in an electrolytic cell, as described in Chapter 1. When a potential exactly equal to the electromotive force of the cell is applied, no reaction takes place. When the applied potential is increased slightly, the reaction proceeds in one direction, and if the applied potential is decreased slightly, the reaction proceeds in the opposite direction. The work involved is the electrical energy supplied or delivered.

Much effort is being directed toward the development of fuel cells in which carbon, hydrogen, or hydrocarbons will react with oxygen and produce electricity directly. If a fuel cell can be developed that utilizes a hydrocarbon fuel and has a sufficiently high efficiency and capacity (for a given volume or weight) drastic changes will be possible in our techniques for generating electricity on a commercial scale. At the present time, however, fuel cells are not competitive with conventional power plants for the production of electricity on a large scale.

12.9   Evaluation of Actual Combustion Processes

In evaluating the performance of an actual combustion process a, number of different parameters can be defined, depending on the nature of the process and the system considered. In the combustion chamber of a gas turbine, for example, the objective is to raise the temperature of the products to a given temperature (usually the maximum temperature the metals in the turbine can withstand). If we had a combustion process in which complete combustion was achieved and which was adiabatic, the temperature of the products would be the adiabatic flame temperature. Let us designate the fuel-air ratio needed to reach a given temperature under these conditions as the ideal fuel-air ratio. In the actual combustion chamber the combustion will be incomplete to some extent and there will be some heat transfer to the surroundings. Therefore more fuel will be required to reach the given temperature, and this we designate as the actual fuel-air ratio. In this case, the combustion efficiency, η_{comb}, is defined as

$$\eta_{comb} = \frac{FA_{ideal}}{FA_{actual}} \tag{12.15}$$

On the other hand, in the furnace of a steam generator (boiler) the purpose is to transfer the maximum possible amount of heat to the steam (water). In practice, the efficiency of a steam generator is defined as the ratio of the heat transferred to the steam to the higher heating value of the fuel. For a coal this is the heating value as measured in a bomb calorimeter, which is the constant-volume heating value, and it corresponds to the internal energy of combustion. One observes a minor inconsistency, since the boiler involves a flow process, and the change in enthalpy is the significant factor. However, in most cases the error thus introduced is less than the experimental error involved in measuring the heating value, and the efficiency of a steam generator is defined by the relation,

$$\eta_{steam\ generator} = \frac{\text{heat transferred to steam/lbm fuel}}{\text{higher heating value of the fuel}} \tag{12.16}$$

In an internal combustion engine the purpose is to do work. The logical way to evaluate the performance of an internal-combustion engine would be to compare the actual work done to the maximum work which would be done by a reversible change of state from the reactants to the products. This, as we noted previously is equal to the decrease in Gibbs function $(h - Ts)$.

However, in practice the efficiency of an internal combustion engine is defined as the ratio of the actual work to the negative of the enthalpy of combustion of the fuel (i.e., the constant-pressure heating value). This is usually called the thermal efficiency, η_{th}

$$\eta_{th} = \frac{w}{(-h_{RP_0})} = \frac{w}{\text{heating value}} \qquad (12.17)$$

The over-all efficiency of a gas turbine or steam power plant is defined in the same way. It should be pointed out that in an internal combustion engine or fuel-burning steam power plant the fact that the combustion is itself irreversible is a significant factor in the relatively low thermal efficiency of these devices.

One other factor should be pointed out regarding efficiency. We have noted that the enthalpy of combustion of a hydrocarbon fuel varies considerably with the phase of the water in the products (which leads to the concept of higher and lower heating values). Therefore, in considering the thermal efficiency of an engine, the heating value used to determine this efficiency must be borne in mind. Two engines made by different manufacturers may have identical performance, but if one manufacturer bases his efficiency on the higher heating value and the other on the lower heating value, the latter will be able to claim a higher thermal efficiency. This claim is not significant, of course, as the performance is the same, and a consideration of the way in which the efficiency was defined would reveal this.

The whole matter of efficiencies of devices involving combustion processes is treated in detail in textbooks dealing with particular applications, and our discussion is intended only as an introduction to the subject. However, a few examples will be cited to illustrate these remarks.

Example 12.19

The combustion chamber of a gas turbine uses a liquid hydrocarbon fuel which has an approximate composition of C_8H_{18}. On test the following data are obtained.

$$T_{air} = 260 \text{ F}(720 \text{ R}) \qquad T_{products} = 1520 \text{ F}(1980 \text{ R})$$

$$V_{air} = 300 \text{ ft/sec} \qquad V_{products} = 450 \text{ ft/sec}$$

$$T_{fuel} = 120 \text{ F} \qquad FA_{actual} = 0.0211 \text{ lbm fuel/lbm air}$$

Calculate the combustion efficiency for this process.

For the ideal chemical reaction the heat transfer is zero. Therefore, writing the first law for a control volume that includes the combustion chamber we have,

$$H_R + KE_R = H_P + KE_P$$

$$H_R + KE_R$$

$$= \sum_R n_i \left[\bar{h}_f^\circ + (\bar{h}^\circ - \bar{h}_{537}^\circ) + \frac{MV^2}{2g_c} \right]_i$$

$$= [\bar{h}_f^\circ + \bar{C}_p(120 - 77)]_{C_8H_{18}(l)} + n_{O_2} \left[(\bar{h}_{720}^\circ - \bar{h}_{537}^\circ) + \frac{MV^2}{2g_c} \right]_{O_2}$$

$$+ 3.76 n_{O_2} \left[(\bar{h}_{720}^\circ - \bar{h}_{537}^\circ) + \frac{MV^2}{2g_c} \right]_{N_2}$$

$$= -107,532 + 0.5(114.23)(43) + n_{O_2} \left[1303 + \frac{32.0 \times (300)^2}{2 \times 32.17 \times 778} \right]$$

$$+ 3.76 n_{O_2} \left[1278 + \frac{28.02 \times (300)^2}{2 \times 32.17 \times 778} \right]$$

$$= (-105,076 + 6355 n_{O_2}) \text{ Btu/lb mole fuel}$$

$$H_P + KE_P$$

$$= \sum_P n_e \left[\bar{h}_f^\circ + (\bar{h}^\circ - \bar{h}_{537}^\circ) + \frac{MV^2}{2g_c} \right]_e$$

$$= 8 \left[\bar{h}_f^\circ + (\bar{h}_{1980}^\circ - \bar{h}_{537}^\circ) + \frac{MV^2}{2g_c} \right]_{CO_2}$$

$$+ 9 \left[\bar{h}_f^\circ + (\bar{h}_{1980}^\circ - \bar{h}_{537}^\circ) + \frac{MV^2}{2g_c} \right]_{H_2O}$$

$$+ (n_{O_2} - 12.5) \left[(\bar{h}_{1980}^\circ - \bar{h}_{537}^\circ) + \frac{MV^2}{2g_c} \right]_{O_2}$$

$$+ 3.76 n_{O_2} \left[(\bar{h}_{1980}^\circ - \bar{h}_{537}^\circ) + \frac{MV^2}{2g_c} \right]_{N_2}$$

$$= 8 \left[-169,297 + 16,733 + \frac{44.01 \times (450)^2}{2 \times 32.17 \times 778} \right]$$

$$+ 9 \left[-104,036 + 12,978 + \frac{18.02 \times (450)^2}{2 \times 32.17 \times 778} \right]$$

$$+ (n_{O_2} - 12.5) \left[11,279 + \frac{32.0 \times (450)^2}{2 \times 32.17 \times 778} \right]$$

$$+ 3.76 n_{O_2} \left[10,651 + \frac{28.02 \times (450)^2}{2 \times 32.17 \times 778} \right]$$

$$= (-2,174,652 + 54,243 n_{O_2}) \text{ Btu/lb mole fuel}$$

Therefore,

$$-105{,}076 + 6355n_{O_2} = -2{,}174{,}652 + 54{,}243n_{O_2}$$

$$n_{O_2} = \frac{2{,}069{,}576}{47{,}888} = 43.2 \text{ moles } O_2/\text{mole fuel}$$

moles air/mole fuel $= 4.76(43.2) = 205.8$

$$FA_{\text{Ideal}} = \frac{114.23}{205.8 \times 28.95} = 0.0194$$

$$\eta_{\text{comb}} = \frac{0.0194}{0.0211} = 0.92 = 92\%$$

Example 12.20

In a certain steam power plant 715,000 lbm of water per hour enter the boiler at a pressure of 1850 lbf/in.^{2} and a temperature of 415 F. Steam leaves the boiler at 1320 lbf/in.^{2}, 925 F. The power output of the turbine is 81,000 kw. Coal is used at the rate of 59,000 lbm/hr, and has a higher heating value of 14,310 Btu/lbm. Determine the efficiency of steam generator and over-all thermal efficiency of the plant.

In power plants the efficiency of both the boiler and the over-all efficiency of the plant are based on the higher heating value of the fuel. The efficiency of the boiler is defined by Eq. 12.16 as

$$\eta_{\text{steam generator}} = \frac{\text{heat transferred to } H_2O/\text{lbm fuel}}{\text{higher heating value}}$$

Therefore

$$\eta_{\text{steam generator}} = \frac{715{,}000}{59{,}000} \times \frac{(1448.0 - 302.8)}{14{,}310} = 89.4\%$$

The thermal efficiency is defined by Eq. 12.17.

$$\eta_{\text{th}} = \frac{w}{\text{heating value}} = \frac{81{,}000 \times 3412}{59{,}000 \times 14{,}310} = 32.7\%$$

PROBLEMS

12.1 Propane is burned with air and an Orsat analysis of the products of combustion is as follows:

CO_2	8.2%
CO	1.3
O_2	7.0
N_2	83.5

Determine the percent of theoretical air used for this combustion process.

12.2 A hydrocarbon fuel is burned with air and the following Orsat analysis is obtained from the products of combustion.

CO_2	10.5%
O_2	5.3
N_2	84.2

Determine the composition of the fuel on a mass basis and the per cent of theoretical air utilized in the combustion process.

12.3 Natural gas B in Table 12.2 is burned with 30% excess air.
(a) What is the dew point of the products if the total pressure is 1 atm?
(b) How many moles of water will be condensed per mole of fuel if the products are cooled to 100 F while the pressure remains at 1 atm?

12.4 Octane is burned with the theoretical air in a constant pressure process ($P = 14.7$ lbf/in.²) and the products are cooled to 80 F.
(a) How many lbm of water are condensed per lbm of fuel?
(b) Suppose the air used for combustion has a relative humidity of 90% and is at a temperature of 80 F and 14.7 lbf/in.² pressure. How many lbm of water will be condensed per lbm of fuel when the products are cooled to 80 F?

12.5 A natural gas consisting of 90% methane and 10% ethane (on a volume basis) is burned with 150% theoretical air in a steady-state, steady-flow process. Heat is transferred from the products of combustion until the temperature reaches 620 F. The fuel enters the combustion chamber at 77 F and the air at 260 F.
Determine the heat transfer per mole of fuel.

12.6 An internal combustion engine burns liquid octane (C_8H_{18}) and uses 120% theoretical air. The air and fuel enter at 77 F, the products leave the engine exhaust ports at 1160 F. In the engine 80% of the carbon burns to CO_2 and the remainder burns to CO. The heat transfer from this engine is just equal to the work done by the engine. Determine:
(a) Power output of the engine if the engine burns 20 lbm fuel/hr
(b) The Orsat analysis and the dew point of the products of combustion.

12.7 Liquid ethanol (C_2H_5OH) is burned with 150% theoretical oxygen in a steady-state, steady-flow process. The reactants enter the combustion chamber at 77 F, and the products are cooled and leave at 150 F, 1 atm pressure. Calculate the heat transfer per mole of ethanol. The enthalpy of formation of $C_2H_5OH(l)$ is $-119{,}441$ Btu/mole.

12.8 Gaseous propane at 77 F is mixed with air at 300 F and burned; 300% theoretical air is used. What is the adiabatic flame temperature?

12.9 Gaseous propane at 77 F is mixed with air at 300 F and burned. What percentage of theoretical air must be used if the temperature of the products is to be 1700 F? Assume an adiabatic process and complete combustion.

12.10 Repeat Problem 12.9 assuming a heat transfer to the surroundings of 100,000 Btu/mole fuel and that 5% of the carbon in the fuel burns to form CO and 95% burns to form CO_2.

12.11 A stoichiometric mixture of CO and air, initially at 77 F, reacts in a steady-state, steady-flow process. What is the adiabatic flame temperature? Assume complete combustion.

12.12 A bomb is charged with 1 mole of CO and 1 mole of O_2. The total pressure is 1 atm and the temperature is 537 R before combustion. Combustion then occurs and the products are cooled to 2520 R. Assume complete combustion. Determine:

(a) The final pressure. (Note that the number of moles changes during combustion.)

(b) The heat transfer.

12.13 Consider the combustion chamber of a gas turbine. Liquid octane enters at 77 F and the air enters at 260 F. Of the carbon in the fuel 95% burns to CO_2 and 5% burns to CO. What amount of excess air will be required if the temperature of the products is to be 1520 F?

12.14 The natural gas A from Table 12.2 is burned with 150% theoretical air. Calculate the adiabatic flame temperature for complete combustion, if the temperature of the reactants is 77 F.

12.15 A thermoelectric generator such as shown in Fig. 1.11 converts heat directly to electrical energy without moving parts. Such a device has been proposed for use in a portable power supply. For the purpose of thermodynamic analysis, the power supply unit may be represented as shown in Fig. 12.8.

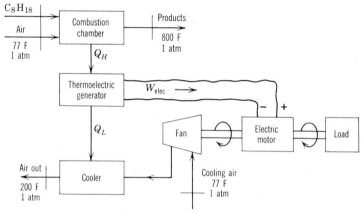

Fig. 12.8   Sketch for Problem 12.15.

Other data are as follows:

$$\eta_{generator} = \frac{W_{elec}}{Q_H} = 0.15$$

$$\eta_{elec.\ motor} = 0.95$$

$$\text{Electric motor output} = 2\ hp$$

$$\text{Fan requirement} = 0.1\ hp$$

Orsat analysis of combustion products

CO_2	9.0%
CO	1.0
O_2	7.0
N_2	83.0

(a) Write the combustion equation per mole of octane, and determine the per cent theoretical air.

(b) Calculate the octane flow rate, lbm/hr.

(c) Calculate the volume flow rate of cooling air required (inlet conditions), ft³/min.

12.16 Consider the analysis of a rocket which uses $C_8H_{18}(l)$ and liquid oxygen for propellants. 100% excess oxygen is used. In a static firing the octane enters the rocket at 14.7 lbf/in.² and 77 F and the liquid oxygen at 14.7 lbf/in.² and its normal boiling point of 162 R.

If complete combustion is achieved in this static firing, and the products leave at 5000 R, what is the velocity of the products of combustion?

12.17 Sulfur at 77 F is burned with 50% excess air, the air being at a temperature of 300 F. Assuming all the sulfur is burned to SO_2, calculate the adiabatic flame temperature. The enthalpy of formation of SO_2 is $-127,700$ Btu/lb mole. The constant-pressure specific heat of SO_2 is given by the relation

$$\bar{C}_p = 7.70 + 0.0029T - 0.26 \times 10^{-6}T^2$$

where $\bar{C}_p$ = Btu/lb mole-R

$T = °R$

12.18 A mixture of 20% methane and 80% ethane on a mole basis is throttled from 150 F, 1500 lbf/in.² to 14.7 lbf/in.² and fed to a combustion chamber where it undergoes complete combustion with air, which enters at 260 F, 14.7 lbf/in.² The amount of air is such that the products of combustion leave at 1700 F, 14.7 lbf/in.² Assuming the combustion process to be adiabatic and that all components behave as ideal gases except the fuel, which behaves as an ideal solution, determine

(1) The per cent theoretical air required
(2) The dew point temperature of the products.

12.19 Consider the cylinder of an internal combustion engine. The contents of the cylinder at top dead center (after compression) and at bottom dead center (after expansion) are as follows:

Constituent	Number of lb moles at T.D.C.	Number of lb moles at B.D.C.
Fuel (C_8H_{18})	0.728×10^{-6}	0
O_2	0.838×10^{-5}	0
N_2	0.326×10^{-5}	0.326×10^{-4}
CO_2	0.166×10^{-6}	0.500×10^{-5}
H_2O	0.210×10^{-6}	0.608×10^{-5}
CO	0.342×10^{-7}	0.102×10^{-5}
H_2	0.161×10^{-7}	0.483×10^{-6}

The specific heat of C_8H_{18} is given by the following relation $(T = R)$

$$\bar{C}_p = a + bT + cT^2 + dT^3$$
$$a = -0.141264 \times 10^1$$
$$b = 0.10221$$
$$c = -0.308597 \times 10^{-4}$$
$$d = 0.361327 \times 10^{-8}$$

At T.D.C. the pressure is 16.1 atm and the temperature is 1220 R. At bottom dead center the pressure is 4.42 atm and the temperature is 2560 R. From a pressure-volume diagram it is found that the work of expansion during the process is 0.705 Btu.

Determine the heat transfer during this process.

12.20 Determine the enthalpy of combustion at 77 F and 1 atm pressure of natural gas B in Table 12.2.

12.21 (a) Determine the enthalpy of formation of liquid benzene at 77 F.
(b) Benzene (l) at 77 F is burned with air at 440 F in a steady-flow process. The products of combustion are cooled to 2060 F and have the following Orsat analysis:

	% by volume
CO_2	10.7
CO	3.6
O_2	5.3
N_2	80.4

Calculate the heat transfer per mole of fuel during the combustion process.

12.22 From data given for the enthalpy of combustion at 77 F of gaseous octane (C_8H_{18}) with vapor H_2O in the products, calculate the enthalpy of combustion of liquid octane at 77 F with liquid H_2O in the products. The enthalpy of vaporization of octane is 156 Btu/lbm.

12.23 The boron hydrides have been considered as a "superfuel." Determine the enthalpy of combustion of pentaborane, B_5H_9 (g). The oxide is B_2O_3 which is a solid at room temperature. The enthalpies of formation at 77 F are as follows:

B_5H_9 (g)	27,000 Btu/lb mole
B_2O_3 (s)	−544,000 Btu/lb mole

Determine the enthalpy of combustion per lbm of fuel. How does this compare with a hydrocarbon fuel?

12.24 Hydrogen peroxide is sometimes used as the oxidizer in special power plants such as torpedoes and rockets. Determine the enthalpy of combustion at 77 F per lbm of reactants for the following combustion process:

$$4H_2O_2 \text{ (l)} + CH_4 \rightarrow 6H_2O + CO_2$$

The enthalpy of formation H_2O_2 (l) is −80,700 Btu/lb mole.

12.25 Nitric acid is sometimes used as the oxidizer in liquid-fuel rockets. As an initial approach to the problem consider the following reactions involving the combustion of C_8H_{18} (l):

$$10HNO_3 + C_8H_{18} \text{ (l)} \rightarrow 8CO_2 + 14H_2O \text{ (g)} + 5N_2$$
$$C_8H_{18} \text{ (l)} + 12.5O_2 \rightarrow 8CO_2 + 9H_2O \text{ (g)}$$

Determine the enthalpy of combustion for these two reactions per lbm of *reactants*. The enthalpy of formation of HNO_3 is −74,530 Btu/lb mole.

12.26 Calculate the internal energy of combustion of gaseous octane with liquid H_2O in the products.

12.27 A certain fuel consisting of a mixture of various compounds has a chemical analysis of 86% carbon, 13% hydrogen, and 1% nitrogen, on a mass basis, and has a higher heating value of 19,200 Btu/lbm. This fuel, at 77 F, is burned with 180% theoretical air at 77 F in a steady-state, steady-flow process. Determine the adiabatic flame temperature.

12.28 The enthalpy of formation of magnesium oxide, MgO (s) is -143.84 k cal/gm mole at 25 C. The melting point of magnesium oxide is approximately 3000 K, and the increase in enthalpy between 298 K and 3000 K is 30.7 k cal/gm mole. The enthalpy of sublimation at 3000 K is estimated at 100 k cal/gm mole, and the specific heat of magnesium-oxide vapor above 3000 K is estimated at 8.9 cal/gm mole-K.

(*a*) Determine the enthalpy of combustion per lbm of magnesium.

(*b*) Estimate the adiabatic flame temperature when magnesium is burned with theoretical oxygen.

12.29 One mole of carbon at 1 atm, 77 F and 1 mole of O_2 at 1 atm, 400 F react to form CO_2 in a steady-state, steady-flow process. The CO_2 leaves at 2000 F, 1 atm pressure. Determine:

(*a*) The heat transfer per mole of fuel.

(*b*) The change of entropy per mole of fuel.

(*c*) The total change of entropy (control volume plus surroundings) if the heat is transferred to the surroundings.

12.30 Consider the combustion of gaseous propane at 14.7 lbf/in.², 77 F, with theoretical air at 14.7 lbf/in.², 77 F in a steady-state, steady-flow process. Assume that combustion is complete and that the products leave at 77 F. Determine the decrease in Gibbs function for the two following cases:

(*a*) The reactants and products are both separated into their various constituents, and each constituent is at 1 atm pressure, 77 F. This is shown schematically in Fig. 12.9.

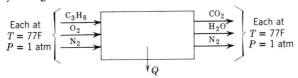

Fig. 12.9   Sketch for Problem 12.30*a*.

(*b*) The reactants and products each consist of a mixture at a total pressure of 1 atm and a temperature of 77 F. This is shown schematically in Fig. 12.10.

Fig. 12.10   Sketch for Problem 12.30*b*.

12.31 Determine the increase of entropy that takes place during the combustion process of Problem 12.11. What is the irreversibility of this process per mole of fuel? The total pressure during this process is 20 lbf/in.²

12.32 Methyl alcohol (CH_3OH) is burned with 140% theoretical air at 20 lbf/in.², after which the products of combustion are passed through a heat exchanger and cooled to 140 F. Considering the process to be steady-flow, calculate the absolute entropy of the products leaving the heat exchanger per mole of alcohol burned.

12.33 A mixture of butane and 100% theoretical air enters a combustor at 537 R, 1 atm, and products of combustion leave at 1520 R, 1 atm. Assuming complete combustion, calculate the heat transfer from the combustor and the irreversibility for the process, both per mole of butane entering.

12.34 The following data are taken from the test of a gas turbine on a test stand.

Fuel—C_4H_{10} (g) at 77 F and 1 atm
Air—300% theoretical air at 77 F and 1 atm
Velocity of inlet air = 200 ft/sec
Velocity of products at exit = 2200 ft/sec
Temperature and pressure of products = 1160 F and 1 atm

Assuming complete combustion, determine
(a) The net heat transfer per mole of fuel.
(b) The net increase of entropy per mole of fuel.

12.35 A small air-cooled gasoline engine is tested, and the output is found to be 1.34 hp. The temperature of the products is measured and found to be 730 F. The products are analyzed with an Orsat, with the following results:

CO_2	11.4%
O_2	1.6
CO	2.9
N_2	84.1

The fuel used may be considered to be C_8H_{18}, and the air and fuel enter the engine at 77 F. The rate at which fuel is used is 1.20 lbm/hr.
(a) Determine the rate of heat transfer from the engine.
(b) What is the efficiency of the engine?

12.36 The insulated combustion chamber of a gas turbine is designed to burn butane (C_4H_{10}) with air at a pressure of 5.0 atmospheres. The temperature of the gases leaving the combustor is limited by metallurgical considerations to 1340 F. The gaseous fuel enters at 77 F and 5.0 atm. The air for combustion enters at 440 F and 5.0 atm.
(a) Calculate the per cent theoretical air required to reach the desired outlet temperature.
(b) Calculate the absolute entropy of the products, per pound mole of the fuel.

12.37 Consider the process described in Problem 12.18.
(a) Calculate the absolute entropy of the fuel mixture before it is throttled into the combustion chamber.
(b) Calculate the irreversibility for the overall process.

12.38 Ethylene at 77 F, 1000 lbf/in.^{2} (Point 1) is fed to a combustion chamber after being throttled to 20 lbf/in.^{2} The flow rate at point 1 is 0.1 ft^3/min. 200% theoretical air enters the chamber at 77 F, 20 lbf/in.^{2}, and the products of combustion exit at 2520 R, 20 lbf/in.^{2}.
Calculate:
(a) The enthalpy and entropy of the C_2H_4 at point 1.
(b) Rate of heat transfer from the combustion chamber, Btu/min.
(c) Rate of irreversibility of the overall process, Btu/min.

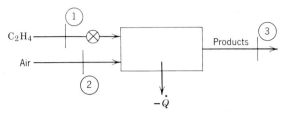

Fig. 12.11   Sketch for Problem 12.38.

12.39 A fuel cell is a device which converts a portion of the energy of a chemical reaction directly into electrical energy. The overall reaction taking place may be described as a controlled-rate combustion process. Consider the fuel cell shown in Fig. 12.12

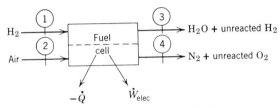

Fig. 12.12   Sketch for Problem 12.39.

The cell temperature is maintained at 540 F by rejecting heat to the surroundings. The following data have been taken:

$$\dot{W}_{elec.} = 3 \text{ kilowatts}$$

$T_1 = 77$ F	$P_1 = 100$ lbf/in.²	$\dot{V}_1 = 0.20$ ft³/min
$T_2 = 77$ F	$P_2 = 100$ lbf/in.²	$\dot{V}_2 = 0.45$ ft³/min
$T_3 = 540$ F	$P_3 = 90$ lbf/in.²	
$T_4 = 540$ F	$P_4 = 90$ lbf/in.²	$(y_{O_2})_4 = 0.05$

(a) Write the overall reaction equation, on a basis of moles/hr for each substance.

(b) Calculate the heat transfer from the cell, Btu/hr.

(c) Calculate the entropy flow at point 4, Btu/R-hr.

12.40 Consider one cylinder of a spark-ignition internal-combustion engine. Before the compression stroke the cylinder is filled with a mixture of air and ethane. Assume that 150% theoretical air has been used, and that the pressure is 1 atm and the temperature 77 F before compression. The compression ratio of the engine is 9 to 1.

(a) Determine the pressure and temperature after compression assuming a reversible adiabatic compression. Assume that the ethane behaves as an ideal gas.

(b) Assume further that complete combustion is achieved while the piston remains at top dead center (i.e., after the reversible adiabatic compression), and that the combustion process is adiabatic. Determine the temperature and pressure after combustion, and the increase in entropy during the combustion process.

(c) What is the irreversibility for this process?

13 Introduction to Phase and Chemical Equilibrium

In most of our considerations up to this point we have assumed that we are dealing either with systems that are in equilibrium or with those in which the deviation from equilibrium is infinitesimal, as in a quasi-equilibrium or reversible process. For irreversible processes we made no attempt to describe the state of the system during the process but dealt only with the initial and final states of the system, at which time we considered the system to be in equilibrium.

In this chapter we shall examine the criteria for equilibrium and from them derive certain relations which will enable us, under certain conditions, to determine the properties of a system when it is in equilibrium. The specific systems we shall consider are those involving equilibrium between phases and those involving chemical equilibrium in a single phase (homogeneous equilibrium) as well as certain related topics.

13.1 Requirements for Equilibrium

As a general requirement for equilibrium we postulate that a system is in equilibrium when there is no possibility that it can do any work when it is isolated from its surroundings. In applying this criterion to a system it is helpful to divide the system into two or more subsystems, and consider the possibility of doing work by any conceivable interaction between these two subsystems. For example, in Fig. 13.1 a system has been divided into two systems and an engine, of any conceivable variety, placed between these subsystems. A system may be so defined as to include the immediate surroundings. In this case we can let the immediate surroundings be a subsystem and thus consider the general case of the equilibrium between a system and its surroundings.

The first requirement for equilibrium is that the two subsystems have the same temperature, for otherwise we could operate a heat engine between the two systems and do work. Thus we conclude that one

Fig. 13.1   Two subsystems that communicate through an engine.

requirement for equilibrium is that a system must be at a uniform temperature to be in equilibrium.   It is also evident that there must be no unbalanced mechanical forces between the two systems, or else one could operate a turbine or piston engine between the two systems and do work.

However, we would like to establish general criteria for equilibrium which would apply to all simple compressible systems, including those that undergo chemical reactions.   We will find that the Gibbs function is a particularly significant property in defining the criteria for equilibrium.

Let us first consider a qualitative example to illustrate this point. Consider a natural gas well that is one mile deep, and let us assume that the temperature of the gas is constant throughout the gas well.   Suppose we have analyzed the composition of the gas at the top of the well, and we would like to know the composition of the gas at the bottom of the well. Further, let us assume that equilibrium conditions prevail in the well.   If this is true we would expect that an engine such as shown in Fig. 13.2 (which operates on the basis of the pressure and composition change with elevation and does not involve combustion) would not be capable of doing any work.

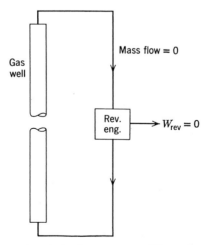

Fig. 13.2   Illustration showing the relation between reversible work and the criteria for equilibrium.

If we consider a steady-state, steady-flow process for a control volume around this engine, we could apply Eq. 8.28,

$$W_{\text{rev}} = m_i \left(g_i + \frac{V_i^2}{2g_c} + Z_i \frac{g}{g_c} \right) - m_e \left(g_e + \frac{V_e^2}{2g_c} + Z_e \frac{g}{g_c} \right)$$

However,

$$W_{\text{rev}} = 0, \qquad m_i = m_e, \quad \text{and} \quad \frac{V_i^2}{2g_c} = \frac{V_e^2}{2g_c}$$

Then we can write,

$$g_i + Z_i \frac{g}{g_c} = g_e + Z_e \frac{g}{g_c}$$

and the requirement for equilibrium in the well between two levels that are a distance dZ apart would be

$$dg_T + g/g_c \, dZ_T = 0$$

In contrast to a deep gas well, most of the systems that we consider are of such size that ΔZ is negligibly small, and therefore we consider the pressure in the system to be uniform.

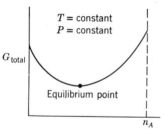

This leads to the general statement of equilibrium that applies to simple compressible systems that may undergo a change in chemical composition, namely, that at equilibrium

$$dG_{T,P} = 0 \qquad (13.1)$$

Fig. 13.3 Illustration of the requirement for chemical equilibrium.

In the case of a chemical reaction, it is helpful to think of the equilibrium state as the state in which the Gibbs function is a minimum. For example, consider a system consisting initially of n_A moles of substance A and n_B moles of substance B, which react in accordance with the relation

$$\nu_A A + \nu_B B \rightleftharpoons \nu_C C + \nu_D D$$

Let the reaction take place at constant pressure and temperature. If we plot G for this system as a function of n_A, the number of moles of A present, we would have a curve as shown in Fig. 13.3. At the minimum point on the curve, $dG_{T,P} = 0$, and this will be the equilibrium composition for this system at the given temperature and pressure. The subject of chemical equilibrium will be developed further in Section 13.6.

13.2   Equilibrium between Two Phases of a Pure Substance

As another example of this requirement for equilibrium, let us consider the equilibrium between two phases of a pure substance. Consider a system consisting of two phases of a pure substance at equilibrium. We know that under these conditions the two phases are at the same pressure and temperature. Consider the change of state associated with a transfer of dn moles from phase 1 to phase 2 while the temperature and pressure remain constant. That is,

$$dn^1 = -dn^2$$

The Gibbs function of this system is given by

$$G = f(T, P, n^1, n^2)$$

where n^1 and n^2 designate the number of moles in each phase. Therefore,

$$dG = \left(\frac{\partial G}{\partial T}\right)_{P,n^1,n^2} dT + \left(\frac{\partial G}{\partial P}\right)_{T,n^1,n^2} dP$$
$$+ \left(\frac{\partial G}{\partial n^1}\right)_{T,P,n^2} dn^1 + \left(\frac{\partial G}{\partial n^2}\right)_{T,P,n^1} dn^2$$

By definition,

$$\left(\frac{\partial G}{\partial n^1}\right)_{T,P,n^2} = \bar{g}^1; \qquad \left(\frac{\partial G}{\partial n^2}\right)_{T,P,n^1} = \bar{g}^2$$

Therefore, at constant temperature and pressure,

$$dG = \bar{g}^1 \, dn^1 + \bar{g}^2 \, dn^2 = dn^1(\bar{g}^1 - \bar{g}^2)$$

Now at equilibrium (Eq. 13.1)

$$dG_{T,P} = 0$$

Therefore, at equilibrium, we have

$$\bar{g}^1 = \bar{g}^2 \tag{13.2}$$

That is, under equilibrium conditions, the Gibbs function of each phase of a pure substance is equal. Let us check this by determining the Gibbs function of saturated liquid (water) and saturated vapor (steam) at 14.7 lbf/in.². From the steam tables:
For the liquid:

$$g_f = h_f - Ts_f = 180.07 - 671.7 \times 0.3120 = -29.5 \text{ Btu/lbm}$$

For the vapor:

$$g_g = h_g - Ts_g = 1150.4 - 671.7 \times 1.7566 = -29.5 \text{ Btu/lbm}$$

Equation 13.2 can also be derived by applying the relation

$$T \, ds = dh - v \, dP$$

to the change of phase that takes place at constant pressure and temperature. For this process this relation can be integrated as follows:

$$\int_f^g T \, ds = \int_f^g dh$$

$$T(s_g - s_f) = (h_g - h_f)$$

$$h_f - Ts_f = h_g - Ts_g$$

$$g_f = g_g$$

The Clapeyron equation, which was derived in Section 10.3 can be derived by an alternate method by considering the fact that the Gibbs functions of two phases in equilibrium are equal. In Chapter 10 we considered the relation (Eq. 10.9) for a simple compressible substance,

$$dg = v \, dP - s \, dT$$

Consider a system that consists of a saturated liquid and a saturated vapor in equilibrium, and let this system undergo a change of pressure dP. The corresponding change in temperature, as determined from the vapor-pressure curve, is dT. Both phases will undergo the change in Gibbs function, dg, but since the phases always have the same value of the Gibbs function when they are in equilibrium, it follows that

$$dg_f = dg_g$$

But, from Eq. 10.9,

$$dg = v \, dP - s \, dT$$

it follows that

$$dg_f = v_f \, dP - s_f \, dT$$
$$dg_g = v_g \, dP - s_g \, dT$$

Since

$$dg_f = dg_g$$

it follows that

$$v_f \, dP - s_f \, dT = v_g \, dP - s_g \, dT$$
$$dP(v_g - v_f) = dT(s_g - s_f)$$

$$\frac{dP}{dT} = \frac{s_{fg}}{v_{fg}} = \frac{h_{fg}}{Tv_{fg}}$$

(13.3)

In summary, when different phases of a pure substance are in equilibrium, each phase has the same value of the Gibbs function per unit mass. This fact is relevant to different solid phases of a pure substance and is important in metallurgical applications of thermodynamics. Example 13.1 illustrates this principle.

Example 13.1

What pressure is required to make diamonds from graphite at a temperature of 25 C? The following data are given for a temperature of 25 C and a pressure of 1 atm.

	Graphite	Diamond
$\bar{g}$	0	1233 Btu/lb mole-R
v	0.00712 ft³/lbm	0.00456 ft³/lbm
β_T	3.0 × 10⁻⁶ atm⁻¹	0.16 × 10⁻⁶ atm⁻¹

The basic principle in the solution is that graphite and diamond can exist in equilibrium when they have the same value of the Gibbs function. At 1 atm pressure the Gibbs function of the diamond is greater than that of the graphite. However, the rate of increase in Gibbs function with pressure is greater for the graphite than the diamond, and therefore, at some pressure they can exist in equilibrium, and our problem is to find this pressure.

We have already considered the relation

$$dg = v \, dP - s \, dT$$

Since we are considering a process that takes place at constant temperature this reduces to

$$dg_T = v \, dP_T \tag{a}$$

Now at any pressure P and the given temperature the specific volume can be found from the following relation, which utilizes the isothermal compressibility factor.

$$v = v° + \int_{P=1}^{P} \left(\frac{\partial v}{\partial P}\right)_T dP = v° + \int_{P=1}^{P} \frac{v}{v}\left(\frac{\partial v}{\partial P}\right)_T dP$$

$$= v° - \int_{P=1}^{P} v\beta_T \, dP \tag{b}$$

The superscript ° will be used in this example to indicate the properties at a pressure of 1 atmosphere and a temperature of 25 C.

The specific volume changes only slightly with pressure, so that $v \approx v°$. Also, we assume that β_T is constant and that we are considering a pressure of many atmospheres. With these assumptions this equation can be integrated to give

$$v = v° - v°\beta_T P = v°(1 - \beta_T P) \tag{c}$$

We can now substitute this into Eq. a to give the relation

$$dg_T = [v°(1 - \beta_T P)]\, dP_T$$

$$g - g° = v°(P - P°) - v°\beta_T \frac{(P^2 - P^{°2})}{2} \tag{d}$$

If we assume that $P° \ll P$ this reduces to

$$g - g° = v° \left[P - \frac{\beta_T P^2}{2} \right] \tag{e}$$

For the graphite, $g° = 0$ and we can write

$$g_G = v_G° \left[P - (\beta_T)_G \frac{P^2}{2} \right]$$

For the diamond, $g°$ has a definite value and we have

$$g_D = g_D° + v_D° \left[P - (\beta_T)_D \frac{P^2}{2} \right]$$

But, at equilibrium the Gibbs function of the graphite and diamond are equal.

$$g_G = g_D$$

Therefore,

$$v_G° \left[P - (\beta_T)_G \frac{P^2}{2} \right] = g_D° + v_D° \left[P - (\beta_T)_D \frac{P^2}{2} \right]$$

$$(v_G° - v_D°)P - [v_G°(\beta_T)_G - v_D°(\beta_T)_D] \frac{P^2}{2} = g_D°$$

$$(0.00712 - 0.00456)P$$

$$- (0.00712 \times 3.0 \times 10^{-6} - 0.00456 \times 0.16 \times 10^{-6}) \frac{P^2}{2}$$

$$= \frac{1233}{12} \times \frac{778}{14.7 \times 144}$$

Solving this for P we find

$$P = 15{,}500 \text{ atm}$$

That is, at 15,500 atm, 25 C, graphite and diamond can exist in equilibrium, and the possibility exists for conversion from graphite to diamonds.

The preceding example could also have been evaluated in terms of the fugacities instead of the Gibbs functions for the two forms of carbon. Similarly, the equilibrium requirement for liquid and vapor water discussed earlier could be expressed in terms of the fugacities of the two phases. That is,

$$f^L = f^V = f^{\text{sat}}$$

where f^{sat} is the fugacity of the substance determined at the given temperature and its saturation pressure P^{sat}.

The fugacity of a pure compressed liquid or solid phase at pressures moderately greater than the saturation pressure can be calculated with considerable accuracy as follows. For a pure substance at constant temperature,

$$dg_T = RT(d \ln f)_T = v \, dP_T$$

Integrating at constant temperature between the saturation state and the pressure P, we have

$$\int_{f_A^{\text{sat}}}^{f_A} RT \, (d \ln f_A)_T = \int_{P_A^{\text{sat}}}^{P} v_A \, dP_T$$

$$RT \ln \frac{f_A}{f_A^{\text{sat}}} = \int_{P_A^{\text{sat}}}^{P} v_A \, dP_T$$

If we assume that v_A is a constant, which often holds with considerable accuracy for liquids and solids, we have

$$RT \ln \frac{f_A}{f_A^{\text{sat}}} \approx v_A(P - P^{\text{sat}}) \qquad (13.4)$$

Equation 13.4 is used to determine the fugacity coefficients of compressed liquid presented in the generalized chart given in Appendix Fig. A.4.

Since v is small for the liquid and solid phases, the quantity $v_A(P - P^{\text{sat}})$ is small for moderate changes of pressure. Therefore, for liquids and solids at moderate pressures we conclude that

$$f_A^{L} \approx f_A^{\text{sat liq}}; \qquad f_A^{S} \approx f_A^{\text{sat sol}} \qquad (13.5)$$

13.3 Equilibrium of a Multicomponent, Multiphase System

As an introduction to more complicated systems, let us consider a system consisting of two components and two phases. In order to be more specific let us consider a system that consists of components A and B that exist in equilibrium in two phases, which we designate with the superscripts 1 and 2.

To show the general characteristics of such a system, consider a mixture of oxygen and nitrogen at a pressure of one atmosphere and in the range of temperature where both the liquid and vapor phases are present.

Figure 13.4 shows the composition of the liquid and vapor phases which are in equilibrium as a function of temperature at a pressure of 1 atm. The upper line, marked "vapor line" gives the composition of the vapor phase, and the lower line gives the composition of the liquid phase.

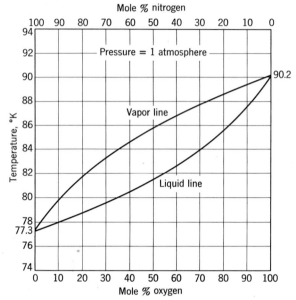

Fig. 13.4   Equilibrium diagram for liquid-vapor phases of the nitrogen-oxygen system at a pressure of 1 atm.

If we have pure nitrogen, the boiling point is 77.3 K.   If we have pure oxygen, the boiling point is 90.2 K.   If we have a mixture of nitrogen and oxygen with both phases present at a temperature of 84 K, the vapor will have a composition of 64 per cent N_2 and 36 per cent O_2.   The liquid will have a composition of 30 per cent N_2 and 70 per cent O_2.

Consider a mixture consisting of 21 per cent oxygen and 79 per cent nitrogen (approximately the composition of air) and at a pressure of one atmosphere and an initial temperature of 74 K.   At this state the mixture will be in the liquid phase.   Let this liquid be slowly heated while the pressure remains constant.   By referring to Fig. 13.4 we note that when the temperature reaches 78.8 K, the first bubble will form.   This vapor will have a composition of approximately 6 per cent O_2 and 94 per cent N_2.   As more heat is added the temperature increases and the mole fraction of oxygen in the liquid increases.   When the last drop of liquid remains, the vapor will have a composition of 21 per cent O_2 and 79 per cent N_2, the temperature will be 81.9 K, and the liquid composition will be 54 per cent O_2 and 46 per cent N_2.

The first question we ask about such a two-component, two-phase system is, "What is the requirement for equilibrium of this system?"   Let us apply our general requirement for equilibrium of a simple compressible system which can undergo a change of composition, namely, that at equilibrium

$$dG_{T,P} = 0$$

In a manner similar to that of Section 11.9, we can write the following relation for each phase of this system, where the superscripts 1 and 2 designate the two phases, and subscripts A and B refer to the two components.

$$G^1 = f(T, P, n_A{}^1, n_B{}^1)$$

$$dG^1 = \left(\frac{\partial G^1}{\partial T}\right)_{P,n_A{}^1,n_B{}^1} dT + \left(\frac{\partial G^1}{\partial P}\right)_{T,n_A{}^1,n_B{}^1} dP$$
$$+ \left(\frac{\partial G^1}{\partial n_A{}^1}\right)_{T,P,n_B{}^1} dn_A{}^1 + \left(\frac{\partial G^1}{\partial n_B{}^1}\right)_{T,P,n_A{}^1} dn_B{}^1$$

$$G^2 = f(T, P, n_A{}^2, n_B{}^2)$$

$$dG^2 = \left(\frac{\partial G^2}{\partial T}\right)_{P,n_A{}^2,n_B{}^2} dT + \left(\frac{\partial G^2}{\partial P}\right)_{T,n_A{}^2,n_B{}^2} dP$$
$$+ \left(\frac{\partial G^2}{\partial n_A{}^2}\right)_{T,P,n_B{}^2} dn_A{}^2 + \left(\frac{\partial G^2}{\partial n_B{}^2}\right)_{T,P,n_A{}^2} dn_B{}^2$$

We have noted previously, Eq. 11.32, that for a single phase mixture the partial molal Gibbs function is defined as

$$\bar{G}_i \equiv \left(\frac{\partial G}{\partial n_i}\right)_{T,P,\text{ all other } n\text{'s}}$$

In a similar way we can define the partial molal Gibbs function for each phase.

$$\bar{G}_i{}^1 \equiv \left(\frac{\partial G^1}{\partial n_i{}^1}\right)_{T,P,\text{ all other } n\text{'s}} \tag{13.6}$$

$$\bar{G}_i{}^2 \equiv \left(\frac{\partial G^2}{\partial n_i{}^2}\right)_{T,P,\text{ all other } n\text{'s}}$$

We also recall that for fixed composition

$$\left(\frac{\partial G}{\partial T}\right)_P = -S; \qquad \left(\frac{\partial G}{\partial P}\right)_T = V$$

Therefore, for the two-phase, two-component mixture under consideration we can write

$$dG^1 = V^1 dP - S^1 dT + \bar{G}_A{}^1 dn_A{}^1 + \bar{G}_B{}^1 dn_B{}^1$$
$$dG^2 = V^2 dP - S^2 dT + \bar{G}_A{}^2 dn_A{}^2 + \bar{G}_B{}^2 dn_B{}^2 \tag{13.7}$$

Let us consider this two-phase, two-component mixture that is in equilibrium as a system, and let each phase be considered as a subsystem. One possible change of state that might occur is for a very small amount of component A to be transferred from phase 1 to phase 2 while the moles of B in each phase and the temperature and pressure remain constant. This is shown schematically in Fig. 13.5.

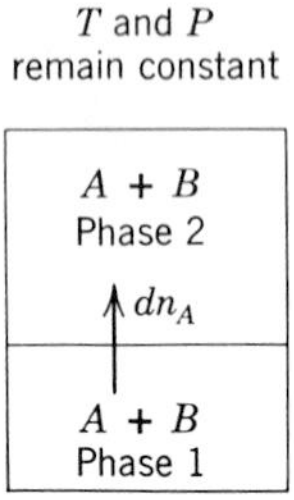

For this change of state

T and *P*
remain constant

$$dn_A{}^2 = -dn_A{}^1 \qquad (13.8)$$

Since this system is in equilibrium, $dG = 0$. Therefore,

$$dG = dG^1 + dG^2 = 0 \qquad (13.9)$$

Since T, P, $n_B{}^1$ and $n_B{}^2$ are all constant, it follows from Eqs. 13.7 and 13.9 that

Fig. 13.5   An equilibrium mixture involving two components and two phases.

$$\begin{aligned}
dG &= \bar{G}_A{}^1 \, dn_A{}^1 + \bar{G}_A{}^2 \, dn_A{}^2 \\
&= \bar{G}_A{}^1 \, dn_A{}^1 - \bar{G}_A{}^2 \, dn_A{}^1 = dn_A{}^1(\bar{G}_A{}^1 - \bar{G}_A{}^2) \\
&= 0
\end{aligned}$$

Therefore, at equilibrium

$$\bar{G}_A{}^1 = \bar{G}_A{}^2 \qquad (13.10)$$

Thus the requirement for equilibrium is that the partial molal Gibbs function of each component is the same in all phases. If the partial molal Gibbs function is not the same in all phases there will be a tendency for mass to pass from one phase to the other. It is this consideration that has led to the adoption of another name for the partial molal Gibbs function, namely, the chemical potential, which is designated μ. The chemical potential can be thought of as the potential tending to cause a change in chemical composition. When the chemical potential of a component is the same in both phases, there is no tendency for a net transfer of mass from one phase to the other.

This requirement for equilibrium is readily extended to multicomponent, multiphase systems, for the chemical potential of each component must be the same in all phases.

$$\mu_A{}^1 = \mu_A{}^2 = \mu_A{}^3 = \cdots \text{ for all phases}$$
$$\mu_B{}^1 = \mu_B{}^2 = \mu_B{}^3 = \cdots \text{ for all phases}$$
$$— \quad — \quad —$$
$$— \quad — \quad — \qquad (13.11)$$
$$— \quad — \quad —$$

for all components

Let us consider some of the consequences of this requirement for equilibrium by considering a two-phase, two-component mixture.

The fugacity of a component in a mixture has been defined as, Eq. 11.48,

$$(d\bar{G}_A)_T = \bar{R}T\, d(\ln \bar{f}_A)_T$$

This expression can be written for each component in each phase.

$$\begin{aligned}
(d\bar{G}_A{}^1)_T &= \bar{R}T\, d(\ln \bar{f}_A{}^1)_T \\
(d\bar{G}_A{}^2)_T &= \bar{R}T\, d(\ln \bar{f}_A{}^2)_T \\
(d\bar{G}_B{}^1)_T &= \bar{R}T\, d(\ln \bar{f}_B{}^1)_T \\
(d\bar{G}_B{}^2)_T &= \bar{R}T\, d(\ln \bar{f}_B{}^2)_T
\end{aligned} \qquad (13.12)$$

It follows therefore, that for equilibrium at constant temperature and pressure the fugacity of each component is the same for each phase. This gives us the clue that we can use this criteria for equilibrium to determine actual equilibrium compositions. But the question remains as to how we determine the fugacity.

The activity and activity coefficient, which were defined and discussed in Section 11.11, are the most general concepts and are utilized for the general case of solutions and phase equilibria.

For many situations at low to moderate pressure, we might reasonably assume that each phase behaves as an ideal solution. In this case we find that certain simplifications in the thermodynamic analysis result, and are a very convenient approach to the solution of such problems.

We might further assume, in those cases where a gaseous phase is present, that the gaseous phase consists of a mixture of ideal gases. We find that still further simplifications in the thermodynamic analysis result, making this an attractive approach when the assumptions are justified.

Let us, in order, examine the consequences of each of these assumptions.

From the definition of activity, Eq. 11.80, it follows that since for a multicomponent, multiphase mixture the fugacities of each component are the same in all phases, the activity of each component depends upon the selection of the standard state and the fugacities of the pure components in that state. The activity coefficient as defined by Eq. 11.84 then similarly depends upon the standard states. In Chapter 11 it was stated that for phase equilibrium calculations standard states are often selected as the pure substance in that phase at the pressure and temperature of the mixture. For such a choice, the activity coefficient of each component is unity for an ideal solution, and departures from unity indicate non-ideality of the system. The Gibbs-Duhem equation as discussed in Chapter 11 is also very useful in correlating and evaluating phase data, especially to test consistency of experimental data. A further discussion of non-ideal systems and behavior is left to a more advanced treatment of the subject.

If we assume that both phases of the mixture are an ideal solution, we can write the Lewis-Randall Rule for each component in each phase.

$$\bar{f}_A^1 = y_A^1 f_A^1; \qquad \bar{f}_B^1 = y_B^1 f_B^1$$

$$\bar{f}_A^2 = y_A^2 f_A^2; \qquad \bar{f}_B^2 = y_B^2 f_B^2 \tag{13.13}$$

At equilibrium

$$\bar{f}_A^1 = \bar{f}_A^2; \qquad \bar{f}_B^1 = \bar{f}_B^2$$

Therefore,

$$y_A^1 f_A^1 = y_A^2 f_A^2; \qquad y_B^1 f_B^1 = y_B^2 f_B^2 \tag{13.14}$$

or

$$\frac{y_A^1}{y_A^2} = \frac{f_A^2}{f_A^1}; \qquad \frac{y_B^1}{y_B^2} = \frac{f_B^2}{f_B^1}$$

That is, for the case where both phases are an ideal solution, the mole fraction of component A in the two phases is inversely proportional to the fugacity of the pure component in these two phases at the pressure and temperature of the mixture. Thus, to evaluate the mole fraction of a given component in the two phases (as in the case of the nitrogen-oxygen mixture referred to earlier) we must be able to evaluate the fugacity of the pure component in the two phases at the pressure and temperature of the mixture. Obviously, one of these two values must correspond to a hypothetical state, since the pure substance at the pressure and temperature of the mixture would actually exist in one phase or the other.

In order to determine the fugacities for these hypothetical states, vapor-phase fugacities have been extrapolated into the liquid region and liquid-phase fugacities extrapolated into the vapor region in a manner so as to give reasonable generalized correlations from Eq. 13.14 with experimental phase equilibrium data. These extrapolated hypothetical values are presented in Fig. 13.6. Fugacities that do not correspond to hypothetical states are found in the conventional manner, using the generalized charts, Fig. A.4, for the vapor phase and also for the liquid phase.

If in addition to assuming ideal solution for both phases and also assuming that Eq. 13.5 applies to the liquid (or solid), we make a third assumption that the vapor phase consists of a mixture of ideal gases, we arrive at a very simple and convenient formula known as Raoult's rule.

If each component in the vapor phase behaves as an ideal gas at the pressure and temperature of the mixture, the fugacity is equal to the pressure, and we can write

$$f_A^V = P \tag{13.15}$$

where the superscript V indicates the vapor phase.

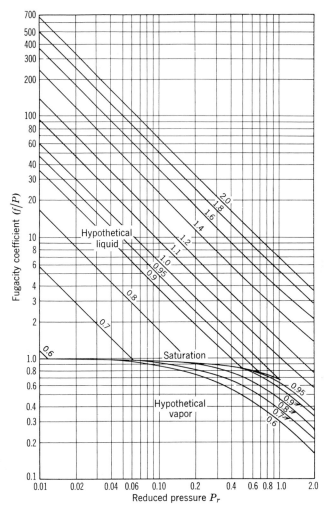

Fig. 13.6 Hypothetical liquid and vapor fugacities.

Further, with the assumption of ideal gas behavior we can write (re-calling that for a pure substance the fugacities of two phases in equilibrium are equal) for liquid-vapor equilibrium.

$$
\begin{aligned}
f_A^{\text{sat liq}} &= f_A^{\text{sat vap}} = P_A^{\text{sat}}; \\
f_B^{\text{sat liq}} &= f_B^{\text{sat vap}} = P_B^{\text{sat}}
\end{aligned}
\tag{13.16}
$$

Similarly, for solid-vapor equilibrium,

$$
\begin{aligned}
f_A^{\text{sat sol}} &= f_A^{\text{sat vap}} = P_A^{\text{sat}} \\
f_B^{\text{sat sol}} &= f_B^{\text{sat sol}} = P_B^{\text{sat}}
\end{aligned}
\tag{13.17}
$$

Let us now rewrite Eq. 13.14 for a mixture which involves an ideal solution of either solid or liquid as one phase and an ideal gas mixture as the other phase. Let us denote mole fractions in the solid or liquid phase as x and mole fractions in the vapor phase as y. Then for the liquid or solid phase we can write, from Eqs. 13.16 and 13.17,

$$x_A f_A^{L\,or\,S} = x_A P_A^{sat};$$
$$x_B f_B^{L\,or\,S} = x_B P_B^{sat}$$

$$(13.18)$$

Substituting Eqs. 13.15 and 13.18 into Eq. 13.14 we have Raoult's rule.

$$x_A P_A^{sat} = y_A P = P_A$$
$$x_B P_B^{sat} = y_B P = P_B$$

$$(13.19)$$

Raoult's rule says, in effect, that the partial pressure of a given component in the vapor, P_i, is equal to the product of the mole fraction of this component in the liquid, x_i, and the saturation pressure of this component at the given temperature, P_i^{sat}. Thus, according to Raoult's rule, the partial pressure of a component in the vapor phase is directly proportional to the number of moles of that component in the liquid and also directly proportional to the vapor pressure of that component. If Raoult's rule held for a mixture of components A and B, the pressure-composition diagram shown in Fig. 13.7 could be drawn with straight lines as indicated.

Raoult's rule holds exactly for the solvent in a very dilute solution. As the mole fraction of the solute increases, the deviation from Raoult's rule

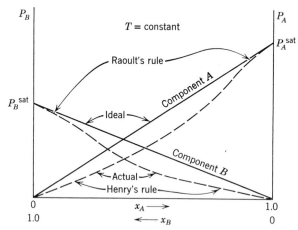

Fig. 13.7   Pressure-composition diagram showing Raoult's rule and Henry's rule.

will, in general, increase, though there is no way of predicting the magnitude of the deviation as a function of mole fraction.

Example 13.2

Air (assumed to be 21% O_2, 79%N_2) is cooled to 80 K, 1 atmosphere pressure. Calculate the composition of the liquid and vapor phases at this condition, assuming (a) Raoult's rule, and (b) Ideal solution in both phases, and compare the results with Fig. 13.4. At 80 K:

$$P_{N_2}^{sat} = 19.71 \text{ lbf/in.}^2, \qquad P_{O_2}^{sat} = 4.36 \text{ lbf/in.}^2$$

For convenience, let $N_2 = A$, and $O_2 = B$ in the calculations.
(a) Assuming Raoult's rule, from Eq. 13.19,

$$x_A P_A^{sat} = y_A P$$
$$x_B P_B^{sat} = y_B P$$

Therefore, at 80 K, 1 atm, pressure,

$$x_A(19.71) = y_A(14.7)$$
$$x_B(4.36) = y_B(14.7)$$

But,

$$x_A + x_B = 1$$
$$y_A + y_B = 1$$

Substituting for y_A, y_B, in the last equation,

$$\frac{19.71}{14.7} x_A + \frac{4.36}{14.7} x_B = 1.34x_A + 0.2965x_B = 1$$

$$4.52x_A + x_B = 3.37$$

Therefore,

$$x_A + (3.37 - 4.52x_A) = 1$$

$$x_A = \frac{2.37}{3.52} = 0.674$$

$$y_A = 1.34x_A = 0.904$$

From Fig. 13.4 at 80 K, 1 atm.,

$$x_A = 0.66, \ y_A = 0.89$$

(b) Assuming ideal solution in both phases, the equilibrium equations are, from Eq. 13.14,

$$x_A f_A{}^L = y_A f_A{}^V$$
$$x_B f_B{}^L = y_B f_B{}^V$$

Since the total pressure is low, Eq. 13.5 is a good approximation for both components. That is,

$$f_A^L \approx f_A^{\text{sat liq}}$$

$$f_B^L \approx f_B^{\text{sat liq}}$$

The critical constants for N_2 are

$$T_{c_A} = 126.2 \text{ K}, \ P_{c_A} = 492 \text{ lbf/in}^2$$

Therefore,

$$T_{r_A} = \frac{80}{126.2} = 0.633$$

$$P_{r_A}^{\text{sat}} = \frac{19.71}{492} = 0.040$$

so that

$$f_A^L = f_A^{\text{sat liq}} = (0.95)19.71 = 18.7 \text{ lbf/in.}^2$$

Also, for the vapor phase fugacity,

$$P_{r_A}^V = \frac{14.7}{492} = 0.0299$$

$$f_A^V = (0.96) \cdot 14.7 = 14.1 \text{ lbf/in.}^2$$

Similarly, for O_2,

$$T_{c_B} = 154.8 \text{ K}, \quad P_{c_B} = 736 \text{ lbf/in}^2.$$

$$T_{r_B} = \frac{80}{154.8} = 0.516$$

$$P_{r_B}^{\text{sat}} = \frac{4.36}{736} = 0.006$$

$$f_B^L = f_B^{\text{sat liq}} = (0.99)4.36 = 4.32 \text{ lbf/in.}^2$$

$$P_{r_B}^V = \frac{14.7}{736} = 0.02$$

$$f_B^V = (0.965)14.7 = 14.18 \text{ lbf/in.}^2$$

Substituting these values into the equilibrium equations,

$$x_A(18.7) = y_A(14.1)$$
$$x_B(4.32) = y_B(14.18)$$

Also,

$$x_A + x_B = 1$$
$$y_A + y_B = 1$$

This set of equations is solved in the same manner as in part (a), giving

$$x_A = 0.681$$
$$y_A = 0.902$$

We find that at this low pressure, both models yield essentially the same result and are quite accurate. At higher pressure, however, the assumption of ideal solution is usually considerably the more accurate of the two.

Closely related to Raoult's rule is Henry's rule, which states that

$$P_i = bx_i \tag{13.20}$$

where b is a constant.

Note that when $b = P^{sat}$, Henry's rule reduces to Raoult's rule. Henry's rule, which is very accurate for the solute in dilute solutions, states that the partial pressure of a given component is proportional to the amount of that component in the liquid phase. When the number of solute atoms is small, as in the case of a dilute solution, there is very little interaction between these solute atoms, and it is quite reasonable that doubling the number of solute atoms would double the vapor pressure. The concentration at which the deviation from Henry's rule becomes significant cannot be predicted theoretically, and varies considerably from one solution to another.

It may be shown that when the solute obeys Henry's rule, the solvent obeys Raoult's rule and vice versa.

13.4 The Gibbs Phase Rule (without Chemical Reaction)

The Gibbs phase rule, which was derived by Professor J. Willard Gibbs of Yale University in 1875, ranks among the truly significant contributions to physical science. In this section we consider the Gibbs phase rule for a system that does not involve a chemical reaction. For such a system the Gibbs phase rule is

$$\mathscr{P} + \mathscr{V} = \mathscr{C} + 2 \tag{13.21}$$

where $\mathscr{P}$ is the number of phases present, $\mathscr{V}$ is the variance, and $\mathscr{C}$ the number of components present. The term variance designates the number of intensive properties that must be specified in order to completely fix the state of the system. For example, in Example 13.2 we considered a two phase mixture of oxygen and nitrogen. For this system the number of phases $\mathscr{P}$ equals 2, the number of components $\mathscr{C}$ is 2, and therefore the variance $\mathscr{V}$ is 2. This is evident from Fig. 13.4, for this diagram is for a fixed pressure (1 atm), and the fixing of one additional intensive property. such as temperature, mole fraction of a given component in the liquid phase, or mole fraction of a given component in the vapor phase, will completely determine all other intensive properties and thus fix the state of the system (although not the relative amounts of the two phases).

Let us consider further the application of the Gibbs phase rule to a pure substance. In this case $\mathscr{C} = 1$. When we have one phase present, such as superheated vapor, $\mathscr{P} = 1$, and we conclude that $\mathscr{V} = \mathscr{C} + 1 - 1 = 2$. That is, two intensive properties must be specified in order to fix the state. We are already familiar with the superheated vapor tables for a number of substances and recognize that these tables are presented with pressure and temperature as the two independent properties. Such a system is referred to as a bivariant system.

Suppose we have two phases of a pure substance in equilibrium, such as saturated liquid and saturated vapor. In this case $\mathscr{C} = 1$, $\mathscr{P} = 2$, and $\mathscr{V} = 1 + 2 - 2 = 1$. That is, one intensive property fixes the value of all other intensive properties and thus determines the state of each phase. Again, from our familiarity with table of thermodynamic properties we recall that either pressure or temperature is used as the independent intensive property for tabulating liquid-vapor equilibrium data for a pure substance. Such a system is known as monovariant.

Consider also the triple point of a pure substance. In this case $\mathscr{C} = 1$ and $\mathscr{P} = 3$. Therefore $\mathscr{V} = 1 + 2 - 3 = 0$. That is, at the triple point all intensive properties are fixed, and if any intensive property is varied, we are no longer at the triple point. This is known as an invariant system.

It might be well at this point to again emphasize that a pure substance can have several phases in the solid state. For example, Fig. 3.6 shows the various phases of water. Note that there are several states at which three phases exist in equilibrium, and each of these is a triple point.

The application of the phase rule to a two-component, two-phase system has already been made. As a final application let us consider a two-component, three-phase system. For such a system $\mathscr{V} = 2 + 2 - 3 = 1$. That is, it is a monovariant system, and specifying one property, such as pressure or temperature fixes the state of the system.

The validity of the Gibbs phase rule can be outlined by considering a system consisting of $\mathscr{C}$ components and $\mathscr{P}$ phases in equilibrium at a given temperature and pressure. Assuming that each component exists in each phase, the state of the system could be completely specified if the concentration of each component in each phase and the temperature and pressure were specified. This would be a total of $\mathscr{C}\mathscr{P} + 2$ intensive properties.

We know, however, that these are not all independent intensive properties. If we determine the number of equations we have between these intensive properties, we can subtract this from the $\mathscr{C}\mathscr{P} + 2$ intensive properties and find the number of independent intensive properties, or, as it has been defined, the variance. The fact that at equilibrium the chemical potential of each component is the same in all phases gives rise to a total of $\mathscr{C}(\mathscr{P} - 1)$ equations between the intensive properties of the mixture.

Further, the fact that the sum of the mole fractions equals unity in each of the $\mathscr{P}$ phases gives $\mathscr{P}$ additional equations. Therefore the variance is

$$\mathscr{V} = \mathscr{C}\mathscr{P} + 2 - \mathscr{P} - \mathscr{C}(\mathscr{P} - 1) = \mathscr{C} + 2 - \mathscr{P}$$

13.5 Metastable Equilibrium

Although the limited scope of this book precludes an extensive treatment of metastable equilibrium, a brief introduction to the subject is presented in this section. Let us first consider an example of metastable equilibrium.

Consider a slightly superheated vapor, such as steam, expanding in a convergent-divergent nozzle, as shown in Fig. 13.8. Assuming the process is reversible and adiabatic, the steam will follow path 1-a on the T-s diagram, and at point a we would expect condensation to occur. However, if point a is reached in the divergent section of the nozzle, it is observed that no condensation occurs until point b is reached, and at this point the condensation occurs very abruptly in what is referred to as a condensation shock. Between points a and b the steam exists as a vapor, but the temperature is below the saturation temperature for the given pressure. This is

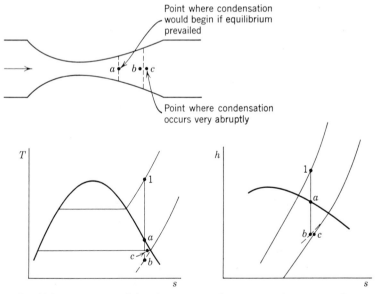

Fig. 13.8 Illustration of the phenomenon of supersaturation in a nozzle.

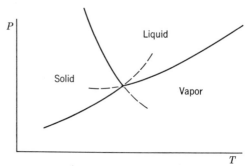

Fig. 13.9   Metastable states for solid-liquid-vapor equilibrium.

known as a metasatable state. The possibility of a metastable state exists with any phase transformation. The dotted lines on the equilibrium diagram shown in Fig. 13.9 represent possible metastable states for solid-liquid-vapor equilibrium.

The nature of a metastable state is often pictured schematically by the kind of diagram shown in Fig. 13.10. The ball is in a stable position (the "metastable state") for small displacements, but with a large displacement it moves to a new equilibrium position. The steam expanding in the nozzle is in a metastable state between a and b. This means that droplets smaller than a certain critical size will re-evaporate, and only when droplets of larger than this critical size have formed (this corresponds to moving the ball out of the depression) will the new equilibrium state appear.

13.6   Chemical Equilibrium

We now turn our attention to chemical equilibrium and consider first a chemical reaction involving only one phase. This is referred to as a homogeneous chemical reaction. It may be helpful to visualize this as a gaseous phase, but the basic considerations apply to any phase.

Consider a vessel, Fig. 13.11, that contains four compounds, A, B, C, and D, which are in chemical equilibrium at a given pressure and temperature. For example, these might consist of CO, CO_2, H_2, and H_2O in

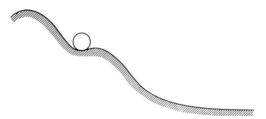

Fig. 13.10   Schematic diagram illustrating a metastable state.

equilibrium. Let the number of moles of each component be designated n_A, n_B, n_C, and n_D. Further, let the chemical reaction which takes place between these four constituents be

$$\nu_A A + \nu_B B \rightleftharpoons \nu_C C + \nu_D D \tag{13.22}$$

where ν's are the stoichiometric coefficients. It should be emphasized that there is a very definite relation between the ν's (the stoichiometric coefficients) whereas the n's (the number of moles present) for any constituent can be varied simply by varying the amount of that component in the reaction vessel.

Let us now consider how the requirement for equilibrium, namely, that $dG_{T,P} = 0$ at equilibrium, applies to a homogeneous chemical reaction. When we considered phase equilibrium (Sec. 13.3) we proceeded by assuming that the two phases were in equilibrium at a given temperature and pressure, and then let a small quantity of one component be transferred from one phase to the other. In a similar manner, let us assume that the four components are in chemical equilibrium and then assume that from this equilibrium state, while the temperature and pressure remain constant, the reaction proceeds an infinitesimal amount toward the right as Eq. 13.22 is written. This results in a decrease in the moles of A and B and an increase in the moles of C and D. Let us designate the degree of reaction by ϵ, and define the degree of reaction by the relations .

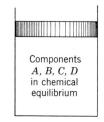

Components A, B, C, D in chemical equilibrium

Fig. 13.11 Schematic diagram for consideration of chemical equilibrium.

$$\begin{aligned}
dn_A &= -\nu_A \, d\epsilon \\
dn_B &= -\nu_B \, d\epsilon \\
dn_C &= +\nu_C \, d\epsilon \\
dn_D &= +\nu_D \, d\epsilon
\end{aligned} \tag{13.23}$$

That is, the change in the number of moles of any component during a chemical reaction is given by the product of the stoichiometric coefficients (the ν's) and the degree of reaction.

Let us evaluate the change in the Gibbs function associated with this chemical reaction that proceeds to the right in the amount $d\epsilon$. In doing so we use, as would be expected, the Gibbs function of each component in the mixture, namely, the partial molal Gibbs function (or its equivalent, the chemical potential)

$$dG_{T,P} = \bar{G}_C \, dn_C + \bar{G}_D \, dn_D + \bar{G}_A \, dn_A + \bar{G}_B \, dn_B$$

Substituting Eq. 13.23, we have

$$dG_{T,P} = (\nu_C \bar{G}_C + \nu_D \bar{G}_D - \nu_A \bar{G}_A - \nu_B \bar{G}_B)\, d\epsilon \qquad (13.24)$$

We have already considered (Sec. 11.12) how to evaluate the partial molal Gibbs function of a given component in terms of the Gibbs function of the pure component at the standard state and the activity of that component. For the component i, we can write (Eq. 11.81)

$$\bar{G}_i = \bar{g}_i{}^\circ + \bar{R}T \ln a_i$$

Substituting this relation into Eq. 13.24 we have

$$dG_{T,P} = [\nu_C(\bar{g}_C{}^\circ + \bar{R}T \ln a_C) + \nu_D(\bar{g}_D{}^\circ + \bar{R}T \ln a_D)$$
$$-\nu_A(\bar{g}_A{}^\circ + \bar{R}T \ln a_A) - \nu_B(\bar{g}_B{}^\circ + \bar{R}T \ln a_B)]\, d\epsilon \quad (13.25)$$

Let us define ΔG° as follows,

$$\Delta G^\circ = \nu_C \bar{g}_C{}^\circ + \nu_D \bar{g}_D{}^\circ - \nu_A \bar{g}_A{}^\circ - \nu_B \bar{g}_B{}^\circ \qquad (13.26)$$

That is, ΔG° is the change in the Gibbs function that would occur if the chemical reaction given by Eq. 13.22 (which involves the stoichiometric amounts of each component) proceeded completely from left to right, with the reactants A and B initially separated and at temperature T and the standard state pressure and the products C and D finally separated and at temperature T and the standard state pressure. Note also that ΔG° for a given reaction is a function of only the temperature. This will be most important to bear in mind as we proceed with our developments of homogeneous chemical equilibrium. Let us now digress from our development to consider an example involving the calculation of ΔG°.

Example 13.3

Determine the value of ΔG° for the reaction $H_2O \rightleftharpoons H_2 + \frac{1}{2}O_2$ at 298 K and at 2000 K, with the H_2O in the gaseous phase.

We take 1 atm as our standard state pressure, and recall that we assume further that $\bar{g}$ for all the elements is zero at one atmosphere pressure and 298 K (537 R). Therefore, at 298 K,

$$(\bar{g}_f{}^\circ)_{H_2} = 0; \qquad (\bar{g}_f{}^\circ)_{O_2} = 0$$

From Table 12.3, at 298 K,

$$(\bar{g}_f{}^\circ)_{H_2O} = -98{,}345 \text{ Btu/lb mole.}$$

$$\Delta G^\circ = (\bar{g}_f{}^\circ)_{H_2} + \tfrac{1}{2}(\bar{g}_f{}^\circ)_{O_2} - (\bar{g}_f{}^\circ)_{H_2O}$$
$$= 0 + 0 - (-98{,}345) = 98{,}345 \text{ Btu}$$

At 2000 K (3600 R), from Table A.11,

$$\bar{g}_{H_2}^{\;\circ} = \bar{g}_{3600}^{\circ} - \bar{g}_{537}^{\circ} = (\bar{h}_{3600}^{\circ} - \bar{h}_{537}^{\circ}) - (3600\,\bar{s}_{3600}^{\circ} - 537\,\bar{s}_{537}^{\circ})$$
$$= 22,772 - 3600(45.004) + 537(31.208)$$
$$= 22,772 - 162,014 + 16,759$$
$$= -122,483 \text{ Btu/lb mole}$$

Similarly, for the O_2 at 2000 K (3600R),

$$\bar{g}_{O_2}^{\;\circ} = (\bar{h}_{3600}^{\circ} - \bar{h}_{537}^{\circ}) - (3600\,\bar{s}_{3600}^{\circ} - 537\,\bar{s}_{537}^{\circ})$$
$$= 25,468 - 3600(64.210) + 537(49.004)$$
$$25,468 - 231,156 + 26,315 = -179,373 \text{ Btu/lb mole}$$

For the H_2O,

$$\bar{g}_{H_2O}^{\circ} = \bar{g}_f^{\;\circ} + \bar{g}_{3600}^{\circ} - \bar{g}_{537}^{\circ}$$
$$= -98,345 + 31,271 - [3600(63.234) - 537(45.106)]$$
$$= -98,345 + 31,271 - 227,642 + 24,222$$
$$= -270,494 \text{ Btu/lb mole}$$

Therefore, at 2000 K

$$\Delta G^{\circ} = -122,483 + \tfrac{1}{2}(-179,373) - (-270,494)$$
$$= 58,324 \text{ Btu.}$$

Returning now to our development, substituting Eq. 13.26 into Eq. 13.25 and rearranging we can write

$$dG_{T,P} = \left[\Delta G^{\circ} + \bar{R}T\ln \frac{a_C^{\;vc} a_D^{\;v_D}}{a_A^{\;v_A} a_B^{\;v_B}}\right] d\epsilon \qquad (13.27)$$

At equilibrium $dG_{T,P} = 0$. Therefore, since $d\epsilon$ is arbitrary,

$$\ln \frac{a_C^{\;vc} a_D^{\;v_D}}{a_A^{\;v_A} a_B^{\;v_B}} = -\frac{\Delta G^{\circ}}{\bar{R}T} \qquad (13.28)$$

The equilibrium constant K is defined as

$$\ln K = \frac{-\Delta G^{\circ}}{\bar{R}T} \qquad (13.29)$$

Note that since ΔG° is defined in terms of the properties of the pure components at a given temperature and the standard state, and is a function of temperature only, the equilibrium constant for a given reaction is also a function of temperature only.

Example 13.4

Determine the equilibrium constant K, expressed as $\ln K$, for the reaction $H_2O \rightleftharpoons H_2 + \frac{1}{2} O_2$ at 537 R and 3600 R.

We have already found, in Example 13.3, $\Delta G°$ for this reaction at these two temperatures. Therefore, at 537 R,

$$(\ln K)_{537} = -\frac{\Delta G°_{537}}{\bar{R}T} = \frac{-98,345}{1.986 \times 537} = -92.21$$

At 3600 R we have,

$$(\ln K)_{3600} = \frac{-\Delta G°_{3600}}{\bar{R}T} = \frac{-58,324}{1.986 \times 3600} = -8.151$$

Table A.12 gives the values of the equilibrium constant for a number of reactions. Note that for each reaction the value of the equilibrium constant is determined from the properties of each of the pure constituents at the standard state pressure and is a function of temperature only.

For other reaction equations, the chemical equilibrium constant can be calculated as in Example 13.4 or can be determined analytically in the following manner. Consider the general reaction Eq. 13.22. The standard-state Gibbs function for each constituent can be expressed by writing Eq. 11.62 at the pressure $P°$. For component A,

$$d\left(\frac{\bar{g}_A°}{T}\right)_{P°} = -\frac{\bar{h}_A°}{T^2} \, dT_{P°} \tag{13.30}$$

Therefore, for the reaction given by Eq. 13.22,

$$d\left(\frac{\Delta G°}{T}\right)_{P°} = -\frac{\Delta H°}{T^2} \, dT_{P°} \tag{13.31}$$

where $\Delta G°$ is defined by Eq. 13.26 and $\Delta H°$ similarly by

$$\Delta H° = v_C \bar{h}_C° + v_D \bar{h}_D° - v_A \bar{h}_A° - v_B \bar{h}_B° \tag{13.32}$$

Now, substituting the definition of the equilibrium constant Eq. 13.29 into Eq. 13.31,

$$d \ln K = \frac{\Delta H°}{\bar{R}T^2} \, dT_{P°} \tag{13.33}$$

which is termed the van't Hoff equation. In integrating this equation, we must be careful to note that $\Delta H°$ as defined by Eq. 13.32 is a function of temperature.

In applying the concept of the equilibrium constant to the determination of the equilibrium composition for a chemical reaction, we must be able to determine the activity of the various constituents. It is at this point that we find considerable simplification results if we can assume that at equilibrium we have an ideal solution. Let us make this assumption and then, at a later point, make the additional assumption that at equilibrium we have a mixture of ideal gases.

For each component in an ideal solution we can write, in accordance with Eq. 11.82,

$$a_i = \frac{y_i f_i}{f_i{}^\circ}$$

Since $f_i{}^\circ$ is, in this application, taken as one atmosphere, we can drop the $f_i{}^\circ$ from this equation provided all the fugacities (and pressures) are expressed in atmospheres. Adopting this procedure, we can derive an expression for the equilibrium constant in terms of fugacity:

$$K = \frac{a_C{}^{\nu_C} a_D{}^{\nu_D}}{a_A{}^{\nu_A} a_B{}^{\nu_B}} = \frac{y_C{}^{\nu_C} y_D{}^{\nu_D}}{y_A{}^{\nu_A} y_B{}^{\nu_B}} P^{\nu_C + \nu_D - \nu_A - \nu_B} \left[\frac{(f/P)_C{}^{\nu_C}(f/P)_D{}^{\nu_D}}{(f/P)_A{}^{\nu_A}(f/P)_B{}^{\nu_B}} \right] \quad (13.34)$$

We have written the equation in this form because it demonstrates quite clearly the influence of various factors on the equilibrium composition (the y's). That is, we know that temperature and pressure both influence the equilibrium composition. From Eq. 13.34 it can be seen that the influence of temperature enters through the value of K (which is a function of temperature only) and the influence of pressure through the term $P^{\nu_C + \nu_D - \nu_A - \nu_B}$ (and through the various fugacity coefficients, f/P). Note that if $\nu_C + \nu_D = \nu_A + \nu_B$ (which means that the total number of moles does not change during a chemical reaction) this term drops out.

If we make the additional assumption that all the constituents in the reaction are ideal gases, the fugacity coefficient f/P is unity for all constituents, and for a reaction involving ideal gases we can write

$$K = \frac{y_C{}^{\nu_C} y_D{}^{\nu_D}}{y_A{}^{\nu_A} y_B{}^{\nu_B}} P^{\nu_C + \nu_D - \nu_A - \nu_B} \quad (13.35)$$

Since for each component in a mixture of ideal gases the partial pressure P_i is defined as

$$P_i = y_i P$$

it follows that

$$P_i{}^{\nu_i} = y_i{}^{\nu_i} P^{\nu_i}$$

and therefore Eq. 13.35 can also be written

$$K = \frac{P_C{}^{\nu_C} P_D{}^{\nu_D}}{P_A{}^{\nu_A} P_B{}^{\nu_B}} \quad (13.36)$$

Equation 13.36 has been called the law of mass action (though it is not properly a law according to the use of the word "law" in this book).

Note that in a sense the last term of Eq. 13.34

$$\left[\frac{(f/P)_C^{\nu_C}\,(f/P)_D^{\nu_D}}{(f/P)_A^{\nu_A}\,(f/P)_B^{\nu_B}}\right]$$

expresses the deviation from ideal gas behavior in the equilibrium composition.

Let us now consider a number of examples that illustrate the procedure for determining the equilibrium composition for a homogeneous reaction and the influence of certain variables on the equilibrium composition.

Example 13.5

One mole of carbon at 77 F and one atmosphere pressure reacts with one mole of oxygen at 77 F and one atmosphere pressure to form an equilibrium mixture of CO_2, CO, and O_2 at 3000 K, one atmosphere pressure, in a steady-flow process. Determine the equilibrium composition and the heat transfer for this process.

It is convenient to view the over-all process as though it occurred in two separate steps, a combustion process followed by a heating and dissociation of the combustion product CO_2, as indicated in Fig. 13.12. This two-step process is represented as follows:

combustion: $C + O_2 \rightarrow CO_2$

dissociation reaction: $CO_2 \rightleftharpoons CO + \tfrac{1}{2}O_2$

That is, the energy released by the combustion of C and O_2 heats the CO_2 formed to high temperature, resulting in the dissociation of part of the CO_2 to CO and O_2. Thus, the over-all reaction can be written

$$C + O_2 \rightarrow aCO_2 + bCO + dO_2$$

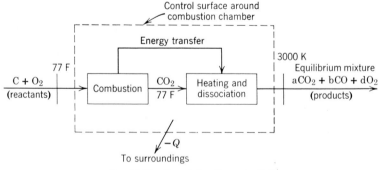

Fig. 13.12   Sketch for Example 13.5.

where the unknown coefficients a, b, and d must be found by solution of the equilibrium equation associated with the dissociation reaction. Once this is accomplished, we can write the first law for a control volume around the combustion chamber to calculate the heat transfer.

$$Q_{c.v.} + H_R = H_P$$

From the combustion equation, we find that the initial composition for the dissociation reaction is 1 mole CO_2. Therefore, letting z be the number of moles of CO_2 dissociated, we find

$$CO_2 \rightleftharpoons CO + \tfrac{1}{2}O_2$$

	CO_2	CO	$\tfrac{1}{2}O_2$
Initial:	1	0	0
Change:	$-z$	$+z$	$+z/2$
At equilibrium:	$(1-z)$	z	$z/2$

Therefore, the over-all reaction is

$$C + O_2 \rightarrow (1-z)CO_2 + z\,CO + \frac{z}{2}\,O_2$$

and the total number of moles at equilibrium is

$$n = (1-z) + z + z/2 = 1 + z/2$$

The equilibrium mole fractions are

$$y_{CO_2} = \frac{1-z}{1+z/2}, \qquad y_{CO} = \frac{z}{1+z/2}, \qquad y_{O_2} = \frac{z/2}{1+z/2}$$

From Table A.12 we find that the value of the equilibrium constant at 3000 K for the dissociation reaction considered here is

$$\ln K = -0.972, \quad K = 0.378$$

Substituting these quantities along with $P = 1$ atm into Eq. 13.35, we have the equilibrium equation,

$$K = 0.378 = \frac{y_{CO}\,y_{O_2}^{1/2}}{y_{CO_2}}\,P^{1+\frac{1}{2}-1}$$

$$= \frac{\left(\dfrac{z}{1+z/2}\right)\left(\dfrac{z/2}{1+z/2}\right)^{1/2}(1)^{1/2}}{\left(\dfrac{1-z}{1+z/2}\right)}$$

or, in more convenient form,

$$\frac{K^2}{P} = \frac{(0.378)^2}{1} = \left(\frac{z}{1-z}\right)^2\left(\frac{z}{2+z}\right)$$

In order to obtain the physically meaningful root of this mathematical relation, we note that the number of moles of each component must be greater than zero. Thus, the root of interest to us must lie in the range

$$0 \leq z \leq 1$$

Solving the equilibrium equation by trial and error, we find

$$z = 0.466$$

Therefore, the over-all process is

$$C + O_2 \rightarrow 0.534\,CO_2 + 0.466\,CO + 0.233\,O_2$$

where the equilibrium mole fractions are

$$y_{CO_2} = \frac{0.534}{1.233} = 0.433$$

$$y_{CO} = \frac{0.466}{1.233} = 0.378$$

$$y_{O_2} = \frac{0.233}{1.233} = 0.189$$

The heat transfer from the combustion chamber to the surroundings can be calculated using the enthalpies of formation and Table A.11. For this process,

$$H_R = (\bar{h}_f{}^\circ)_C + (\bar{h}_f{}^\circ)_{O_2} = 0 + 0$$

The equilibrium products leave the chamber at 3000 K, or 5400 R. Therefore,

$$
\begin{aligned}
H_p &= n_{CO_2}(\bar{h}_f{}^\circ + \bar{h}_{5400}^\circ - \bar{h}_{537}^\circ)_{CO_2} \\
&\quad + n_{CO}(\bar{h}_f{}^\circ + \bar{h}_{5400}^\circ - \bar{h}_{537}^\circ)_{CO} \\
&\quad + n_{O_2}(\bar{h}_f{}^\circ + \bar{h}_{5400}^\circ - \bar{h}_{537}^\circ)_{O_2} \\
&= 0.534(-169{,}297 + 65{,}763) \\
&\quad + 0.466(-47{,}551 + 40{,}243) \\
&\quad + 0.233(0 + 42{,}203) \\
&= -48{,}860 \text{ Btu/mole C burned}
\end{aligned}
$$

Substituting into the first law,

$$Q_{c.v.} = H_P - H_R$$
$$= -48{,}860 \text{ Btu/mole C burned}$$

Example 13.6

One mole of carbon at 77 F reacts with two moles of oxygen at 77 F to form an equilibrium mixture of CO_2, CO, and O_2 at 3000 K, 1 atmosphere pressure. Determine the equilibrium composition.

The over-all process can be imagined to occur in two steps as in the previous example. The combustion process is

$$C + 2O_2 \rightarrow CO_2 + O_2$$

and the subsequent dissociation reaction is

	CO_2	$\rightleftharpoons$	CO	$+$	$\frac{1}{2}O_2$
Initial:	1		O		1
Change:	$-z$		$+z$		$+z/2$
At equilibrium:	$(1-z)$		z		$(1+z/2)$

We find that in this case the over-all process is

$$C + 2O_2 \rightarrow (1-z)CO_2 + zCO + (1+z/2)O_2$$

and the total number of moles at equilibrium is

$$n = (1-z) + z + (1+z/2) = 2 + z/2$$

The mole fractions are

$$y_{CO_2} = \frac{1-z}{2+z/2}, \qquad y_{CO} = \frac{z}{2+z/2}, \qquad y_{O_2} = \frac{1+z/2}{2+z/2}$$

The equilibrium constant for the reaction $CO_2 \rightleftharpoons CO + \frac{1}{2}O_2$ at 3000 K was found in Example 13.5 to be 0.378. Therefore, the equilibrium equation is, substituting these quantities and $P = 1$ atm.,

$$K = 0.378 = \frac{y_{CO}y_{O_2}^{1/2}}{y_{CO_2}} p^{1+1/2-1}$$

$$= \frac{\left(\dfrac{z}{2+z/2}\right)\left(\dfrac{1+z/2}{2+z/2}\right)^{1/2}}{\left(\dfrac{1-z}{2+z/2}\right)} (1)^{1/2}$$

or,

$$\frac{K^2}{P} = \frac{(0.378)^2}{1} = \left(\frac{z}{1-z}\right)^2 \left(\frac{2+z}{4+z}\right)$$

We note that in order for the number of moles of each component to be greater than zero,

$$0 \le z \le 1$$

Solving the equilibrium equation for z, we find

$$z = 0.340$$

so that the over-all process is

$$C + 2O_2 \rightarrow 0.66\ CO_2 + 0.34\ CO + 1.17O_2$$

The mole fractions of the components in the equilibrium mixture are

$$y_{CO_2} = \frac{0.66}{2.17} = 0.304$$

$$y_{CO} = \frac{0.34}{2.17} = 0.157$$

$$y_{O_2} = \frac{1.17}{2.17} = 0.539$$

The heat transferred from the chamber in this process could be found by the same procedure followed in Example 13.5, considering the over-all process as expressed above.

13.7   Simultaneous Reactions

In developing the equilibrium equation and equilibrium constant expressions of Section 13.6, it was assumed that there was only a single chemical reaction equation relating the substances present in the system. To demonstrate the more general situation in which there is more than one chemical reaction, we will now analyze a system involving two simultaneous reactions by a procedure analogous to that followed in Section 13.6. These results are then readily extended to systems involving several simultaneous reactions.

Consider a mixture of substances A, B, C, D, L, M, and N as indicated in Fig. 13.13. These substances are assumed to exist at a condition of chemical equilibrium at temperature T and pressure P, and are related by the two independent reactions

(1) $v_{A_1}A + v_B B \rightleftharpoons v_C C + v_D D$ (13.37)

(2) $v_{A_2}A + v_L L \rightleftharpoons v_M M + v_N N$ (13.38)

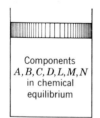

Components
A, B, C, D, L, M, N
in chemical
equilibrium

Fig. 13.13 Sketch demonstrating simultaneous reactions.

We have considered the situation where one of the components (substance A) is involved in each of the reactions in order to demonstrate the effect of this condition on the resulting equations. As in the previous section, the changes in amount of the components are related by the various stoichiometric coefficients, which are not the same as the number of moles of each substance present in the vessel. We also realize that the coefficients ν_{A_1}, and ν_{A_2} are not necessarily the same. That is, substance A does not in general take part in each of the reactions to the same extent.

Development of the requirement for equilibrium is completely analogous to that of Section 13.6. We consider that each reaction proceeds an infinitesimal amount toward the right side. This results in a decrease in the number of moles of A, B, and L, and an increase in the moles of C, D, M, and N. Letting the degrees of reaction be ϵ_1 and ϵ_2 for reactions 1 and 2, respectively, the changes in the number of moles are, for infinitesimal shifts from the equilibrium composition,

$$
\begin{aligned}
dn_A &= -\nu_{A_1}d\epsilon_1 - \nu_{A_2}\,d\epsilon_2 \\
dn_B &= -\nu_B d\epsilon_1 \\
dn_L &= -\nu_L d\epsilon_2 \\
dn_C &= +\nu_C d\epsilon_1 \\
dn_D &= +\nu_D d\epsilon_1 \\
dn_M &= +\nu_M d\epsilon_2 \\
dn_N &= +\nu_N d\epsilon_2
\end{aligned}
\tag{13.39}
$$

The change in Gibbs function for the mixture in the vessel at constant temperature and pressure is

$$
\begin{aligned}
dG_{T,P} = \bar{G}_A dn_A + \bar{G}_B dn_B + \bar{G}_C dn_C + \bar{G}_D dn_D \\
+ \bar{G}_L dn_L + \bar{G}_M dn_M + \bar{G}_N dn_N
\end{aligned}
$$

Substituting the expressions of Eq. 13.39 and collecting terms,

$$
\begin{aligned}
dG_{T,P} = (\nu_C \bar{G}_C + \nu_D \bar{G}_D - \nu_{A_1}\bar{G}_A - \nu_B \bar{G}_B)d\epsilon_1 \\
+ (\nu_M \bar{G}_M + \nu_N \bar{G}_N - \nu_{A_2}\bar{G}_A - \nu_L \bar{G}_L)d\epsilon_2 \quad (13.40)
\end{aligned}
$$

It is convenient to again express each of the partial molal Gibbs functions in terms of the activity as

$$
\bar{G}_i = \bar{g}_i{}^\circ + \bar{R}T \ln a_i
$$

Equation 13.40 written in this form becomes

$$
\begin{aligned}
dG_{T,P} = \left[\Delta G_1{}^\circ + \bar{R}T \ln \frac{a_C{}^{\nu_C} a_D{}^{\nu_D}}{a_A{}^{\nu_{A_1}} a_B{}^{\nu_B}}\right] d\epsilon_1 \\
+ \left[\Delta G_2{}^\circ + \bar{R}T \ln \frac{a_M{}^{\nu_M} a_N{}^{\nu_N}}{a_A{}^{\nu_{A_2}} a_L{}^{\nu_L}}\right] d\epsilon_2 \quad (13.41)
\end{aligned}
$$

In this equation the standard-state change in Gibbs function for each reaction is defined as

$$\Delta G_1^\circ = \nu_C \bar{g}_C^\circ + \nu_D \bar{g}_D^\circ - \nu_{A_1} \bar{g}_A^\circ - \nu_B \bar{g}_B^\circ \qquad (13.42)$$

$$\Delta G_2^\circ = \nu_M \bar{g}_M^\circ + \nu_N \bar{g}_N^\circ - \nu_{A_2} \bar{g}_A^\circ - \nu_L \bar{g}_L^\circ \qquad (13.43)$$

Equation 13.41 expresses the change in Gibbs function of the system at constant T, P, for infinitesimal degrees of reaction of both reactions 1 and 2, Eqs. 13.37 and 13.38. The requirement for equilibrium is that $dG_{T,P} = 0$. Therefore, since reactions 1 and 2 are independent, $d\epsilon_1$ and $d\epsilon_2$ can be independently varied. It follows that at equilibrium each of the bracketed terms of Eq. 13.41 must be zero. Defining equilibrium constants for the two reactions by

$$\ln K_1 = -\frac{\Delta G_1^\circ}{\bar{R}T} \qquad (13.44)$$

and

$$\ln K_2 = -\frac{\Delta G_2^\circ}{\bar{R}T} \qquad (13.45)$$

we find that, at equilibrium

$$K_1 = \frac{a_C^{\nu_C} a_D^{\nu_D}}{a_A^{\nu_{A_1}} a_B^{\nu_B}} \qquad (13.46)$$

and

$$K_2 = \frac{a_M^{\nu_M} a_N^{\nu_N}}{a_A^{\nu_{A_2}} a_L^{\nu_L}} \qquad (13.47)$$

can be expressed in terms of the mole fractions for the appropriate model of the mixture, after which these expressions must be solved simultaneously for the equilibrium composition of the mixture. The following example is presented to demonstrate and clarify this procedure.

Example 13.7

One mole of H_2O vapor is heated to 3000K, 1 atm. pressure. Determine the equilibrium composition, assuming that H_2O, H_2, O_2, and OH are present.

There are two independent reactions relating the four components of the mixture at equilibrium. These can be written as:

$$(1) \quad H_2O \rightleftharpoons H_2 + \tfrac{1}{2}O_2$$
$$(2) \quad H_2O \rightleftharpoons \tfrac{1}{2}H_2 + OH$$

Let a be the number of moles of H_2O dissociating according to reaction (1) during the heating, and b the number of moles of H_2O dissociating according to reaction (2). Since the initial composition is 1 mole H_2O, the changes according to the two reactions are

$$(1) \quad H_2O \rightleftharpoons H_2 + \tfrac{1}{2}O_2$$

Change: $\qquad\qquad\qquad -a \quad +a +\tfrac{1}{2}a$

$$(2) \quad H_2O \rightleftharpoons \tfrac{1}{2}H_2 + OH$$

Change: $\qquad\qquad\qquad -b \quad +\tfrac{1}{2}b \quad +b$

Therefore, the number of moles of each component at equilibrium is its initial number plus the change, so that at equilibrium

$$n_{H_2O} = 1 - a - b$$
$$n_{H_2} = a + \tfrac{1}{2}b$$
$$n_{O_2} = \tfrac{1}{2}a$$
$$\underline{n_{OH} = b}$$
$$n = 1 + \tfrac{1}{2}a + \tfrac{1}{2}b$$

The overall chemical reaction that occurs during the heating process can be written

$$H_2O \rightarrow (1 - a - b)H_2O + (a + \tfrac{1}{2}b)H_2 + \tfrac{1}{2}aO_2 + bOH$$

The right-hand side of this expression is the equilibrium composition of the system. Since the number of moles of each substance must necessarily be greater than zero, we find that the possible values of a and b are restricted to

$$a \geq 0$$
$$b \geq 0$$
$$(a + b) \leq 1$$

The two equilibrium equations are, assuming the mixture to behave as an ideal gas,

$$K_1 = \frac{y_{H_2}y_{O_2}^{1/2}}{y_{H_2O}} p^{1+1/2-1}$$

$$K_2 = \frac{y_{H_2}^{1/2}y_{OH}}{y_{H_2O}} p^{1/2+1-1}$$

where the pressure is given in atmospheres. Since the mole fraction of each component is the ratio of the number of moles of the component to the total number of moles of the mixture, these equations can be written in the form,

$$K_1 = \frac{\left(\dfrac{a + \frac{1}{2}b}{1 + \frac{1}{2}a + \frac{1}{2}b}\right)\left(\dfrac{\frac{1}{2}a}{1 + \frac{1}{2}a + \frac{1}{2}b}\right)^{1/2}}{\left(\dfrac{1 - a - b}{1 + \frac{1}{2}a + \frac{1}{2}b}\right)} P^{1/2}$$

$$= \left(\frac{a + \frac{1}{2}b}{1 - a - b}\right)\left(\frac{\frac{1}{2}a}{1 + \frac{1}{2}a + \frac{1}{2}b}\right)^{1/2} P^{1/2}$$

and

$$K_2 = \frac{\left(\dfrac{a + \frac{1}{2}b}{1 + \frac{1}{2}a + \frac{1}{2}b}\right)^{1/2}\left(\dfrac{b}{1 + \frac{1}{2}a + \frac{1}{2}b}\right)}{\left(\dfrac{1 - a - b}{1 + \frac{1}{2}a + \frac{1}{2}b}\right)} P^{1/2}$$

$$= \left(\frac{a + \frac{1}{2}b}{1 + \frac{1}{2}a + \frac{1}{2}b}\right)^{1/2}\left(\frac{b}{1 - a - b}\right) P^{1/2}$$

giving two equations in the two unknowns a and b, since $P = 1$ atmosphere and the values of K_1, K_2 are known. From Table A.12 at 3000 K, we find

$$K_1 = 0.0457, \quad K_2 = 0.0543$$

Therefore, the equations can be solved simultaneously for a and b. The values satisfying the equations are

$$a = 0.1074, \quad b = 0.1110$$

Substituting these values into the expressions for the number of moles of each component and of the mixture, we find the equilibrium mole fractions to be

$$y_{H_2O} = 0.7045$$
$$y_{H_2} = 0.1468$$
$$y_{O_2} = 0.0485$$
$$y_{OH} = 0.1002$$

The methods used in this section can readily be extended to equilibrium systems involving more than two independent reactions. In each case, the number of simultaneous equilibrium equations is equal to the number of independent reactions. Solution of a large set of nonlinear simultaneous equations naturally becomes quite difficult, however, and is not easily accomplished by hand calculations. Instead, solution of these problems is normally made using iterative procedures on a digital computer.

13.8   Ionization

In the final section of this chapter, we shall consider the equilibrium of systems involving ionized gases, or plasmas, a field that has found increasing application and study in recent years. In previous sections we have discussed chemical equilibrium, with a particular emphasis on molecular dissociation, as for example the reaction

$$N_2 \rightleftharpoons 2N$$

which occurs to an appreciable extent for most molecules only at high temperature (of the order of magnitude 3000–10,000 K). At still higher temperatures, such as found in electric arcs, the gas becomes ionized. That is, some of the atoms lose an electron, according to the reaction

$$N \rightleftharpoons N^+ + e^-$$

where N^+ denotes a singly-ionized nitrogen atom (one that has lost one electron and consequently has a positive charge) and e^- represents the free electron. As temperature is increased still further, many of the ionized atoms lose another electron, according to the reaction

$$N^+ \rightleftharpoons N^{++} + e^-$$

and thus become doubly-ionized. As the temperature is increased further, the process continues until a temperature is reached at which all the electrons have been stripped from the nucleus.

Ionization generally is appreciable only at high temperature. However, dissociation and ionization both tend to occur to greater extents at low pressure, and consequently dissociation and ionization may be appreciable in such environments as the upper atmosphere, even at moderate temperature. Other effects such as radiation will also cause ionization, but these effects are not considered here.

The problems involved with analyzing the composition in a plasma become much more difficult than for an ordinary chemical reaction, since in an electric field the free electrons in the mixture do not exchange energy with the positive ions and neutral atoms at the same rate as they do with the field. Consequently, in a plasma in an electric field, the electron gas is not at exactly the same temperature as the heavy particles. However, for moderate fields, it is a reasonable approximation to assume a condition of thermal equilibrium in the plasma, at least for preliminary calculations. Under this condition, we can treat the ionization equilibrium in exactly the same manner as an ordinary chemical equilibrium analysis.

At these extremely high temperatures, we may assume that the plasma behaves as an ideal gas mixture of neutral atoms, positive ions, and electron gas. Thus, for the ionization of some atomic species A,

$$A \rightleftharpoons A^+ + e^- \qquad (13.48)$$

we may write the ionization equilibrium equation in the form

$$K = \frac{y_{A^+} y_{e^-}}{y_A} P^{1+1-1} \qquad (13.49)$$

The ionization-equilibrium constant K is defined in the ordinary manner as

$$\ln K = -\frac{\Delta G^\circ}{RT} \qquad (13.50)$$

and is a function of temperature only. The standard-state Gibbs function change for reaction 13.48 is found from

$$\Delta G^\circ = \bar{g}_{A^+}{}^\circ + \bar{g}_{e^-}{}^\circ - \bar{g}_A{}^\circ \qquad (13.51)$$

The standard-state Gibbs function for each component at the given plasma temperature can be calculated using the procedures of statistical thermo-dynamics, so that ionization-equilibrium constants can be tabulated as functions of temperature.

Solution of the ionization-equilibrium equation, Eq. 13.49, is then accomplished in the same manner as for an ordinary chemical-reaction equilibrium.

Example 13.8

Calculate the equilibrium composition if argon gas is heated in an arc to 10,000 K, 0.01 atm, assuming the plasma to consist of Ar, Ar$^+$, e^-. The ionization-equilibrium constant for the reaction

$$Ar \rightleftharpoons Ar^+ + e^-$$

at this temperature is 0.00042.

Consider an initial composition of 1 mole neutral argon, and let z be the number of moles ionized during the heating process. Therefore,

$$Ar \rightleftharpoons Ar^+ + e^-$$

Initial:	1	0	0
Change:	$-z$	$+z$	$+z$
Equilibrium:	$(1-z)$	z	z

and $n = (1-z) + z + z = 1 + z$

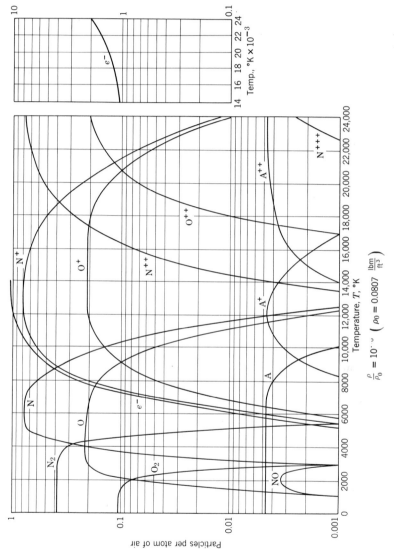

Fig. 13.14   Equilibrium composition of air (W. E. Moeckel & K. C. Weston, NACA TN 4265 (1958)).

Since the number of moles of each component must be positive, the variable z is restricted to the range

$$0 \leq z \leq 1$$

The equilibrium mole fractions are

$$y_{Ar} = \frac{n_{Ar}}{n} = \frac{1 - z}{1 + z}$$

$$y_{Ar^+} = \frac{n_{Ar^+}}{n} = \frac{z}{1 + z}$$

$$y_{e^-} = \frac{n_{e^-}}{n} = \frac{z}{1 + z}$$

The equilibrium equation is

$$K = \frac{y_{Ar^+} y_{e^-}}{y_{Ar}} P^{1+1-1} = \frac{\left(\dfrac{z}{1 + z}\right)\left(\dfrac{z}{1 + z}\right)}{\left(\dfrac{1 - z}{1 + z}\right)} P$$

so that, at 10,000 K, 0.01 atm,

$$0.00042 = \left(\frac{z^2}{1 - z^2}\right)(0.01)$$

Solving,

$$z = 0.201$$

and the composition is found to be

$$y_{Ar} = 0.666$$
$$y_{Ar^+} = 0.167$$
$$y_{e^-} = 0.167$$

Simultaneous reactions, such as simultaneous molecular dissociation and ionization reactions or multiple ionization reactions, can be analyzed in the same manner as the ordinary simultaneous chemical reactions of Section 13.7. In doing so, we again make the assumption of thermal equilibrium in the plasma, which as mentioned before is, in many cases, a reasonable approximation. Figure 13.14 shows the equilibrium composition of air at high temperature and low density, and indicates the overlapping regions of the various dissociation and ionization processes.

PROBLEMS

13.1 Show that at the triple point of water all three phases have the same value of the Gibbs function.

13.2 Consider a gas well one mile deep filled with pure ethane. The temperature may be assumed to be uniform throughout the well at 100 F. The pressure is measured at the top of the well and found to be 1000 lbf/in.² What is the pressure at the bottom of the well?

13.3 Consider a gas well containing a mixture of methane and ethane at a uniform temperature of 100 F. The pressure at the top of the well is 2000 lbf/in.², and the molar composition is 90% CH_4, 10% C_2H_6. Determine the pressure and composition at a depth of one mile, assuming

(a) ideal gas mixture.

(b) ideal solution.

13.4 Consider the liquid-vapor equilibrium system methane-carbon monoxide at −150 F, 600 lbf/in.² Calculate the equilibrium composition, assuming ideal solution for both phases. (The values determined experimentally at this condition are $x_{CO} = 0.211$, $y_{CO} = 0.339.$*)

13.5 An air-water vapor mixture is in equilibrium with liquid water (assuming the mole fraction of air in the liquid to be negligible) at 120 F, 500 lbf/in.² Calculate the mole fraction of H_2O in the gas phase, assuming

(a) Raoult's rule—Ideal gas (the method used for saturated air-H_2O mixtures in Chapter 11).

(b) Ideal solution.

13.6 Consider the effect of gaseous nitrogen on the equilibrium of solid-vapor carbon dioxide at 190 K and a pressure of 100 atmospheres. Assume that the mole fraction of nitrogen in the solid phase is negligible.

Determine the mole fraction of CO_2 in the vapor by the following methods:

(a) Ideal gas.

(b) Ideal solution.

(c) Van der Waals' equation of state using a linear combination for b and square-root for a.

(The experimental value for this pressure and temperature is $y_{CO_2} = 0.0324$.†)

For carbon dioxide at 190 K,

$$P_{\text{sublimation}} = 0.679 \text{ atm} \qquad v_{\text{solid}} = 0.0280 \frac{\text{lit}}{\text{gm mole-K}}$$

13.7 Calculate the equilibrium composition of the liquid and vapor phases in the binary system carbon dioxide-sulfur dioxide at 30 C, 40 atmospheres, assuming that both phases behave as ideal solutions. Compare the results with the experimental values $x_{CO_2} = 0.46$, $y_{CO_2} = 0.88$, and evaluate the assumption of ideal solution for the two phases at this point.

13.8 Calculate the equilibrium constant for the reaction

$$NO + \tfrac{1}{2}O_2 \rightleftharpoons NO_2$$

at 537 R and at 1800 R.

13.9 Plot to scale the values of ln K vs. $1/T$ for the reaction $CO_2 \rightleftharpoons CO + \tfrac{1}{2}O_2$. Write an equation for the ln K as a function of temperature.

13.10 (a) One mole of oxygen at 77 F and 1 atm pressure is heated to 5000 K

---

* A. Toyama, P. S. Chappelear, T. W. Leland, and R. Kobayashi, *Adv. in Cryog. Eng.*, **7**, 125 (1962).

† G. E. Smith, R. E. Sonntag, and G. J. Van Wylen, *Adv. in Cryog. Eng.*, **9**, 197 (1964).

in a constant-pressure process. What is the composition at 5000 K and 1 atm pressure, assuming that O_2 and O are the constituents present?

(b) Repeat part a for a pressure of 0.1 atm.

13.11 Oxygen is heated from room temperature in a steady-flow process at a constant pressure of 10 atm. At what temperature will the mole fraction of O_2 in the mixture of O_2 and O be 30%? (That is, the mole fraction of the O_2 is 30% and of the O, 70%.)

13.12 A mixture of 1 mole CO_2, $\frac{1}{2}$ mole CO, and 2 moles O_2 at 77 F and 20 lbf/in.² pressure is heated in a constant pressure steady-flow process to 3000 K. Determine the equilibrium composition at 3000 K on a per cent basis, assuming the reaction equation to be

$$CO_2 \rightleftharpoons CO + \tfrac{1}{2}O_2$$

13.13 Repeat Problem 13.12 for the case where the initial mixture also includes 2 moles N_2, which does not dissociate during the process.

13.14 Calculate the equilibrium constant at 3000 K for the reaction

$$2CO_2 \rightleftharpoons 2CO + O_2$$

Repeat Problem 13.12 using this reaction equation instead of the one specified in Problem 13.12.

13.15 (a) One mole of hydrogen at 537 R, 30 lbf/in.², is heated to 5400 R at constant pressure in a steady-state, steady-flow process.

Determine the equilibrium composition at the outlet and the heat transfer per mole of H_2 entering.

(b) Plot the equilibrium composition of hydrogen (H_2 and H) as a function of temperature for 1 atm and for 0.01 atm pressure.

13.16 Diatomic fluorine gas (F_2) enters a heat exchanger at 77 F, 100 lbf/in.² at the rate of 1 mole/min. The gas is heated to 3000 R, during which process some of the fluorine dissociates according to the reaction

$$F_2 \rightleftharpoons 2 F$$

Calculate:

(a) The equilibrium constant for the reaction at 3000 R.

(b) The composition of the mixture leaving the heat exchanger at 3000 R, 100 lbf/in.²

(c) The heat transfer rate, Btu/min.

	$(\bar{h}_f°)_{537} \left(\dfrac{\text{Btu}}{\text{mole}}\right)$	$\bar{s}°_{537} \left(\dfrac{\text{Btu}}{\text{mole-R}}\right)$	$\bar{C}_{po} \left(\dfrac{\text{Btu}}{\text{mole-R}}\right)$
F_2	0	48.45	$6.5 + 5.5 \times 10^{-4}T$
F	34020	37.92	4.968

13.17 A mixture of 40% CO_2, 40% O_2, 20% N_2 (by volume) at 77 F, 25 lbf/in.², is fed to a steady-flow heater at the rate of 1 mole/min. An equilibrium mixture of CO_2, CO, O_2, N_2 leaves the heater at 4500 F, 25 lbf/in.² Determine

(a) The composition of the mixture leaving the heater.

(b) Heat transfer to the heater/min.

13.18 One mole of carbon monoxide at 1 atm pressure, 1000 K, reacts with one mole of oxygen at 1 atm pressure, 1000 K to form an equilibrium mixture at 2800 K and a total pressure of 1 atm.

(a) Determine the heat transfer for this process, assuming that the reaction takes place in a steady-state, steady-flow process.

(b) Calculate the irreversibility for this process.

13.19 One mole of water vapor at 1 atm pressure and 400 K temperature is heated to 3000 K in a steady-flow constant-pressure process. Determine the final composition and heat transfer for this process, assuming that H_2, O_2, and H_2O are present in the final state.

13.20 One mole of hydrogen at 77 F and 1 atm pressure reacts with 2 moles of oxygen at 77 F and 1 atm pressure in a steady-flow adiabatic process. The products are at 1 atm pressure and consist of H_2, O_2, and H_2O. Determine the adiabatic flame temperature.

13.21 Calculate the net entropy change for the process described in Problem 13.20.

13.22 Many combustion processes involve products of combustion at temperatures not greater than 2000 F. A gas turbine is a typical example. Usually the effects of dissociation are ignored at these temperatures. Is this justified for CO_2 and H_2O?

13.23 As a preliminary study of a rocket fuel combination, consider the combustion of octane with 200% theoretical oxygen. The products leave the combustion chamber at 5000 R, 200 lbf/in.^{2} Due to the high temperature, some of the CO_2 formed will have dissociated to CO and O_2 (neglect any other dissociation reactions). Assuming a condition of chemical equilibrium, determine the composition of the products.

13.24 A mixture of 1 mole CO_2 and 2 moles O_2 at 77 F, 1 atm., is slowly heated to 5400 R in a closed tank. Determine the equilibrium composition at the final state, assuming that only CO_2, CO, and O_2 are present.

13.25 A mixture of 2 moles CO_2, 2 moles O_2, and b moles N_2 at room temperature and 50 lbf/in.^{2} is heated to 3500 F in a steady-flow process. Consider that at the outlet the mixture consists of CO_2, O_2, N_2, CO in equilibrium. Determine the minimum value for b if the mole fraction of CO at the outlet is to be kept below 0.001.

13.26 Consider the reaction

$$2NH_3 \rightleftharpoons N_2 + 3H_2$$

(a) Using the data given below, calculate the equilibrium constant at 750 R.

(b) For an initial composition of 1 mole NH_3, calculate the equilibrium composition at 750 R, 150 atm, assuming

     (1) Ideal gas mixture.

     (2) Ideal solution.

For NH_3: $(\bar{h}_f)_{537} = -19{,}872 \, \dfrac{\text{Btu}}{\text{mole}}$; $(\bar{g}_f°)_{537} = -7157 \, \dfrac{\text{Btu}}{\text{mole}}$

$$\bar{C}_{po} = 6.086 + 8.812 \times 10^{-3}T - 1.506 \times 10^{-6}T^2 \, \dfrac{\text{Btu}}{\text{mole-R}}$$

13.27 A gas mixture at 77 F, 15 lbf/in.^{2}, which consists of 50% CO_2 and 50% CO (by volume) is fed to a chemical reactor at the rate of 2 moles/min. Steam from a line at 400 F, 200 lbf/in.^{2} is also fed to the reactor at the rate of 2 moles/min. In the reactor the gases are heated in the presence of a catalyst such that the mixture leaving the reactor at 1340 F, 15 lbf/in.^{2} may be assumed to be in equilibrium according to the reaction

$$CO + H_2O \rightleftharpoons CO_2 + H_2$$

Assume that all the constituents are ideal gases except for the inlet steam. Calculate:

(a) The equilibrium constant for this reaction at 1340 F using the values from Table A.12.

(b) Enthalpy of the inlet steam relative to the elements at 77 F, 1 atm.

(c) Composition (on a mole basis) of the mixture leaving the reactor.

(d) Heat transfer to the reactor per minute.

13.28 A mixture of one mole H_2O and one mole O_2 at 400 K is heated to 3000 K, 2 atm pressure, in a steady-state, steady-flow process. Determine the equilibrium composition at the outlet of the heat exchanger, assuming that H_2O, H_2, O_2, and OH are present.

13.29 One lb mole of air (assume 78% N_2, 21% O_2, 1% Ar) at room temperature is heated to 7200 R, 30 lbf/in.^{2} Find the equilibrium composition at this temperature and pressure, assuming that only N_2, O_2, NO, O, and Ar are present.

13.30 Calculate the heat transfer required for the process described in Problem 13.29, assuming a steady-state, steady-flow process.

13.31 One mole of water vapor at 1 atm pressure and 400 K is heated to 3000 K in a steady-flow constant-pressure process. Determine the final composition, assuming that H_2O, H_2, H, O_2, and OH are present at equilibrium.

13.32 Methane is burned with theoretical oxygen in a steady-state, steady-flow process. The products leave the combustion chamber at 5300 F, 100 lbf/in.^{2}, and because of the high temperature some of the CO_2 and H_2O will have dissociated. Calculate the equilibrium composition, assuming that CO_2, H_2O, CO, H_2, O_2, and OH are present.

13.33 One gm mole of argon at room temperature is heated to 20,000 K, 1 atm pressure. Assume that the plasma at this condition consists of an equilibrium mixture of Ar, Ar^+, A^{++}, e^-, according to the simultaneous reactions

(1) $Ar \rightleftharpoons Ar^+ + e^-$

(2) $Ar^+ \rightleftharpoons Ar^{++} + e^-$

The ionization-equilibrium constants for these reactions at 20,000 K have been calculated from spectroscopic data as: $\ln K_1 = 3.11$; $\ln K_2 = -4.92$. Determine the equilibrium composition of the plasma.

13.34 Plot the equilibrium composition of nitrogen at 0.1 atm pressure (assume N_2, N, N^+, e^- present) from 5000 K to 15,000 K. For the reaction

$$N \rightleftharpoons N^+ + e^-$$

the ionization-equilibrium constant K has been calculated from spectroscopic data* as

$T(°K)$	K
10,000	6.26×10^{-4}
12,000	1.51×10^{-2}
14,000	0.151
16,000	0.92

* F. Martinek, "Thermodynamic and Electrical Properties of Nitrogen at High Temperatures." *Thermodynamic and Transport Properties of Gases, Liquids and Solids*, p. 130. A.S.M.E., McGraw-Hill Book Co., Inc. (1959).

14 Flow through Nozzles and Blade Passages*

This chapter deals with the thermodynamic aspects of one-dimensional flow through nozzles and blade passages. In addition, the momentum equation for the control volume is developed and applied to these same problems. The sonic velocity is defined in terms of thermodynamic properties, and the importance of the Mach number as a variable in compressible flow is noted.

14.1 Stagnation Properties

In dealing with problems involving flow, many discussions and equations can be simplified by introducing the concept of the isentropic stagnation state and the properties associated with it. The isentropic stagnation state is the state a flowing fluid would attain if it underwent a reversible adiabatic deceleration to zero velocity. This state is designated in this chapter with the subscript 0. From the first law for a steady-state, steady-flow process we conclude that

$$h + \frac{V^2}{2g_c} = h_0 \tag{14.1}$$

The actual and the isentropic stagnation states for a typical gas or vapor

---

* As indicated in the preface, the basic idea of the Thermal and Transport Sciences Series is to present basic texts in thermodynamics, fluid mechanics, heat transfer, and statistical thermodynamics, followed by certain applications of these subjects. As the first book in this series, the original intention had been to limit the coverage in this book to thermodynamics, and to encourage the use of the next volume in this series, *Fluid Mechanics*, by A. G. Hansen, for a thorough coverage of fluid mechanics. However, this final chapter has been included in order to make the book complete in itself and perhaps even to contribute to the continuity of the series. It should be emphasized however, that a complete analysis of fluid flow problems involves not only thermodynamics, but many other topics, such as viscosity, turbulence, similarity locus, and boundary layer theory.

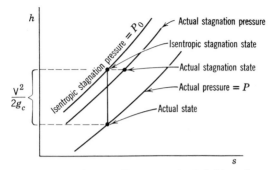

Fig. 14.1   Enthalpy-entropy diagram illustrating the definition of stagnation state.

are shown on the *h-s* diagram of Fig. 14.1. Sometimes it is advantageous to make a distinction between the actual and the isentropic stagnation states. The actual stagnation state is the state achieved after an actual deceleration to zero velocity (as at the nose of a body placed in a fluid stream), and there may be irreversibilities associated with the deceleration process. Therefore, the term stagnation property is sometimes reserved for the properties associated with the actual state, and the term total property is used for the isentropic stagnation state.

It is evident from Fig. 14.1 that the enthalpy is the same for both the actual and isentropic stagnation states (assuming that the actual process is adiabatic). Therefore, for an ideal gas, the actual stagnation temperature is the same as the isentropic stagnation temperature. However, the actual stagnation pressure may be less than the isentropic stagnation pressure and for this reason the term total pressure (meaning isentropic stagnation pressure) has particular meaning compared to the actual stagnation pressure.

Example 14.1

Air flows in a duct at a pressure of 20 lbf/in.^{2} with a velocity of 600 ft/sec. The temperature of the air is 80 F. Determine the isentropic stagnation pressure and temperature.

If we assume that the air is an ideal gas with constant specific heat as given in Table A.8, the calculation is as follows. From Eq. 14.1

$$\frac{V^2}{2g_c} = h_0 - h = C_{po}(T_0 - T)$$

$$\frac{(600)^2}{64.34 \times 778} = 0.240(T_0 - T)$$

$$T_0 = 570 \text{ R} = 110 \text{ F}$$

The stagnation pressure can be found from the relation

$$\frac{T_0}{T} = \left(\frac{P_0}{P}\right)^{(k-1)/k}$$

$$\frac{570}{540} = \left(\frac{P_0}{P}\right)^{0.286}$$

$$\frac{P_0}{P} = 1.210$$

$$P_0 = 20(1.210) = 24.2 \text{ lbf/in.}^2$$

The Air Tables, Table A.10, which are abridged from Keenan and Kayes' *Gas Tables* could also have been used, and then the variation of specific heat with temperature would have been taken into account. Since the actual and stagnation states have the same entropy, we proceed as follows: Using Table 1 of the *Gas Tables* (Appendix Table A.10),

$$T = 540 \text{ R} \qquad h = 129.06 \qquad P_r = 1.3860$$

$$h_0 = h + \frac{V^2}{2g_c} = 129.06 + \frac{(600)^2}{64.34 \times 778} = 136.26$$

$$T_0 = 570 \text{ R} \qquad P_{r0} = 1.6748$$

$$P_0 = P \times \frac{P_{r0}}{P_r} = 20.0 \times \frac{1.6748}{1.3860} = 24.2 \text{ lbf/in.}^2$$

14.2 The Momentum Equation for the Control Volume

Before proceeding it will be advantageous to develop the momentum equation for the control volume. Newton's second law states that the sum of the external forces acting on a body in a given direction is proportional to the rate of change of momentum in the given direction. Writing this in equation form for the x-direction we have

$$\sum F_x \propto \frac{d(mV_x)}{dt}$$

For the system of units used in this book it is convenient to introduce the constant g_c.

$$\sum F_x = \frac{1}{g_c} \frac{d(mV_x)}{dt} \tag{14.2}$$

Equation 14.2 has been written for a body of fixed mass, or in thermodynamic parlance, for a system. We now proceed to write the momentum equation for a control volume, and follow a procedure similar to that used

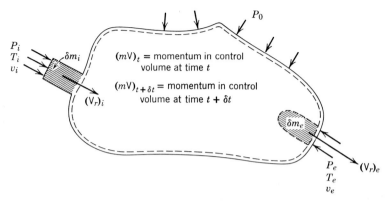

Fig. 14.2   Schematic diagram for the development of the momentum equation for a control volume.

in writing the continuity equation and the first and second laws of thermodynamics for a control volume.

Consider the system and control volume shown in Fig. 14.2. Let the control volume be fixed relative to its coordinate frame. During the time interval δt, the mass δm_i enters the control volume with a velocity $(V_r)_i$ and velocity components $(V_x)_i$, $(V_y)_i$, and $(V_z)_i$. During this same time interval the mass δm_e leaves the control volume, with velocity $(V_r)_e$ and velocity components $(V_x)_e$, $(V_y)_e$, and $(V_z)_e$.

If we write the x-momentum equation for the system during this time interval we have

$$(\textstyle\sum F_x)_{\text{av}} = \frac{1}{g_c}\frac{\Delta(mV_x)}{\delta t} = \frac{1}{g_c}\frac{(mV_x)_2 - (mV_x)_1}{\delta t} \tag{14.3}$$

Let $(mV_x)_t = x$-momentum in the control volume at time t.

$(mV_x)_{t+\delta t} = x$-momentum in the control volume at time $t + \delta t$.

Then

$(mV_x)_1 = (mV_x)_t + (V_x)_i\,\delta m_i = x$-momentum of the system at time t.

$(mV_x)_2 = (mV_x)_{t+\delta t} + (V_x)_e\,\delta m_e = x$-momentum of the system at time $t + \delta t$.

It follows that

$$(mV_x)_2 - (mV_x)_1 = [(mV_x)_{t+\delta t} - (mV_x)_t] + [(V_x)_e\,\delta m_e - (V_x)_i\,\delta m_i] \tag{14.4}$$

The first bracketed term on the right side of Eq. 14.4 represents the change of x-momentum within the control volume during the time interval

δt. This can be written as a volume integral in the form

$$(m\mathbf{V}_x)_{t+\delta t} - (m\mathbf{V}_x)_t = \delta \int_V \mathbf{V}_x \rho \, dV \qquad (14.5)$$

Dividing by δt, we have

$$\frac{(m\mathbf{V}_x)_{t+\delta t} - (m\mathbf{V}_x)_t}{\delta t} = \frac{\delta}{\delta t} \int_V \mathbf{V}_x \rho \, dV \qquad (14.6)$$

The second bracketed term in Eq. 14.4 represents the momentum flow across the control surface during δt, and can be written as a surface integral.

$$(\mathbf{V}_x)_e \, \delta m_e - (\mathbf{V}_x)_i \, \delta m_i = \left[\int_A \mathbf{V}_x \rho \mathbf{V}_r \cos \alpha \, dA \right]_{av} \delta t \qquad (14.7)$$

Dividing by δt we have the average rate at which momentum crosses the control surface during δt.

$$\frac{(\mathbf{V}_x)_e \, \delta m_e - (\mathbf{V}_x)_i \, \delta m_i}{\delta t} = \left[\int_A \mathbf{V}_x \rho \mathbf{V}_r \cos \alpha \, dA \right]_{av} \qquad (14.8)$$

Substituting Eqs. 14.4, 14.6, and 14.8 into Eq. 14.3 we have

$$(\textstyle\sum F_x)_{av} = \frac{1}{g_c} \left\{ \frac{\delta}{\delta t} \int_V \mathbf{V}_x \rho \, dV + \left[\int_A \mathbf{V}_x \rho \mathbf{V}_r \cos \alpha \, dA \right]_{av} \right\} \qquad (14.9)$$

We now establish the limit for each of these terms as $\delta t \to 0$.

$$\lim_{\delta t \to 0} (\textstyle\sum F_x)_{av} = \textstyle\sum F_x$$

$$\lim_{\delta t \to 0} \frac{\delta}{\delta t} \int_V \mathbf{V}_x \rho \, dV = \frac{d}{dt} \int_V \mathbf{V}_x \rho \, dV \qquad (14.10)$$

$$\lim_{\delta t \to 0} \left[\int_A \mathbf{V}_x \rho \mathbf{V}_r \cos \alpha \, dA \right]_{av} = \int_A \mathbf{V}_x \rho \mathbf{V}_r \cos \alpha \, dA$$

Thus, as $\delta t \to 0$ we have a rate form of the momentum equation for the control volume.

$$\textstyle\sum F_x = \frac{1}{g_c} \left[\frac{d}{dt} \int_V \mathbf{V}_x \rho \, dV + \int_A \mathbf{V}_x \rho \mathbf{V}_r \cos \alpha \, dA \right] \qquad (14.11)$$

Similar equations can also be written for y and z directions.

$$\textstyle\sum F_y = \frac{1}{g_c} \left[\frac{d}{dt} \int_V \mathbf{V}_y \rho \, dV + \int_A \mathbf{V}_y \rho \mathbf{V}_r \cos \alpha \, dA \right] \qquad (14.12)$$

$$\textstyle\sum F_z = \frac{1}{g_c} \left[\frac{d}{dt} \int_V \mathbf{V}_z \rho \, dV + \int_A \mathbf{V}_z \rho \mathbf{V}_r \cos \alpha \, dA \right] \qquad (14.13)$$

In this chapter we will be concerned primarily with steady-state, steady-flow processes in which there is a single flow with uniform properties into the control surface, and a single flow with uniform properties out of the control surface. The assumption of steady-state, steady-flow means that the volume integrals in Eqs. 14.11, 14.12, and 14.13 are equal to zero. That is

$$\frac{d}{dt}\int_V V_x \rho \, dV = 0; \qquad \frac{d}{dt}\int_V V_y \rho \, dV = 0; \qquad \frac{d}{dt}\int_V V_z \rho \, dV = 0$$

The assumption of uniform properties both into and out of the control volume means that we can write

$$\int_A V_x \rho V_r \cos \alpha \, dA = \sum \dot{m}_e(V_e)_x - \sum \dot{m}_i(V_i)_x$$

$$\int_A V_y \rho V_r \cos \alpha \, dA = \sum \dot{m}_e(V_e)_y - \sum \dot{m}_i(V_i)_y \qquad (14.14)$$

$$\int_A V_z \rho V_r \cos \alpha \, dA = \sum \dot{m}_e(V_e)_y - \sum \dot{m}_i(V_i)_z$$

Therefore, for such a process the momentum equation for the control volume reduces to

$$\sum F_x = \frac{1}{g_c}[\sum \dot{m}_e(V_e)_x - \sum \dot{m}_i(V_i)_x]$$

$$\sum F_y = \frac{1}{g_c}[\sum \dot{m}_e(V_e)_y - \sum \dot{m}_i(V_i)_y] \qquad (14.15)$$

$$\sum F_z = \frac{1}{g_c}[\sum \dot{m}_e(V_e)_z - \sum \dot{m}_i(V_i)_z]$$

If with these same assumptions, there is a single flow into and out of the control volume these equations reduce to

$$\sum F_x = \frac{\dot{m}}{g_c}[(V_e)_x - (V_i)_x]$$

$$\sum F_y = \frac{\dot{m}}{g_c}[(V_e)_y - (V_i)_y] \qquad (14.16)$$

$$\sum F_z = \frac{\dot{m}}{g_c}[(V_e)_z - (V_i)_z]$$

Example 14.2

On a level floor a man is pushing a wheelbarrow (Fig. 14.3) into which sand is falling at the rate of 1 lbm/sec. The man is walking at the rate of

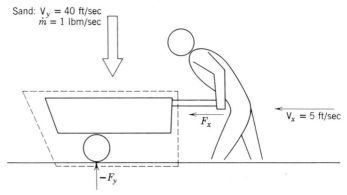

Fig. 14.3   Sketch for Example 14.2.

5 ft/sec and the sand has a velocity of 40 ft/sec as it falls into the wheelbarrow. Determine the force the man must exert on the wheelbarrow and
the force the floor exerts on the wheelbarrow due to the falling sand.

Consider a control surface around the wheelbarrow. Consider first the
x-direction. From Eq. 14.11

$$\sum F_x = F_x = \frac{1}{g_c}\left[\frac{d}{dt}\int_V V_x\rho\,dV + \int_A V_x\rho V_r \cos \alpha\,dA\right]$$

Let us analyze this problem from the point of view of an observer riding
on the wheelbarrow. For this observer, V_x of the material in the wheelbarrow is zero and therefore,

$$\frac{d}{dt}\int_V V_x\rho\,dV = 0$$

However, for this observer the sand crossing the control surface has an
x-component velocity of -5 ft/sec, and $\int_A \rho V_r \cos \alpha\,dA$, the mass flow
out of the control volume is -1 lbm/sec. Therefore,

$$F_x = \frac{1\ \text{lbm/sec} \times 5\ \text{ft/sec}}{32.17\ \text{lbm-ft/lbf-sec}^2} = 0.155\ \text{lbf}$$

If one considers this from the point of view of an observer who is
stationary on the earth's surface we conclude that V_x of the falling sand is
zero and therefore

$$\int_A V_x\rho V_r \cos \alpha\,dA = 0$$

However for this observer there is a change of momentum within the control volume, namely,

$$F_x = \frac{1}{g_c}\left[\frac{d}{dt}\int_V V_x\rho\,dV\right] = \frac{5\text{ ft/sec} \times 1\text{ lbm/sec}}{32.17\text{ lbm-ft/lbf-sec}^2} = 0.155\text{ lbf}$$

Next consider the vertical (y) direction.

$$\sum F_y = F_y = \frac{1}{g_c}\left[\int_V V_y\rho\,dV + \int_A V_y\rho V_r\cos\alpha\,dA\right]$$

For both the stationary and moving observer the first term drops out because V_y of the mass within the control volume is zero. However, for the mass crossing the control surface, $V_y = 40$ ft/sec and

$$\int_A \rho V_r\cos\alpha\,dA = -1\text{ lbm/sec}$$

Therefore,

$$F_y = \frac{40\text{ ft/sec} \times (-1\text{ lbm/sec})}{32.17\text{ lbm-ft/lbf-sec}^2} = -1.24\text{ lbf}$$

The minus sign indicates that the force is in the opposite direction to V_y.

14.3   Forces Acting on a Control Surface

In the last section we considered the momentum equation for the control volume. We now wish to evaluate the net force on a control surface which causes this change in momentum. Let us do this by considering the system shown in Fig. 14.4, which involves a pipe bend. The control surface is designated by the dotted lines, and is so chosen that at the point where the fluid crosses the system boundary the flow is perpendicular to the control surface. The shear forces at the section where the fluid crosses the boundary of the system are assumed to be negligible. Figure 14.4a shows the velocities and Fig. 14.4b shows the forces involved.

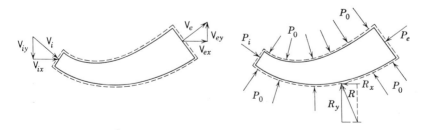

Fig. 14.4   Forces acting on a control surface.

The force R is the result of all external forces on the system, except for the pressure of the surroundings. The pressure of the surroundings, P_0, acts on the entire boundary except at A_i and A_e, where the fluid crosses the control surface. P_i and P_e represent the absolute pressures at these points.

The net forces acting on the system in the x and y directions, F_x and F_y, are the sum of the pressure forces and the external force R in their respective directions. The influence of the pressure of the surroundings, P_0, is most easily taken into account by noting that it acts over the entire system boundary except at A_i and A_e. Therefore, we can write

$$\sum F_x = (P_i A_i)_x - (P_0 A_i)_x + (P_e A_e)_x - (P_0 A_e)_x + R_x$$
$$\sum F_y = (P_i A_i)_y - (P_0 A_i)_y + (P_e A_e)_y - (P_0 A_e)_y + R_y$$

This equation may be simplified by combining the pressure terms.

$$\sum F_x = [(P_i - P_0)A_i]_x + [(P_e - P_0)A_e]_x + R_x$$
$$\sum F_y = [(P_i - P_0)A_i]_y + [(P_e - P_0)A_e]_y + R_y$$

(14.17)

The proper sign for each pressure and force must of course be used in all calculations.

Equations 14.15 and 14.17 may be combined to give

$$\sum F_x = \frac{1}{g_c} [\sum \dot{m}_e(V_e)_x - \sum \dot{m}_i(V_i)_x] = \sum [(P_i - P_0)A_i]_x$$
$$+ \sum [(P_e - P_0)A_e]_x + R_x \quad (14.18)$$
$$\sum F_y = \frac{1}{g_c} [\sum \dot{m}_e(V_e)_y - \sum \dot{m}_i(V_i)_y] = \sum [(P_i - P_0)A_i]_y$$
$$+ \sum [(P_e - P_0)A_e]_y + R_y$$

If there is a single flow across the control surface, Eqs. 14.16 and 14.17 can be combined to give

$$\sum F_x = \frac{\dot{m}}{g_c}(V_e - V_i)_x = [(P_i - P_0)A_i]_x + [(P_e - P_0)A_e]_x + R_x$$

(14.19)

$$\sum F_y = \frac{\dot{m}}{g_c}(V_e - V_i)_y = [(P_i - P_0)A_i]_y + [(P_e - P_0)A_e]_y + R_y$$

A similar equation could be written for the z-direction. These equations are very useful in analyzing the forces involved in a control volume analysis.

Example 14.3

A jet engine is being tested on a test stand (Fig. 14.5). The inlet area to the compressor is 1.8 ft², and air enters the compressor at 14.0 lbf/in.², 300 ft/sec. The pressure of the atmosphere is 14.7 lbf/in.². The exit area

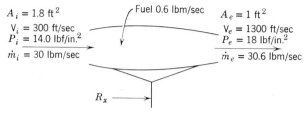

$A_i = 1.8 \text{ ft}^2$
$V_i = 300 \text{ ft/sec}$
$P_i = 14.0 \text{ lbf/in.}^2$
$\dot{m}_i = 30 \text{ lbm/sec}$

Fuel 0.6 lbm/sec

$A_e = 1 \text{ ft}^2$
$V_e = 1300 \text{ ft/sec}$
$P_e = 18 \text{ lbf/in.}^2$
$\dot{m}_e = 30.6 \text{ lbm/sec}$

R_x

Fig. 14.5 Sketch for Example 14.3.

of the engine is 1 ft², and the products of combustion leave the exit plane at a pressure of 18 lbf/in.² and a velocity of 1300 ft/sec. The air-fuel ratio is 50 lbm air/lbm fuel, and the fuel enters with a low velocity. The rate of air flow entering the engine is 30 lbm/sec. Determine the thrust on the engine.

In the solution that follows it is assumed that forces and velocities to the right are positive.

Using Eq. 14.19

$$R_x + [(P_i - P_0)A_i]_x + [(P_e - P_0)A_e]_x = \frac{1}{g_c}(\dot{m}_e V_e - \dot{m}_i V_i)_x$$

$$R_x + [(14.0 - 14.7)144 \text{ lbf/ft}^2 \times 1.8 \text{ ft}^2]$$

$$- [(18.0 - 14.7)144 \text{ lbf/ft}^2 \times 1.0 \text{ ft}^2]$$

$$= \frac{(30.6 \times 1300 - 30 \times 300) \text{ lbm ft/sec}^2}{32.17 \text{ lbm-ft/lbf-sec}^2}$$

$$R_x = 957 + 180 + 475 = 1612 \text{ lbf}$$

(Note that the momentum of the fuel entering has been neglected.)

14.4 Adiabatic, One-Dimensional, Steady-State, Steady Flow of an Incompressible Fluid through a Nozzle

A nozzle is a device in which the kinetic energy of a fluid is increased in an adiabatic process. This increase involves a decrease in pressure and is accomplished by the proper change in flow area. A diffuser is a device that has the opposite function namely, to increase the pressure by decelerating the fluid. In this section we discuss both nozzles and diffusers, but to minimize words we shall use only the term nozzle.

Consider the nozzle shown in Fig. 14.6, and assume an adiabatic, one-dimensional, steady-state, steady-flow process of an incompressible fluid.

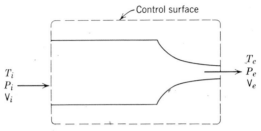

Fig. 14.6   Schematic sketch of a nozzle.

From the continuity equation we conclude that

$$\dot{m}_e = \dot{m}_i = \rho A_i V_i = \rho A_e V_e$$

or
$$\frac{A_i}{A_e} = \frac{V_e}{V_i} \qquad (14.20)$$

The first law for this process is

$$h_e - h_i + \frac{V_e^{\,2} - V_i^{\,2}}{2g_c} + \frac{(Z_e - Z_i)g}{g_c} = 0 \qquad (14.21)$$

From the second law we conclude that $s_e \geq s_i$, where the equality holds for a reversible process. Therefore, from the relation

$$T\,ds = dh - v\,dP$$

we conclude that for the reversible process

$$h_e - h_i = \int_i^e v\,dP \qquad (14.22)$$

If we assume that the fluid is incompressible, Eq. 14.22 can be integrated to give

$$h_e - h_i = v(P_e - P_i) \qquad (14.23)$$

Substituting this in Eq. 14.21 we have

$$v(P_e - P_i) + \frac{V_e^{\,2} - V_i^{\,2}}{2g_c} + \frac{(Z_e - Z_i)g}{g_c} = 0 \qquad (14.24)$$

This is of course the Bernoulli Equation which was derived in Section 7.8, Eq. 7.39, and for the reversible, adiabatic one-dimensional steady-state, steady-flow of an incompressible fluid through a nozzle the Bernoulli Equation represents a combined statement of the first and second laws of thermodynamics.

Example 14.4

Water enters the diffuser in a pump casing with a velocity of 100 ft/sec, a pressure of 50 lbf/in.², and a temperature of 80 F. It leaves the diffuser with a velocity of 20 ft/sec and a pressure of 90 lbf/in.². Determine the exit pressure for a reversible diffuser with these inlet conditions and exit velocity. Determine the increase in enthalpy, internal energy, and entropy for the actual diffuser.

Consider first a control surface around a reversible diffuser with the given inlet conditions and exit velocity. Equation 14.24, the Bernoulli equation, is a statement of the first and second laws of thermodynamics for this process. Since there is no change in elevation this equation reduces to

$$v[(P_e)_s - P_i] + \frac{V_e{}^2 - V_i{}^2}{2g_c} = 0$$

where $(P_e)_s$ represents the exit pressure for the reversible diffuser. From the steam tables, $v = 0.01608$ ft³/lbm.

$$P_{es} - P_1 = \frac{(100)^2 - (20)^2}{0.01608 \times 2 \times 32.17 \times 144} = 64.5 \text{ lbf/in.}^2$$

$$P_{es} = 50 + 64.5 = 114.5 \text{ lbf/in.}^2$$

Next consider a control surface around the actual diffuser. The change in enthalpy can be found from the first law for this process, Eq. 14.21.

$$h_e - h_i = \frac{V_i{}^2 - V_e{}^2}{2g_c} = \frac{(100)^2 - (20)^2}{2 \times 32.17 \times 778} = 0.192 \text{ Btu/lbm}$$

The change in internal energy can be found from the definition of enthalpy, $h_e - h_i = (u_e - u_i) + (P_e v_e - P_i v_i)$.

Thus, for an incompressible fluid

$$u_e - u_i = h_e - h_i - v(P_e - P_i)$$

$$= 0.192 \text{ Btu/lbm} - 0.01608 \text{ ft}^3/\text{lbm} \times \frac{(90 - 50)144 \text{ lbf/ft}^2}{778 \text{ ft-lbf/Btu}}$$

$$= 0.192 - 0.119 = 0.073 \text{ Btu/lbm}$$

The change of entropy can be approximated from the familiar relation

$$T\, ds = du + P\, dv$$

by assuming that the temperature is constant (which is approximately true in this case) and noting that for an incompressible fluid $dv = 0$. With these assumptions

$$s_e - s_i = \frac{u_e - u_i}{T} = \frac{0.073}{540} = 0.000135 \text{ Btu/lbm-R}$$

Since this is an irreversible adiabatic process, the entropy will increase, as the above calculation indicates.

14.5 Velocity of Sound in an Ideal Gas

When a pressure disturbance occurs in a compressible fluid, the disturbance travels with a velocity that depends on the state of the fluid. A sound wave is a very small pressure disturbance; the velocity of sound, also called the sonic velocity, is an important parameter in compressible-fluid flow. We proceed now to determine an expression for the sonic velocity of an ideal gas in terms of the properties of the gas.

Let a disturbance be set up by the movement of the piston at the end of the tube, Fig. 14.7a. A wave travels down the tube with a velocity c, which is the sonic velocity. Assume that after the wave has passed the properties of the gas have changed an infinitesimal amount and that the gas is moving with the velocity dV toward the wave front.

In Fig. 14.7b this process is shown from the point of view of an observer who travels with the wave front. Consider the control surface shown in Fig. 14.7b. From the first law for this steady-state, steady-flow process we can write,

$$h + \frac{c^2}{2g_c} = (h + dh) + \frac{(c - dV)^2}{2g_c}$$

$$dh - \frac{c\,dV}{g_c} = 0$$

(14.25)

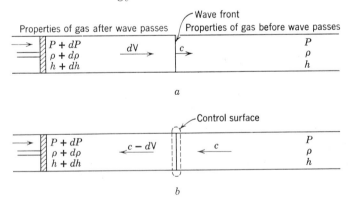

Fig. 14.7 Diagram illustrating sonic velocity. (a) Stationary observer. (b) Observer traveling with wave front.

From the continuity equation we can write

$$\rho Ac = (\rho + d\rho)A(c - dV)$$
$$c\,d\rho - \rho\,dV = 0$$

$$(14.26)$$

Consider also the relation between properties

$$T\,ds = dh - \frac{dP}{\rho}$$

If the process is isentropic, $ds = 0$, and this equation can be combined with Eq. 14.25 to give the relation

$$\frac{dP}{\rho} - \frac{c\,dV}{g_c} = 0$$

$$(14.27)$$

This can be combined with Eq. 14.26 to give the relation

$$\frac{dP}{d\rho} = \frac{c^2}{g_c}$$

Since we have assumed the process to be isentropic this is better written as a partial derivative.

$$\left(\frac{\partial P}{\partial \rho}\right)_s = \frac{c^2}{g_c}$$

$$(14.28)$$

An alternate derivation is to introduce the momentum equation. For the control volume of Fig. 14.7b the momentum equation is

$$PA - (P + dP)A = \frac{\dot{m}}{g_c}(c - dV - c) = \frac{\rho Ac}{g_c}(c - dV - c)$$

$$dV = \frac{g_c}{\rho c}\,dP$$

$$(14.29)$$

On combining this with Eq. 14.26 we obtain Eq. 14.28.

$$\left(\frac{\partial P}{\partial \rho}\right)_s = \frac{c^2}{g_c}$$

It will be of particular advantage to solve Eq. 14.28 for the velocity of sound in an ideal gas.

When an ideal gas undergoes an isentropic change of state, we found in Chapter 7 that, for this process, assuming constant specific heat,

$$\frac{dP}{P} - k\frac{d\rho}{\rho} = 0$$

or
$$\left(\frac{\partial P}{\partial \rho}\right)_s = \frac{kP}{\rho}$$

Substituting this equation in Eq. 14.28 we have an equation for the velocity of sound in an ideal gas,

$$c^2 = \frac{kPg_c}{\rho} \tag{14.30}$$

Since for an ideal gas

$$\frac{P}{\rho} = RT$$

this equation may also be written

$$c^2 = kg_cRT \tag{14.31}$$

Example 14.5

Determine the velocity of sound in air at 80 F and at 1000 F. Using Eq. 14.31

$$c = \sqrt{kg_cRT}$$
$$= \sqrt{1.4 \times 32.17 \text{ lbm-ft/lbf-sec}^2 \times 53.34 \text{ ft-lbf/lbm-R} \times 540 \text{ R}}$$
$$= 1138 \text{ ft/sec}$$

Similarly, at 1000 F, using $k = 1.4$,

$$c = \sqrt{1.4 \times 32.17 \times 53.34 \times 1460}$$
$$= 1862 \text{ ft/sec}$$

Note the significant increase in sonic velocity as the temperature increases.

The Mach number, M, is defined as the ratio of the actual velocity V to the sonic velocity c.

$$M = \frac{V}{c} \tag{14.32}$$

When $M > 1$ the flow is supersonic; when $M < 1$ the flow is subsonic: and when $M = 1$ the flow is sonic. The importance of the Mach number as a parameter in fluid-flow problems will be evident in the paragraphs which follow.

14.6   Reversible, Adiabatic, One-Dimensional, Steady Flow of an Ideal Gas through a Nozzle

A nozzle or diffuser with both a converging and diverging section is shown in Fig. 14.8. The minimum cross-sectional area is called the throat.

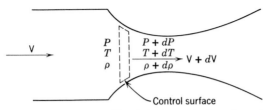

Fig. 14.8   One-dimensional reversible adiabatic steady flow through a nozzle.

Our first consideration concerns the conditions that determine whether a nozzle or diffuser should be converging or diverging, and the conditions that prevail at the throat.   For the control volume shown the following relations can be written.
First law:

$$dh + \frac{V \, dV}{g_c} = 0 \tag{14.33}$$

Property relation:

$$T \, ds = dh - \frac{dP}{\rho} = 0 \tag{14.34}$$

Continuity equation:

$$\rho A V = \dot{m} = \text{constant}$$

$$\frac{d\rho}{\rho} + \frac{dA}{A} + \frac{dV}{V} = 0 \tag{14.35}$$

Combining Eqs. 14.33 and 14.34 we have

$$dh = \frac{dP}{\rho} = \frac{-V \, dV}{g_c}$$

$$dV = - \frac{g_c}{\rho V} \, dP$$

Substituting this in Eq. 14.35

$$\frac{dA}{A} = \left(-\frac{d\rho}{\rho} - \frac{dV}{V} \right) = -\frac{d\rho}{\rho} \left(\frac{dP}{dP} \right) + \frac{g_c}{\rho V^2} \, dP$$

$$= \frac{-dP}{\rho} \left(\frac{d\rho}{dP} - \frac{g_c}{V^2} \right) = \frac{dP}{\rho} \left(-\frac{1}{(dP/d\rho)} + \frac{g_c}{V^2} \right)$$

Since the flow is isentropic

$$\frac{dP}{d\rho} = \frac{c^2}{g_c} = \frac{V^2}{M^2 g_c}$$

and therefore,

$$\frac{dA}{A} = \frac{dP}{\rho V^2/g_c} (1 - M^2) \tag{14.36}$$

This is a very significant equation, for from it we can draw the following conclusions about the proper shape for nozzles and diffusers:

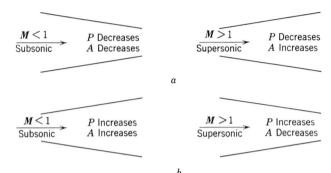

$M < 1$ Subsonic →	P Decreases A Decreases		$M > 1$ Supersonic →	P Decreases A Increases

a

$M < 1$ Subsonic →	P Increases A Increases		$M > 1$ Supersonic →	P Increases A Decreases

b

Fig. 14.9   Required area changes for (*a*) nozzles, and (*b*) diffusers.

For a nozzle, $dP < 0$. Therefore,

for a subsonic nozzle, $M < 1$, $dA < 0$, and the nozzle is converging.

for a supersonic nozzle, $M > 1$, $dA > 0$, and the nozzle is diverging.

For a diffuser, $dP > 0$. Therefore,

for a subsonic diffuser, $M < 1$, $dA > 0$, and the diffuser is diverging.

for a supersonic diffuser, $M > 1$, $dA < 0$, and the diffuser is converging.

When $M = 1$, $dA = 0$, which means that sonic velocity can be achieved only at the throat of a nozzle or diffuser. These conclusions are summarized in Fig. 14.9.

We will now develop a number of relations between the actual properties, stagnation properties, and Mach number. These relations are very useful in dealing with isentropic flow of an ideal gas in a nozzle.

Equation 14.1 gives the relation between enthalpy, stagnation enthalpy, and kinetic energy.

$$h + \frac{V^2}{2g_c} = h_0$$

For an ideal gas with constant specific heat Eq. 14.1 can be written

$$V^2 = 2g_c C_{p_0}(T_0 - T) = 2g_c \frac{kRT}{k-1}\left(\frac{T_0}{T} - 1\right)$$

Since

$$c^2 = kg_c RT$$

$$V^2 = \frac{2c^2}{k-1}\left(\frac{T_0}{T} - 1\right)$$

$$\frac{V^2}{c^2} = M^2 = \frac{2}{k-1}\left(\frac{T_0}{T} - 1\right)$$

$$\frac{T_0}{T} = 1 + \frac{(k-1)}{2}M^2 \tag{14.37}$$

For an isentropic process,

$$\left(\frac{T_0}{T}\right)^{k/(k-1)} = \frac{P_0}{P} \qquad \left(\frac{T_0}{T}\right)^{1/(k-1)} = \frac{\rho_0}{\rho}$$

Therefore,

$$\frac{P_0}{P} = \left[1 + \frac{(k-1)}{2}M^2\right]^{k/(k-1)} \tag{14.38}$$

$$\frac{\rho_0}{\rho} = \left[1 + \frac{(k-1)}{2}M^2\right]^{1/(k-1)} \tag{14.39}$$

Values of P/P_0, ρ/ρ_0, and T/T_0 are given as a function of M in Tables 30 to 35 of the *Gas Tables*, each table being for a given value of k. Table A.13 of the Appendix has been abstracted from Table 30 of the *Gas Tables*, and applies to an ideal gas with $k = 1.4$.

The conditions at the throat of the nozzle can be found by noting that $M = 1$ at the throat. The properties at the throat are denoted by an asterisk.* Therefore,

$$\frac{T^*}{T_0} = \frac{2}{k+1} \tag{14.40}$$

$$\frac{P^*}{P_0} = \left(\frac{2}{k+1}\right)^{k/(k-1)} \tag{14.41}$$

$$\frac{\rho^*}{\rho_0} = \left(\frac{2}{k+1}\right)^{1/(k-1)} \tag{14.42}$$

These properties at the throat of a nozzle when $M = 1$ are frequently referred to as critical pressure, critical temperature, and critical density and the ratios given by Eqs. 14.40, 14.41, and 14.42 are referred to as the critical-temperature ratio, critical-pressure ratio, and critical-density ratio. Table 14.1 gives these ratios for various values of k.

TABLE 14.1

Critical Pressure, Density, and Temperature Ratios
for Isentropic Flow of an Ideal Gas

	$k = 1.1$	$k = 1.2$	$k = 1.3$	$k = 1.4$	$k = 1.67$
P^*/P_0	0.5847	0.5644	0.5457	0.5283	0.4867
ρ^*/ρ_0	0.6139	0.6209	0.6276	0.6340	0.6497
T^*/T_0	0.9524	0.9091	0.8696	0.8333	0.7491

14.7 Mass Rate of Flow of an Ideal Gas through an Isentropic Nozzle

We now turn our attention to a consideration of the mass rate of flow per unit area, $\dot{m}/A$, in a nozzle. From the continuity equation we proceed as follows:

$$\frac{\dot{m}}{A} = \rho V = \frac{PV}{RT}\sqrt{\frac{kg_cT_0}{kg_cT_0}}$$

$$= \frac{PV}{\sqrt{kg_cRT}}\sqrt{\frac{g_ck}{R}}\sqrt{\frac{T_0}{T}}\sqrt{\frac{1}{T_0}}$$

$$= \frac{PM}{\sqrt{T_0}}\sqrt{\frac{kg_c}{R}}\sqrt{1 + \frac{k-1}{2}M^2} \tag{14.43}$$

By substituting Eq. 14.38 into Eq. 14.42 the flow per unit area can be expressed in terms of stagnation pressure, stagnation temperature, Mach number, and gas properties.

$$\frac{\dot{m}}{A} = \frac{P_0}{\sqrt{T_0}}\sqrt{\frac{kg_c}{R}} \times \frac{M}{\left(1 + \dfrac{k-1}{2}M^2\right)^{(k+1)/2(k-1)}} \tag{14.44}$$

At the throat, $M = 1$, and therefore the flow per unit area at the throat, $\dot{m}/A^*$, can be found by setting $M = 1$ in Eq. 14.44.

$$\frac{\dot{m}}{A^*} = \frac{P_0}{\sqrt{T_0}}\sqrt{\frac{kg_c}{R}} \times \frac{1}{\left(\dfrac{k+1}{2}\right)^{(k+1)/2(k-1)}} \tag{14.45}$$

The area ratio A/A^* can be obtained by dividing Eq. 14.45 by Eq. 14.44.

$$\frac{A}{A^*} = \frac{1}{M}\left[\left(\frac{2}{k+1}\right)\left(1 + \frac{k-1}{2}M^2\right)\right]^{(k+1)/2(k-1)} \tag{14.46}$$

The area ratio A/A^* is the ratio of the area at the point where the Mach number is M to the throat area, and values of A/A^* as a function of Mach number are given in Tables 30 through 35 of the *Gas Tables* and in Table A.13 in the Appendix. Figure 14.10 shows a plot of A/A^* vs. M, which is in accordance with our previous conclusion that a subsonic nozzle is converging and a supersonic nozzle is diverging.

The final point to be made regarding the isentropic flow of an ideal

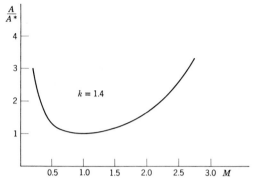

Fig. 14.10   Area ratio as a function of Mach number for a reversible adiabatic nozzle.

gas through a nozzle involves the effect of varying the back pressure (the pressure outside the nozzle exit) on the mass rate of flow.

Consider first a convergent nozzle as shown in Fig. 14.11, which also shows the pressure ratio P/P_0 along the length of the nozzle. The conditions upstream are the stagnation conditions, which are assumed to be constant. The pressure at the exit plane of the nozzle is designated P_E, and the back pressure P_B. Let us consider how the mass rate of flow $\dot{m}$ and the exit plane pressure P_E/P_0, vary as the back pressure P_B is decreased. These quantities are plotted in Fig. 14.12.

When $P_B/P_0 = 1$ there is of course no flow, and $P_E/P_0 = 1$ as designated by point a. Next let the back pressure P_B be lowered to that designated by point b, so that P_B/P_0 is greater than the critical-pressure ratio. The mass rate of flow has a certain value and $P_E = P_B$. The exit Mach number is less than 1. Next let the back pressure be lowered to the critical pressure, designated by point c. The Mach number at the exit is now unity, and P_E is equal to P_B. When P_B is decreased below the critical pressure, designated by point d, there is no further increase in the mass rate of flow,

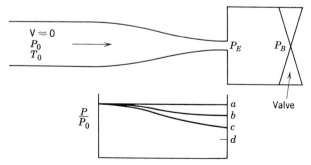

Fig. 14.11   Pressure ratio as a function of back pressure for a convergent nozzle.

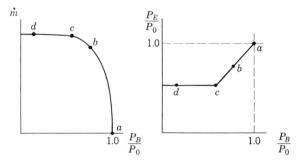

Fig. 14.12   Mass rate of flow and exit pressure as a function of back pressure for a convergent nozzle.

and P_E remains constant at a value equal to the critical pressure, and the exit Mach number is unity. The drop in pressure from P_E to P_B takes place outside the nozzle exit. Under these conditions the nozzle is said to be choked, which means that for given stagnation conditions the nozzle is passing the maximum possible mass flow.

Consider next a convergent-divergent nozzle in a similar arrangement, Fig. 14.13. Point a designates the condition when $P_B = P_0$ and there is no flow. When P_B is decreased to the pressure indicated by point b, so that P_B/P_0 is less than 1 but considerably greater than the critical-pressure ratio, the velocity increases in the convergent section, but $M < 1$ at the throat. Therefore, the diverging section acts as a subsonic diffuser in which the pressure increases and velocity decreases. Point c designates the back pressure at which $M = 1$ at the throat, but the diverging section acts as a subsonic diffuser (with $M = 1$ at the inlet) in which the pressure increases and velocity decreases. Point d designates one other back pressure that permits isentropic flow, and in this case the diverging section acts as a supersonic nozzle, with a decrease in pressure and an increase in

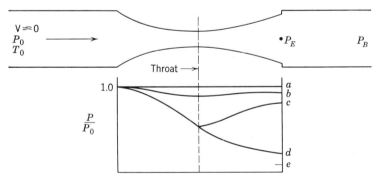

Fig. 14.13   Nozzle pressure ratio as a function of back pressure for a reversible convergent-divergent nozzle.

velocity. Between the back pressures designated by points c and d, an isentropic solution is not possible, and shock waves will be present. This matter is discussed in the section that follows. When the back pressure is decreased below that designated by point d, the exit-plane pressure P_E remains constant, and the drop in pressure from P_E to P_B takes place outside the nozzle. This is designated by point e.

Example 14.6

A convergent nozzle has an exit area of 1 in.². Air enters the nozzle with a stagnation pressure of 100 lbf/in.² and a stagnation temperature of 200 F. Determine the mass rate of flow for back pressures of 80 lbf/in.², 52.8 lbf/in.², and 30 lbf/in.², assuming isentropic flow.

For air $k = 1.4$ and Table 30 of the *Gas Tables* (or Table A.13 in the Appendix) may be used. The critical-pressure ratio, P^*/P_0, is 0.528. Therefore, for a back pressure of 52.8 lbf/in.² $M = 1$ at the nozzle exit and the nozzle is choked. Decreasing the back pressure below 52.8 lbf/in.² will not increase the flow.

For a back pressure of 52.8 lbf/in.²

$$\frac{T^*}{T} = 0.833 \qquad T^* = 0.833(660) = 550 \text{ R}$$

At the exit

$$V = c = \sqrt{kg_cRT}$$
$$= \sqrt{1.4 \times 32.17 \times 53.34 \times 550} = 1152 \text{ ft/sec}$$
$$\rho^* = \frac{P^*}{RT^*} = \frac{52.8 \times 144}{53.34 \times 550} = 0.259 \text{ lbm/ft}^3$$
$$\dot{m} = \rho A V$$

Applying this relation to the throat section,

$$\dot{m} = 0.259 \text{ lbm/ft}^3 \times \tfrac{1}{144} \text{ ft}^2 \times 1152 \text{ ft/sec} = 2.07 \text{ lbm/sec}$$

For a back pressure of 80 lbf/in.², $P_E/P_0 = 0.8$ (subscript E designates the properties in the exit plane). From Table A.13,

$$M_E = 0.573 \qquad T_E/T_0 = 0.938$$
$$T_E = 0.938(660) = 619 \text{ R}$$
$$c_E = \sqrt{kg_cRT_E} = \sqrt{1.4 \times 32.17 \times 53.34 \times 619} = 1222 \text{ ft/sec}$$
$$V_E = M_E c_E = 0.573(1222) = 700 \text{ ft/sec}$$
$$\rho_E = \frac{P_E}{RT_E} = \frac{80 \times 144}{53.34 \times 619} = 0.35 \text{ lbm/ft}^3$$
$$\dot{m} = \rho A V$$

Applying this relation to the exit section,

$$\dot{m} = 0.35 \text{ lbm/ft}^3 \times \tfrac{1}{144} \text{ ft}^2 \times 700 \text{ ft/sec} = 1.69 \text{ lbm/sec}$$

For a back pressure less than the critical pressure, which in this case is 52.8 lbf/in.², the nozzle is choked and the mass rate of flow is the same as that for the critical pressure. Therefore, for an exhaust pressure of 30 lbf/in.², the mass rate of flow is 2.07 lbm/sec.

Example 14.7

A converging-diverging nozzle has an exit area to throat area ratio of 2. Air enters this nozzle with a stagnation pressure of 100 lbf/in.² and a stagnation temperature of 200 F. The throat area is 1 in.². Determine the mass rate of flow, exit pressure, exit temperature, exit Mach number, and exit velocity for the following conditions:

(a) Sonic velocity at the throat, diverging section acting as a nozzle. (Corresponds to point d in Fig. 14.13.)

(b) Sonic velocity at the throat, diverging section acting as a diffuser. (Corresponds to point c in Fig. 14.13.)

(a) In Table A.13 of the Appendix we find that there are two Mach numbers listed for $A/A^* = 2$. One of these is greater than unity and one is less than unity. When the diverging section acts as a supersonic nozzle we use the value for $M > 1$. The following are from Table A.13.

$$\frac{A_E}{A^*} = 2.0 \qquad M_E = 2.197 \qquad \frac{P_E}{P_0} = 0.0939 \qquad \frac{T_E}{T_0} = 0.5089$$

Therefore,

$$P_E = 0.0939(100) = 9.39 \text{ lbf/in.}^2$$

$$T_E = 0.5089(660) = 336 \text{ R}$$

$$c_E = \sqrt{kg_cRT_E} = \sqrt{1.4 \times 32.17 \times 53.34 \times 336} = 900 \text{ ft/sec}$$

$$V_E = M_Ec_E = 2.197(900) = 1977 \text{ ft/sec}$$

The mass rate of flow can be determined by considering either the throat section or the exit section. However, in general it is preferable to determine the mass rate of flow from conditions at the throat. Since in this case $M = 1$ at the throat, the calculation is identical to the calculation for the flow in the convergent nozzle of Example 14.6 when it is choked.

(b) The following are from Table A.13

$$\frac{A_E}{A^*} = 2.0 \qquad M_E = 0.306 \qquad \frac{P_E}{P_0} = 0.9371 \qquad \frac{T_E}{T_0} = 0.9816$$

$$P_E = 0.9371(100) = 93.7 \text{ lbf/in.}^2$$

$$T_E = 0.9816(660) = 649 \text{ R}$$

$$c_E = \sqrt{kg_cRT_E} = \sqrt{1.4 \times 32.17 \times 53.34 \times 649} = 1250 \text{ ft/sec}$$

$$V_E = M_Ec_E = 0.306(1250) = 383 \text{ ft/sec}$$

Since $M = 1$ at the throat, the mass rate of flow is the same as in (*a*), which is also equal to the flow in the convergent nozzle of Example 14.6 when it is choked.

In the example above a solution assuming isentropic flow is not possible if the back pressure is between 93.7 lbf/in.² and 9.39 lbf/in.². If the back pressure is in this range there will either be a normal shock in the nozzle or oblique shock waves outside the nozzle. The matter of normal shock waves is considered in the following section.

14.8   Normal Shock in an Ideal Gas Flowing through a Nozzle

A shock wave involves an extremely rapid and abrupt change of state. In a normal shock this change of state takes place across a plane normal to the direction of the flow. Figure 14.14 shows a control surface that includes such a normal shock. We can now determine the relations that govern the flow. Assuming steady-state, steady-flow we can write the following relations, where subscripts x and y denote the conditions upstream and downstream of the shock respectively. Note that no heat and work cross the control surface.
First law:

$$h_x + \frac{V_x^{\,2}}{2g_c} = h_y + \frac{V_y^{\,2}}{2g_c} = h_{0x} = h_{0y} \qquad (14.47)$$

Continuity equation:

$$\frac{\dot{m}}{A} = \rho_x V_x = \rho_y V_y \qquad (14.48)$$

Momentum equation:

$$A(P_x - P_y) = \frac{\dot{m}}{g_c}(V_y - V_x) \qquad (14.49)$$

Second law: Since the process is adiabatic

$$s_y - s_x \geq 0 \qquad (14.50)$$

The energy and continuity equations can be combined to give an

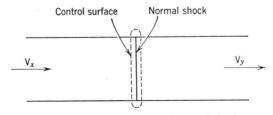

Fig. 14.14   One-dimensional normal shock.

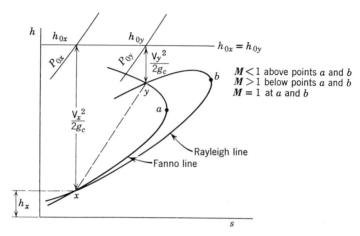

Fig. 14.15 End states for a one-dimensional normal shock on an enthalpy-entropy
diagram.

equation which when plotted on the h-s diagram is called the Fanno line.
Similarly, the momentum and continuity equations can be combined to
give an equation, the plot of which on the h-s diagram is known as the
Rayleigh line. Both of these lines are shown on the h-s diagram of Fig.
14.15. It can be shown that the point of maximum entropy on each
line, points a and b, correspond to $M = 1$. The lower part of each line
corresponds to supersonic velocities, and the upper part to subsonic
velocities.

The two points where all three equations are satisfied are points x and
y, x being in the supersonic region and y in the subsonic region. Since
the second law requires that $s_y - s_x \geq 0$ in an adiabatic process, we
conclude that the normal shock can proceed only from x to y. This
means that the velocity changes from supersonic ($M > 1$) before the
shock to subsonic ($M < 1$) after the shock.

The equations governing normal shock waves will now be developed.
If we assume constant specific heats we conclude from Eq. 14.47, the
energy equation, that

$$T_{0x} = T_{0y} \tag{14.51}$$

That is, there is no change in stagnation temperature across a normal
shock. Introducing Eq. 14.37

$$\frac{T_{0x}}{T_x} = 1 + \frac{k-1}{2} M_x^{\ 2} \qquad \frac{T_{0y}}{T_y} = 1 + \frac{k-1}{2} M_y^{\ 2}$$

and substituting into Eq. 14.51 we have,

$$\frac{T_y}{T_x} = \frac{1 + \frac{k-1}{2} M_x^2}{1 + \frac{k-1}{2} M_y^2} \tag{14.52}$$

The equation of state, the definition of Mach number, and the relation $c = \sqrt{kg_cRT}$ can be introduced into the continuity equation as follows:

$$\rho_x V_x = \rho_y V_y$$

But

$$\rho_x = \frac{P_x}{RT_x} \qquad \rho_y = \frac{P_y}{RT_y}$$

$$\frac{T_y}{T_x} = \frac{P_y V_y}{P_x V_x} = \frac{P_y M_y c_y}{P_x M_x c_x} = \frac{P_y M_y \sqrt{T_y}}{P_x M_x \sqrt{T_x}}$$

$$= \left(\frac{P_y}{P_x}\right)^2 \left(\frac{M_y}{M_x}\right)^2 \tag{14.53}$$

Combining Eqs. 14.52 and 14.53, which involves combining the energy equation and the continuity equation, gives the equation of the Fanno line.

$$\frac{P_y}{P_x} = \frac{M_x \sqrt{1 + \frac{k-1}{2} M_x^2}}{M_y \sqrt{1 + \frac{k-1}{2} M_y^2}} \tag{14.54}$$

The momentum and continuity equations can be combined as follows to give the equation of the Rayleigh line.

$$P_x - P_y = \frac{\dot{m}}{Ag_c}(V_y - V_x) = \frac{\rho_y V_y^2 - \rho_x V_x^2}{g_c}$$

$$P_x g_c + \rho_x V_x^2 = P_y g_c + \rho_y V_y^2$$

$$P_x g_c + \rho_x M_x^2 c_x^2 = P_y g_c + \rho_y M_y^2 c_y^2$$

$$P_x g_c + \frac{P_x M_x^2}{RT_x}(kg_cRT_x) = P_y g_c + \frac{P_y M_y^2}{RT_y}(kg_cRT_y)$$

$$P_x(1 + kM_x^2) = P_y(1 + kM_y^2)$$

$$\frac{P_y}{P_x} = \frac{1 + kM_x^2}{1 + kM_y^2} \tag{14.55}$$

Equations 14.54 and 14.55 can be combined to give the following equation relating M_x and M_y.

$$M_y^2 = \frac{M_x^2 + \dfrac{2}{k-1}}{\dfrac{2k}{k-1} M_x^2 - 1} \tag{14.56}$$

Tables 48 through 53 of the *Gas Tables* give the normal shock functions, which include M_y as a function of M_x. Table A.14 of the Appendix has been abstracted from Table 48 of the *Gas Tables*, and applies to an ideal gas with $k = 1.4$. Note that M_x is always supersonic and M_y is always subsonic, which agrees with the previous statement that in a normal shock the velocity changes from supersonic to subsonic. These tables also give the pressure, density, temperature, and stagnation pressure ratios across a normal shock as a function of M_x. These are found from Eqs. 14.52, 14.53, and the equation of state. Note that there is always a drop in stagnation pressure across a normal shock and an increase in the static pressure.

Example 14.8

Consider the convergent-divergent nozzle of Ex. 14.7 in which the diverging section acts as a supersonic nozzle (Fig. 14.16). Assume that a normal shock stands in the exit plane of the nozzle. Determine the static pressure and temperature and the stagnation pressure just downstream of the normal shock.

From Table 48 of the *Gas Tables* (Table A.14 of the Appendix)

$$M_x = 2.197 \qquad M_y = 0.548 \qquad \frac{P_y}{P_x} = 5.46 \qquad \frac{T_y}{T_x} = 1.854 \qquad \frac{P_{0y}}{P_{0x}} = 0.631$$

$P_y = 5.46 \times P_x = 5.46 \times 9.39 = 51.2 \text{ lbf/in.}^2$

$T_y = 1.854 \times T_x = 1.854 \times 336 = 622 \text{ R}$

$P_{0y} = 0.631 \times P_{0x} = 0.631 \times 100 = 63.1 \text{ lbf/in.}^2$

In the light of this example we can conclude the discussion concerning the flow through a convergent-divergent nozzle. Figure 14.13 is repeated here as Fig. 14.17 for convenience, except that points f, g, and h have been added. Consider point d. We have already noted that with this back pressure the exit plane pressure P_E is just equal to the back pressure P_B, and isentropic flow is maintained in the nozzle. Let the back pressure be raised to that designated by point f. The exit-plane pressure P_E is not influenced by this increase in back pressure, and the increase in pressure from P_E to P_B takes place outside the nozzle. Let the back pressure be

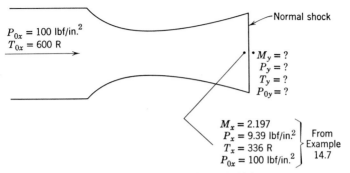

$P_{0x} = 100$ lbf/in.^{2}
$T_{0x} = 600$ R

Normal shock

$^{\bullet}M_y = ?$
$P_y = ?$
$T_y = ?$
$P_{0y} = ?$

$M_x = 2.197$
$P_x = 9.39$ lbf/in.^{2}
$T_x = 336$ R
$P_{0x} = 100$ lbf/in.^{2}

From Example 14.7

Fig. 14.16   Sketch for Example 14.8.

raised to that designated by point g, which is just sufficient to cause a normal shock to stand in the exit plane of the nozzle. The exit-plane pressure P_E (downstream of the shock) is equal to the back pressure P_B, and $M < 1$ leaving the nozzle. This is the case in Ex. 14.8. Now let the back pressure be raised to that corresponding to point h. As the back pressure is raised from g to h the normal shock moves into the nozzle as indicated. Since $M < 1$ downstream of the normal shock, the diverging part of the nozzle which is downstream of the shock acts as a subsonic diffuser. As the back pressure is increased from h to c the shock moves further upstream and disappears at the nozzle throat where the back pressure corresponds to c. This is reasonable since there are no supersonic velocities involved when the back pressure corresponds to c, and hence no shock waves are possible.

Example 14.9
Consider the convergent-divergent nozzle of Examples 14.7 and 14.8. Assume that there is a normal shock wave standing at the point where

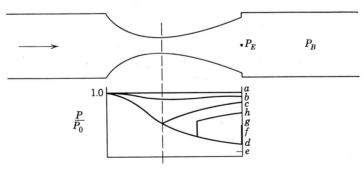

$\bullet P_E$ P_B

$\dfrac{P}{P_0}$

1.0

a
b
c
h
g
f
d
e

Fig. 14.17   Nozzle pressure ratio as a function of back pressure for a convergent-divergent nozzle.

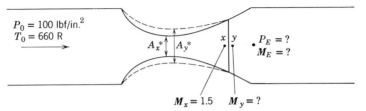

$P_0 = 100$ lbf/in.^{2}
$T_0 = 660$ R

A_x^* A_y^* $x|y$ $\bullet \, P_E = ?$
$\quad M_E = ?$

$M_x = 1.5$ $M_y = ?$

Fig. 14.18 Sketch for Example 14.9.

$M = 1.5$. Determine the exit-plane pressure, temperature, and Mach number. Assume isentropic flow except for the normal shock (Fig. 14.18).

The properties at point x can be determined from Table A.13, because the flow is isentropic to point x.

$$M_x = 1.5 \qquad \frac{P_x}{P_{0x}} = 0.272 \qquad \frac{T_x}{T_{0x}} = 0.690 \qquad \frac{A_x}{A_x^*} = 1.176$$

Therefore,

$$P_x = 0.272(100) = 27.2 \text{ lbf/in.}^2$$
$$T_x = 0.690(660) = 455 \text{ R}$$

The properties at point y can be determined from the normal shock functions, Table A.14.

$$M_y = 0.701 \qquad \frac{P_y}{P_x} = 2.458 \qquad \frac{T_y}{T_x} = 1.320 \qquad \frac{P_{0y}}{P_{0x}} = 0.9298$$

$$P_y = 2.458 P_x = 2.458(27.2) = 66.9 \text{ lbf/in.}^2$$
$$T_y = 1.320 T_x = 1.320(455) = 601 \text{ R}$$
$$P_{0y} = 0.9298 P_{0x} = 0.9298(100) = 93.0 \text{ lbf/in.}^2$$

Since there is no change in stagnation temperature across a normal shock,

$$T_{0x} = T_{0y} = 660 \text{ R}$$

From y to E the diverging section acts as a subsonic diffuser. In solving this problem it is convenient to think of the flow at y as having come from an isentropic nozzle having a throat area A_y^*. Such a hypothetical nozzle is shown by the dotted line. From the table of isentropic flow functions, Table A.13, we find the following for $M_y = 0.701$:

$$M_y = 0.701 \qquad \frac{A_y}{A_y^*} = 1.094 \qquad \frac{P_y}{P_{0y}} = 0.721 \qquad \frac{T_y}{T_{0y}} = 0.911$$

From the statement of the problem

$$\frac{A_E}{A_x^*} = 2.0$$

Also, since the flow from y to E is isentropic,

$$\frac{A_E}{A_E^*} = \frac{A_E}{A_y^*} = \frac{A_E}{A_x^*} \times \frac{A_x^*}{A_x} \times \frac{A_x}{A_y} \times \frac{A_y}{A_y^*}$$

$$= \frac{A_E}{A_y^*} = 2.0 \times \frac{1}{1.176} \times 1 \times 1.094 = 1.897$$

From the table of isentropic flow functions for $A/A^* = 1.897$ and $M < 1$

$$M_E = 0.343 \qquad \frac{P_E}{P_{0E}} = 0.922 \qquad \frac{T_E}{T_{0E}} = 0.977$$

$$\frac{P_E}{P_{0E}} = \frac{P_E}{P_{0y}} = 0.922$$

$$P_E = 0.922(P_{0y}) = 0.922(93.0) = 85.7 \text{ lbf/in.}^2$$

$$T_E = 0.977(T_{0E}) = 0.977(660) = 645 \text{ R}$$

In conclusion it should be pointed out that in considering the normal shock we have ignored the effect of viscosity and thermal conductivity, which are certain to be present. The actual shock wave will occur over some finite thickness. However, the development as given here gives a very good qualitative picture of normal shocks, and also provides a basis for fairly accurate quantitative results.

14.9   Flow of a Vapor through a Nozzle

In this section we consider a vapor to be a substance that is in the gaseous phase but with limited superheat. Therefore, the vapor will probably deviate significantly from the ideal-gas relations, and the possibility of condensation must be considered. The most familiar example is the flow of steam through the nozzles of a steam turbine.

The principles that have been developed for the isentropic flow of an ideal gas apply also to the isentropic flow of a vapor. However, because the vapor deviates from the ideal-gas relationships, the appropriate tables of thermodynamic properties must be used. Further, the possibility of condensation must be borne in mind, as indicated in Fig. 14.19. If steam expands isentropically from state 1 to state 2, and if equilibrium is maintained throughout the nozzle, condensation would begin at point a, and at pressures below this a mixture of liquid droplets and vapor would be present. In an actual nozzle the formation of the liquid tends to be delayed due to an effect known as supersaturation. This will be considered in a later paragraph.

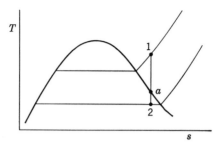

Fig. 14.19   Reversible adiabatic expansion of a vapor.

Let us consider first the isentropic flow of steam in a nozzle without condensation. The value of the specific-heat ratio k for steam varies, but $k = 1.3$ is a good approximation over a considerable range. Therefore, the critical pressure ratio, P^*/P_0, can be found by the relation

$$\frac{P^*}{P_0} = \left(\frac{2}{k+1}\right)^{k/(k-1)} = 0.545 \qquad (14.57)$$

This is also the value given in Table 14.1. Knowing, therefore, the critical-pressure ratio, the throat area for a given flow can be calculated. The exit area of the nozzle can be calculated in a similar manner. The example below illustrates this procedure.

Example 14.10

Steam at a stagnation pressure of 100 lbf/in.^{2} and a stagnation temperature of 600 F expands in a nozzle to 20 lbf/in.^{2}. Determine the throat area and exit area required for a flow of 20,000 lbm/hr, assuming reversible adiabatic flow.

First consider the properties and flow at the throat.

$$\frac{P^*}{P_0} = 0.545 \qquad\qquad P^* = 54.5 \text{ lbf/in.}^2$$

$$s^* = s_0 = 1.7581 \text{ Btu/lbm-R} \qquad h_0 = 1329.1 \text{ Btu/lbm}$$

$$T^* = 460 \text{ F} \qquad\qquad h^* = 1264.0 \text{ Btu/lbm}$$

$$h_0 = h^* + \frac{V^{*2}}{2g_c} \qquad\qquad V^* = \sqrt{2g_c}\sqrt{h_0 - h^*}$$

$$V^* = 223.7\sqrt{1329.1 - 1264.0} = 223.7\sqrt{65.1} = 1800 \text{ ft/sec}$$

$$v^* = 9.961 \text{ (from the steam tables)}$$

$$\dot{m}v^* = A^*V^*$$

$$A^* = \frac{20,000 \times 9.961}{3600 \times 1800} = 0.0307 \text{ ft}^2 = 4.42 \text{ in.}^2$$

At the nozzle exit

$$P_E = 20 \text{ lbf/in.}^2 \qquad s_E = s_0 = 1.7581 \text{ Btu/lbm-R}$$

$$h_E = 1174.9 \text{ Btu/lbm} \qquad v_E = 21.28 \text{ lbf/in.}^2$$

$$V_E = \sqrt{2g_c}\,\sqrt{h_0 - h_E} = 223.7\sqrt{1329.1 - 1174.4} = 223.7\sqrt{154.2}$$

$$= 2780 \text{ ft/sec}$$

$$\dot{m}v_E = A_E V_E$$

$$A_E = \frac{20,000 \times 21.28}{3600 \times 2780} = 0.0426 \text{ ft}^2 = 6.13 \text{ in.}^2$$

For steam initially saturated the critical-pressure ratio is usually taken as

$$\frac{P^*}{P_0} = 0.577 \qquad\qquad (14.58)$$

If the flow with initially saturated steam is assumed to be isentropic there will be a certain amount of liquid entrained with the vapor. Calculation of throat and exit areas under most conditions is similar to the example above.

When the steam flowing through a nozzle is initially superheated, there will be a certain point in the nozzle where the steam becomes saturated.

However, as noted in Section 13.5 in connection with a discussion of metastable equilibrium, if the point at which condensation would occur under equilibrium conditions (point a in Fig. 13.9) occurs in the divergent section of the nozzle, a condition of metastable equilibrium exists. That is, the formation of droplets is delayed, and the vapor temperature is less than the saturation temperature for the given pressure. This is frequently referred to as supersaturation.

This phenomenon of supersaturation is observed only in the diverging portions of the nozzle. In a nozzle in which supersaturation occurs the rate of mass flow might be slightly greater than that obtained in an isentropic flow without supersaturation.

Supersaturation may also be present in a supersonic wind tunnel. An abrupt condensation of the moisture in the air would disturb the flow pattern, and for this reason most of the moisture is removed from the air to be used in the tunnel.

A similar phenomenon may occur in the flow of a saturated liquid through a nozzle or valve. When a saturated liquid flows through a nozzle or valve some of it will vaporize as the pressure is reduced. In practice the formation of the vapor is delayed, because a metastable state exists.

14.10   Nozzle and Diffuser Coefficients

Up to this point we have considered only isentropic flow and normal shocks. As was pointed out in Chapter 7, isentropic flow through a nozzle provides a standard to which the performance of an actual nozzle can be compared. For nozzles, the three important parameters by which actual flow can be compared to the ideal flow are nozzle efficiency, velocity coefficient, and discharge coefficient. These are defined as follows:
The nozzle efficiency η_N is defined as

$$\eta_N = \frac{\text{Actual kinetic energy at nozzle exit}}{\text{Kinetic energy at nozzle exit with isentropic flow to same exit pressure}}$$

(14.59)

The efficiency can be defined in terms of properties. On the h-s diagram of Fig. 14.20 state $0i$ represents the stagnation state of the fluid entering the nozzle; state e represents the actual state at the nozzle exit; and state s represents the state that would have been achieved at the nozzle exit if the flow had been reversible and adiabatic to the same exit pressure. Therefore, in terms of these states the nozzle efficiency is

$$\eta_N = \frac{h_{0i} - h_e}{h_{0i} - h_s}$$

Nozzle efficiencies vary in general from 90 to 99 per cent. Large nozzles usually have higher efficiencies than small nozzles, and nozzles with straight axes have higher efficiencies than nozzles with curved axes. The irreversibilities, which cause the departure from isentropic flow, are primarily due to frictional effects, and are confined largely to the boundary layer. The

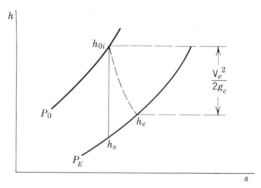

Fig. 14.20   Enthalpy-entropy diagram showing the effects of irreversibility in a nozzle.

rate of change of cross-sectional area along the nozzle axis (i.e., the nozzle contour) is an important parameter in the design of an efficient nozzle, particularly in the divergent section. Detailed consideration of this matter is beyond the scope of this text, and the reader is referred to standard references on the subject.

The velocity coefficient C_V is defined as

$$C_V = \frac{\text{Actual velocity at nozzle exit}}{\text{Velocity at nozzle exit with isentropic flow and same exit pressure}}$$

(14.60)

It follows that the velocity coefficient is equal to the square root of the nozzle efficiency

$$C_V = \sqrt{\eta_N} \qquad (14.61)$$

The coefficient of discharge C_D is defined by the relation

$$C_D = \frac{\text{Actual mass rate of flow}}{\text{Mass rate of flow with isentropic flow}}$$

In determining the mass rate of flow with isentropic conditions, the actual back pressure is used if the nozzle is not choked. If the nozzle is choked, the isentropic mass rate of flow is based on isentropic flow and sonic velocity at the minimum section (i.e., sonic velocity at the exit of a convergent nozzle and at the throat of a convergent-divergent nozzle).

The performance of a diffuser is usually given in terms of diffuser efficiency, which is best defined with the aid of an h-s diagram. On the h-s diagram of Fig. 14.21 states 1 and 01 are the actual and stagnation states of the fluid entering the diffuser. States 2 and 02 are the actual and stagnation states of the fluid leaving the diffuser. State 3 is not attained in the diffuser, but it is the state that has the same entropy as the initial state and the pressure of the isentropic stagnation state leaving the diffuser. The efficiency of the diffuser η_D is defined as

$$\eta_D = \frac{\Delta h_s}{V_1^2/2g_c} = \frac{h_3 - h_1}{h_{01} - h_1} = \frac{h_3 - h_1}{h_{02} - h_1} \qquad (14.62)$$

If we assume an ideal gas with constant specific heat this reduces to

$$\eta_D = \frac{T_3 - T_1}{T_{02} - T_1} = \frac{\dfrac{(T_3 - T_1)}{T_1} T_1}{\dfrac{V_1^2}{2g_c C_{po}}}$$

$$C_{po} = \frac{kR}{k-1} \qquad T_1 = \frac{c_1^2}{kg_c R} \qquad V_1^2 = M_1^2 c_1^2 \qquad \frac{T_3}{T_1} = \left(\frac{P_{02}}{P_1}\right)^{(k-1)/k}$$

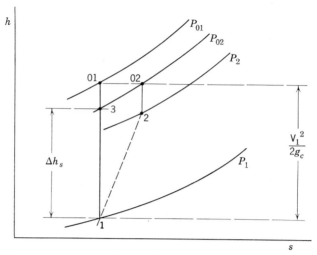

Fig. 14.21 Enthalpy-entropy diagram showing the definition of diffuser efficiency.

Therefore,

$$\eta_D = \frac{\left(\dfrac{P_{02}}{P_1}\right)^{(k-1)/k} - 1}{\dfrac{k-1}{2} M_1^{\,2}}$$

$$\left(\frac{P_{02}}{P_1}\right)^{(k-1)/k} = \left(\frac{P_{01}}{P_1}\right)^{(k-1)/k} \times \left(\frac{P_{02}}{P_{01}}\right)^{(k-1)/k}$$

$$= \left(1 + \frac{k-1}{2} M_1^{\,2}\right)\left(\frac{P_{02}}{P_{01}}\right)^{(k-1)/k}$$

$$\eta_D = \frac{\left(1 + \dfrac{k-1}{2} M_1^{\,2}\right)\left(\dfrac{P_{02}}{P_{01}}\right)^{(k-1)/k} - 1}{\dfrac{k-1}{2} M_1^{\,2}} \qquad (14.63)$$

14.11 Nozzles and Orifices as Flow-Measuring Devices

The mass rate of flow of a fluid flowing in a pipe is frequently determined by measuring the pressure drop across a nozzle or orifice in the line, as shown in Fig. 14.22. The ideal process for such a nozzle or orifice is assumed to be isentropic flow through a nozzle which has the measured pressure drop from inlet to exit and a minimum cross-sectional area equal

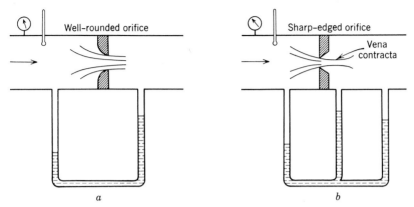

Fig. 14.22 Nozzles and orifices as flow-measuring devices.

to the minimum area of the nozzle or orifice. The actual flow is related to the ideal flow by the coefficient of discharge which is defined by Eq. 14.62.

The pressure difference measured across an orifice depends upon the location of the pressure taps as indicated in Fig. 14.22. Since the ideal flow is based on the measured pressure difference, it follows that the coefficient of discharge depends on the locations of the pressure taps. Also, the coefficient of discharge for a sharp-edged orifice is considerably less than that for a well-rounded nozzle, primarily due to a contraction of the stream, known as the vena contracta, as it flows through a sharp-edged orifice.

There are two approaches to determining the discharge coefficient of a nozzle or orifice. One is to follow a standard design procedure, such as the ones established by the American Society of Mechanical Engineers,* and use the coefficient of discharge given for a particular design. A more accurate method is to calibrate a given nozzle or orifice, and determine the discharge coefficient for a given installation by accurately measuring the actual mass rate of flow. The procedure to be followed will depend on the accuracy desired and other factors involved (such as time, expense, availability of calibration facilities) in a given situation.

For incompressible fluids flowing through an orifice the ideal flow for a given pressure drop can be found by the procedure outlined in Section 14.4. Actually, it is advantageous to combine Eqs. 14.24 and 14.20 to give the following relation, which is valid for reversible flow.

$$v(P_2 - P_1) + \frac{V_2^2 - V_1^2}{2g_c} = v(P_2 - P_1) + \frac{V_2^2 - (A_2/A_1)^2 V_2^2}{2g_c} = 0 \quad (14.64)$$

*Fluid Meters, Their Theory and Application, ASME, 1959. Flow Measurement, ASME, 1959.

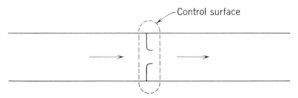

Fig. 14.23   Analysis of a nozzle as a flow-measuring device.

or
$$v(P_2 - P_1) + \frac{V_2^2}{2g_c}\left[1 - \left(\frac{A_2}{A_1}\right)^2\right] = 0$$

$$V_2 = \sqrt{\frac{2g_c v(P_1 - P_2)}{[1 - (A_2/A_1)^2]}} \qquad (14.65)$$

For an ideal gas it is frequently advantageous to use the following simplified procedure when the pressure drop across an orifice or nozzle is small. Consider the nozzle shown in Fig. 14.23. From the first law we conclude that

$$h_i + \frac{V_i^2}{2g_c} = h_e + \frac{V_e^2}{2g_c}$$

Assuming constant specific heat, this reduces to

$$\frac{V_e^2 - V_i^2}{2g_c} = h_i - h_e = C_{po}(T_i - T_e)$$

Let ΔP and ΔT be the decrease in pressure and temperature across the nozzle. Since we are considering reversible adiabatic flow we note that

$$\frac{T_e}{T_i} = \left(\frac{P_e}{P_i}\right)^{(k-1)/k}$$

or
$$\frac{T_i - \Delta T}{T_i} = \left(\frac{P_i - \Delta P}{P_i}\right)^{(k-1)/k}$$

$$1 - \frac{\Delta T}{T_i} = \left(1 - \frac{\Delta P}{P_i}\right)^{(k-1)/k}$$

Using the binomial expansion on the right side of the equation we have

$$1 - \frac{\Delta T}{T_i} = 1 - \frac{k-1}{k}\frac{\Delta P}{P_i} - \frac{k-1}{2k^2}\frac{\Delta P^2}{P_i^2}\cdots$$

If $\Delta P/P_i$ is small this reduces to

$$\frac{\Delta T}{T_i} = \frac{k-1}{k}\frac{\Delta P}{P_i}$$

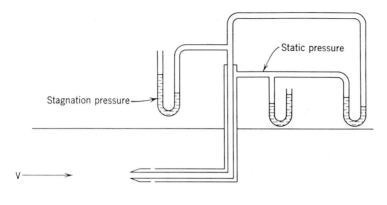

Fig. 14.24   Schematic arrangement of a Pitot tube.

Substituting this into the first-law equation we have

$$\frac{V_e^{\,2} - V_i^{\,2}}{2g_c} = C_{po} \frac{k-1}{k} \Delta P \frac{T_i}{P_i}$$

But for an ideal gas

$$C_{po} = \frac{kR}{k-1} \qquad \text{and} \qquad v_i = R \frac{T_i}{P_i}$$

Therefore,

$$\frac{V_e^{\,2} - V_i^{\,2}}{2g_c} = v_i \Delta P$$

which is the same as Eq. 14.64, which was developed for incompressible flow. Therefore, when the pressure drop across a nozzle or orifice is small, the flow can be calculated with high accuracy by assuming incompressible flow.

The Pitot tube, Fig. 14.24, is an important instrument for measuring the velocity of a fluid. In calculating the flow with a Pitot tube it is assumed that the fluid is decelerated isentropically in front of the Pitot tube, and therefore the stagnation pressure of the free stream can be measured.

Applying the first law to this process we have

$$h + \frac{V^2}{2g_c} = h_0$$

If we assume incompressible flow for this isentropic process, the first law reduces to (because $T\,ds = dh - v\,dp$)

$$\frac{V^2}{2g_c} = h_0 - h = v(P_0 - P)$$

or

$$V = \sqrt{2g_c v(P_0 - P)} \qquad (14.66)$$

If we consider the compressible flow of an ideal gas with constant specific heat, the velocity can be found from the relations

$$\frac{V^2}{2g_c} = h_0 - h = C_{po}(T_0 - T) = C_{po}T\left(\frac{T_0}{T} - 1\right)$$

$$= C_{po}T\left[\left(\frac{P_0}{P}\right)^{(k-1)/k} - 1\right] \tag{14.67}$$

It is of interest to know the error introduced by assuming incompressible flow when using the Pitot tube to measure the velocity of an ideal gas. In order to do so we introduce Eq. 14.38 and rearrange it as follows:

$$\frac{P_0}{P} = \left(1 + \frac{k-1}{2}M^2\right)^{k/(k-1)} = \left[1 + \left(\frac{k-1}{2}\right)\left(\frac{V^2}{c^2}\right)\right]^{k/(k-1)} \tag{14.68}$$

But

$$\frac{V^2}{2g_c} + C_{po}T = C_{po}T_0$$

$$\frac{V^2}{2g_c} + \frac{kRc^2}{(k-1)kg_cR} = \frac{kRc_0^2}{(k-1)kg_cR}$$

$$1 + \frac{2c^2}{(k-1)V^2} = \frac{2c_0^2}{(k-1)V^2}, \quad \text{where } c_0 = \sqrt{kg_cRT_0}$$

$$\frac{c^2}{V^2} = \frac{k-1}{2}\left[\left(\frac{2}{k-1}\right)\left(\frac{c_0^2}{V^2}\right) - 1\right] = \frac{c_0^2}{V^2} - \frac{k-1}{2}$$

or

$$\frac{c^2}{V^2} = \frac{c_0^2}{V^2} - \frac{k-1}{2} \tag{14.69}$$

Substituting this into Eq. 14.68 and rearranging

$$\frac{P}{P_0} = \left[1 - \frac{k-1}{2}\left(\frac{V}{c_0}\right)^2\right]^{k/(k-1)} \tag{14.70}$$

Expanding this equation by the binomial theorem, and including terms through $(V/c_0)^4$ we have

$$\frac{P}{P_0} = 1 - \frac{k}{2}\left(\frac{V}{c_0}\right)^2 + \frac{k}{8}\left(\frac{V}{c_0}\right)^4$$

On rearranging this we have

$$\frac{P_0 - P}{\rho_0 V^2/2g_c} = 1 - \frac{1}{4}\left(\frac{V}{c_0}\right)^2 \tag{14.71}$$

For incompressible flow the corresponding equation is

$$\frac{P_0 - P}{\rho_0 V^2/2g_c} = 1$$

Therefore, the second term on the right side of Eq. 14.71 represents the error involved if incompressible flow is assumed. The error in pressure for a given velocity, and the error in velocity for a given pressure which would result from assuming incompressible flow are given in Table 14.2

TABLE 14.2

V/c_0	Approximate Room-Temperature Velocity, ft/sec	Error in Pressure for a Given Velocity, %	Error in Velocity for a Given Pressure, %
0.0	0	0	0
0.1	110	0.25	−0.13
0.2	220	1.0	−0.50
0.3	330	2.25	−1.2
0.4	440	4.0	−2.1
0.5	550	6.25	−3.3

14.12 Flow through Blade Passages

We will now apply the principles we have been considering in this chapter to the flow of fluids through blade passages. We will limit our consideration to uniform, parallel, one-dimensional flow.

There are a number of different devices that involve flow through blade passages. Some of the familiar ones are steam and gas turbines, axial-flow compressors, and certain types of blowers, pumps, and torque converters. Some of these devices, such as the steam turbine, are made up of a number of stages. One stage consists of a nozzle (or blade passages which act as a nozzle) and the moving row of blades that follows. Sometimes the blades are also called buckets, but in this text the term blade will be used.

In the analysis of such problems it is necessary to discuss both absolute and relative velocities. By absolute velocity we mean the velocity a stationary observer would detect. The relative velocity is the velocity an observer traveling with the blade would detect, which is designated with a subscript R. The velocity of the blade is designated V_B.

It is advantageous to show these velocities on a vector diagram. Figure 14.25 shows typical vector diagrams for both a turbine and a compressor. In each case the first sketch shows the velocity vectors in relation to the blades, and the second sketch shows how these vector diagrams are usually

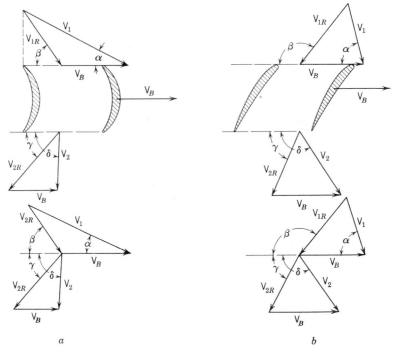

Fig. 14.25   Velocity vector diagrams for (a) a turbine, and (b) a compressor.

drawn. In these diagrams V_1 represents the velocity of the fluid entering the blade passage, and α designates the angle at which it enters. V_{1R} represents the relative velocity of the fluid entering the blade passage and β the angle at which it enters. Similarly, V_2 and V_{2R} represent the velocity and relative velocity of the fluid leaving at the angles are δ and γ, respectively.

In analyzing the flow through a blade passage it is convenient to consider the control surface shown in Fig. 14.26, which is shown both from a stationary and a moving observer's point of view.

Let us begin the analysis by writing the first law for both cases, assuming steady, adiabatic flow through the blade passage. The stationary observer is aware that work is being done on the blade, and the steady-flow equation for the first law is

$$h_1 + \frac{V_1^2}{2g_c} = h_2 + \frac{V_2^2}{2g_c} + w \qquad (14.72)$$

The moving observer is not aware of any work being done on the blade, and in this case the first law is

$$h_1 + \frac{V_{1R}^2}{2g_c} = h_2 + \frac{V_{2R}^2}{2g_c} \qquad (14.73)$$

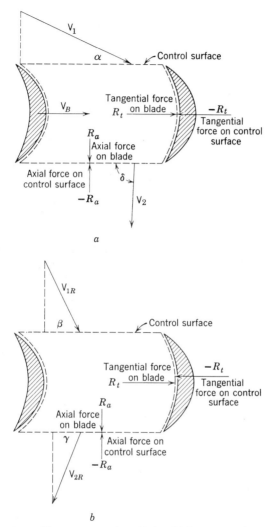

Fig. 14.26   Analysis of forces on a turbine blade. (*a*) Stationary observer. (*b*) Observer moving with the blade.

By combining Eqs. 14.72 and 14.73, we can derive the relation

$$w = \frac{(V_1^2 - V_{1R}^2) - (V_2^2 - V_{2R}^2)}{2g_c} \tag{14.74}$$

Applying the second law of thermodynamics to this process we conclude, since the process is adiabatic, that

$$s_2 \geq s_1$$

We will next consider the momentum equation, and evaluate both the tangential force R_t and the axial force R_a on the blade. For our sign convention we assume that tangential velocities and forces in the direction of the movement of the blade are positive and axial velocities and forces in the direction of the axial component of the velocity are positive.

Let us first apply the momentum equation in the tangential direction to the control volume as viewed by the stationary observer. In doing so we make the reasonable assumption that the pressure forces in the tangential direction balance. Then, using Eq. 14.19

$$-R_t = \frac{\dot{m}}{g_c}(-V_2 \cos \delta - V_1 \cos \alpha)$$

or

$$R_t = \frac{\dot{m}}{g_c}(V_1 \cos \alpha + V_2 \cos \delta) \qquad (14.75)$$

Similarly, for the control volume as viewed by the moving observer we have

$$-R_t = \frac{\dot{m}}{g_c}(-V_{2R} \cos \gamma - V_{1R} \cos \beta)$$

or

$$R_t = \frac{\dot{m}}{g_c}(V_{1R} \cos \beta + V_{2R} \cos \gamma) \qquad (14.76)$$

Equation 14.76 could have been developed from Eq. 14.75 and from the geometry of the vector diagram by noting that

$$V_1 \cos \alpha - V_B = V_{1R} \cos \beta$$

and

$$V_2 \cos \delta + V_B = V_{2R} \cos \gamma$$

Therefore,

$$V_1 \cos \alpha + V_2 \cos \delta = V_{1R} \cos \beta + V_{2R} \cos \gamma \qquad (14.77)$$

The work done by the control volume on the blade in time dt as the blade moves a distance dx is

$$\delta W = R_t \, dx$$

The rate at which work is done, or the power, is

$$\frac{\delta W}{dt} = R_t \frac{dx}{dt} = R_t V_B$$

Substituting for R_t from Eqs. 14.75 and 14.76

$$\frac{\delta W}{dt} = \dot{W}_{\text{c.v.}} = \frac{\dot{m}}{g_c} V_B(V_1 \cos \alpha + V_2 \cos \delta)$$

$$\frac{\delta W}{\delta t} = \dot{W}_{\text{c.v.}} = \frac{\dot{m}}{g_c} V_B(V_{1R} \cos \beta + V_{2R} \cos \gamma) \qquad (14.78)$$

The work w per pound of fluid flowing is therefore

$$\dot{W}_{\text{c.v.}}/\dot{m} = w = \frac{V_B}{g_c}(V_1 \cos \alpha + V_2 \cos \delta) \tag{14.79}$$

or

$$\dot{W}_{\text{c.v.}}/\dot{m} = w = \frac{V_B}{g_c}(V_{1R} \cos \beta + V_{2R} \cos \gamma) \tag{14.80}$$

The axial thrust on the blade can be found by applying the momentum equation in the axial direction. We must recognize that the pressure at the inlet section may be different from the pressure at the exit section. Consider first the control volume as viewed by the stationary observer. Again we use Eq. 14.19.

$$R_a = \frac{\dot{m}}{g_c}(V_2 \sin \delta - V_1 \sin \alpha) - (P_1 A_1 - P_2 A_2) \tag{14.81}$$

As viewed by the moving observer we have

$$R_a = \frac{\dot{m}}{g_c}(V_{2R} \sin \gamma - V_{1R} \sin \beta) - (P_1 A_1 - P_2 A_2) \tag{14.82}$$

Since there is no motion in the axial direction there is no work involved. However, adequate thrust bearings must be provided to handle the axial force. It is important to note in Eqs. 14.81 and 14.82 that if the pressure changes across the moving blade, the axial forces will be significantly influenced. This will be discussed more fully in the next section when the difference between an impulse and a reaction stage is considered.

Example 14.11

Steam enters the blade passage of one stage of a steam turbine with a velocity of 1800 ft/sec and at an angle (α) of 20°. The steam leaves the blade (as seen by the moving observer) at an angle (γ) of 50°. There is no pressure change across the blade and there are no irreversibilities (which means that there is no change in the magnitude of the relative velocity during the flow through the blade passage). Determine the work per pound of steam and the axial thrust.

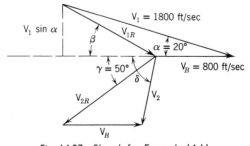

Fig. 14.27   Sketch for Example 14.11.

We first draw the vector diagram as shown in Fig. 14.27.

$$V_{1R} \sin \beta = V_1 \sin \alpha = 1800 \sin 20° = 1800(0.3240) = 616 \text{ ft/sec}$$
$$V_{1R} \cos \beta + V_B = V_1 \cos \alpha = 1800(0.9397) = 1691 \text{ ft/sec}$$
$$V_{1R} \cos \beta = 1691 - 800 = 891 \text{ ft/sec}$$
$$\tan \beta = \frac{V_{1R} \sin \beta}{V_{1R} \cos \beta} = \frac{616}{891} = 0.692$$
$$\beta = 34° 41'$$
$$V_{1R} \sin \beta = 616$$
$$V_{1R} = \frac{616}{\sin 34° 41'} = \frac{616}{0.569} = 1084 \text{ ft/sec}$$

$$V_{2R} = V_{1R} = 1084 \text{ ft/sec}$$
$$V_2 \sin \delta = V_{2R} \sin \gamma = 1084 \sin 50° = 1084(0.766)$$
$$= 830 \text{ ft/sec}$$
$$V_2 \cos \delta + V_B = V_{2R} \cos \gamma = 1084 \cos 50° = 1084(0.6428)$$
$$= 696 \text{ ft/sec}$$
$$V_2 \cos \delta = 696 - 800 = -104 \text{ ft/sec}$$

This implies that we drew our vector diagram slightly wrong and it should have been as shown in Fig. 14.28

$$\cot \delta = \frac{V_2 \cos \delta}{V_2 \sin \delta} = \frac{-104}{830} = -0.1253$$
$$\delta = 97° 9'$$
$$V_2 = \sqrt{(V_2 \sin \delta)^2 + (V_2 \cos \delta)^2} = \sqrt{(830)^2 + (104)^2}$$
$$= 842 \text{ ft/sec}$$

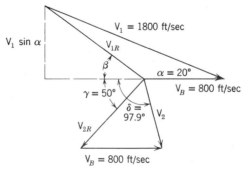

Fig. 14.28   Sketch for Example 14.11.

14.13   Impulse and Reaction Stages for Turbines

Two terms used in connection with turbines are impulse stage and reaction stage. A turbine stage is defined as the fixed nozzle or blade and the moving blades that follow it. Figure 14.29*a* shows an impulse stage. In an impulse stage the entire pressure drop takes place in a stationary nozzle, and the pressure remains constant as the fluid flows through the blade passage. There is a decrease in the kinetic energy of the fluid as it flows through the blade passage, and the enthalpy will increase due to irreversibilities associated with the fluid flow.

In the pure reaction stage the entire pressure drop occurs as the fluid flows through the moving blades. Thus, the moving blade acts as a nozzle, and the blade passage must have the proper contour for a nozzle (converging if the exit pressure is greater than the critical pressure and converging-diverging if the exit pressure is less than the critical pressure). In the pure reaction stage the only purpose of the stationary blade is to direct the fluid into the moving blade at the proper angle and velocity.

The pure reaction stage is used relatively infrequently. Rather, most turbines that are classified as reaction turbines have a pressure and enthalpy drop in both the fixed and moving blades. The degree of reaction is defined as the fraction of the enthalpy drop that occurs in the moving blades. Thus, in the 50 per cent reaction stage, which is very commonly

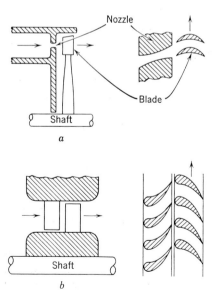

Fig. 14.29   Schematic arrangement for (*a*) an impulse stage, and (*b*) a reaction stage.

used, half of the enthalpy drop across the stage occurs in the fixed blade and the other half in the moving blade.

A few comparisons between the impulse and reaction blade may be noted here. Since there is a pressure drop across both the fixed and moving blades in the reaction stage, there is a tendency for leakage to occur across the tip of the blade. Therefore, very close clearances must be maintained at the blade tips. Further, the pressure drop across the moving blade of the reaction stage gives rise to axial forces that must be balanced in order to prevent axial motion in reaction turbines. In an impulse stage it is possible to utilize only part of the periphery for admission of steam. This is usually termed partial admission. In fact, in turbines that utilize an impulse stage for the first stage the power output can be controlled by opening and closing nozzles. The main advantage of the reaction stage is that lower fluid velocities are utilized, and higher efficiencies can be attained at lower velocities. This will be discussed more fully in the following sections.

14.14   Some Further Considerations of Impulse Stages

Figure 14.30 shows a typical velocity diagram for an impulse stage. The blade velocity coefficient k_B is defined as the ratio of the relative velocity leaving the blade to the relative velocity entering the blade. That is,

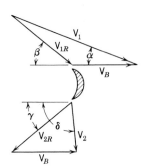

Fig. 14.30   A velocity vector diagram for an impulse blade.

$$k_B = \frac{V_{2R}}{V_{1R}} \qquad (14.83)$$

In the ideal impulse stage $V_{2R} = V_{1R}$ and $k_B = 1$, but in the actual impulse stage V_{2R} will be less than V_{1R} due to irreversibilities in the fluid as it flows through the blade passage.

The blade efficiency η_B is defined as the ratio of the actual work per pound of fluid flowing to the kinetic energy of the fluid entering the blade passage.

$$\eta_B = \frac{w}{V_1^2/2g_c} \qquad (14.84)$$

Thus, a blade efficiency of 100 per cent means that the work is exactly equal to the kinetic energy of the fluid entering the blade, and the kinetic energy of the fluid leaving the blade is zero.

Quite obviously, the fluid must have some axial velocity if it is to flow out the blade passage. However, it is of interest to consider a turbine having a zero axial velocity and to determine the blade-speed ratio that will give an efficiency of 100 per cent. The blade-speed ratio is the ratio of

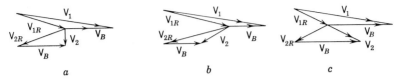

Fig. 14.31   A velocity vector diagram illustrating optimum blade-speed ratio.

the blade speed V_B to the velocity of the fluid leaving the nozzle V_1 and the ratio is designated V_B/V_1.

Figure 14.31a shows a reversible impulse stage that has a very small entrance and blade exit angle, and a blade-speed ratio of 0.5. It is evident that as the angles α and γ (the inlet and blade exit angles) approach zero that the exit velocity V_2 will also approach zero. Such a stage would have an efficiency of 100 per cent. Figures 14.31b and c show reversible impulse stages with essentially zero angles, but with blade-speed ratios considerably less and considerably greater than 0.5. In both of these the exit velocity is large, and therefore the blade efficiency is considerably less than 100 per cent. We conclude, therefore, that for a reversible, zero-angle impulse turbine the optimum blade-speed ratio is 0.5   The curve marked impulse stage on Fig. 14.34 shows the variation of blade efficiency with blade-speed ratio for a reversible stage.

An expression for the blade efficiency as a function of the angles α and γ (the inlet angle and blade exit angles), the blade-speed ratio, and the blade velocity coefficient can be derived.

From Eq. 14.79

$$w = \frac{V_B}{g_c}(V_1 \cos \alpha + V_2 \cos \delta)$$

$$V_{2R} = k_B V_{1R}$$

From the vector diagram we note that

$$V_2 \cos \delta = V_{2R} \cos \gamma - V_B = k_B V_{1R} \cos \gamma - V_B$$

$$V_{1R} = \frac{V_1 \cos \alpha - V_B}{\cos \beta}$$

Therefore,

$$w = \frac{V_B}{g_c}\left(V_1 \cos \alpha + k_B \cos \gamma \frac{V_1 \cos \alpha - V_B}{\cos \beta} - V_B\right)$$

$$= \frac{V_B}{g_c}\left[(V_1 \cos \alpha - V_B)\left(1 + \frac{k_B \cos \gamma}{\cos \beta}\right)\right]$$

$$\eta_B = \frac{w}{V_1^2/2g_c} = \frac{2V_B}{V_1^2}(V_1 \cos \alpha - V_B)\left(1 + k_B \frac{\cos \gamma}{\cos \beta}\right)$$

$$= \frac{2V_B^2}{V_1^2}\left(\frac{V_1}{V_B}\cos \alpha - 1\right)\left(1 + k_B \frac{\cos \gamma}{\cos \beta}\right)$$

But

$$\cos \beta = \frac{V_1 \cos \alpha - V_B}{\sqrt{(V_1 \cos \alpha - V_B)^2 + (V_1 \sin \alpha)^2}}$$

$$= \frac{\cos \alpha - V_B/V_1}{\sqrt{(\cos \alpha - V_B/V_1)^2 + \sin^2 \alpha}}$$

$$\eta_B = 2 \frac{V_B}{V_1}\left(\cos \alpha - \frac{V_B}{V_1}\right)\left[1 + \frac{k_B \cos \gamma}{\dfrac{\cos \alpha - V_B/V_1}{\sqrt{(\cos \alpha - V_B/V_1)^2 + \sin^2 \alpha}}}\right] \qquad (14.85)$$

This relation gives the blade efficiency as a function of the blade speed-ratio V_B/V_1, the angles α and γ, and the blade velocity coefficient k_B. From this relation it can be shown that for the usual values of angles and blade velocity coefficient, the optimum efficiency is obtained with blade velocity coefficient of approximately 0.5, which was the value obtained for the reversible zero-angle impulse stage.

This leads to consideration of the velocity-compounded turbine. Suppose one was attempting to build a turbine having one impulse stage, and that it was to receive steam at 100 lbf/in.², 500 F and exhaust at a pressure of 2 lbf/in.² The velocity of the steam leaving the nozzle would be about 3500 ft/sec. In order to have maximum efficiency a blade-speed ratio of 0.5 must be used, and this would require a blade speed of 1750 ft/sec. Blade speeds of this magnitude result in very high stresses due to centrifugal force, and further, the irreversibilities associated with fluid flow increase as the fluid velocity increases.

For these reasons velocity compounding is used, and a schematic diagram and a vector diagram for a velocity-compounded stage are shown in Fig. 14.32. The stationary blade serves to change the direction of the fluid so that it will enter the second row of moving blades properly. It can be shown that for a reversible zero-angle turbine having two moving rows the blade-speed ratio for optimum efficiency is 1/4. Sometimes velocity-compounded turbines are built with as many as three moving rows.

Velocity-compounded turbines have a lower efficiency than comparable turbines that have a number of impulse or reaction stages. However, they are relatively inexpensive and are therefore frequently used in small sizes where initial cost is more important than efficiency. A velocity-compounded stage is also frequently used as the first stage in large steam turbines in order to have a large pressure and temperature drop before the steam enters the moving blades.

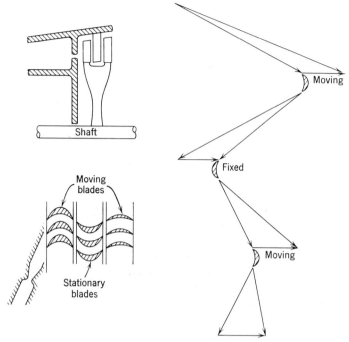

Fig. 14.32   A velocity-compounded impulse stage.

14.15   Some Further Considerations of Reaction Stages

First a remark should be made regarding the blade efficiency of a reaction stage. Both the fixed blades and moving blades act as a nozzle. Therefore, the efficiency of the moving blades can be defined in the same way as the efficiency of a nozzle if the relative velocities are used.

The second matter to consider is the blade-speed ratio for maximum efficiency of a reaction stage. Let us consider a reversible reaction stage in which the isentropic enthalpy drops across the fixed and moving blades are equal (i.e., a 50 per cent reaction stage). For a zero-angle turbine it is evident from Fig. 14.33 that for zero kinetic energy leaving the blade, a blade-speed ratio of 1.0 is required. Thus, maximum efficiency in a reaction stage is obtained for a blade-speed ratio of 1.0.

This leads us to a comparison of the impulse stage with the reaction stage regarding the blade-speed ratio for maximum efficiency.

If we compare reversible impulse and reaction stages for a given velocity from the stationary nozzle or blade, it is evident that for maximum efficiency the blade velocity for the reaction stage would be twice the blade velocity of the impulse stage. However, this is not a good comparison

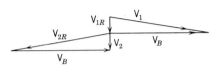

Fig. 14.33   A velocity vector diagram for a reaction stage.

because the reaction stage would have a greater enthalpy drop (due to the enthalpy drop in the moving row) than the impulse stage.

A better comparison can be made by considering equal enthalpy drops across the stage. Let this enthalpy drop be denoted Δh_s, and let the velocity V_0 be defined by the relation

$$V_0 = \sqrt{2g_c\,\Delta h_s}$$

That is, V_0 would be the velocity leaving the nozzle of the reversible impulse stage that has this enthalpy drop. That is, for the impulse stage

$$V_1 = V_0$$

For the reversible 50 per cent reaction stage the velocity leaving the fixed blades would be

$$V_1 = \sqrt{\tfrac{1}{2} \times 2g_c\,\Delta h_s} = \frac{V_0}{\sqrt{2}}$$

For maximum efficiency in the impulse stage, $V_B/V_1 = 0.5$. Therefore, for for the impulse stage

$$\frac{V_B}{V_1} = \frac{V_B}{V_0} = 0.5$$

For maximum efficiency in the reaction stage, $V_B/V_1 = 1.0$. Therefore, for the reaction stage

$$\frac{V_B}{V_1} = \frac{V_B\sqrt{2}}{V_0} \qquad \frac{V_B}{V_0} = \frac{1}{\sqrt{2}}$$

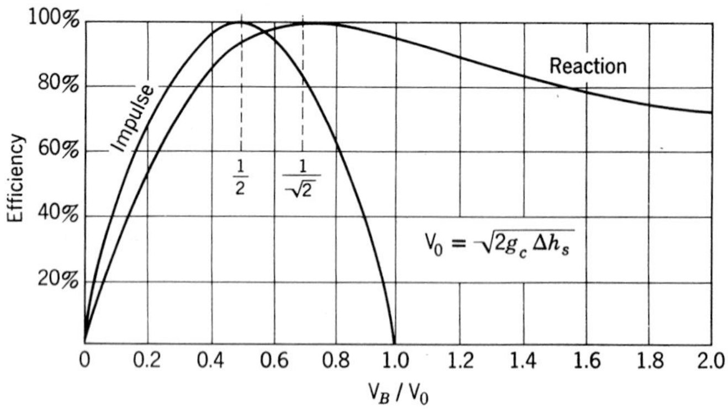

Fig. 14.34   Efficiency of an ideal impulse and reaction stage as a function of V_B/V_0.

Thus, for a given enthalpy drop per stage, the reaction stage requires a higher blade speed for maximum efficiency than the impulse stage. Conversely, for a given blade speed the reaction turbine requires more stages than an impulse stage, and in this case the fluid velocity is lower in the reaction stage than in the impulse stage.

Figure 14.34 shows the blade efficiency as a function of V_B/V_0 for an impulse stage and reaction stage.

PROBLEMS

14.1 Air leaves the compressor of a jet engine at a temperature of 300 F, a pressure of 20 lbf/in.², and a velocity of 400 ft/sec. Determine the isentropic stagnation temperature and pressure.

14.2 The products of combustion of a jet engine leave the engine with a velocity relative to the plane of 1200 ft/sec, a temperature of 900 F, and a pressure of 12 lbf/in.² Assuming that $k = 1.34$, $C_p = 0.271$ Btu/lbm-R for the products, determine the stagnation pressure and temperature of the products (relative to the airplane).

14.3 Steam leaves a nozzle with a velocity of 800 ft/sec. The stagnation pressure is 100 lbf/in.², and the stagnation temperature is 500 F. What is the static pressure and temperature?

14.4 Water is pumped from a lake and discharged through a nozzle as shown in Fig. 14.35. At the pump discharge the pressure is 100 lbf/in.², and the temperature is 80 F. The nozzle is located 30 ft above the pump. Assume standard

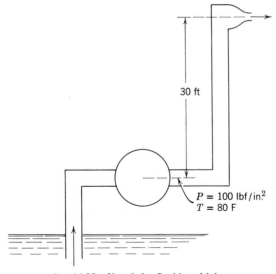

30 ft

$P = 100$ lbf/in²
$T = 80$ F

Fig. 14.35   Sketch for Problem 14.4.

atmospheric pressure and reversible flow throughout. Determine the velocity of the water leaving the nozzle.

14.5 In a water turbine that utilizes nozzles the water enters the nozzle at 50 lbf/in.², 80 F and leaves at standard atmospheric pressure. If the flow through the nozzle is reversible and adiabatic, determine the velocity and kinetic energy per lbm of water leaving the nozzle.

14.6 Air is expanded in a nozzle from 200 lbf/in.², 400 F, to 20 lbf/in.² The mass rate of flow through the nozzle is 600 lbm/min. Assume the flow to be reversible and adiabatic.

(*a*) Determine specific volume, velocity, Mach number, and cross-sectional area for each 20 lbf/in.² decrease of pressure, and plot these as a function of pressure.

(*b*) Determine the throat and exit areas for the nozzle.

14.7 Consider the nozzle of Problem 14.6 and determine what back pressure will cause a normal shock to stand in the exit plane of the nozzle. What is the mass rate of flow under these conditions?

14.8 At what Mach number will the normal shock occur in the nozzle of Problem 14.6 if the back pressure is 140 lbf/in.²?

14.9 Consider the nozzle of Problem 14.6. What back pressure will be required to cause subsonic flow throughout the entire nozzle with $M = 1$ at the throat?

14.10 Determine the mass rate of flow through the nozzle of Problem 14.6 for a back pressure of 190 lbf/in.²

14.11 A nozzle is designed assuming reversible adiabatic flow with an exit Mach number of 2.6 while flowing air having a stagnation pressure and temperature of 300 lbf/in.² and 300 F, respectively. The mass rate of flow is 10 lbm/sec, and k may be assumed to be 1.40 and constant.

(*a*) Determine the exit pressure, temperature, and area, and the throat area.

(*b*) Suppose that the back pressure at the nozzle exit is raised to 200 lbf/in.², and that the flow remains isentropic except for a normal shock wave. Determine the exit Mach number and temperature, and the mass flow through the nozzle.

14.12 A jet plane travels through the air with a speed of 600 miles/hr at an altitude of 20,000 ft, where the pressure is 6.75 lbf/in.² and the temperature is −12 C. Consider the diffuser of the engine. The air leaves the diffuser with a velocity of 300 ft/sec. Determine the pressure and temperature leaving the diffuser, and the ratio of inlet to exit area of the diffuser, assuming the flow to be reversible and adiabatic.

14.13 The products of combustion enter the nozzle of a jet engine at a total pressure of 18 lbf/in.², and a total temperature of 1200 F. The atmospheric pressure is 6.75 lbf/in.² The nozzle is convergent, and the rate of flow is 50 lbm/sec. Assume the flow to be reversible and adiabatic. Determine the exit area of the nozzle.

14.14 Air is expanded in a nozzle from 100 lbf/in.², 400 F, to 20 lbf/in.² in a nozzle having an efficiency of 90%. The mass rate of flow is 600 lbm/min. Determine the exit area of the nozzle, the exit velocity, and the increase of entropy per lbm of fluid. Compare these results with those of the reversible adiabatic nozzle of Problem 14.6.

14.15 Repeat Problem 14.12 assuming a diffuser efficiency of 80%.

14.16 Consider the diffuser of a supersonic aircraft flying at $M = 1.4$ at such an altitude that the temperature is -10 F, and the atmosphere pressure is 7 lbf/in.^{2} Consider two possible ways in which this diffuser might operate, and for each case calculate the throat area required for a flow of 100 lbm/sec.

(a) The diffuser operates as a reversible adiabatic diffuser with subsonic exit velocity.

(b) A normal shock stands at the entrance to the diffuser. Except for the normal shock the flow is reversible and adiabatic, and the exit velocity is subsonic. This is shown in Fig. 14.36. Assume a convergent-divergent diffuser with $M = 1$ at the throat.

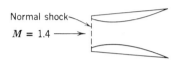

Fig. 14.36 Sketch for Problem 14.16.

14.17 Air enters a diffuser with a velocity of 600 ft/sec, a static pressure of 10 lbf/in.^{2}, and a temperature of 20 F. The velocity leaving the diffuser is 200 ft/sec and the static pressure at the diffuser exit is 11.7 lbf/in.^{2} Determine the static temperature at the diffuser exit and the diffuser efficiency. Compare the stagnation pressures at the diffuser inlet and exit.

14.18 Steam at a pressure of 100 lbf/in.^{2} and a temperature of 600 F expands to a pressure of 20 lbf/in.^{2} in a nozzle having an efficiency of 90%. The mass rate of flow is 20 lbm/sec. Determine the nozzle exit area.

14.19 Steam at an initial pressure of 100 lbf/in.^{2} and a temperature of 600 F flows through a convergent-divergent nozzle having a throat area of 0.5 in.^{2} The pressure at the exit plane is 20 lbf/in.^{2} and the exit velocity is 2600 ft/sec. The flow from the nozzle entrance to the throat is reversible and adiabatic. Determine the exit area of the nozzle, the over-all nozzle efficiency, and the increase in entropy per lbm of fluid.

14.20 A sharp-edged orifice is used to measure the flow of air in a pipe. The pipe diameter is 4 in. and the diameter of the orifice is 1 in. Upstream of the orifice the absolute pressure is 20 lbf/in.^{2} and the temperature is 100 F. The pressure drop across the orifice is 4 in. of mercury, and the coefficient of discharge is 0.62. Determine the mass rate of flow in the pipeline.

14.21 A steam turbine utilizes convergent nozzles. An estimate of the rate of steam flow is to be made from the pressure drop across the nozzles of one stage. The inlet conditions to these nozzles are 80 lbf/in.^{2}, 500 F. The exit pressure is 50 lbf/in.^{2} The coefficient of discharge is estimated to be 0.94. The total exit area of the nozzles in this stage is 5 in.^{2} Determine the rate of flow under these conditions.

14.22 The coefficient of discharge of a sharp-edged orifice is determined at one set of conditions by use of an accurately calibrated gasometer. The orifice has a diameter of 0.75 in. and the pipe diameter is 2.0 in. The absolute upstream pressure is 30 lbf/in.^{2} and the pressure drop across the orifice is 3.2 in. of mercury. The temperature of the air entering the orifice is 80 F. The mass rate of flow as measured by the gasometer is 5.30 lbm/min. What is the coefficient of discharge of the orifice under these conditions?

14.23 Consider the flow of air through an impulse blade passage. The air enters the blade passage at an angle of 18° with a velocity of 1500 ft/sec, a pressure of 16 lbf/in.², and a temperature of 200 F. The blade velocity is 800 ft/sec and the air leaves the blade passage at an angle of 45° relative to the blade. The mass rate of flow is 20 lbm/sec, and it is assumed that the flow is reversible and adiabatic

(a) Draw the velocity diagram to scale.

(b) What is the hp output of the turbine?

(c) If the blade wheel to which the blades are attached has a diameter of 1 ft, what is the length of each blade?

14.24 Steam enters an impulse turbine in which all processes are assumed to be reversible and adiabatic. The inlet pressure is 100 lbf/in.² and the inlet temperature is 800 F. The exhaust pressure is 16 lbf/in.² The steam leaves the nozzle and enters the turbine at an angle of 20°. The blade-speed ratio is 0.5 and the blade exit angle is 50°. Determine the blade efficiency of this turbine.

14.25 Consider an impulse turbine having the same inlet conditions as Problem 14.24. The nozzle efficiency is 92% and the blade velocity coefficient is 0.96. The blade-speed ratio is 0.5. Determine the work per lbm of steam and draw the velocity diagram to scale.

14.26 Consider a two stage, reversible, velocity-compounded impulse turbine that has the same inlet conditions as Problem 14.24. Assume a blade-velocity coefficient of 0.25, and an inlet angle of 20°. Both the moving and fixed blades have equal inlet and exit angles (i.e., the angle at which the steam enters relative to the blade is equal to the relative angle at which it leaves). Determine the blade efficiency of the turbine and draw the velocity diagram to scale.

14.27 Consider a single-stage reaction turbine having equal enthalpy drops across the fixed and moving blades. Consider the same inlet conditions and exit pressure as Problem 14.24. All processes are reversible and adiabatic. The blade inlet angle is 20° and the blade-speed ratio is 0.9.

(a) What is the pressure at the exit of the fixed blades?

(b) Draw the velocity vector diagram to scale.

(c) What is the net work per lbm of steam flowing through the turbine?

14.28 A single-stage air turbine having 50% reaction operates with inlet pressure and temperature of 50 lbf/in.², 1800 R, and exhaust pressure of 14.7 lbf/in.² The fixed-blade exit angle is 18°, and exhaust from the turbine is in the axial direction. The blade-speed ratio is 0.9, and all processes are reversible and adiabatic. Determine:

(a) All velocities and angles, and draw the velocity vector diagram.

(b) The work/lbm of air flowing through the turbine.

Appendix

TABLE A.I

Thermodynamic Properties of Steam

TABLE A.1.1. DRY SATURATED STEAM: TEMPERATURE TABLE *

Temp., F t	Abs. Press., lbf/in.² P	Specific Volume, ft³/lbm			Enthalpy, Btu/lbm			Entropy, Btu/lbm R		
		Sat. Liquid v_f	Evap. v_{fg}	Sat. Vapor v_g	Sat. Liquid h_f	Evap. h_{fg}	Sat. Vapor h_g	Sat. Liquid s_f	Evap. s_{fg}	Sat. Vapor s_g
32	0.08854	0.01602	3306	3306	0.00	1075.8	1075.8	0.0000	2.1877	2.1877
35	0.09995	0.01602	2947	2947	3.02	1074.1	1077.1	0.0061	2.1709	2.1770
40	0.12170	0.01602	2444	2444	8.05	1071.3	1079.3	0.0162	2.1435	2.1597
45	0.14752	0.01602	2036.4	2036.4	13.06	1068.4	1081.5	0.0262	2.1167	2.1429
50	0.17811	0.01603	1703.2	1703.2	18.07	1065.6	1083.7	0.0361	2.0903	2.1264
60	0.2563	0.01604	1206.6	1206.7	28.06	1059.9	1088.0	0.0555	2.0393	2.0948
70	0.3631	0.01606	867.8	867.9	38.04	1054.3	1092.3	0.0745	1.9902	2.0647
80	0.5069	0.01608	633.1	633.1	48.02	1048.6	1096.6	0.0932	1.9428	2.0360
90	0.6982	0.01610	468.0	468.0	57.99	1042.9	1100.9	0.1115	1.8972	2.0087
100	0.9492	0.01613	350.3	350.4	67.97	1037.2	1105.2	0.1295	1.8531	1.9826
110	1.2748	0.01617	265.3	265.4	77.94	1031.6	1109.5	0.1471	1.8106	1.9577
120	1.6924	0.01620	203.25	203.27	87.92	1025.8	1113.7	0.1645	1.7694	1.9339
130	2.2225	0.01625	157.32	157.34	97.90	1020.0	1117.9	0.1816	1.7296	1.9112
140	2.8886	0.01629	122.99	123.01	107.89	1014.1	1122.0	0.1984	1.6910	1.8894
150	3.718	0.01634	97.06	97.07	117.89	1008.2	1126.1	0.2149	1.6537	1.8685
160	4.741	0.01639	77.27	77.29	127.89	1002.3	1130.2	0.2311	1.6174	1.8485
170	5.992	0.01645	62.04	62.06	137.90	996.3	1134.2	0.2472	1.5822	1.8293
180	7.510	0.01651	50.21	50.23	147.92	990.2	1138.1	0.2630	1.5480	1.8109
190	9.339	0.01657	40.94	40.96	157.95	984.1	1142.0	0.2785	1.5147	1.7932
200	11.526	0.01663	33.62	33.64	167.99	977.9	1145.9	0.2938	1.4824	1.7762

Temp.	Press.	v_f			h_f	h_{fg}	h_g	s_f	s_{fg}	s_g
210	14.123	0.01670	27.80	27.82	178.05	971.6	1149.7	0.3090	1.4508	1.7598
212	14.696	0.01672	26.78	26.80	180.07	970.3	1150.4	0.3120	1.4446	1.7566
220	17.186	0.01677	23.13	23.15	188.13	965.2	1153.4	0.3239	1.4201	1.7440
230	20.780	0.01684	19.365	19.382	198.23	958.8	1157.0	0.3387	1.3901	1.7288
240	24.969	0.01692	16.306	16.323	208.34	952.2	1160.5	0.3531	1.3609	1.7140
250	29.825	0.01700	13.804	13.821	218.48	945.5	1164.0	0.3675	1.3323	1.6998
260	35.429	0.01709	11.746	11.763	228.64	938.7	1167.3	0.3817	1.3043	1.6860
270	41.858	0.01717	10.044	10.061	238.84	931.8	1170.6	0.3958	1.2769	1.6727
280	49.203	0.01726	8.628	8.645	249.06	924.7	1173.8	0.4096	1.2501	1.6597
290	57.556	0.01735	7.444	7.461	259.31	917.5	1176.8	0.4234	1.2238	1.6472
300	67.013	0.01745	6.449	6.466	269.59	910.1	1179.7	0.4369	1.1980	1.6350
310	77.68	0.01755	5.609	5.626	279.92	902.6	1182.5	0.4504	1.1727	1.6231
320	89.66	0.01765	4.896	4.914	290.28	894.9	1185.2	0.4637	1.1478	1.6115
330	103.06	0.01776	4.289	4.307	300.68	887.0	1187.7	0.4769	1.1233	1.6002
340	118.01	0.01787	3.770	3.788	311.13	879.0	1190.1	0.4900	1.0992	1.5891
350	134.63	0.01799	3.324	3.342	321.63	870.7	1192.3	0.5029	1.0754	1.5783
360	153.04	0.01811	2.939	2.957	332.18	862.2	1194.4	0.5158	1.0519	1.5677
370	173.37	0.01823	2.606	2.625	342.79	853.5	1196.3	0.5286	1.0287	1.5573
380	195.77	0.01836	2.317	2.335	353.45	844.6	1198.1	0.5413	1.0059	1.5471
390	220.37	0.01850	2.0651	2.0836	364.17	835.4	1199.6	0.5539	0.9832	1.5371
400	247.31	0.01864	1.8447	1.8633	374.97	826.0	1201.0	0.5664	0.9608	1.5272
410	276.75	0.01878	1.6512	1.6700	385.83	816.3	1202.1	0.5788	0.9386	1.5174
420	308.83	0.01894	1.4811	1.5000	396.77	806.3	1203.1	0.5912	0.9166	1.5078
430	343.72	0.01910	1.3308	1.3499	407.79	796.0	1203.8	0.6035	0.8947	1.4982
440	381.59	0.01926	1.1979	1.2171	418.90	785.4	1204.3	0.6158	0.8730	1.4887

* Abridged from *Thermodynamic Properties of Steam*, by Joseph H. Keenan and Frederick G. Keyes. Copyright 1936, by Joseph H. Keenan and Frederick G. Keyes. Published by John Wiley & Sons, Inc., New York.

TABLE A.1

Steam Tables (Continued)

TABLE A.1.1. DRY SATURATED STEAM: TEMPERATURE TABLE (Continued)

Temp., F, t	Abs. Press., lbf/in.², P	Specific Volume, ft³/lbm			Enthalpy, Btu/lbm			Entropy, Btu/lbm R		
		Sat. Liquid v_f	Evap. v_{fg}	Sat. Vapor v_g	Sat. Liquid h_f	Evap. h_{fg}	Sat. Vapor h_g	Sat. Liquid s_f	Evap. s_{fg}	Sat. Vapor s_g
450	422.6	0.0194	1.0799	1.0993	430.1	774.5	1204.6	0.6280	0.8513	1.4793
460	466.9	0.0196	0.9748	0.9944	441.4	763.2	1204.6	0.6402	0.8298	1.4700
470	514.7	0.0198	0.8811	0.9009	452.8	751.5	1204.3	0.6523	0.8083	1.4606
480	566.1	0.0200	0.7972	0.8172	464.4	739.4	1203.7	0.6645	0.7868	1.4513
490	621.4	0.0202	0.7221	0.7423	476.0	726.8	1202.8	0.6766	0.7653	1.4419
500	680.8	0.0204	0.6545	0.6749	487.8	713.9	1201.7	0.6887	0.7438	1.4325
520	812.4	0.0209	0.5385	0.5594	511.9	686.4	1198.2	0.7130	0.7006	1.4136
540	962.5	0.0215	0.4434	0.4649	536.6	656.6	1193.2	0.7374	0.6568	1.3942
560	1133.1	0.0221	0.3647	0.3868	562.2	624.2	1186.4	0.7621	0.6121	1.3742
580	1325.8	0.0228	0.2989	0.3217	588.9	588.4	1177.3	0.7872	0.5659	1.3532
600	1542.9	0.0236	0.2432	0.2668	617.0	548.5	1165.5	0.8131	0.5176	1.3307
620	1786.6	0.0247	0.1955	0.2201	646.7	503.6	1150.3	0.8398	0.4664	1.3062
640	2059.7	0.0260	0.1538	0.1798	678.6	452.0	1130.5	0.8679	0.4110	1.2789
660	2365.4	0.0278	0.1165	0.1442	714.2	390.2	1104.4	0.8987	0.3485	1.2472
680	2708.1	0.0305	0.0810	0.1115	757.3	309.9	1067.2	0.9351	0.2719	1.2071
700	3093.7	0.0369	0.0392	0.0761	823.3	172.1	995.4	0.9905	0.1484	1.1389
705.4	3206.2	0.0503	0	0.0503	902.7	0	902.7	1.0580	0	1.0580

TABLE A.1

Steam Tables (Continued)

TABLE A.1.2. DRY SATURATED STEAM: PRESSURE TABLE *

Abs. Press., lbf/in.² P	Temp., F t	Specific Volume, ft³/lbm		Enthalpy, Btu/lbm			Entropy, Btu/lbm R			Internal Energy, Btu/lbm	
		Sat. Liquid v_f	Sat. Vapor v_g	Sat. Liquid h_f	Evap. h_{fg}	Sat. Vapor h_g	Sat. Liquid s_f	Evap. s_{fg}	Sat. Vapor s_g	Sat. Liquid u_f	Sat. Vapor u_g
1.0	101.74	0.01614	333.6	69.70	1036.3	1106.0	0.1326	1.8456	1.9782	69.70	1044.3
2.0	126.08	0.01623	173.73	93.99	1022.2	1116.2	0.1749	1.7451	1.9200	93.98	1051.9
3.0	141.48	0.01630	118.71	109.37	1013.2	1122.6	0.2008	1.6855	1.8863	109.36	1056.7
4.0	152.97	0.01636	90.63	120.86	1006.4	1127.3	0.2198	1.6427	1.8625	120.85	1060.2
5.0	162.24	0.01640	73.52	130.13	1001.0	1131.1	0.2347	1.6094	1.8441	130.12	1063.1
6.0	170.06	0.01645	61.98	137.96	996.2	1134.2	0.2472	1.5820	1.8292	137.94	1065.4
7.0	176.85	0.01649	53.64	144.76	992.1	1136.9	0.2581	1.5586	1.8167	144.74	1067.4
8.0	182.86	0.01653	47.34	150.79	988.5	1139.3	0.2674	1.5383	1.8057	150.77	1069.2
9.0	188.28	0.01656	42.40	156.22	985.2	1141.4	0.2759	1.5203	1.7962	156.19	1070.8
10	193.21	0.01659	38.42	161.17	982.1	1143.3	0.2835	1.5041	1.7876	161.14	1072.2
14.696	212.00	0.01672	26.80	180.07	970.3	1150.4	0.3120	1.4446	1.7566	180.02	1077.5
15	213.03	0.01672	26.29	181.11	969.7	1150.8	0.3135	1.4415	1.7549	181.06	1077.8
20	227.96	0.01683	20.089	196.16	960.1	1156.3	0.3356	1.3962	1.7319	196.10	1081.9
25	240.07	0.01692	16.303	208.42	952.1	1160.6	0.3533	1.3606	1.7139	208.34	1085.1
30	250.33	0.01701	13.746	218.82	945.3	1164.1	0.3680	1.3313	1.6993	218.73	1087.8
35	259.28	0.01708	11.898	227.91	939.2	1167.1	0.3807	1.3063	1.6870	227.80	1090.1
40	267.25	0.01715	10.498	236.03	933.7	1169.7	0.3919	1.2844	1.6763	235.90	1092.0
45	274.44	0.01721	9.401	243.36	928.6	1172.0	0.4019	1.2650	1.6669	243.22	1093.7

* Abridged from *Thermodynamic Properties of Steam*, by Joseph H. Keenan and Frederick G. Keyes. Copyright 1936, by Joseph H. Keenan and Frederick G. Keyes. Published by John Wiley & Sons, Inc., New York.

TABLE A.1
Steam Tables (Continued)

TABLE A.1.2. DRY SATURATED STEAM: PRESSURE TABLE (Continued)

Abs. Press., lbf/in.² P	Temp., F t	Specific Volume, ft³/lbm		Enthalpy, Btu/lbm			Entropy, Btu/lbm R			Internal Energy, Btu/lbm	
		Sat. Liquid v_f	Sat. Vapor v_g	Sat. Liquid h_f	Evap. h_{fg}	Sat. Vapor h_g	Sat. Liquid s_f	Evap. s_{fg}	Sat. Vapor s_g	Sat. Liquid u_f	Sat. Vapor u_g
50	281.01	0.01727	8.515	250.09	924.0	1174.1	0.4110	1.2474	1.6585	249.93	1095.3
55	287.07	0.01732	7.787	256.30	919.6	1175.9	0.4193	1.2316	1.6509	256.12	1096.7
60	292.71	0.01738	7.175	262.09	915.5	1177.6	0.4270	1.2168	1.6438	261.90	1097.9
65	297.97	0.01743	6.655	267.50	911.6	1179.1	0.4342	1.2032	1.6374	267.29	1099.1
70	302.92	0.01748	6.206	272.61	907.9	1180.6	0.4409	1.1906	1.6315	272.38	1100.2
75	307.60	0.01753	5.816	277.43	904.5	1181.9	0.4472	1.1787	1.6259	277.19	1101.2
80	312.03	0.01757	5.472	282.02	901.1	1183.1	0.4531	1.1676	1.6207	281.76	1102.1
85	316.25	0.01761	5.168	286.39	897.8	1184.2	0.4587	1.1571	1.6158	286.11	1102.9
90	320.27	0.01766	4.896	290.56	894.7	1185.3	0.4641	1.1471	1.6112	290.27	1103.7
95	324.12	0.01770	4.652	294.56	891.7	1186.2	0.4692	1.1376	1.6068	294.25	1104.5
100	327.81	0.01774	4.432	298.40	888.8	1187.2	0.4740	1.1286	1.6026	298.08	1105.2
110	334.77	0.01782	4.049	305.66	883.2	1188.9	0.4832	1.1117	1.5948	305.30	1106.5
120	341.25	0.01789	3.728	312.44	877.9	1190.4	0.4916	1.0962	1.5878	312.05	1107.6
130	347.32	0.01796	3.455	318.81	872.9	1191.7	0.4995	1.0817	1.5812	318.38	1108.6
140	353.02	0.01802	3.220	324.82	868.2	1193.0	0.5069	1.0682	1.5751	324.35	1109.6
150	358.42	0.01809	3.015	330.51	863.6	1194.1	0.5138	1.0556	1.5694	330.01	1110.5
160	363.53	0.01815	2.834	335.93	859.2	1195.1	0.5204	1.0436	1.5640	335.39	1111.2

170	368.41	0.01822	2.675	341.09	854.9	1196.0	0.5266	1.0324	1.5590	340.52	1111.9
180	373.06	0.01827	2.532	346.03	850.8	1196.9	0.5325	1.0217	1.5542	345.42	1112.5
190	377.51	0.01833	2.404	350.79	846.8	1197.6	0.5381	1.0116	1.5497	350.15	1113.1
200	381.79	0.01839	2.288	355.36	843.0	1198.4	0.5435	1.0018	1.5453	354.68	1113.7
250	400.95	0.01865	1.8438	376.00	825.1	1201.1	0.5675	0.9588	1.5263	375.14	1115.8
300	417.33	0.01890	1.5433	393.84	809.0	1202.8	0.5879	0.9225	1.5104	392.79	1117.1
350	431.72	0.01913	1.3260	409.69	794.2	1203.9	0.6056	0.8910	1.4966	408.45	1118.0
400	444.59	0.0193	1.1613	424.0	780.5	1204.5	0.6214	0.8630	1.4844	422.6	1118.5
450	456.28	0.0195	1.0320	437.2	767.4	1204.6	0.6356	0.8378	1.4734	435.5	1118.7
500	467.01	0.0197	0.9278	449.4	755.0	1204.4	0.6487	0.8147	1.4634	447.6	1118.6
550	476.94	0.0199	0.8424	460.8	743.1	1203.9	0.6608	0.7934	1.4542	458.8	1118.2
600	486.21	0.0201	0.7698	471.6	731.6	1203.2	0.6720	0.7734	1.4454	469.4	1117.7
650	494.90	0.0203	0.7083	481.8	720.5	1202.3	0.6826	0.7548	1.4374	479.4	1117.1
700	503.10	0.0205	0.6554	491.5	709.7	1201.2	0.6925	0.7371	1.4296	488.8	1116.3
750	510.86	0.0207	0.6092	500.8	699.2	1200.0	0.7019	0.7204	1.4223	498.0	1115.4
800	518.23	0.0209	0.5687	509.7	688.9	1198.6	0.7108	0.7045	1.4153	506.6	1114.4
850	525.26	0.0210	0.5327	518.3	678.8	1197.1	0.7194	0.6891	1.4085	515.0	1113.3
900	531.98	0.0212	0.5006	526.6	668.8	1195.4	0.7275	0.6744	1.4020	523.1	1112.1
950	538.43	0.0214	0.4717	534.6	659.1	1193.7	0.7355	0.6602	1.3957	530.9	1110.8
1000	544.61	0.0216	0.4456	542.4	649.4	1191.8	0.7430	0.6467	1.3897	538.4	1109.4
1100	556.31	0.0220	0.4001	557.4	630.4	1187.8	0.7575	0.6205	1.3780	552.9	1106.4
1200	567.22	0.0223	0.3619	571.7	611.7	1183.4	0.7711	0.5956	1.3667	566.7	1103.0
1300	577.46	0.0227	0.3293	585.4	593.2	1178.6	0.7840	0.5719	1.3559	580.0	1099.4
1400	587.10	0.0231	0.3012	598.7	574.7	1173.4	0.7963	0.5491	1.3454	592.7	1095.4
1500	596.23	0.0235	0.2765	611.6	556.3	1167.9	0.8082	0.5269	1.3351	605.1	1091.2
2000	635.82	0.0257	0.1878	671.7	463.4	1135.1	0.8619	0.4230	1.2849	662.2	1065.6
2500	668.13	0.0287	0.1307	730.6	360.5	1091.1	0.9126	0.3197	1.2322	717.3	1030.6
3000	695.36	0.0346	0.0858	802.5	217.8	1020.3	0.9731	0.1885	1.1615	783.4	972.7
3206.2	705.40	0.0503	0.0503	902.7	0	902.7	1.0580	0	1.0580	872.9	872.9

TABLE A.1

Steam Tables (Continued)

TABLE A.1.3. PROPERTIES OF SUPERHEATED STEAM *

Temperature, F

Abs. Press., lbf/in.² (Sat. Temp.)		200	220	300	350	400	450	500	550	600	700	800	900	1000
1 (101.74)	v	392.6	404.5	452.3	482.2	512.0	541.8	571.6	601.4	631.2	690.8	750.4	809.9	869.5
	h	1150.4	1159.5	1195.8	1218.7	1241.7	1264.9	1288.3	1312.0	1335.7	1383.8	1432.8	1482.7	1533.5
	s	2.0512	2.0647	2.1153	2.1444	2.1720	2.1983	2.2233	2.2468	2.2702	2.3137	2.3542	2.3923	2.4283
5 (162.24)	v	78.16	80.59	90.25	96.26	102.26	108.24	114.22	120.19	126.16	138.10	150.03	161.95	173.87
	h	1148.8	1158.1	1195.0	1218.1	1241.2	1264.5	1288.0	1311.7	1335.4	1383.6	1432.7	1482.6	1533.4
	s	1.8718	1.8857	1.9370	1.9664	1.9942	2.0205	2.0456	2.0692	2.0927	2.1361	2.1767	2.2148	2.2509
10 (193.21)	v	38.85	40.09	45.00	48.03	51.04	54.05	57.05	60.04	63.03	69.01	74.98	80.95	86.92
	h	1146.6	1156.2	1193.9	1217.2	1240.6	1264.0	1287.5	1311.3	1335.1	1383.4	1432.5	1482.4	1533.2
	s	1.7927	1.8071	1.8595	1.8892	1.9172	1.9436	1.9689	1.9924	2.0160	2.0596	2.1002	2.1383	2.1744
14.696 (212.00)	v		27.15	30.53	32.62	34.68	36.73	38.78	40.82	42.86	46.94	51.00	55.07	59.13
	h		1154.4	1192.8	1216.4	1239.9	1263.5	1287.1	1310.9	1334.8	1383.2	1432.8	1482.3	1533.1
	s		1.7624	1.8160	1.8460	1.8743	1.9008	1.9261	1.9498	1.9734	2.0170	2.0576	2.0958	2.1319
20 (227.96)	v			22.36	23.91	25.43	26.95	28.46	29.97	31.47	34.47	37.46	40.45	43.44
	h			1191.6	1215.6	1239.2	1262.9	1286.6	1310.5	1334.4	1382.9	1432.1	1482.1	1533.0
	s			1.7808	1.8112	1.8396	1.8664	1.8918	1.9160	1.9392	1.9829	2.0235	2.0618	2.0978
40 (267.25)	v			11.040	11.843	12.628	13.401	14.168	14.93	15.688	17.198	18.702	20.20	21.70
	h			1186.8	1211.9	1236.5	1260.7	1284.8	1308.9	1333.1	1381.9	1431.3	1481.4	1532.4
	s			1.6994	1.7314	1.7608	1.7881	1.8140	1.8384	1.8619	1.9058	1.9467	1.9850	2.0214
60 (292.71)	v			7.259	7.818	8.357	8.884	9.403	9.916	10.427	11.441	12.449	13.452	14.454
	h			1181.6	1208.2	1233.6	1258.5	1283.0	1307.4	1331.8	1380.9	1430.5	1480.8	1531.9
	s			1.6492	1.6830	1.7135	1.7416	1.7678	1.7926	1.8162	1.8605	1.9015	1.9400	1.9762

Abs. Press. (Sat. Temp.)											
80 (312.03)	v	5.803	6.220	6.624	7.020	7.410	7.797	8.562	9.322	10.077	10.830
	h	1204.3	1230.7	1256.1	1281.1	1305.8	1330.5	1379.9	1429.7	1480.1	1531.3
	s	1.6475	1.6791	1.7078	1.7346	1.7598	1.7836	1.8281	1.8694	1.9079	1.9442
100 (327.81)	v	4.592	4.937	5.268	5.589	5.905	6.218	6.835	7.446	8.052	8.656
	h	1200.1	1227.6	1253.7	1279.1	1304.2	1329.1	1378.9	1428.9	1479.5	1530.8
	s	1.6188	1.6518	1.6813	1.7085	1.7339	1.7581	1.8029	1.8443	1.8829	1.9193
120 (341.25)	v	3.783	4.081	4.363	4.636	4.902	5.165	5.683	6.195	6.702	7.207
	h	1195.7	1224.4	1251.3	1277.2	1302.5	1327.7	1377.8	1428.1	1478.8	1530.2
	s	1.5944	1.6287	1.6591	1.6869	1.7127	1.7370	1.7822	1.8237	1.8625	1.8990
140 (353.02)	v		3.468	3.715	3.954	4.186	4.413	4.861	5.301	5.738	6.172
	h		1221.1	1248.7	1275.2	1300.9	1326.4	1376.8	1427.3	1478.2	1529.7
	s		1.6087	1.6399	1.6683	1.6945	1.7190	1.7645	1.8063	1.8451	1.8817
160 (363.53)	v		3.008	3.230	3.443	3.648	3.849	4.244	4.631	5.015	5.396
	h		1217.6	1246.1	1273.1	1299.3	1325.0	1375.7	1426.4	1477.5	1529.1
	s		1.5908	1.6230	1.6519	1.6785	1.7033	1.7491	1.7911	1.8301	1.8667
180 (373.06)	v		2.649	2.852	3.044	3.229	3.411	3.764	4.110	4.452	4.792
	h		1214.0	1243.5	1271.0	1297.6	1323.5	1374.7	1425.6	1476.8	1528.6
	s		1.5745	1.6077	1.6373	1.6642	1.6894	1.7355	1.7776	1.8167	1.8534
200 (381.79)	v		2.361	2.549	2.726	2.895	3.060	3.380	3.693	4.002	4.309
	h		1210.3	1240.7	1268.9	1295.8	1322.1	1373.6	1424.8	1476.2	1528.0
	s		1.5594	1.5937	1.6240	1.6513	1.6767	1.7232	1.7655	1.8048	1.8415
220 (389.86)	v		2.125	2.301	2.465	2.621	2.772	3.066	3.352	3.634	3.913
	h		1206.5	1237.9	1266.7	1294.1	1320.7	1372.6	1424.0	1475.5	1527.5
	s		1.5453	1.5808	1.6117	1.6395	1.6652	1.7120	1.7545	1.7939	1.8308
240 (397.37)	v		1.9276	2.094	2.247	2.393	2.533	2.804	3.068	3.327	3.584
	h		1202.5	1234.9	1264.5	1292.4	1319.2	1371.5	1423.2	1474.8	1526.9
	s		1.5319	1.5686	1.6003	1.6286	1.6546	1.7017	1.7444	1.7839	1.8209

* Abridged from *Thermodynamic Properties of Steam*, by Joseph H. Keenan and Frederick G. Keyes. Copyright 1936, by Joseph H. Keenan and Frederick G. Keyes. Published by John Wiley & Sons, Inc., New York.

TABLE A.1

Steam Tables (Continued)

TABLE A.1.3. PROPERTIES OF SUPERHEATED STEAM (Continued)

Temperature, F

Abs. Press., lbf/in.² (Sat. Temp.)		200	220	300	350	400	450	500	550	600	700	800	900	1000
260	v						1.9183	2.063	2.199	2.330	2.582	2.827	3.067	3.305
(404.42)	h						1232.0	1262.3	1290.5	1317.7	1370.4	1422.3	1474.2	1526.3
	s						1.5573	1.5897	1.6184	1.6447	1.6922	1.7352	1.7748	1.8118
280	v						1.7674	1.9047	2.033	2.156	2.392	2.621	2.845	3.066
(411.05)	h						1228.9	1260.0	1288.7	1316.2	1369.4	1421.5	1473.5	1525.8
	s						1.5464	1.5796	1.6087	1.6354	1.6834	1.7265	1.7662	1.8033
300	v						1.6364	1.7675	1.8891	2.005	2.227	2.442	2.652	2.859
(417.33)	h						1225.8	1257.6	1286.8	1314.7	1368.3	1420.6	1472.8	1525.2
	s						1.5360	1.5701	1.5998	1.6268	1.6751	1.7184	1.7582	1.7954
350	v						1.3734	1.4923	1.6010	1.7036	1.8980	2.084	2.266	2.445
(431.72)	h						1217.7	1251.5	1282.1	1310.9	1365.5	1418.5	1471.1	1523.8
	s						1.5119	1.5481	1.5792	1.6070	1.6563	1.7002	1.7403	1.7777
400	v						1.1744	1.2851	1.3843	1.4770	1.6508	1.8161	1.9767	2.134
(444.59)	h						1208.8	1245.1	1277.2	1306.9	1362.7	1416.4	1469.4	1522.4
	s						1.4892	1.5281	1.5607	1.5894	1.6398	1.6842	1.7247	1.7623

Temperature, F

Abs. Press., lbf/in.² (Sat. Temp.)		500	550	600	620	640	660	680	700	800	900	1000	1200	1400	1600
450	v	1.1231	1.2155	1.3005	1.3332	1.3652	1.3967	1.4278	1.4584	1.6074	1.7516	1.8928	2.170	2.443	2.714
(456.28)	h	1238.4	1272.0	1302.8	1314.6	1326.2	1337.5	1348.8	1359.9	1414.3	1467.7	1521.0	1628.6	1738.7	1851.9
	s	1.5095	1.5437	1.5735	1.5845	1.5951	1.6054	1.6153	1.6250	1.6699	1.7108	1.7486	1.8177	1.8803	1.9381

Abs. Press. (Sat. Temp.)															
500 (467.01)	v	0.9927	1.0800	1.1591	1.1893	1.2188	1.2478	1.2763	1.3044	1.4405	1.5715	1.6996	1.9504	2.197	2.442
	h	1231.3	1266.8	1298.6	1310.7	1322.6	1334.2	1345.7	1357.0	1412.1	1466.0	1519.6	1627.6	1737.9	1851.3
	s	1.4919	1.5280	1.5588	1.5701	1.5810	1.5915	1.6016	1.6115	1.6571	1.6982	1.7363	1.8056	1.8683	1.9262
550 (476.94)	v	0.8852	0.9686	1.0431	1.0714	1.0989	1.1259	1.1523	1.1783	1.3038	1.4241	1.5414	1.7706	1.9957	2.219
	h	1223.7	1261.2	1294.3	1306.8	1318.9	1330.8	1342.5	1354.0	1409.9	1464.3	1518.2	1626.6	1737.1	1850.6
	s	1.4751	1.5131	1.5451	1.5568	1.5680	1.5787	1.5890	1.5991	1.6452	1.6868	1.7250	1.7946	1.8575	1.9155
600 (486.21)	v	0.7947	0.8753	0.9463	0.9729	0.9988	1.0241	1.0489	1.0732	1.1899	1.3013	1.4096	1.6208	1.8279	2.033
	h	1215.7	1255.5	1289.9	1302.7	1315.2	1327.4	1339.3	1351.1	1407.7	1462.5	1516.7	1625.5	1736.3	1850.0
	s	1.4586	1.4990	1.5323	1.5443	1.5558	1.5667	1.5773	1.5875	1.6343	1.6762	1.7147	1.7846	1.8476	1.9056
700 (503.10)	v	—	0.7277	0.7934	0.8177	0.8411	0.8639	0.8860	0.9077	1.0108	1.1082	1.2024	1.3853	1.5641	1.7405
	h	—	1243.2	1280.6	1294.3	1307.5	1320.3	1332.8	1345.0	1403.2	1459.0	1513.9	1623.9	1734.8	1848.8
	s	—	1.4722	1.5084	1.5212	1.5333	1.5449	1.5559	1.5665	1.6147	1.6573	1.6963	1.7666	1.8299	1.8881
800 (518.23)	v	—	0.6154	0.6779	0.7006	0.7223	0.7433	0.7635	0.7833	0.8763	0.9633	1.0470	1.2088	1.3662	1.5214
	h	—	1229.8	1270.7	1285.4	1299.4	1312.9	1325.9	1338.6	1398.6	1455.4	1511.0	1621.4	1733.2	1847.5
	s	—	1.4467	1.4863	1.5000	1.5129	1.5250	1.5366	1.5476	1.5972	1.6407	1.6801	1.7510	1.8146	1.8729
900 (531.98)	v	—	0.5264	0.5873	0.6089	0.6294	0.6491	0.6680	0.6863	0.7716	0.8506	0.9262	1.0714	1.2124	1.3509
	h	—	1215.0	1260.1	1275.9	1290.9	1305.1	1318.8	1332.1	1393.9	1451.8	1508.1	1619.3	1731.6	1846.3
	s	—	1.4216	1.4653	1.4800	1.4938	1.5066	1.5187	1.5303	1.5814	1.6257	1.6656	1.7371	1.8009	1.8595
1000 (544.61)	v	—	0.4533	0.5140	0.5350	0.5546	0.5733	0.5912	0.6084	0.6878	0.7604	0.8294	0.9615	1.0893	1.2146
	h	—	1198.3	1248.8	1265.9	1281.9	1297.0	1311.4	1325.3	1389.2	1448.2	1505.1	1617.3	1730.0	1845.0
	s	—	1.3961	1.4450	1.4610	1.4757	1.4893	1.5021	1.5141	1.5670	1.6121	1.6525	1.7245	1.7886	1.8474
1100 (556.31)	v	—	—	0.4532	0.4738	0.4929	0.5110	0.5281	0.5445	0.6191	0.6866	0.7503	0.8716	0.9885	1.1031
	h	—	—	1236.7	1255.3	1272.4	1288.5	1303.7	1318.3	1384.3	1444.5	1502.2	1615.2	1728.4	1843.8
	s	—	—	1.4251	1.4425	1.4583	1.4728	1.4862	1.4989	1.5535	1.5995	1.6405	1.7130	1.7775	1.8363
1200 (567.22)	v	—	—	0.4016	0.4222	0.4410	0.4586	0.4752	0.4909	0.5617	0.6250	0.6843	0.7967	0.9046	1.0101
	h	—	—	1223.5	1243.9	1262.4	1279.6	1295.7	1311.0	1379.3	1440.7	1499.2	1613.1	1726.9	1842.5
	s	—	—	1.4052	1.4243	1.4413	1.4568	1.4710	1.4843	1.5409	1.5879	1.6293	1.7025	1.7672	1.8263
1400 (587.10)	v	—	—	0.3174	0.3390	0.3580	0.3753	0.3912	0.4062	0.4714	0.5281	0.5805	0.6789	0.7727	0.8640
	h	—	—	1193.0	1218.4	1240.4	1260.3	1278.5	1295.5	1369.1	1433.1	1493.2	1608.9	1723.7	1840.0
	s	—	—	1.3639	1.3877	1.4079	1.4258	1.4419	1.4567	1.5177	1.5666	1.6093	1.6836	1.7489	1.8083

TABLE A.1

Steam Tables (Continued)

TABLE A.1.3. PROPERTIES OF SUPERHEATED STEAM (Continued)

Abs. Press., lbf/in.² (Sat. Temp.)		500	550	600	620	640	660	680	700	800	900	1000	1200	1400	1600
											Temperature, F				
1600 (604.90)	v				0.2733	0.2936	0.3112	0.3271	0.3417	0.4034	0.4553	0.5027	0.5906	0.6738	0.7545
	h				1187.8	1215.2	1238.7	1259.6	1278.7	1358.4	1425.3	1487.0	1604.6	1720.5	1837.5
	s				1.3489	1.3741	1.3952	1.4137	1.4303	1.4964	1.5476	1.5914	1.6669	1.7328	1.7926
1800 (621.03)	v					0.2407	0.2597	0.2760	0.2907	0.3502	0.3986	0.4421	0.5218	0.5968	0.6693
	h					1185.1	1214.0	1238.5	1260.3	1347.2	1417.4	1480.8	1600.4	1717.3	1835.0
	s					1.3377	1.3638	1.3855	1.4044	1.4765	1.5301	1.5752	1.6520	1.7185	1.7786
2000 (635.82)	v					0.1936	0.2161	0.2337	0.2489	0.3074	0.3532	0.3935	0.4668	0.5352	0.6011
	h					1145.6	1184.9	1214.8	1240.0	1335.5	1409.2	1474.5	1596.1	1714.1	1832.5
	s					1.2945	1.3300	1.3564	1.3783	1.4576	1.5139	1.5603	1.6384	1.7055	1.7660
2500 (668.13)	v							0.1484	0.1686	0.2294	0.2710	0.3061	0.3678	0.4244	0.4784
	h							1132.3	1176.8	1303.6	1387.8	1458.4	1585.3	1706.1	1826.2
	s							1.2687	1.3073	1.4127	1.4772	1.5273	1.6088	1.6775	1.7389
3000 (695.36)	v								0.0984	0.1760	0.2159	0.2476	0.3018	0.3505	0.3966
	h								1060.7	1267.2	1365.0	1441.8	1574.3	1698.0	1819.9
	s								1.1966	1.3690	1.4439	1.4984	1.5837	1.6540	1.7163
3206.2 (705.40)	v									0.1583	0.1981	0.2288	0.2806	0.3267	0.3703
	h									1250.5	1355.2	1434.7	1569.8	1694.6	1817.2
	s									1.3508	1.4309	1.4874	1.5742	1.6452	1.7080
3500	v								0.0306	0.1364	0.1762	0.2058	0.2546	0.2977	0.3381
	h								780.5	1224.9	1340.7	1424.5	1563.3	1689.8	1813.6
	s								0.9515	1.3241	1.4127	1.4723	1.5615	1.6336	1.6968

4000	v	0.0287	0.1052	0.1462	0.1743	0.2192	0.2581	0.2943
	h	763.8	1174.8	1314.4	1406.8	1552.1	1681.7	1807.2
	s	0.9347	1.2757	1.3827	1.4482	1.5417	1.6154	1.6795
4500	v	0.0276	0.0798	0.1226	0.1500	0.1917	0.2273	0.2602
	h	753.5	1113.9	1286.5	1388.4	1540.8	1673.5	1800.9
	s	0.9235	1.2204	1.3529	1.4253	1.5235	1.5990	1.6640
5000	v	0.0268	0.0593	0.1036	0.1303	0.1696	0.2027	0.2329
	h	746.4	1047.1	1256.5	1369.5	1529.5	1665.3	1794.5
	s	0.9152	1.1622	1.3231	1.4034	1.5066	1.5839	1.6499
5500	v	0.0262	0.0463	0.0880	0.1143	0.1516	0.1825	0.2106
	h	741.3	985.0	1224.1	1349.3	1518.2	1657.0	1788.1
	s	0.9090	1.1093	1.2930	1.3821	1.4908	1.5699	1.6369

TABLE A.1
Steam Tables (Continued)
TABLE A.1.4. COMPRESSED LIQUID *

Temperature, F

Abs. Press., lbf/in.² (Sat. Temp.)	Saturated Liquid		32	100	200	300	400	500	600	700
	P		0.08854	0.9492	11.526	67.013	247.31	680.8	1542.9	3093.7
	v_f		0.016022	0.016132	0.016634	0.017449	0.018639	0.020432	0.023629	0.03692
	h_f		0	67.97	167.99	269.59	374.97	487.82	617.0	823.3
	s_f		0	0.12948	0.29382	0.43694	0.56638	0.68871	0.8131	0.9905
200 (381.79)	$(v - v_f) \cdot 10^5$		-1.1	-1.1	-1.1	-1.1				
	$(h - h_f)$		$+0.61$	$+0.54$	$+0.41$	$+0.23$				
	$(s - s_f) \cdot 10^3$		$+0.03$	-0.05	-0.21	-0.21				
400 (444.59)	$(v - v_f) \cdot 10^5$		-2.3	-2.1	-2.2	-2.8	-2.1			
	$(h - h_f)$		$+1.21$	$+1.09$	$+0.88$	$+0.61$	$+0.16$			
	$(s - s_f) \cdot 10^3$		$+0.04$	-0.16	-0.47	-0.56	-0.40			
800 (518.23)	$(v - v_f) \cdot 10^5$		-4.6	-4.0	-4.4	-5.6	-6.5	-1.7		
	$(h - h_f)$		$+2.39$	$+2.17$	$+1.78$	$+1.35$	$+0.61$	-0.05		
	$(s - s_f) \cdot 10^3$		$+0.10$	-0.40	-0.97	-1.27	-1.48	-0.53		
1000 (544.61)	$(v - v_f) \cdot 10^5$		-5.7	-5.1	-5.4	-6.9	-8.7	-6.4		
	$(h - h_f)$		$+2.99$	$+2.70$	$+2.21$	$+1.75$	$+0.84$	-0.14		
	$(s - s_f) \cdot 10^3$		$+0.15$	-0.53	-1.20	-1.64	-2.00	-1.41		

1500	$(v - v_f) \cdot 10^5$	-8.4	-7.5	-8.1	-10.4	-14.1	-17.3	
	$(h - h_f)$	$+4.48$	$+3.99$	$+3.36$	$+2.70$	$+1.44$	-0.29	
(596.23)	$(s - s_f) \cdot 10^3$	$+0.20$	-0.86	-1.79	-2.53	-3.32	-3.56	
2000	$(v - v_f) \cdot 10^5$	-11.0	-9.9	-10.8	-13.8	-19.5	-27.8	-32.6
	$(h - h_f)$	$+5.97$	$+5.31$	$+4.51$	$+3.64$	$+2.03$	-0.38	-2.5
(635.82)	$(s - s_f) \cdot 10^3$	$+0.22$	-1.18	-2.39	-3.42	-4.57	-5.58	-4.3
3000	$(v - v_f) \cdot 10^5$	-16.3	-14.7	-16.0	-20.7	-30.0	-47.1	-87.9
	$(h - h_f)$	$+9.00$	$+7.88$	$+6.76$	$+5.49$	$+3.33$	-0.41	-6.9
(695.36)	$(s - s_f) \cdot 10^3$	$+0.28$	-1.79	-3.56	-5.12	-7.03	-9.42	-12.4
4000	$(v - v_f) \cdot 10^5$	-21.5	-19.2	-21.0	-27.5	-40.0	-64.5	-132.2 -821
	$(h - h_f)$	$+11.88$	$+10.49$	$+9.03$	$+7.41$	$+4.71$	-0.16	-10.0 -59.5
	$(s - s_f) \cdot 10^3$	$+0.29$	-2.42	-4.74	-6.77	-9.40	-13.03	-19.3 -55.8
5000	$(v - v_f) \cdot 10^5$	-26.7	-23.6	-26.0	-34.0	-49.6	-80.5	-169.3 -1017
	$(h - h_f)$	$+14.75$	$+13.08$	$+11.30$	$+9.36$	$+6.08$	$+0.25$	-12.1 -76.9
	$(s - s_f) \cdot 10^3$	$+0.22$	-3.07	-5.92	-8.40	-11.74	-16.47	-25.3 -75.3

* Abridged from *Thermodynamic Properties of Steam*, by Joseph H. Keenan and Frederick G. Keyes. Copyright 1936, by Joseph H. Keenan and Frederick G. Keyes. Published by John Wiley & Sons, Inc., New York.

TABLE A.1
Steam Tables (Continued)

TABLE A.1.5. SATURATION: SOLID-VAPOR *

Temp., F t	Abs. Press., lbf/in.² P	Specific Volume, ft³/lbm		Enthalpy, Btu/lbm			Entropy, Btu/lbm R		
		Sat. Solid v_i	Sat. Vapor $v_g \times 10^{-3}$	Sat. Solid h_i	Subl. h_{ig}	Sat. Vapor h_g	Sat. Solid s_i	Subl. s_{ig}	Sat. Vapor s_g
32	0.0885	0.01747	3.306	−143.35	1219.1	1075.8	−0.2916	2.4793	2.1877
30	0.0808	0.01747	3.609	−144.35	1219.3	1074.9	−0.2936	2.4897	2.1961
20	0.0505	0.01745	5.658	−149.31	1219.9	1070.6	−0.3038	2.5425	2.2387
10	0.0309	0.01744	9.05	−154.17	1220.4	1066.2	−0.3141	2.5977	2.2836
0	0.0185	0.01742	14.77	−158.93	1220.7	1061.8	−0.3241	2.6546	2.3305
−10	0.0108	0.01741	24.67	−163.59	1221.0	1057.4	−0.3346	2.7143	2.3797
−20	0.0062	0.01739	42.2	−168.16	1221.2	1053.0	−0.3448	2.7764	2.4316
−30	0.0035	0.01738	74.1	−172.63	1221.2	1048.6	−0.3551	2.8411	2.4860
−40	0.0019	0.01737	133.9	−177.00	1221.2	1044.2	−0.3654	2.9087	2.5433

* Abridged from *Thermodynamic Properties of Steam*, by Joseph H. Keenan and Frederick G. Keyes. Copyright 1936, by Joseph H. Keenan and Frederick G. Keyes. Published by John Wiley & Sons, Inc., New York.

TABLE A.2

Thermodynamic Properties of Ammonia *

TABLE A.2.1. SATURATED AMMONIA

Temp., F	Abs. Press., lbf/in.^{2} P	Specific Volume, ft^3/lbm			Enthalpy, Btu/lbm			Entropy, Btu/lbm R		
		Sat. Liquid v_f	Evap. v_{fg}	Sat. Vapor v_g	Sat. Liquid h_f	Evap. h_{fg}	Sat. Vapor h_g	Sat. Liquid s_f	Evap. s_{fg}	Sat. Vapor s_g
−60	5.55	0.0228	44.707	44.73	−21.2	610.8	589.6	−0.0517	1.5286	1.4769
−55	6.54	0.0229	38.357	38.38	−15.9	607.5	591.6	−0.0386	1.5017	1.4631
−50	7.67	0.0230	33.057	33.08	−10.6	604.3	593.7	−0.0256	1.4753	1.4497
−45	8.95	0.0231	28.597	28.62	−5.3	600.9	595.6	−0.0127	1.4495	1.4368
−40	10.41	0.02322	24.837	24.86	0	597.6	597.6	0.000	1.4242	1.4242
−35	12.05	0.02333	21.657	21.68	5.3	594.2	599.5	0.0126	1.3994	1.4120
−30	13.90	0.0235	18.947	18.97	10.7	590.7	601.4	0.0250	1.3751	1.4001
−25	15.98	0.0236	16.636	16.66	16.0	587.2	603.2	0.0374	1.3512	1.3886
−20	18.30	0.0237	14.656	14.68	21.4	583.6	605.0	0.0497	1.3277	1.3774
−15	20.88	0.02381	12.946	12.97	26.7	580.0	606.7	0.0618	1.3044	1.3664
−10	23.74	0.02393	11.476	11.50	32.1	576.4	608.5	0.0738	1.2820	1.3558
−5	26.92	0.02406	10.206	10.23	37.5	572.6	610.1	0.0857	1.2597	1.3454
0	30.42	0.02419	9.092	9.116	42.9	568.9	611.8	0.0975	1.2377	1.3352
5	34.27	0.02432	8.1257	8.150	48.3	565.0	613.3	0.1092	1.2161	1.3253
10	38.51	0.02446	7.2795	7.304	53.8	561.1	614.9	0.1208	1.1949	1.3157
15	43.14	0.02460	6.5374	6.562	59.2	557.1	616.3	0.1323	1.1739	1.3062
20	48.21	0.02474	5.8853	5.910	64.7	553.1	617.8	0.1437	1.1532	1.2969
25	53.73	0.02488	5.3091	5.334	70.2	548.9	619.1	0.1551	1.1328	1.2879
30	59.74	0.02503	4.8000	4.825	75.7	544.8	620.5	0.1663	1.1127	1.2790
35	66.26	0.02518	4.3478	4.373	81.2	540.5	621.7	0.1775	1.0929	1.2704
40	73.32	0.02533	3.9457	3.971	86.8	536.2	623.0	0.1885	1.0733	1.2618
45	80.96	0.02548	3.5885	3.614	92.3	531.8	624.1	0.1996	1.0539	1.2535
50	89.19	0.02564	3.2684	3.294	97.9	527.3	625.2	0.2105	1.0348	1.2453
55	98.06	0.02581	2.9822	3.008	103.5	522.8	626.3	0.2214	1.0159	1.2373
60	107.6	0.02597	2.7250	2.751	109.2	518.1	627.3	0.2322	0.9972	1.2294
65	117.8	0.02614	2.4939	2.520	114.8	513.4	628.2	0.2430	0.9786	1.2216
70	128.8	0.02632	2.2857	2.312	120.5	508.6	629.1	0.2537	0.9603	1.2140
75	140.5	0.02650	2.0985	2.125	126.2	503.7	629.9	0.2643	0.9422	1.2065
80	153.0	0.02668	1.9283	1.955	132.0	498.7	630.7	0.2749	0.9242	1.1991
85	166.4	0.02687	1.7741	1.801	137.8	493.6	631.4	0.2854	0.9064	1.1918
90	180.6	0.02707	1.6339	1.661	143.5	488.5	632.0	0.2958	0.8888	1.1846
95	195.8	0.02727	1.5067	1.534	149.4	483.2	632.6	0.3062	0.8713	1.1775
100	211.9	0.02747	1.3915	1.419	155.2	477.8	633.0	0.3166	0.8539	1.1705
105	228.9	0.02769	1.2853	1.313	161.1	472.3	633.4	0.3269	0.8366	1.1635
110	247.0	0.02790	1.1891	1.217	167.0	466.7	633.7	0.3372	0.8194	1.1566
115	266.2	0.02813	1.0999	1.128	173.0	460.9	633.9	0.3474	0.8023	1.1497
120	286.4	0.02836	1.0186	1.047	179.0	455.0	634.0	0.3576	0.7851	1.1427
125	307.8	0.02860	0.9444	0.973	185.1	448.9	634.0	0.3679	0.7679	1.1358

* Reprinted by permission from National Bureau of Standards Circular No. 142, *Tables of Thermodynamic Properties of Ammonia.*

TABLE A.2

Thermodynamic Properties of Ammonia (*Continued*)

TABLE A.2.2. SUPERHEATED AMMONIA

Abs. Press., lbf/in.² (Sat. Temp.)		0	20	40	60	80	100	120	140	160	180	200	220
						Temperature, F							
10 (−41.34)	v	28.58	29.90	31.20	32.49	33.78	35.07	36.35	37.62	38.90	40.17	41.45	
	h	618.9	629.1	639.3	649.5	659.7	670.0	680.3	690.6	701.1	711.6	722.2	
	s	1.477	1.499	1.520	1.540	1.559	1.578	1.596	1.614	1.631	1.647	1.664	
15 (−27.29)	v	18.92	19.82	20.70	21.58	22.44	23.31	24.17	25.03	25.88	26.74	27.59	
	h	617.2	627.8	638.2	648.5	658.9	669.2	679.6	690.0	700.5	711.1	721.7	
	s	1.427	1.450	1.471	1.491	1.511	1.529	1.548	1.566	1.583	1.599	1.616	
20 (−16.64)	v	14.09	14.78	15.45	16.12	16.78	17.43	18.08	18.73	19.37	20.02	20.66	21.3
	h	615.5	626.4	637.0	647.5	658.0	668.5	678.9	689.4	700.0	710.6	721.2	732.0
	s	1.391	1.414	1.436	1.456	1.476	1.495	1.513	1.531	1.549	1.565	1.582	1.598
25 (−7.96)	v	11.19	11.75	12.30	12.84	13.37	13.90	14.43	14.95	15.47	15.99	16.50	17.02
	h	613.8	625.0	635.8	646.5	657.1	667.7	678.2	688.8	699.4	710.1	720.8	731.6
	s	1.362	1.386	1.408	1.429	1.449	1.468	1.486	1.504	1.522	1.539	1.555	1.571
30 (−.57)	v	9.25	9.731	10.20	10.65	11.10	11.55	11.99	12.43	12.87	13.30	13.73	14.16
	h	611.9	623.5	634.6	645.5	656.2	666.9	677.5	688.2	698.8	709.6	720.3	731.1
	s	1.337	1.362	1.385	1.406	1.426	1.446	1.464	1.482	1.500	1.517	1.533	1.550
35 (5.89)	v		8.287	8.695	9.093	9.484	9.869	10.25	10.63	11.00	11.38	11.75	12.12
	h		622.0	633.4	644.4	655.3	666.1	676.8	687.6	698.3	709.1	719.9	730.7
	s		1.341	1.365	1.386	1.407	1.427	1.445	1.464	1.481	1.498	1.515	1.531
40 (11.66)	v		7.203	7.568	7.922	8.268	8.609	8.945	9.278	9.609	9.938	10.27	10.59
	h		620.4	632.1	643.4	654.4	665.3	676.1	686.9	697.7	708.5	719.4	730.3
	s		1.323	1.347	1.369	1.390	1.410	1.429	1.447	1.465	1.482	1.499	1.515
46 (17.87)	v		6.213	6.538	6.851	7.157	7.457	7.753	8.045	8.335	8.623	8.909	9.194
	h		618.5	630.5	642.1	653.3	664.4	675.3	686.2	697.1	707.9	718.8	729.8
	s		1.304	1.328	1.351	1.372	1.392	1.411	1.430	1.448	1.465	1.482	1.498
50 (21.67)	v			5.988	6.280	6.564	6.843	7.117	7.387	7.655	7.921	8.185	8.448
	h			629.5	641.2	652.6	663.7	674.7	685.7	696.6	707.5	718.5	729.4
	s			1.317	1.340	1.361	1.382	1.401	1.420	1.437	1.455	1.472	1.488
60 (30.21)	v			4.933	5.184	5.428	5.665	5.897	6.126	6.352	6.576	6.798	7.019
	h			626.8	639.0	650.7	662.1	673.3	684.4	695.5	706.5	717.5	728.6
	s			1.2913	1.3152	1.3373	1.3581	1.3778	1.3966	1.4148	1.4323	1.4493	1.4658

TABLE A.2

Thermodynamic Properties of Ammonia (Continued)

TABLE A.2.2. SUPERHEATED AMMONIA (Continued)

Abs. Press., lbf/in.² (Sat. Temp.)		Temperature, F											
		60	80	100	120	140	160	180	200	240	280	320	360
70 (37.7)	v	4.401	4.615	4.822	5.025	5.224	5.420	5.615	5.807	6.187	6.563		
	h	636.6	648.7	660.4	671.8	683.1	694.3	705.5	716.6	738.9	761.4		
	s	1.294	1.317	1.338	1.358	1.377	1.395	1.413	1.430	1.463	1.494		
80 (44.4)	v	3.812	4.005	4.190	4.371	4.548	4.722	4.893	5.063	5.398	5.73		
	h	634.3	646.7	658.7	670.4	681.8	693.2	704.4	715.6	738.1	760.7		
	s	1.275	1.298	1.320	1.340	1.360	1.378	1.396	1.414	1.447	1.478		
90 (50.47)	v	3.353	3.529	3.698	3.862	4.021	4.178	4.332	4.484	4.785	5.081		
	h	631.8	644.7	657.0	668.9	680.5	692.0	703.4	714.7	737.3	760.0		
	s	1.257	1.281	1.304	1.325	1.344	1.363	1.381	1.400	1.432	1.464		
100 (56.05)	v	2.985	3.149	3.304	3.454	3.600	3.743	3.883	4.021	4.294	4.562		
	h	629.3	642.6	655.2	667.3	679.2	690.8	702.3	713.7	736.5	759.4		
	s	1.241	1.266	1.289	1.310	1.331	1.349	1.368	1.385	1.419	1.451		
140 (74.79)	v		2.166	2.288	2.404	2.515	2.622	2.727	2.830	3.030	3.227	3.420	
	h		633.8	647.8	661.1	673.7	686.0	698.0	709.9	733.3	756.7	780.0	
	s		1.214	1.240	1.263	1.284	1.305	1.324	1.342	1.376	1.409	1.440	
180 (89.78)	v			1.720	1.818	1.910	1.999	2.084	2.167	2.328	2.484	2.637	
	h			639.9	654.4	668.0	681.0	693.6	705.9	730.1	753.9	777.7	
	s			1.199	1.225	1.248	1.269	1.289	1.308	1.344	1.377	1.408	
220 (102.42)	v				1.443	1.525	1.601	1.675	1.745	1.881	2.012	2.140	2.265
	h				647.3	662.0	675.8	689.1	701.9	726.8	751.1	775.3	799.5
	s				1.192	1.217	1.239	1.260	1.280	1.317	1.351	1.383	1.413
240 (108.09)	v				1.302	1.380	1.452	1.521	1.587	1.714	1.835	1.954	2.069
	h				643.5	658.8	673.1	686.7	699.8	725.1	749.8	774.1	798.4
	s				1.176	1.203	1.226	1.248	1.268	1.305	1.339	1.371	1.402
260 (113.42)	v				1.182	1.257	1.326	1.391	1.453	1.572	1.686	1.796	1.904
	h				639.5	655.6	670.4	684.4	697.7	723.4	748.4	772.9	797.4
	s				1.162	1.189	1.213	1.235	1.256	1.294	1.329	1.361	1.391
280 (118.45)	v				1.078	1.151	1.217	1.279	1.339	1.451	1.558	1.661	1.762
	h				535.4	652.2	667.6	681.9	695.6	721.8	747.0	771.7	796.3
	s				1.147	1.176	1.201	1.224	1.245	1.283	1.318	1.351	1.382

TABLE A.3

Thermodynamic Properties of Freon-12 (Dichlorodifluoromethane) *

TABLE A.3.1. SATURATED FREON-12

Temp., F t	Abs. Press., lbf/in.² P	Specific Volume, ft³/lbm			Enthalpy, Btu/lbm			Entropy, Btu/lbm R		
		Sat. Liquid v_f	Evap. v_{fg}	Sat. Vapor v_g	Sat. Liquid h_f	Evap. h_{fg}	Sat. Vapor h_g	Sat. Liquid s_f	Evap. s_{fg}	Sat. Vapor s_g
−130	0.41224	0.009736	70.7203	70.730	−18.609	81.577	62.968	−0.04983	0.24743	0.19760
−120	0.64190	0.009816	46.7312	46.741	−16.565	80.617	64.052	−0.04372	0.23731	0.19359
−110	0.97034	0.009899	31.7671	31.777	−14.518	79.663	65.145	−0.03779	0.22780	0.19002
−100	1.4280	0.009985	21.1541	22.164	−12.466	78.714	66.248	−0.03200	0.21883	0.18683
−90	2.0509	0.010073	15.8109	15.821	−10.409	77.764	67.355	−0.02637	0.21034	0.18398
−80	2.8807	0.010164	11.5228	11.533	−8.3451	76.812	68.467	−0.02086	0.20229	0.18143
−70	3.9651	0.010259	8.5584	8.5687	−6.2730	75.853	69.580	−0.01548	0.19464	0.17916
−60	5.3575	0.010357	6.4670	6.4774	−4.1919	74.885	70.693	−0.01021	0.18716	0.17714
−50	7.1168	0.010459	4.9637	4.9742	−2.1011	73.906	71.805	−0.00506	0.18038	0.17533
−40	9.3076	0.010564	3.8644	3.8750	0	72.913	72.913	0	0.17373	0.17373
−30	11.999	0.010674	3.0478	3.0585	2.1120	71.903	74.015	0.00496	0.16733	0.17229
−20	15.267	0.010788	2.4321	2.4429	4.2357	70.874	75.110	0.00983	0.16119	0.17102
−10	19.189	0.010906	1.9628	1.9727	6.3716	69.824	76.196	0.01462	0.15527	0.16989
0	23.849	0.011030	1.5979	1.6089	8.5207	68.750	77.271	0.01932	0.14956	0.16888

10	29.335	0.011160	1.3129	1.3241	10.684	67.651	78.335	0.02395	0.14403	0.16798
20	35.736	0.011296	1.0875	1.0988	12.863	66.522	79.385	0.02852	0.13867	0.16719
30	43.148	0.011438	0.90736	0.91880	15.058	65.361	80.419	0.03301	0.13347	0.16648
40	51.667	0.011588	0.76198	0.77357	17.273	64.163	81.436	0.03745	0.12841	0.16586
50	61.394	0.011746	0.64362	0.65537	19.507	62.926	82.433	0.04184	0.12346	0.16530
60	72.433	0.011913	0.54648	0.55839	21.766	61.643	83.409	0.04618	0.11861	0.16479
70	84.888	0.012089	0.46609	0.47818	24.050	60.309	84.359	0.05048	0.11386	0.16434
80	98.870	0.012277	0.39907	0.41135	26.365	58.917	85.282	0.05475	0.10917	0.16392
90	114.49	0.012478	0.34281	0.35529	28.713	57.461	86.174	0.05900	0.10453	0.16353
100	131.86	0.012693	0.29525	0.30794	31.100	55.929	87.029	0.06323	0.09992	0.16315
110	151.11	0.012924	0.25577	0.26769	33.531	54.313	87.844	0.06745	0.09534	0.16279
120	172.35	0.013174	0.22019	0.23326	36.013	52.597	88.610	0.07168	0.09073	0.16241
130	195.71	0.013447	0.19019	0.20364	38.553	50.768	89.321	0.07583	0.08609	0.16202
140	221.32	0.013746	0.16424	0.17799	41.162	48.805	89.967	0.08021	0.08138	0.16159
150	249.31	0.014078	0.14156	0.15564	43.850	46.684	90.534	0.08453	0.07657	0.16110
160	279.82	0.014449	0.12159	0.13604	46.633	44.373	91.006	0.08893	0.07260	0.16053
170	313.00	0.014871	0.10386	0.11873	49.529	41.830	91.359	0.09342	0.06643	0.15985
180	349.00	0.015360	0.08794	0.10330	52.562	38.999	91.561	0.09804	0.06096	0.15900
190	387.98	0.015942	0.073476	0.089418	55.769	35.792	91.561	0.10284	0.05511	0.15793
200	430.09	0.016659	0.060069	0.076728	59.203	32.075	91.278	0.10789	0.04862	0.15651
210	475.52	0.017601	0.047242	0.064843	62.959	27.599	90.558	0.11332	0.03921	0.15453
220	524.43	0.018986	0.035154	0.053140	67.246	21.790	89.036	0.11943	0.03206	0.15149
230	577.03	0.021854	0.017581	0.039435	72.893	12.229	85.122	0.12739	0.01773	0.14512
233.6 (critical)	596.9	0.02870	0	0.02870	78.86	0	78.86	0.1359	0	0.1359

* Copyright 1955 and 1956, E. I. du Pont de Nemours & Company, Inc.   Reprinted by permission.

TABLE A.3

Thermodynamic Properties of Freon-12

TABLE A.3.2.   SUPERHEATED FREON-12

Temp., F	v	h	s	v	h	s	v	h	s
		5 lbf/in.²			10 lbf/in.²			15 lbf/in.²	
0	8.0611	78.582	0.19663	3.9809	78.246	0.18471	2.6201	77.902	0.17751
20	8.4265	81.309	0.20244	4.1691	81.014	0.19061	2.7494	80.712	0.18349
40	8.7903	84.090	0.20812	4.3556	83.828	0.19635	2.8770	83.561	0.18931
60	9.1528	86.922	0.21367	4.5408	86.689	0.20197	3.0031	86.451	0.19498
80	9.5142	89.806	0.21912	4.7248	89.596	0.20746	3.1281	89.383	0.20051
100	9.8747	92.738	0.22445	4.9079	92.548	0.21283	3.2521	92.357	0.20593
120	10.234	95.717	0.22968	5.0903	95.546	0.21809	3.3754	95.373	0.21122
140	10.594	98.743	0.23481	5.2720	98.586	0.22325	3.4981	98.429	0.21640
160	10.952	101.812	0.23985	5.4533	101.669	0.22830	3.6202	101.525	0.22148
180	11.311	104.925	0.24479	5.6341	104.793	0.23326	3.7419	104.661	0.22646
200	11.668	108.079	0.24964	5.8145	107.957	0.23813	3.8632	107.835	0.23135
220	12.026	111.272	0.25441	5.9946	111.159	0.24291	3.9841	111.046	0.23614
		20 lbf/in.²			25 lbf/in.²			30 lbf/in.²	
20	2.0391	80.403	0.17829	1.6125	80.088	0.17414	1.3278	79.765	0.17065
40	2.1373	83.289	0.18419	1.6932	83.012	0.18012	1.3969	82.730	0.17671
60	2.2340	86.210	0.18992	1.7723	85.965	0.18591	1.4644	85.716	0.18257
80	2.3295	89.168	0.19550	1.8502	88.950	0.19155	1.5306	88.729	0.18826
100	2.4241	92.164	0.20095	1.9271	91.968	0.19704	1.5957	91.770	0.19379
120	2.5179	95.198	0.20628	2.0032	95.021	0.20240	1.6600	94.843	0.19918
140	2.6110	98.270	0.21149	2.0786	98.110	0.20763	1.7237	97.948	0.20445
160	2.7036	101.380	0.21659	2.1535	101.234	0.21276	1.7868	101.086	0.20960
180	2.7957	104.528	0.22159	2.2279	104.393	0.21778	1.8494	104.258	0.21463
200	2.8874	107.712	0.22649	2.3019	107.588	0.22269	1.9116	107.464	0.21957
220	2.9789	110.932	0.23130	2.3756	110.817	0.22752	1.9735	110.702	0.22440
240	3.0700	114.186	0.23602	2.4491	114.080	0.23225	2.0351	113.973	0.22915
		35 lbf/in.²			40 lbf/in.²			50 lbf/in.²	
40	1.1850	82.442	0.17375	1.0258	82.148	0.17112	0.80248	81.540	0.16655
60	1.2442	85.463	0.17968	1.0789	85.206	0.17712	0.84713	84.676	0.17271
80	1.3021	88.504	0.18542	1.1306	88.277	0.18292	0.89025	87.811	0.17862
100	1.3589	91.570	0.19100	1.1812	91.367	0.18854	0.93216	90.953	0.18434
120	1.4148	94.663	0.19643	1.2309	94.480	0.19401	0.97313	94.110	0.18988
140	1.4701	97.785	0.20172	1.2798	97.620	0.19933	1.0133	97.286	0.19527
160	1.5248	100.938	0.20689	1.3282	100.788	0.20453	1.0529	100.485	0.20051
180	1.5789	104.122	0.21195	1.3761	103.985	0.20961	1.0920	103.708	0.20563
200	1.6327	107.338	0.21690	1.4236	107.212	0.21457	1.1307	106.958	0.21064
220	1.6862	110.586	0.22175	1.4707	110.469	0.21944	1.1690	110.235	0.21553
240	1.7394	113.865	0.22651	1.5176	113.757	0.22420	1.2070	113.539	0.22032
260	1.7923	117.175	0.23117	1.5642	117.074	0.22888	1.2447	116.871	0.22502
		60 lbf/in.²			70 lbf/in.²			80 lbf/in.²	
60	0.69210	84.126	0.16892	0.58088	83.552	0.16556	...	...	...
80	0.72964	87.330	0.17497	0.61458	86.832	0.17175	0.52795	86.316	0.16885
100	0.76588	90.528	0.18079	0.64685	90.091	0.17768	0.55734	89.640	0.17489
120	0.80110	93.731	0.18641	0.67803	93.343	0.18339	0.58556	92.945	0.18070
140	0.83551	96.945	0.19186	0.70836	96.597	0.18891	0.61286	96.242	0.18629
160	0.86928	100.776	0.19716	0.73800	99.862	0.19427	0.63943	99.542	0.19170
180	0.90252	103.427	0.20233	0.76708	103.141	0.19948	0.66543	102.851	0.19696
200	0.93531	106.700	0.20736	0.79571	106.439	0.20455	0.69095	106.174	0.20207
220	0.96775	109.997	0.21229	0.82397	109.756	0.20951	0.71609	109.513	0.20706
240	0.99988	113.319	0.21710	0.85191	113.096	0.21435	0.74090	112.872	0.21193
260	1.0318	116.666	0.22182	0.87959	116.459	0.21909	0.76544	116.251	0.21669
280	1.0634	120.039	0.22644	0.90705	119.846	0.22373	0.78975	119.652	0.22135

TABLE A.3

Thermodynamic Properties of Freon-12 (*Continued*)

TABLE A.3.2.   SUPERHEATED FREON-12 (*Continued*)

Temp., F	v	h	s	v	h	s	v	h	s
		90 lbf/in.²			100 lbf/in.²			125 lbf/in.²	
100	0.48749	89.175	0.17234	0.43138	88.694	0.16996	0.32943	87.407	0.16455
120	0.51346	92.536	0.17824	0.45562	92.116	0.17597	0.35086	91.008	0.17087
140	0.53845	95.879	0.18391	0.47881	95.507	0.18172	0.37098	94.537	0.17686
160	0.56268	99.216	0.18938	0.50118	98.884	0.18726	0.39015	98.023	0.18258
180	0.58629	102.557	0.19469	0.52291	102.257	0.19262	0.40857	101.484	0.18807
200	0.60941	105.905	0.19984	0.54413	105.633	0.19782	0.42642	104.934	0.19338
220	0.63213	109.267	0.20486	0.56492	109.018	0.20287	0.44380	108.380	0.19853
240	0.65451	112.644	0.20976	0.58538	112.415	0.20780	0.46081	111.829	0.20353
260	0.67662	116.040	0.21455	0.60554	115.828	0.21261	0.47750	115.287	0.20840
280	0.69849	119.456	0.21923	0.62546	119.258	0.21731	0.49394	118.756	0.21316
300	0.72016	122.892	0.22381	0.64518	122.707	0.22191	0.51016	122.238	0.21780
320	0.74166	126.349	0.22830	0.66472	126.176	0.22641	0.52619	125.737	0.22235
		150 lbf/in.²			175 lbf/in.²			200 lbf/in.²	
120	0.28007	89.800	0.16629	...	...	...	...	...	...
140	0.29845	93.498	0.17256	0.24595	92.373	0.16859	0.20579	91.137	0.16480
160	0.31566	97.112	0.17849	0.26198	96.142	0.17478	0.22121	95.100	0.17130
180	0.33200	100.675	0.18415	0.27697	99.823	0.18062	0.23535	98.921	0.17737
200	0.34769	104.206	0.18958	0.29120	103.447	0.18620	0.24860	102.652	0.18311
220	0.36285	107.720	0.19483	0.30485	107.036	0.19156	0.26117	106.325	0.18860
240	0.37761	111.226	0.19992	0.31804	110.605	0.19674	0.27323	109.962	0.19387
260	0.39203	114.732	0.20485	0.33087	114.162	0.20175	0.28489	113.576	0.19896
280	0.40617	118.242	0.20967	0.34339	117.717	0.20662	0.29623	117.178	0.20390
300	0.42008	121.761	0.21436	0.35567	121.273	0.21137	0.30730	120.775	0.20870
320	0.43379	125.290	0.21894	0.36773	124.835	0.21599	0.31815	124.373	0.21337
340	0.44733	128.833	0.22343	0.37963	128.407	0.22052	0.32881	127.974	0.21793
		250 lbf/in.²			300 lbf/in.²			400 lbf/in.²	
160	0.16249	92.717	0.16462	...	...	...	...	...	...
180	0.17605	96.925	0.17130	0.13482	94.556	0.16537	...	...	...
200	0.18824	100.930	0.17747	0.14697	98.975	0.17217	0.091005	93.718	0.16092
220	0.19952	104.809	0.18326	0.15774	103.136	0.17838	0.10316	99.046	0.16888
240	0.21014	108.607	0.18877	0.16761	107.140	0.18419	0.11300	103.735	0.17568
260	0.22027	112.351	0.19404	0.17685	111.043	0.18969	0.12163	108.105	0.18183
280	0.23001	116.060	0.19913	0.18562	114.879	0.19495	0.12949	112.286	0.18756
300	0.23944	119.747	0.20405	0.19402	118.670	0.20000	0.13680	116.343	0.19298
320	0.24862	123.420	0.20882	0.20214	122.430	0.20489	0.14372	120.318	0.19814
340	0.25759	127.088	0.21346	0.21002	126.171	0.20963	0.15032	124.235	0.20310
360	0.26639	130.754	0.21799	0.21770	129.900	0.21423	0.15668	128.112	0.20789
380	0.27504	134.423	0.22241	0.22522	133.624	0.21872	0.16285	131.961	0.21253
		500 lbf/in.²			600 lbf/in.²				
220	0.064207	92.397	0.15683	...	...	...			
240	0.077620	99.218	0.16672	0.047488	91.024	0.15335			
260	0.087054	104.526	0.17421	0.061922	99.741	0.16566			
280	0.094923	109.277	0.18072	0.070859	105.637	0.17374			
300	0.10190	113.729	0.18666	0.078059	110.729	0.18053			
320	0.10829	117.997	0.19221	0.084333	115.420	0.18663			
340	0.11426	122.143	0.19746	0.090017	119.871	0.19227			
360	0.11992	126.205	0.20247	0.095289	124.167	0.19757			
380	0.12533	130.207	0.20730	0.10025	128.355	0.20262			
400	0.13054	134.166	0.21196	0.10498	132.466	0.20746			
420	0.13559	138.096	0.21648	0.10952	136.523	0.21213			
440	0.14051	142.004	0.22087	0.11391	140.539	0.21664			

TABLE A.4

Thermodynamic Properties of Oxygen*

Table A4.1 Saturated Oxygen

Abs. Press. lbf/in.² P	Temp. °R	Specific Volume, ft³/lbm			Enthalpy, Btu/lbm			Entropy, Btu/lbm-R		
		Sat. Liquid v_f	Evap. v_{fg}	Sat. Vapor v_g	Sat. Liquid h_f	Evap. h_{fg}	Sat. Vapor h_g	Sat. Liquid s_f	Evap. s_{fg}	Sat. Vapor s_g
2.00	134.454	0.01323	22.3837	22.397	49.512	97.601	147.113	0.62913	0.72590	1.35503
5.00	145.875	0.01353	9.63547	9.6490	53.891	95.514	149.405	0.66032	0.65476	1.31508
10.00	156.026	0.01384	5.09496	5.1088	57.939	93.385	151.324	0.68705	0.59853	1.28558
14.70	162.362	0.01406	3.57294	3.5870	60.535	91.915	152.450	0.70329	0.56611	1.26940
20.00	167.840	0.01425	2.68835	2.7026	62.819	90.552	153.371	0.71704	0.53952	1.25656
50.00	186.783	0.01501	1.14139	1.1564	70.946	85.165	156.111	0.76244	0.45596	1.21840
80.00	198.375	0.01556	0.72694	0.7425	76.050	81.328	157.378	0.78851	0.40998	1.19849
100.00	204.415	0.01587	0.58383	0.5997	78.742	79.150	157.892	0.80159	0.38720	1.18879
200.00	225.751	0.01721	0.28459	0.3018	88.492	70.221	158.713	0.84552	0.31106	1.15658
300.00	240.287	0.01845	0.17755	0.1960	95.584	62.505	158.089	0.87454	0.26013	1.13467
400.00	251.622	0.01978	0.12052	0.1403	101.716	54.859	156.575	0.89803	0.21802	1.11605
500.00	261.019	0.02133	0.08357	0.1049	107.449	46.761	154.210	0.91891	0.17915	1.09806
600.00	269.092	0.02340	0.05584	0.07924	113.520	37.197	150.717	0.94028	0.13823	1.07851

* Private communication, Richard B. Stewart, Cryogenic Data Center, Cryogenic Engineering Laboratory, National Bureau of Standards, Boulder, Colorado.

Table A.4.2 Superheated Oxygen

Temp. °R	14.7 lbf/in.² v ft³/lbm	h Btu/lbm	s Btu/lbm-R	20 lbf/in.² v ft³/lbm	h Btu/lbm	s Btu/lbm-R	50 lbf/in.² v ft³/lbm	h Btu/lbm	s Btu/lbm-R
200	4.4835	160.867	1.31604	3.2735	160.638	1.29618	1.2577	159.281	1.23480
250	5.6526	171.926	1.36540	4.1406	171.772	1.34588	1.6238	170.885	1.28663
300	6.8099	182.909	1.40545	4.9956	182.799	1.38609	1.9762	182.165	1.32777
350	7.9613	193.855	1.43920	5.8447	193.771	1.41992	2.3222	193.294	1.36208
400	9.1095	204.782	1.46838	6.6905	204.716	1.44915	2.6650	204.342	1.39159
450	10.256	215.703	1.49411	7.5344	215.650	1.47490	3.0057	215.349	1.41752
500	11.401	226.636	1.51715	8.3770	226.593	1.49796	3.3451	226.347	1.44070
540	12.316	235.412	1.53403	9.0505	235.375	1.51486	3.6160	235.163	1.45766

Temp.	100 lbf/in.² v ft³/lbm	h Btu/lbm	s Btu/lbm-R	200 lbf/in.² v ft³/lbm	h Btu/lbm	s Btu/lbm-R	500 lbf/in.² v ft³/lbm	h Btu/lbm	s Btu/lbm-R
250	0.78360	169.329	1.23938	0.36060	165.849	1.18664			
300	0.96931	181.083	1.28227	0.46515	178.812	1.23399	0.15953	170.799	1.15776
350	1.1480	192.487	1.31744	0.56068	190.835	1.27108	0.20768	185.528	1.20328
400	1.3231	203.715	1.34743	0.65215	202.445	1.30209	0.24960	198.517	1.23800
450	1.4961	214.847	1.37365	0.74139	213.838	1.32893	0.28876	210.774	1.26688
500	1.6678	225.937	1.39702	0.82926	225.116	1.35270	0.32638	222.652	1.29192
540	1.8046	234.811	1.41410	0.89890	234.107	1.37000	0.35577	232.007	1.30992

Temp.	1000 lbf/in.² v ft³/lbm	h Btu/lbm	s Btu/lbm-R	2000 lbf/in.² v ft³/lbm	h Btu/lbm	s Btu/lbm-R	3000 lbf/in.² v ft³/lbm	h Btu/lbm	s Btu/lbm-R
300	0.04695	146.731	1.04897	0.02227	123.294	0.95394	0.01998	121.041	0.93350
350	0.08936	175.302	1.13834	0.03543	154.051	1.04870	0.02571	144.893	1.00697
400	0.11579	191.622	1.18204	0.05156	177.942	1.11278	0.03424	168.196	1.06929
450	0.13844	205.606	1.21502	0.06521	195.728	1.15476	0.04320	187.861	1.11570
500	0.15931	218.583	1.24237	0.07729	210.969	1.18691	0.05160	204.703	1.15123
540	0.17525	228.575	1.26160	0.08626	222.225	1.20857	0.05791	216.946	1.17479

TABLE A.5

Thermodynamic Properties of Nitrogen*

Table A.5.1 Saturated Nitrogen

Temp. °R	Abs. Press. lbf/in.² P	Specific Volume, ft³/lbm			Enthalpy, Btu/lbm			Entropy, Btu/lbm-R		
		Sat. Liquid v_f	Evap. v_{fg}	Sat. Vapor v_g	Sat. Liquid h_f	Evap. h_{fg}	Sat. Vapor h_g	Sat. Liquid s_f	Evap. s_{fg}	Sat. Vapor s_g
113.670	1.813	0.01845	23.793	23.812	0.000	92.891	92.891	0.00000	0.81720	0.81720
120.000	3.337	0.01875	13.570	13.589	3.113	91.224	94.337	0.02661	0.76020	0.78681
130.000	7.654	0.01929	6.3208	6.3401	8.062	88.432	96.494	0.06610	0.68025	0.74634
139.255	14.696	0.01984	3.4592	3.4791	12.639	85.668	98.306	0.09992	0.61518	0.71510
140.000	15.425	0.01989	3.3072	3.3271	13.006	85.436	98.443	0.10253	0.61026	0.71279
150.000	28.120	0.02056	1.8865	1.9071	17.945	82.179	100.124	0.13628	0.54786	0.68414
160.000	47.383	0.02132	1.1469	1.1682	22.928	78.548	101.476	0.16795	0.49093	0.65888
170.000	74.991	0.02219	0.7299	0.7521	28.045	74.383	102.427	0.19829	0.43754	0.63584
180.000	112.808	0.02323	0.4789	0.5021	33.411	69.478	102.889	0.22805	0.38599	0.61404
190.000	162.761	0.02449	0.3190	0.3435	39.153	63.582	102.735	0.25789	0.33464	0.59254
200.000	226.853	0.02613	0.2119	0.2380	45.283	56.474	101.757	0.28780	0.28237	0.57017
210.000	307.276	0.02845	0.1354	0.1639	52.061	47.474	99.536	0.31894	0.22607	0.54501
220.000	406.739	0.03249	0.0750	0.1075	60.336	34.536	94.872	0.35494	0.15698	0.51192
226.000	477.104	0.03806	0.0374	0.0755	68.123	20.423	88.546	0.38789	0.09037	0.47826

* Abstracted from National Bureau of Standards Technical Note 129A, The Thermodynamic Properties of Nitrogen from 114 to 540 R between 1.0 and 3000 PSIA. Supplement A (British Units) by Thomas R. Strobridge.

Table A.5.2 Superheated Nitrogen

Temp. °R	14.7 lbf/in.² v ft³/lbm	14.7 lbf/in.² h Btu/lbm	14.7 lbf/in.² s Btu/lbm-R	20 lbf/in.² v ft³/lbm	20 lbf/in.² h Btu/lbm	20 lbf/in.² s Btu/lbm-R	50 lbf/in.² v ft³/lbm	50 lbf/in.² h Btu/lbm	50 lbf/in.² s Btu/lbm-R
150	3.7782	101.086	0.7343	2.7395	100.715	0.7109			
200	5.1366	113.849	0.8078	3.7538	113.625	0.7852	1.4534	112.315	0.7159
250	6.4680	126.443	0.8640	4.7397	126.293	0.8418	1.8663	125.432	0.7744
300	7.7876	138.958	0.9096	5.7138	138.850	0.8875	2.2662	138.239	0.8212
350	9.1015	151.432	0.9481	6.6820	151.351	0.9261	2.6599	150.896	0.8602
400	10.412	163.882	0.9814	7.6469	163.821	0.9594	3.0502	163.471	0.8938
450	11.721	176.319	1.0107	8.6098	176.271	0.9887	3.4385	175.997	0.9233
500	13.028	188.748	1.0368	9.5714	188.710	1.0149	3.8255	188.492	0.9496
540	14.073	198.690	1.0560	10.340	198.657	1.0341	4.1344	198.474	0.9688

Temp. °R	100 lbf/in.² v ft³/lbm	100 lbf/in.² h Btu/lbm	100 lbf/in.² s Btu/lbm-R	200 lbf/in.² v ft³/lbm	200 lbf/in.² h Btu/lbm	200 lbf/in.² s Btu/lbm-R	500 lbf/in.² v ft³/lbm	500 lbf/in.² h Btu/lbm	500 lbf/in.² s Btu/lbm-R
200	0.6834	109.931	0.6585	0.2884	103.911	0.5875			
250	0.9078	123.948	0.7212	0.4272	120.763	0.6631	0.1321	108.378	0.5608
300	1.1169	137.205	0.7696	0.5420	135.076	0.7153	0.1966	128.168	0.6335
350	1.3192	150.133	0.8094	0.6490	148.589	0.7570	0.2473	143.838	0.6819
400	1.5181	162.888	0.8435	0.7522	161.718	0.7921	0.2932	158.205	0.7202
450	1.7149	175.540	0.8733	0.8532	174.630	0.8225	0.3368	171.93	0.7526
500	1.9103	188.129	0.8998	0.9529	187.408	0.8494	0.3790	185.292	0.7807
540	2.0660	198.170	0.9192	1.0319	197.567	0.8690	0.4120	195.807	0.8010

Temp. °R	1000 lbf/in.² v ft³/lbm	1000 lbf/in.² h Btu/lbm	1000 lbf/in.² s Btu/lbm-R	2000 lbf/in.² v ft³/lbm	2000 lbf/in.² h Btu/lbm	2000 lbf/in.² s Btu/lbm-R	3000 lbf/in.² v ft³/lbm	3000 lbf/in.² h Btu/lbm	3000 lbf/in.² s Btu/lbm-R
250	0.0384	78.1260	0.4145	0.0286	70.2898	0.3596	0.0261	69.7185	0.3371
300	0.0828	115.224	0.5514	0.0398	97.8200	0.4599	0.0321	93.2156	0.4228
350	0.1150	135.789	0.6150	0.0552	122.614	0.5366	0.0403	116.066	0.4933
400	0.1417	152.487	0.6597	0.0699	142.869	0.5908	0.0493	136.883	0.5490
450	0.1659	167.637	0.6954	0.0833	160.406	0.6321	0.0582	155.522	0.5930
500	0.1887	181.969	0.7256	0.0958	176.411	0.6659	0.0667	172.551	0.6289
540	0.2063	193.069	0.7470	0.1053	188.526	0.6892	0.0732	185.361	0.6535

TABLE A.6

Thermodynamic Properties of Saturated Mercury *

Press., lbf/in.^{2}	Temp., F	Enthalpy, Btu/lbm			Entropy, Btu/lbm R			Specific Volume Sat. Vapor, ft^3/lbf
		Sat. Liquid	Evap.	Sat. Vapor	Sat. Liquid	Evap.	Sat. Vapor	
0.020	259.88	7.532	127.614	135.146	0.01259	0.17735	0.18994	1893
0.040	288.32	8.463	127.486	135.949	0.01386	0.17044	0.18430	986
0.075	316.19	9.373	127.361	136.734	0.01504	0.16415	0.17919	545
0.100	329.73	9.814	127.300	137.114	0.01561	0.16126	0.17687	416
0.200	364.25	10.936	127.144	138.080	0.01699	0.15432	0.17131	217.3
0.400	401.98	12.159	126.975	139.134	0.01844	0.14736	0.16580	113.7
0.600	425.82	12.929	126.868	139.797	0.01932	0.14328	0.16260	77.84
0.800	443.50	13.500	126.788	140.288	0.01994	0.14038	0.16032	59.58
1.00	457.72	13.959	126.724	140.683	0.02045	0.13814	0.15859	48.42
2.00	504.93	15.476	126.512	141.988	0.02205	0.13116	0.15321	25.39
4.00	557.85	17.161	126.275	143.436	0.02373	0.12434	0.14787	13.38
6.00	591.2	18.233	126.124	144.357	0.02477	0.12002	0.14479	9.26
8.00	616.5	19.035	126.011	145.046	0.02551	0.11712	0.14262	7.12
10	637.0	19.685	125.919	145.604	0.02610	0.11483	0.14093	5.81
20	706.0	21.864	125.609	147.473	0.02800	0.10779	0.13579	3.09
40	784.4	24.345	125.255	149.600	0.03004	0.10068	0.13072	1.648
60	835.7	25.940	125.024	150.964	0.03127	0.09652	0.12779	1.144
80	874.8	27.159	124.849	152.008	0.03218	0.09356	0.12574	0.885
100	906.8	28.152	124.706	152.858	0.03290	0.09127	0.12417	0.725
120	934.3	29.005	124.582	153.587	0.03350	0.08938	0.12288	0.617
140	958.3	29.748	124.474	154.222	0.03401	0.08778	0.12179	0.538
160	979.9	30.415	124.376	154.791	0.03447	0.08640	0.12087	0.478
180	999.5	31.018	124.288	155.306	0.03488	0.08518	0.12006	0.431
200	1017.2	31.560	124.209	155.769	0.03523	0.08411	0.11934	0.392
225	1038.0	32.204	124.115	156.319	0.03565	0.08287	0.11852	0.354
250	1057.2	32.784	124.029	156.813	0.03603	0.08178	0.11781	0.322
275	1074.8	33.322	123.950	157.272	0.03637	0.08079	0.11716	0.297
300	1091.2	33.824	123.876	157.700	0.03669	0.07989	0.11658	0.276
350	1121.4	34.747	123.740	158.487	0.03725	0.07828	0.11553	0.241
400	1148.4	35.565	123.620	159.185	0.03775	0.07688	0.11463	0.215
500	1196.0	37.006	123.406	160.412	0.03861	0.07455	0.11316	0.177
600	1236.8	38.245	123.221	161.466	0.03932	0.07264	0.11196	0.151
800	1306.1	40.324	122.910	163.234	0.04047	0.06961	0.11008	0.118
1000	1364.0	42.056	122.649	164.705	0.04139	0.06726	0.10865	0.098
1100	1390.0	42.828	122.533	165.361	0.04179	0.06625	0.10804	0.090

* Abridged from *Thermodynamic Properties of Mercury Vapor*, by Lucian A. Sheldon. Courtesy of General Electric Company.

TABLE A.7

Critical Constants *

Substance	Formula	Molecular Weight	Temperature		Pressure		Volume, ft^3/lb-mole
			K	R	atm	lbf/in.^{2}	
Ammonia	NH$_3$	17.03	405.5	729.8	111.3	1636	1.16
Argon	A	39.944	151	272	48.0	705	1.20
Bromine	Br$_2$	159.832	584	1052	102	1500	2.17
Carbon dioxide	CO$_2$	44.01	304.2	547.5	72.9	1071	1.51
Carbon monoxide	CO	28.01	133	240	34.5	507	1.49
Chlorine	Cl$_2$	70.914	417	751	76.1	1120	1.99
Deuterium (Normal)	D$_2$	4.00	38.4	69.1	16.4	241	...
Helium	He	4.003	5.3	9.5	2.26	33.2	0.926
Helium^3	He	3.00	3.34	6.01	1.15	16.9	...
Hydrogen (Normal)	H$_2$	2.016	33.3	59.9	12.8	188.1	1.04
Krypton	Kr	83.7	209.4	376.9	54.3	798	1.48
Neon	Ne	20.183	44.5	80.1	26.9	395	0.668
Nitrogen	N$_2$	28.016	126.2	227.1	33.5	492	1.44
Nitrous oxide	N$_2$O	44.02	309.7	557.4	71.7	1054	1.54
Oxygen	O$_2$	32.00	154.8	278.6	50.1	736	1.25
Sulfur dioxide	SO$_2$	64.06	430.7	775.2	77.8	1143	1.95
Water	H$_2$O	18.016	647.4	1165.3	218.3	3208	0.90
Xenon	Xe	131.3	289.75	521.55	58.0	852	1.90
Benzene	C$_6$H$_6$	78.11	562	1012	48.6	714	4.17
n-Butane	C$_4$H$_{10}$	58.120	425.2	765.2	37.5	551	4.08
Carbon tetrachloride	CCl$_4$	153.84	556.4	1001.5	45.0	661	4.42
Chloroform	CHCl$_3$	119.39	536.6	965.8	54.0	794	3.85
Dichlorodifluoromethane	CCl$_2$F$_2$	120.92	384.7	692.4	39.6	582	3.49
Dichlorofluoromethane	CHCl$_2$F	102.93	451.7	813.0	51.0	749	3.16
Ethane	C$_2$H$_5$	30.068	305.5	549.8	48.2	708	2.37
Ethyl alcohol	C$_2$H$_5$OH	46.07	516.0	929.0	63.0	926	2.68
Ethylene	C$_2$H$_4$	28.052	282.4	508.3	50.5	742	1.99
n-Hexane	C$_6$H$_{14}$	86.172	507.9	914.2	29.9	439	5.89
Methane	CH$_4$	16.042	191.1	343.9	45.8	673	1.59
Methyl alcohol	CH$_3$OH	32.04	513.2	923.7	78.5	1154	1.89
Methyl chloride	CH$_3$Cl	50.49	416.3	749.3	65.9	968	2.29
Propane	C$_3$H$_8$	44.094	370.0	665.9	42.0	617	3.20
Propene	C$_3$H$_6$	42.078	365.0	656.9	45.6	670	2.90
Propyne	C$_3$H$_4$	40.062	401	722	52.8	776	...
Trichlorofluoromethane	CCl$_3$F	137.38	471.2	848.1	43.2	635	3.97

* K. A. Kobe and R. E. Lynn, Jr., *Chem. Rev.*, **52**, 117–236 (1953).

TABLE A.8

Zero-Pressure Properties of Gases

C_{po}, C_{vo}, and k are at 80 F

Gas	Chemical Formula	Molecular Weight	R ft-lbf/ lbm R	C_{po} Btu/ lbm R	C_{vo} Btu/ lbm R	k
Air	...	28.95	53.34	0.240	0.171	1.400
Argon	Ar	39.94	38.66	0.1253	0.0756	1.668
Carbon Dioxide	CO_2	44.01	35.10	0.203	0.158	1.285
Carbon Monoxide	CO	28.01	55.16	0.249	0.178	1.399
Helium	He	4.003	386.0	1.25	0.753	1.66
Hydrogen	H_2	2.016	766.4	3.43	2.44	1.404
Methane	CH_4	16.04	96.35	0.532	0.403	1.32
Nitrogen	N_2	28.016	55.15	0.248	0.177	1.400
Oxygen	O_2	32.000	48.28	0.219	0.157	1.395
Steam	H_2O	18.016	85.76	0.445	0.335	1.329

TABLE A.9

Constant-Pressure Specific Heats of Various Substances at Zero Pressure *

Gas or Vapor	Equation, $\bar{C}_{po}$ in Btu/lb mole-R T in degrees Rankine	Range, R	Max. Error, %
O_2	$\bar{C}_{po} = 11.515 - \dfrac{172}{\sqrt{T}} + \dfrac{1530}{T}$	540–5000	1.1
	$= 11.515 - \dfrac{172}{\sqrt{T}} + \dfrac{1530}{T}$ $+ \dfrac{0.05}{1000}(T - 4000)$	5000–9000	0.3
N_2	$\bar{C}_{po} = 9.47 - \dfrac{3.47 \times 10^3}{T} + \dfrac{1.16 \times 10^6}{T^2}$	540–9000	1.7
CO	$\bar{C}_{po} = 9.46 - \dfrac{3.29 \times 10^3}{T} + \dfrac{1.07 \times 10^6}{T^2}$	540–9000	1.1
H_2	$\bar{C}_{po} = 5.76 + \dfrac{0.578}{1000}T + \dfrac{20}{\sqrt{T}}$	540–4000	0.8
	$= 5.76 + \dfrac{0.578}{1000}T + \dfrac{20}{\sqrt{T}}$ $- \dfrac{0.33}{1000}(T - 4000)$	4000–9000	1.4
H_2O	$\bar{C}_{po} = 19.86 - \dfrac{597}{\sqrt{T}} + \dfrac{7500}{T}$	540–5400	1.8
CO_2	$\bar{C}_{po} = 16.2 - \dfrac{6.53 \times 10^3}{T} + \dfrac{1.41 \times 10^6}{T^2}$	540–6300	0.8
CH_4	$\bar{C}_{po} = 4.52 + 0.00737T$	540–1500	1.2
C_2H_4	$\bar{C}_{po} = 4.23 + 0.01177T$	350–1100	1.5
C_2H_6	$\bar{C}_{po} = 4.01 + 0.01636T$	400–1100	1.5
C_3H_8	$\bar{C}_{po} = 2.258 + 0.0320T - 5.43 \times 10^{-6}T^2$	415–2700	1.8
C_4H_{10}	$\bar{C}_{po} = 4.36 + 0.0403T - 6.83 \times 10^{-6}T^2$	540–2700	1.7
C_8H_{18}	$\bar{C}_{po} = 7.92 + 0.0601T$	400–1100	est. 4
$C_{12}H_{26}$	$\bar{C}_{po} = 8.68 + 0.0889T$	400–1100	est. 4

* From *Bulletin No. 2*, Ga. School of Technology, by R. L. Sweigert and M. W. Beardsley, 1938, except C_3H_8 and C_4H_{10}, which are from H. M. Spencer, *J. of Am. Chem. Soc.*, **67**, 1859 (1945).

TABLE A.10

Thermodynamic Properties of Air at Low Pressure *

T, R	h, Btu/lbm	P_r	u, Btu/lbm	v_r	ϕ, Btu/lbm R
200	47.67	0.04320	33.96	1714.9	0.36303
220	52.46	0.06026	37.38	1352.5	0.38584
240	57.25	0.08165	40.80	1088.8	0.40666
260	62.03	0.10797	44.21	892.0	0.42582
280	66.82	0.13986	47.63	741.6	0.44356
300	71.61	0.17795	51.04	624.5	0.46007
320	76.40	0.22290	54.46	531.8	0.47550
340	81.18	0.27545	57.87	457.2	0.49002
360	85.97	0.3363	61.29	396.6	0.50369
380	90.75	0.4061	64.70	346.6	0.51663
400	95.53	0.4858	68.11	305.0	0.52890
420	100.32	0.5760	71.52	270.1	0.54058
440	105.11	0.6776	74.93	240.6	0.55172
460	109.90	0.7913	78.36	215.33	0.56235
480	114.69	0.9182	81.77	193.65	0.57255
500	119.48	1.0590	85.20	174.90	0.58233
520	124.27	1.2147	88.62	158.58	0.59173
540	129.06	1.3860	92.04	144.32	0.60078
560	133.86	1.5742	95.47	131.78	0.60950
580	138.66	1.7800	98.90	120.70	0.61793
600	143.47	2.005	102.34	110.88	0.62607
620	148.28	2.249	105.78	102.12	0.63395
640	153.09	2.514	109.21	94.30	0.64159
660	157.92	2.801	112.67	87.27	0.64902
680	162.73	3.111	116.12	80.96	0.65621
700	167.56	3.446	119.58	75.25	0.66321
720	172.39	3.806	123.04	70.07	0.67002
740	177.23	4.193	126.51	65.38	0.67665
760	182.08	4.607	129.99	61.10	0.68312
780	186.94	5.051	133.47	57.20	0.68942
800	191.81	5.526	136.97	53.63	0.69558
820	196.69	6.033	140.47	50.35	0.70160
840	201.56	6.573	143.98	47.34	0.70747
860	206.46	7.149	147.50	44.57	0.71323

* Abridged from Table 1 in *Gas Tables*, by Joseph H. Keenan and Joseph Kaye. Copyright 1948, by Joseph H. Keenan and Joseph Kaye. Published by John Wiley & Sons, Inc., New York.

TABLE A.10

Thermodynamic Properties of Air at Low Pressure (Continued)

T, R	h, Btu/lbm	P_r	u, Btu/lbm	v_r	ϕ, Btu/lbm R
880	211.35	7.761	151.02	42.01	0.71886
900	216.26	8.411	154.57	39.64	0.72438
920	221.18	9.102	158.12	37.44	0.72979
940	226.11	9.834	161.68	35.41	0.73509
960	231.06	10.610	165.26	33.52	0.74030
980	236.02	11.430	168.83	31.76	0.74540
1000	240.98	12.298	172.43	30.12	0.75042
1020	245.97	13.215	176.04	28.59	0.75536
1040	250.95	14.182	179.66	27.17	0.76019
1060	255.96	15.203	183.29	25.82	0.76496
1080	260.97	16.278	186.93	24.58	0.76964
1100	265.99	17.413	190.58	23.40	0.77426
1120	271.03	18.604	194.25	22.30	0.77880
1140	276.08	19.858	197.94	21.27	0.78326
1160	281.14	21.18	201.63	20.293	0.78767
1180	286.21	22.56	205.33	19.377	0.79201
1200	291.30	24.01	209.05	18.514	0.79628
1220	296.41	25.53	212.78	17.700	0.80050
1240	301.52	27.13	216.53	16.932	0.80466
1260	306.65	28.80	220.28	16.205	0.80876
1280	311.79	30.55	224.05	15.518	0.81280
1300	316.94	32.39	227.83	14.868	0.81680
1320	322.11	34.31	231.63	14.253	0.82075
1340	327.29	36.31	235.43	13.670	0.82464
1360	332.48	38.41	239.25	13.118	0.82848
1380	337.68	40.59	243.08	12.593	0.83229
1400	342.90	42.88	246.93	12.095	0.83604
1420	348.14	45.26	250.79	11.622	0.83975
1440	353.37	47.75	254.66	11.172	0.84341
1460	358.63	50.34	258.54	10.743	0.84704
1480	363.89	53.04	262.44	10.336	0.85062
1500	369.17	55.86	266.34	9.948	0.85416
1520	374.47	58.78	270.26	9.578	0.85767
1540	379.77	61.83	274.20	9.226	0.86113
1560	385.08	65.00	278.13	8.890	0.86456
1580	390.40	68.30	282.09	8.569	0.86794
1600	395.74	71.73	286.06	8.263	0.87130
1620	401.09	75.29	290.04	7.971	0.87462

TABLE A.10

T, R	h, Btu/lbm	P_r	u, Btu/lbm	v_r	ϕ, Btu/lbm R
1640	406.45	78.99	294.03	7.691	0.87791
1660	411.82	82.83	298.02	7.424	0.88116
1680	417.20	86.82	302.04	7.168	0.88439
1700	422.59	90.95	306.06	6.924	0.88758
1720	428.00	95.24	310.09	6.690	0.89074
1740	433.41	99.69	314.13	6.465	0.89387
1760	438.83	104.30	318.18	6.251	0.89697
1780	444.26	109.08	322.24	6.045	0.90003
1800	449.71	114.03	326.32	5.847	0.90308
1820	455.17	119.16	330.40	5.658	0.90609
1840	460.63	124.47	334.50	5.476	0.90908
1860	466.12	129.95	338.61	5.302	0.91203
1880	471.60	135.64	342.73	5.134	0.91497
1900	477.09	141.51	346.85	4.974	0.91788
1920	482.60	147.59	350.98	4.819	0.92076
1940	488.12	153.87	355.12	4.670	0.92362
1960	493.64	160.37	359.28	4.527	0.92645
1980	499.17	167.07	363.43	4.390	0.92926
2000	504.71	174.00	367.61	4.258	0.93205
2020	510.26	181.16	371.79	4.130	0.93481
2040	515.82	188.54	375.98	4.008	0.93756
2060	521.39	196.16	380.18	3.890	0.94026
2080	526.97	204.02	384.39	3.777	0.94296
2100	532.55	212.1	388.60	3.667	0.94564
2120	538.15	220.5	392.83	3.561	0.94829
2140	543.74	229.1	397.05	3.460	0.95092
2160	549.35	238.0	401.29	3.362	0.95352
2180	554.97	247.2	405.53	3.267	0.95611
2200	560.59	256.6	409.78	3.176	0.95868
2220	566.23	266.3	414.05	3.088	0.96123
2240	571.86	276.3	418.31	3.003	0.96376
2260	577.51	286.6	422.59	2.921	0.96626
2280	583.16	297.2	426.87	2.841	0.96876
2300	588.82	308.1	431.16	2.765	0.97123
2320	594.49	319.4	435.46	2.691	0.97369
2340	600.16	330.9	439.76	2.619	0.97611
2360	605.84	342.8	444.07	2.550	0.97853
2380	611.53	355.0	448.38	2.483	0.98092
2400	617.22	367.6	452.70	2.419	0.98331

TABLE A.11*

Enthalpy of Formation at 25 C, Ideal Gas Enthalpy, and Absolute Entropy at One Atmosphere Pressure

Temp °K	Temp °R	Nitrogen, Diatomic (N₂) (Mar. 31, 1961) $(h_f^\circ)_{298} = 0$ cal/gm mole $= 0$ Btu/lb mole $M = 28.016$			Nitrogen, Monatomic (N) (Mar. 31, 1961) $(h_f^\circ)_{298} = 112,965$ cal/gm mole $= 203,337$ Btu/lb mole $M = 14.008$		
		$(h^\circ - h_{298}^\circ)$ cal/gm mole	s°: cal/gm mole-K Btu/lb mole-R	$(h^\circ - h_{537}^\circ)$ Btu/lb mole	$(h^\circ - h_{298}^\circ)$ cal/gm mole	s°: cal/gm mole-K Btu/lb mole-R	$(h^\circ - h_{537}^\circ)$ Btu/lb mole
0	0	-2,072	0	-3,730	-1,401	0	-2,522
100	180	-1,387	38.113	-2,497	-984	31.187	-1,771
200	360	-684	42.986	-1,231	-488	34.631	-878
298	537	0	45.770	0	0	36.614	0
300	540	13	45.813	23	9	36.645	16
400	720	710	47.818	1,278	506	38.074	911
500	900	1,413	49.386	2,543	1,003	39.183	1,805
600	1,080	2,125	50.685	3,825	1,500	40.089	2,700
700	1,260	2,853	51.806	5,135	1,996	40.855	3,593
800	1,440	3,596	52.798	6,473	2,493	41.518	4,487
900	1,620	4,355	53.692	7,839	2,990	42.103	5,382
1000	1,800	5,129	54.507	9,232	3,487	42.627	6,277
1100	1,980	5,917	55.258	10,651	3,984	43.100	7,171
1200	2,160	6,718	55.955	12,092	4,481	43.532	8,066
1300	2,340	7,529	56.604	13,552	4,977	43.930	8,959
1400	2,520	8,350	57.212	15,030	5,474	44.298	9,853
1500	2,700	9,179	57.784	16,522	5,971	44.641	10,748

* The thermochemical data in Table A.11 are from the JANAF Thermochemical Tables, Thermal Research Laboratory, The Dow Chemical Company, Midland, Michigan. The date each table was issued is indicated.

TABLE A.11 (Continued)

Enthalpy of Formation at 25 C, Ideal Gas Enthalpy, and Absolute Entropy at One Atmosphere Pressure

Temp °K	Temp °R	Nitrogen, Diatomic (N_2) (Mar. 31, 1961) $(h_f°)_{298} = 0$ cal/gm mole $= 0$ Btu/lb mole $M = 28.016$			Nitrogen, Monatomic (N) (Mar. 31, 1961) $(h_f°)_{298} = 112{,}965$ cal/gm mole $= 203{,}337$ Btu/lb mole $M = 14.008$		
		$(h° - h°_{298})$ cal/gm mole	$\bar{s}°$: cal/gm mole-K Btu/lb mole-R	$(h° - h°_{537})$ Btu/lb mole	$(h° - h°_{298})$ cal/gm mole	$\bar{s}°$: cal/gm mole-K Btu/lb mole-R	$(h° - h°_{537})$ Btu/lb mole
1600	2,880	10,015	58.324	18,027	6,468	44.962	11,642
1700	3,060	10,858	58.835	19,544	6,965	45.263	12,537
1800	3,240	11,707	59.320	21,073	7,461	45.547	13,430
1900	3,420	12,560	59.782	22,608	7,958	45.815	14,324
2000	3,600	13,418	60.222	24,152	8,455	46.070	15,219
2100	3,780	14,280	60.642	25,704	8,952	46.313	16,114
2200	3,960	15,146	61.045	27,263	9,449	46.544	17,008
2300	4,140	16,015	61.431	28,827	9,946	46.765	17,903
2400	4,320	16,886	61.802	30,395	10,444	46.977	18,799
2500	4,500	17,761	62.159	31,970	10,941	47.180	19,694

2600	4,680	18,638	62.503	33,548	11,439	47.375	20,590
2700	4,860	19,517	62.835	35,131	11,938	47.563	21,488
2800	5,040	20,398	63.155	36,716	12,437	47.745	22,387
2900	5,220	21,280	63.465	38,304	12,936	47.920	23,285
3000	5,400	22,165	63.765	39,897	13,437	48.090	24,187
3200	5,760	23,939	64.337	43,090	14,441	48.414	25,994
3400	6,120	25,719	64.877	46,294	15,451	48.720	27,812
3600	6,480	27,505	65.387	49,509	16,469	49.011	29,644
3800	6,840	29,295	65.871	52,731	17,495	49.288	31,491
4000	7,200	31,089	66.331	55,960	18,531	49.554	33,356
4200	7,560	32,888	66.770	59,198	19,580	49.810	35,244
4400	7,920	34,690	67.189	62,442	20,643	50.057	37,157
4600	8,280	36,496	67.591	65,693	21,721	50.297	39,098
4800	8,640	38,306	67.976	68,951	22,816	50.530	41,069
5000	9,000	40,119	68.346	72,214	23,928	50.757	43,070
5200	9,360	41,935	68.702	75,483	25,059	50.978	45,106
5400	9,720	43,755	69.045	78,759	26,210	51.195	47,178
5600	10,180	45,579	69.377	82,042	27,380	51.408	49,284
5800	10,540	47,406	69.698	85,331	28,570	51.617	51,426
6000	10,800	49,237	70.008	88,627	29,780	51.822	53,604

TABLE A.II (Continued)

Enthalpy of Formation at 25 C, Ideal Gas Enthalpy, and Absolute Entropy at One Atmosphere Pressure

		Oxygen, Diatomic (O_2) (Mar. 31, 1961) $(h_f^\circ)_{298} = 0$ cal/gm mole = 0 Btu/lb mole, $M = 32.00$			Oxygen, Monatomic (O) (June 30, 1962) $(h_f^\circ)_{298} = 59{,}559$ cal/gm mole = 107,206 Btu/lb mole, $M = 16.00$			
Temp °K	Temp °R	$(h^\circ - h_{298}^\circ)$ cal/gm mole	$\bar{s}^\circ$: cal/gm mole-K Btu/lb mole-R	$(h^\circ - h_{537}^\circ)$ Btu/lb mole	$(h_f^\circ)_{298}$	$(h^\circ - h_{298}^\circ)$ cal/gm mole	$\bar{s}^\circ$: cal/gm mole-K Btu/lb mole-R	$(h^\circ - h_{537}^\circ)$ Btu/lb mole
0	0	-2,075	0	-3,735		-1,608	0	-2,894
100	180	-1,362	41.522	-2,452		-1,080	32.466	-1,944
200	360	-682	46.233	-1,228		-523	36.340	-941
298	537	0	49.004	0		0	38.468	0
300	540	13	49.047	23		10	38.501	18
400	720	724	51.091	1,303		528	39.991	950
500	900	1,455	52.722	2,619		1,038	41.131	1,868
600	1,080	2,210	54.098	3,978		1,544	42.054	2,779
700	1,260	2,988	55.297	5,378		2,048	42.831	3,686
800	1,440	3,786	56.361	6,815		2,550	43.501	4,590
900	1,620	4,600	57.320	8,280		3,052	44.092	5,494
1000	1,800	5,427	58.192	9,769		3,552	44.619	6,394
1100	1,980	6,266	58.991	11,279		4,051	45.095	7,292
1200	2,160	7,114	59.729	12,805		4,551	45.529	8,192
1300	2,340	7,971	60.415	14,348		5,049	45.928	9,088
1400	2,520	8,835	61.055	15,903		5,548	46.298	9,986
1500	2,700	9,706	61.656	17,471		6,046	46.642	10,883
1600	2,880	10,583	62.222	19,049		6,544	46.963	11,779

1700	3,060	11,465	62.757	20,637	7,042	47.265	12,676
1800	3,240	12,354	63.265	22,237	7,540	47.550	13,572
1900	3,420	13,249	63.749	23,848	8,038	47.819	14,468
2000	3,600	14,149	64.210	25,468	8,536	48.074	15,365
2100	3,780	15,054	64.652	27,097	9,034	48.317	16,261
2200	3,960	15,966	65.076	28,739	9,532	48.549	17,158
2300	4,140	16,882	65.483	30,388	10,029	48.770	18,052
2400	4,320	17,804	65.876	32,047	10,527	48.982	18,949
2500	4,500	18,732	66.254	33,718	11,026	49.185	19,847
2600	4,680	19,664	66.620	35,395	11,524	49.381	20,743
2700	4,860	20,602	66.974	37,084	12,023	49.569	21,641
2800	5,040	21,545	67.317	38,781	12,522	49.751	22,540
2900	5,220	22,493	67.650	40,487	13,022	49.926	23,440
3000	5,400	23,446	67.973	42,203	13,522	50.096	24,340
3200	5,760	25,365	68.592	45,657	14,524	50.419	26,143
3400	6,120	27,302	69.179	49,144	15,529	50.724	27,952
3600	6,480	29,254	69.737	52,657	16,537	51.012	29,767
3800	6,840	31,221	70.269	56,198	17,549	51.285	31,588
4000	7,200	33,201	70.776	59,762	18,565	51.546	33,417
4200	7,560	35,193	71.262	63,347	19,586	51.795	35,255
4400	7,920	37,196	71.728	66,953	20,611	52.033	37,100
4600	8,280	39,208	72.176	70,574	21,641	52.262	38,954
4800	8,640	41,229	72.606	74,212	22,676	52.482	40,817
5000	9,000	43,257	73.019	77,863	23,715	52.695	42,687
5200	9,360	45,292	73.418	81,526	24,760	52.899	44,568
5400	9,720	47,332	73.803	85,198	25,809	53.097	46,456
5600	10,180	49,377	74.175	88,879	26,863	53.289	48,353
5800	10,540	51,426	74.535	92,567	27,921	53.475	50,258
6000	10,800	53,479	74.883	96,262	28,984	53.655	25,171

TABLE A.II (Continued)

Enthalpy of Formation at 25 C, Ideal Gas Enthalpy, and Absolute Entropy at One Atmosphere Pressure

		Carbon Dioxide (CO$_2$) (Mar. 31, 1961) $(h_f{}^\circ)_{298} = -94,054$ cal/gm mole $= -169,297$ Btu/lb mole, $M = 44.011$			Carbon Monoxide (CO) (Mar. 31, 1961) $(h_f{}^\circ)_{298} = -26,417$ cal/gm mole $= -47,551$ Btu/lb mole, $M = 28.011$		
Temp °K	Temp °R	$(h^\circ - h_{298}^\circ)$ cal/gm mole	$\bar{s}^\circ$: cal/gm mole-K / Btu/lb mole-R	$(h^\circ - h_{537}^\circ)$ Btu/lb mole	$(h^\circ - h_{298}^\circ)$ cal/gm mole	$\bar{s}^\circ$: cal/gm mole-K / Btu/lb mole-R	$(h^\circ - h_{537}^\circ)$ Btu/lb mole
0	0	−2,238	0	−4,028	−2,073	0	−3,731
100	180	−1,471	43.276	−2,648	−1,393	39.517	−2,507
200	360	−807	47.807	−1,453	−685	44.426	−1,233
298	537	0	51.072	0	0	47.214	0
300	540	16	51.127	29	13	47.257	23
400	720	958	53.830	1,724	711	49.265	1,280
500	900	1,987	56.122	3,577	1,417	50.841	2,551
600	1,080	3,087	58.126	5,557	2,137	52.152	3,847
700	1,260	4,245	59.910	7,641	2,873	53.287	5,171
800	1,440	5,453	61.522	9,815	3,627	54.293	6,529
900	1,620	6,702	62.992	12,064	4,397	55.200	7,915
1000	1,800	7,984	64.344	14,371	5,183	56.028	9,329
1100	1,980	9,296	65.594	16,733	5,983	56.790	10,769
1200	2,160	10,632	66.756	19,138	6,794	57.496	12,229
1300	2,340	11,988	67.841	21,578	7,616	58.154	13,709
1400	2,520	13,362	68.859	24,052	8,446	58.769	15,203
1500	2,700	14,750	69.817	26,550	9,285	59.348	16,713
1600	2,880	16,152	70.722	29,074	10,130	59.893	18,234

1700	3,060	17,565	71.578	31,617	10,980	60.409	19,764
1800	3,240	18,987	72.391	34,177	11,836	60.898	21,305
1900	3,420	20,418	73.165	36,752	12,697	61.363	22,855
2000	3,600	21,857	73.903	39,343	13,561	61.807	24,410
2100	3,780	23,303	74.608	41,945	14,430	62.230	25,974
2200	3,960	24,755	75.284	44,559	15,301	62.635	27,542
2300	4,140	26,212	75.931	47,182	16,175	63.024	29,115
2400	4,320	27,674	76.554	49,813	17,052	63.397	30,694
2500	4,500	29,141	77.153	52,454	17,931	63.756	32,276
2600	4,680	30,613	77.730	55,103	18,813	64.102	33,863
2700	4,860	32,088	78.286	57,758	19,696	64.435	35,453
2800	5,040	33,567	78.824	60,421	20,582	64.757	37,048
2900	5,220	35,049	79.344	63,088	21,469	65.069	38,644
3000	5,400	36,535	79.848	65,763	22,357	65.370	40,243
3200	5,760	39,515	80.810	71,127	24,139	65.945	43,450
3400	6,120	42,507	81.717	76,513	25,927	66.487	46,669
3600	6,480	45,508	82.574	81,914	27,719	66.999	49,894
3800	6,840	48,518	83.388	87,332	29,516	67.485	53,129
4000	7,200	51,538	84.162	92,768	31,316	67.946	56,369
4200	7,560	54,566	84.901	98,219	33,121	68.387	59,618
4400	7,920	57,601	85.607	103,682	34,930	68.807	62,874
4600	8,280	60,644	86.284	109,159	36,741	69.210	66,134
4800	8,640	63,695	86.933	114,651	38,557	69.596	69,403
5000	9,000	66,753	87.557	120,155	40,375	69.967	72,675
5200	9,360	69,819	88.158	125,674	42,196	70.325	75,953
5400	9,720	72,893	88.738	131,207	44,021	70.669	79,238
5600	10,180	75,976	89.299	136,757	45,849	71.001	82,528
5800	10,540	79,068	89.841	142,322	47,679	71.322	85,822
6000	10,800	82,168	90.367	147,902	49,513	71.633	89,123

TABLE A.11 (Continued)

Enthalpy of Formation at 25 C, Ideal Gas Enthalpy, and Absolute Entropy at One Atmosphere Pressure

Temp °K	Temp °R	Water (H_2O) (Mar. 31, 1961) $(\bar{h}_f°)_{298} = -57,798$ cal/gm mole $= -104,036$ Btu/lb mole $M = 18.016$			Hydroxyl (OH) (Dec. 31, 1960) $(\bar{h}_f°)_{298} = 9330$ cal/gm mole $= 16,794$ Btu/lb mole $M = 17.008$		
		$(h° - h°_{298})$ cal/gm mole	$s°$: cal/gm mole-K Btu/lb mole-R	$(h° - h°_{537})$ Btu/lb mole	$(h° - h°_{298})$ cal/gm mole	$s°$: cal/gm mole-K Btu/lb mole-R	$(h° - h°_{537})$ Btu/lb mole
0	0	−2,367	0	−4,261	−2,107	0	−3,793
100	180	−1,581	36.396	−2,846	−1,451	35.852	−2,612
200	360	−784	41.916	−1,411	−707	41.021	−1,273
298	537	0	45.106	0	0	43.918	0
300	540	15	45.155	27	13	43.962	23
400	720	825	47.484	1,485	724	46.006	1,303
500	900	1,654	49.334	2,977	1,430	47.582	2,574
600	1,080	2,509	50.891	4,516	2,134	48.867	3,841
700	1,260	3,390	52.249	6,102	2,841	49.956	5,114
800	1,440	4,300	53.464	7,740	3,553	50.906	6,395
900	1,620	5,240	54.570	9,432	4,272	51.753	7,690
1000	1,800	6,209	55.592	11,176	5,000	52.520	9,000
1100	1,980	7,210	56.545	12,978	5,738	53.223	10,328
1200	2,160	8,240	57.441	14,832	6,487	53.875	11,677
1300	2,340	9,298	58.288	16,736	7,247	54.483	13,045
1400	2,520	10,384	59.092	18,691	8,018	55.055	14,432
1500	2,700	11,495	59.859	20,691	8,800	55.594	15,840
1600	2,880	12,630	60.591	22,734	9,591	56.105	17,264

1700	3,060	13,787	61.293	24,817	10,392	56.590	18,706
1800	3,240	14,964	61.965	26,935	11,202	57.053	20,164
1900	3,420	16,160	62.612	29,088	12,019	57.495	21,634
2000	3,600	17,373	63.234	31,271	12,844	57.918	23,119
2100	3,780	18,602	63.834	33,484	13,676	58.324	24,617
2200	3,960	19,846	64.412	35,723	14,514	58.714	26,125
2300	4,140	21,103	64.971	37,985	15,358	59.089	27,644
2400	4,320	22,372	65.511	40,270	16,208	59.451	29,174
2500	4,500	23,653	66.034	42,575	17,063	59.800	30,713
2600	4,680	24,945	66.541	44,901	17,923	60.137	32,261
2700	4,860	26,246	67.032	47,243	18,787	60.463	33,817
2800	5,040	27,556	67.508	49,601	19,655	60.779	35,379
2900	5,220	28,875	67.971	51,975	20,528	61.085	36,950
3000	5,400	30,201	68.421	54,362	21,404	61.382	38,527
3200	5,760	32,876	69.284	59,177	23,166	61.951	41,699
3400	6,120	35,577		64,039	24,940	62.488	44,892
3600	6,480	38,300	70.881	68,940	26,726	62.999	48,107
3800	6,840	41,043	71.622	73,877	28,522	63.484	51,340
4000	7,200	43,805	72.331	78,849	30,327	63.947	54,589
4200	7,560	46,583	73.008	83,849	32,140	64.389	57,852
4400	7,920	49,375	73.658	88,875	33,962	64.813	61,132
4600	8,280	52,181	74.281	93,926	35,790	65.219	64,422
4800	8,640	55,000	74.881	99,000	37,626	65.610	67,727
5000	9,000	57,829	75.459	104,092	39,467	65.986	71,041
5200	9,360	60,669	76.016	109,204	41,316	66.348	74,369
5400	9,720	63,520	76.553	114,336	43,171	66.699	77,708
5600	10,180	66,381	77.074	119,486	45,032	67.037	81,058
5800	10,540	69,251	77.577	124,652	46,898	67.364	84,416
6000	10,800	72,131	78.065	129,836	48,769	67.681	87,784

TABLE A.II (Continued)

Enthalpy of Formation at 25 C, Ideal Gas Enthalpy, and Absolute Entropy at One Atmosphere Pressure

Temp °K	Temp °R	Hydrogen, Diatomic (H_2) (Mar. 31, 1961) $(\bar{h}_f{}^\circ)_{298} = 0$ cal/gm mole $= 0$ Btu/lb mole $M = 2.016$			Hydrogen, Monatomic (H) (Dec. 31, 1960) $(\bar{h}_f{}^\circ)_{298} = 52,102$ cal/gm mole $= 93,784$ Btu/lb mole $M = 1.008$		
		$(h^\circ - h^\circ_{298})$ cal/gm mole	$\bar{s}^\circ$: cal/gm mole-K Btu/lb mole-R	$(h^\circ - h^\circ_{537})$ Btu/lb mole	$(h^\circ - h^\circ_{298})$ cal/gm mole	$\bar{s}^\circ$: cal/gm mole-K Btu/lb mole-R	$(h^\circ - h^\circ_{537})$ Btu/lb mole
0	0	-2,024	0	-3,643	-1,481	0	-2,666
100	180	-1,265	24.387	-2,277	-984	21.965	-1,771
200	360	-662	28.520	-1,192	-488	25.408	-878
298	537	0	31.208	0	0	27.392	0
300	540	13	31.251	23	9	27.423	16
400	720	707	33.247	1,273	506	28.852	911
500	900	1,406	34.806	2,531	1,003	29.961	1,805
600	1,080	2,106	36.082	3,791	1,500	30.867	2,700
700	1,260	2,808	37.165	5,054	1,996	31.632	3,593
800	1,440	3,514	38.107	6,325	2,493	32.296	4,487
900	1,620	4,226	38.946	7,607	2,990	32.881	5,382
1000	1,800	4,944	39.702	8,899	3,487	33.404	6,277
1100	1,980	5,670	40.394	10,206	3,984	33.878	7,171
1200	2,160	6,404	41.033	11,527	4,481	34.310	8,066
1300	2,340	7,148	41.628	12,866	4,977	34.708	8,959
1400	2,520	7,902	42.187	14,224	5,474	35.076	9,853
1500	2,700	8,668	42.716	15,602	5,971	35.419	10,748
1600	2,880	9,446	43.217	17,003	6,468	35.739	11,642

1700	3,060	10,233	43.695	18,419	6,965	36.041	12,537
1800	3,240	11,030	44.150	19,854	7,461	36.325	13,430
1900	3,420	11,836	44.586	21,305	7,958	36.593	14,324
2000	3,600	12,651	45.004	22,772	8,455	36.848	15,219
2100	3,780	13,475	45.406	24,255	8,952	37.090	16,114
2200	3,960	14,307	45.793	25,753	9,449	37.322	17,008
2300	4,140	15,146	46.166	27,263	9,945	37.542	17,901
2400	4,320	15,993	46.527	28,787	10,442	37.754	18,796
2500	4,500	16,848	46.875	30,326	10,939	37.957	19,690
2600	4,680	17,708	47.213	31,874	11,436	38.152	20,585
2700	4,860	18,575	47.540	33,435	11,933	38.339	21,479
2800	5,040	19,448	47.857	35,006	12,430	38.520	22,374
2900	5,220	20,326	48.166	36,587	12,926	38.694	23,267
3000	5,400	21,210	48.465	38,178	13,423	38.862	24,161
3200	5,760	22,992	49.040	41,386	14,417	39.183	25,951
3400	6,120	24,794	49.586	44,629	15,410	39.484	27,738
3600	6,400	26,616	50.107	47,909	16,404	39.768	29,527
3800	6,840	28,457	50.605	51,223	17,398	40.037	31,316
4000	7,200	30,317	51.082	54,571	18,391	40.292	33,104
4200	7,560	32,194	51.540	57,949	19,385	40.534	34,893
4400	7,920	34,088	51.980	61,358	20,379	40.765	36,682
4600	8,280	35,999	52.405	64,798	21,372	40.986	38,470
4800	8,640	37,926	52.815	68,267	22,366	41.198	40,259
5000	9,000	39,868	53.211	71,762	23,359	41.400	42,046
5200	9,360	41,825	53.595	75,285	24,353	41.595	43,835
5400	9,720	43,797	53.967	78,835	25,347	41.783	45,625
5600	10,180	45,783	54.328	82,409	26,340	41.963	47,412
5800	10,540	47,783	54.679	86,009	27,334	42.138	49,201
6000	10,800	49,796	55.020	89,633	28,328	42.306	50,990

TABLE A.II (Continued)

Enthalpy of Formation at 25 C, Ideal Gas Enthalpy, and Absolute Entropy at One Atmosphere Pressure

Temp °K	Temp °R	Nitric Oxide (NO) (June 30, 1963) $(\bar{h}_f{}^\circ)_{298} = 21{,}652$ cal/gm mole $= 38{,}974$ Btu/lb mole $M = 30.008$			Nitrogen Dioxide (NO$_2$) (June 30, 1963) $(\bar{h}_f{}^\circ)_{298} = 8060$ cal/gm mole $= 14{,}508$ Btu/lb mole $M = 46.008$			
		$(h^\circ - h^\circ_{298})$ cal/gm mole	s°: cal/gm mole-K Btu/lb mole-R	$(h^\circ - h^\circ_{537})$ Btu/lb mole	$(h^\circ - h^\circ_{298})$ cal/gm mole	$\bar{s}$: cal/gm mole-K Btu/lb mole-R	$(h^\circ - h^\circ_{537})$ Btu/lb mole
0	0	−2,197	0	−3,955	−2,437	0	−4,387
100	180	−1,451	42.286	−2,612	−1,642	48.356	−2,956
200	360	−705	47.477	−1,269	−837	53.925	−1,507
298	537	0	50.347	0	0	57.324	0
300	540	13	50.392	23	16	57.379	29
400	720	727	52.444	1,309	944	60.041	1,699
500	900	1,448	54.053	2,606	1,948	62.279	3,506
600	1,080	2,186	55.397	3,935	3,021	64.234	5,438
700	1,260	2,942	56.562	5,296	4,151	65.975	7,472
800	1,440	3,716	57.596	6,689	5,327	67.544	9,589
900	1,620	4,507	58.528	8,113	6,539	68.971	11,770
1000	1,800	5,313	59.377	9,563	7,780	70.278	14,004
1100	1,980	6,131	60.157	11,036	9,043	71.482	16,277
1200	2,160	6,960	60.878	12,528	10,324	72.597	18,583
1300	2,340	7,798	61.548	14,036	11,620	73.634	20,916
1400	2,520	8,644	62.175	15,559	12,929	74.604	23,272
1500	2,700	9,496	62.763	17,093	14,247	75.513	25,645
1600	2,880	10,354	63.317	18,637	15,573	76.369	28,031

1700	3,060	11,217	20,191	63.840	16,907	77.178	30,433
1800	3,240	12,084	21,751	64.335	18,247	77.943	32,845
1900	3,420	12,955	23,319	64.806	19,591	78.670	35,264
2000	3,600	13,829	24,892	65.255	20,940	79.362	37,692
2100	3,780	14,706	26,471	65.683	22,293	80.022	40,127
2200	3,960	15,587	28,057	66.092	23,649	80.653	42,568
2300	4,140	16,469	29,644	66.484	25,008	81.257	45,014
2400	4,320	17,354	31,237	66.861	26,370	81.837	47,466
2500	4,500	18,241	32,834	67.223	27,734	82.394	49,921
2600	4,680	19,129	34,432	67.571	29,100	82.930	52,380
2700	4,860	20,020	36,036	67.907	30,468	83.446	54,842
2800	5,040	20,911	37,640	68.232	31,837	83.944	57,307
2900	5,220	21,805	39,249	68.545	33,208	84.425	59,774
3000	5,400	22,700	40,860	68.849	34,580	84.890	62,244
3200	5,760	24,493	44,087	69.427	37,328	85.777	67,190
3400	6,120	26,291	47,324	69.973	40,080	86.611	72,144
3600	6,480	28,094	50,569	70.488	42,835	87.398	77,103
3800	6,840	29,900	53,820	70.976	45,593	88.144	82,067
4000	7,200	31,710	57,078	71.440	48,353	88.852	87,035
4200	7,560	33,523	60,341	71.882	51,115	89.525	92,007
4400	7,920	35,340	63,612	72.305	53,879	90.168	96,982
4600	8,280	37,159	66,886	72.709	56,645	90.783	101,961
4800	8,640	38,982	70,168	73.097	59,412	91.372	106,942
5000	9,000	40,807	73,453	73.470	62,180	91.937	111,924
5200	9,360	42,634	76,741	73.828	64,950	92.480	116,910
5400	9,720	44,465	80,037	74.173	67,720	93.003	121,896
5600	10,180	46,297	83,335	74.507	70,491	93.507	126,884
5800	10,540	48,133	86,639	74.829	73,263	93.993	131,873
6000	10,800	49,970	89,946	75.140	76,035	94.463	136,863

TABLE A.12

Logarithms to the Base e of the Equilibrium Constant K

For the reaction $\nu_A A + \nu_B B \rightleftharpoons \nu_C C + \nu_D D$ the equilibrium constant K is defined in terms of the activity a as

$$K = \frac{a_C^{\nu_C} a_D^{\nu_D}}{a_A^{\nu_A} a_B^{\nu_B}} \qquad \left(\text{For ideal gases, } K = \frac{p_C^{\nu_C} p_D^{\nu_D}}{p_A^{\nu_A} p_B^{\nu_B}}\right)$$

Based on thermodynamic data given in the JANAF Thermochemical Tables, Thermal Research Laboratory, The Dow Chemical Company, Midland, Michigan.

Temperature °K	$H_2 \rightleftharpoons 2H$	$O_2 \rightleftharpoons 2O$	$N_2 \rightleftharpoons 2N$	$H_2O \rightleftharpoons H_2 + \frac{1}{2}O_2$	$H_2O \rightleftharpoons \frac{1}{2}H_2 + OH$	$CO_2 \rightleftharpoons CO + \frac{1}{2}O_2$	$\frac{1}{2}N_2 + \frac{1}{2}O_2 \rightleftharpoons NO$
298	−164.008	−186.988	−367.493	−92.214	−106.023	−103.768	−35.052
500	−92.836	−105.643	−213.385	−52.697	−60.167	−57.622	−20.295
1000	−39.816	−45.163	−99.140	−23.169	−25.973	−23.535	−9.388
1200	−30.887	−35.018	−80.024	−18.188	−20.231	−17.877	−7.569
1400	−24.476	−27.755	−66.342	−14.615	−16.054	−13.848	−6.270
1600	−19.650	−22.298	−56.068	−11.927	−13.026	−10.836	−5.294
1800	−15.879	−18.043	−48.064	−9.832	−10.622	−8.503	−4.536
2000	−12.853	−14.635	−41.658	−8.151	−8.695	−6.641	−3.931
2200	−10.366	−11.840	−36.404	−6.774	−7.117	−5.126	−3.433
2400	−8.289	−9.510	−32.024	−5.625	−5.803	−3.866	−3.019
2600	−6.530	−7.534	−28.317	−4.654	−4.693	−2.807	−2.671
2800	−5.015	−5.839	−25.130	−3.818	−3.739	−1.900	−2.372
3000	−3.698	−4.370	−22.372	−3.092	−2.913	−0.972	−2.114
3200	−2.547	−3.085	−19.950	−2.457	−2.190	−0.435	−1.888
3400	−1.529	−1.948	−17.813	−1.897	−1.552	0.163	−1.690
3600	−0.622	−0.939	−15.911	−1.398	−0.986	0.695	−1.513
3800	0.189	−0.032	−14.212	−0.951	−0.479	1.170	−1.356
4000	0.921	0.783	−12.673	−0.548	−0.025	1.593	−1.216
4500	2.473	2.500	−9.427	0.306	0.939	2.484	−0.921
5000	3.712	3.882	−6.820	0.990	1.706	3.191	−0.686
5500	4.730	5.010	−4.679	1.554	2.335	3.765	−0.497
6000	5.577	5.950	−0.288	2.026	2.858	4.239	−0.341

TABLE A.13

One-Dimensional Isentropic Compressible-Flow Functions for an Ideal Gas
with Constant Specific Heat and Molecular Weight and $k = 1.4$ *

M	$M*$	$\dfrac{A}{A*}$	$\dfrac{P}{P_o}$	$\dfrac{\rho}{\rho_o}$	$\dfrac{T}{T_o}$
0	0	∞	1.00000	1.00000	1.00000
0.10	0.10943	5.8218	0.99303	0.99502	0.99800
0.20	0.21822	2.9635	0.97250	0.98027	0.99206
0.30	0.32572	2.0351	0.93947	0.95638	0.98232
0.40	0.43133	1.5901	0.89562	0.92428	0.96899
0.50	0.53452	1.3398	0.84302	0.88517	0.95238
0.60	0.63480	1.1882	0.78400	0.84045	0.93284
0.70	0.73179	1.09437	0.72092	0.79158	0.91075
0.80	0.82514	1.03823	0.65602	0.74000	0.88652
0.90	0.91460	1.00886	0.59126	0.68704	0.86058
1.00	1.00000	1.00000	0.52828	0.63394	0.83333
1.10	1.08124	1.00793	0.46835	0.58169	0.80515
1.20	1.1583	1.03044	0.41238	0.53114	0.77640
1.30	1.2311	1.06631	0.36092	0.48291	0.74738
1.40	1.2999	1.1149	0.31424	0.43742	0.71839
1.50	1.3646	1.1762	0.27240	0.39498	0.68965
1.60	1.4254	1.2502	0.23527	0.35573	0.66138
1.70	1.4825	1.3376	0.20259	0.31969	0.63372
1.80	1.5360	1.4390	0.17404	0.28682	0.60680
1.90	1.5861	1.5552	0.14924	0.25699	0.58072
2.00	1.6330	1.6875	0.12780	0.23005	0.55556
2.10	1.6769	1.8369	0.10935	0.20580	0.53135
2.20	1.7179	2.0050	0.09352	0.18405	0.50813
2.30	1.7563	2.1931	0.07997	0.16458	0.48591
2.40	1.7922	2.4031	0.06840	0.14720	0.46468
2.50	1.8258	2.6367	0.05853	0.13169	0.44444
2.60	1.8572	2.8960	0.05012	0.11787	0.42517
2.70	1.8865	3.1830	0.04295	0.10557	0.40684
2.80	1.9140	3.5001	0.03685	0.09462	0.38941
2.90	1.9398	3.8498	0.03165	0.08489	0.37286
3.00	1.9640	4.2346	0.02722	0.07623	0.35714
3.50	2.0642	6.7896	0.01311	0.04523	0.28986
4.00	2.1381	10.719	0.00658	0.02766	0.23810
4.50	2.1936	16.562	0.00346	0.01745	0.19802
5.00	2.2361	25.000	$189(10)^{-5}$	0.01134	0.16667
6.00	2.2953	53.180	$633(10)^{-6}$	0.00519	0.12195
7.00	2.3333	104.143	$242(10)^{-6}$	0.00261	0.09259
8.00	2.3591	190.109	$102(10)^{-6}$	0.00141	0.07246
9.00	2.3772	327.189	$474(10)^{-7}$	0.000815	0.05814
10.00	2.3904	535.938	$236(10)^{-7}$	0.000495	0.04762
∞	2.4495	∞	0	0	0

* Abridged from Table 30 in *Gas Tables*, by Joseph H. Keenan and Joseph
Kaye. Copyright 1948, by Joseph H. Keenan and Joseph Kaye. Published
by John Wiley & Sons, Inc., New York.

TABLE A.14

One-Dimensional Normal-Shock Functions for an Ideal Gas with Constant Specific Heat and Molecular Weight and $k = 1.4$ *

M_x	M_y	$\dfrac{P_y}{P_x}$	$\dfrac{\rho_y}{\rho_x}$	$\dfrac{T_y}{T_x}$	$\dfrac{P_{oy}}{P_{ox}}$	$\dfrac{P_{oy}}{P_x}$
1.00	1.00000	1.00000	1.00000	1.00000	1.00000	1.8929
1.10	0.91177	1.2450	1.1691	1.06494	0.99892	2.1328
1.20	0.84217	1.5133	1.3416	1.1280	0.99280	2.4075
1.30	0.78596	1.8050	1.5157	1.1909	0.97935	2.7135
1.40	0.73971	2.1200	1.6896	1.2547	0.95819	3.0493
1.50	0.70109	2.4583	1.8621	1.3202	0.92978	3.4133
1.60	0.66844	2.8201	2.0317	1.3880	0.89520	3.8049
1.70	0.64055	3.2050	2.1977	1.4583	0.85573	4.2238
1.80	0.61650	3.6133	2.3592	1.5316	0.81268	4.6695
1.90	0.59562	4.0450	2.5157	1.6079	0.76735	5.1417
2.00	0.57735	4.5000	2.6666	1.6875	0.72088	5.6405
2.10	0.56128	4.9784	2.8119	1.7704	0.67422	6.1655
2.20	0.54706	5.4800	2.9512	1.8569	0.62812	6.7163
2.30	0.53441	6.0050	3.0846	1.9468	0.58331	7.2937
2.40	0.52312	6.5533	3.2119	2.0403	0.54015	7.8969
2.50	0.51299	7.1250	3.3333	2.1375	0.49902	8.5262
2.60	0.50387	7.7200	3.4489	2.2383	0.46012	9.1813
2.70	0.49563	8.3383	3.5590	2.3429	0.42359	9.8625
2.80	0.48817	8.9800	3.6635	2.4512	0.38946	10.569
2.90	0.48138	9.6450	3.7629	2.5632	0.35773	11.302
3.00	0.47519	10.333	3.8571	2.6790	0.32834	12.061
4.00	0.43496	18.500	4.5714	4.0469	0.13876	21.068
5.00	0.41523	29.000	5.0000	5.8000	0.06172	32.654
10.00	0.38757	116.50	5.7143	20.388	0.00304	129.217
∞	0.37796	∞	6.000	∞	0	∞

* Abridged from Table 48 in *Gas Tables*, by Joseph H. Keenan and Joseph Kaye. Copyright 1948, by Joseph H. Keenan and Joseph Kaye. Published by John Wiley & Sons, Inc., New York.

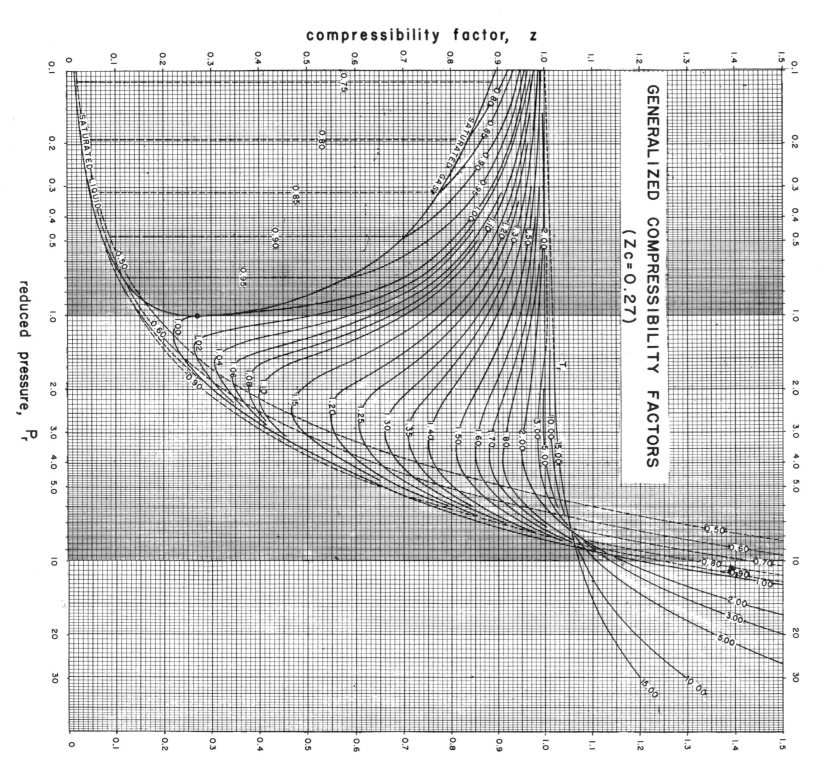

Fig. A.I. Generalized compressibility chart

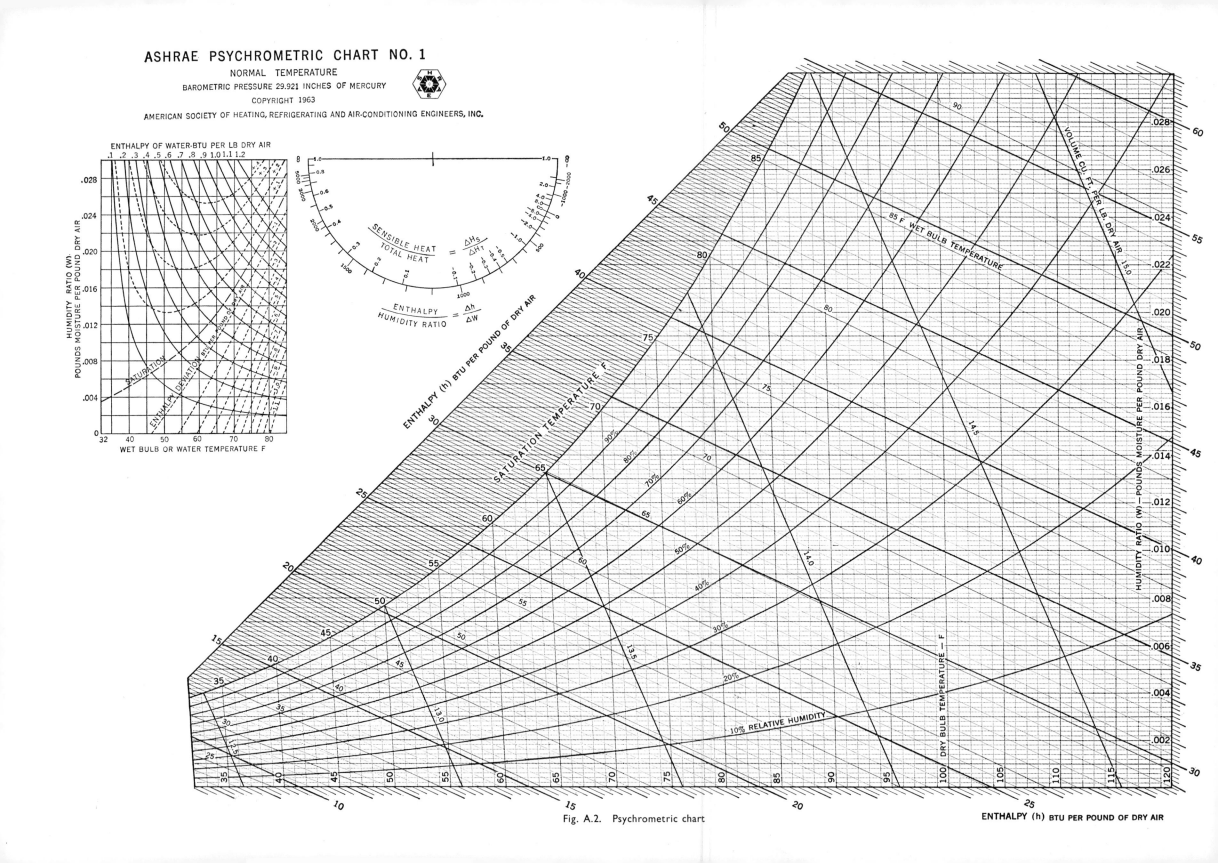

Fig. A.2. Psychrometric chart

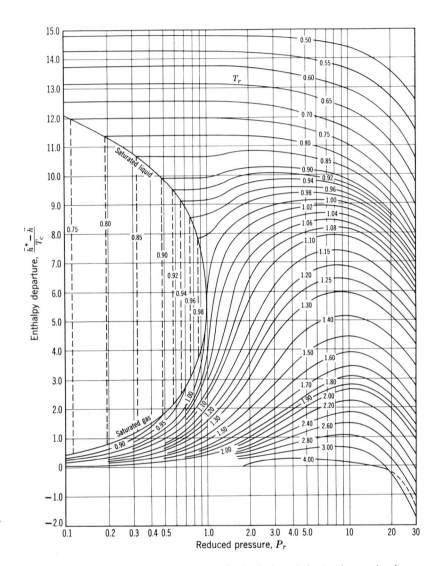

Fig. A.3.   Generalized enthalpy departure from ideal gas behavior (per mole of gas or liquid, $Z_c = 0.27$)

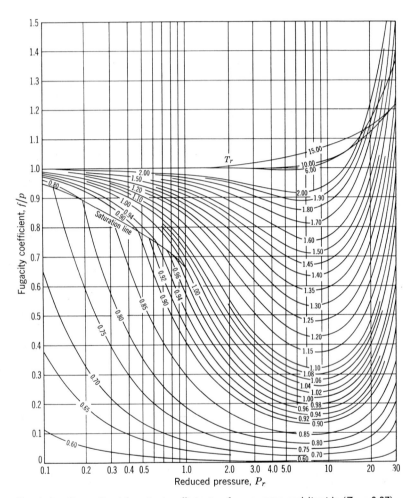

Fig. A.4. Generalized fugacity coefficients of pure gases and liquids ($Z_c = 0.27$)

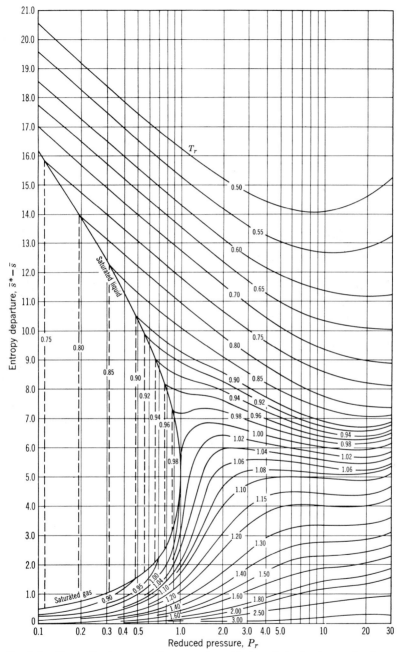

Fig. A.5. Generalized entropy departure from ideal gas behavior (per mole of gas or liquid, $Z_c = 0.27$)

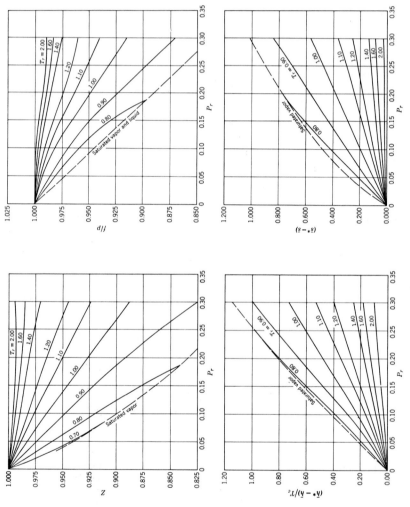

Fig. A.6.   Low-pressure generalized charts

Some Selected References

H. B. Callen: *Thermodynamics*, John Wiley and Sons, New York, 1960.

B. F. Dodge: *Chemical Engineering Thermodynamics*, McGraw-Hill Book Co., New York, 1944.

G. N. Hatsopoulos and J. H. Keenan: *Principles of General Thermodynamics*, John Wiley and Sons, New York, 1965.

O. A. Hougen, K. M. Watson, and R. A. Ragatz: *Chemical Process Principles, Part Two: Thermodynamics*, Second Edition, John Wiley and Sons, New York, 1959.

J. B. Jones and G. A. Hawkins: *Engineering Thermodynamics*, John Wiley and Sons, New York, 1960.

J. H. Keenan: *Thermodynamics*, John Wiley and Sons, New York, 1941.

E. F. Obert: *Concepts of Thermodynamics*, McGraw-Hill Book Co., New York, 1960.

W. C. Reynolds: *Thermodynamics*, McGraw-Hill Book Co., New York, 1965.

F. D. Rossini: *Chemical Thermodynamics*, John Wiley and Sons, New York, 1950.

A. H. Shapiro: *The Dynamics and Thermodynamics of Compressible Fluid Flow*, The Ronald Press Co., New York, 1953.

M. W. Zemansky: *Heat and Thermodynamics*, McGraw-Hill Book Co., New York, 1957.

Answers to Selected Problems

2.3 1440 lbm
2.6 45.3 lbf/in.², 3.09 atm
2.9 9.31 lbm
2.12 0.48 in.
2.15 59.4 lbf/in.²

3.3 (a) 756 R
    (b) 35 lbf/in.²
3.6 (a) 2.640 ft³/lbm
    (b) 0.1631 ft³/lbm
    (c) 0.4371 ft³/lbm
    (d) 0.4800 ft³/lbm
3.12 66.8% vapor
3.15 (a) 62.4 lbm/ft³
    (b) 62.4 lbm/ft³
    (c) 56.4 lbm/ft³
    (d) 49.0 lbm/ft³
3.18 (a) 0.652 lbm
    (b) 2.062 lbm
    (c) 33%
3.21 3900 lbf/in.²
3.24 10.6 ft³/hr

4.3 (b) 4680 ft lbf
    (c) 2190 ft lbf
4.6 (a) −442 ft lbf
    (b) 233 F

4.9 $\quad -w = A\rho \dfrac{g}{g_c} L_2\left[L_1 - \dfrac{L_2}{2}\right]$

4.12 −90.4 dyne-cm
4.15 $W = 73.9$ watts, $Q = 0$

5.3 975.4 Btu
5.6 15.9 Btu
5.9 −350 Btu

5.12 2300 Btu
5.15 (a) 300 lbf/in.²
    (b) 948 F
    (c) 212 Btu
    (d) 2132 Btu
5.18 $V_0 = V_{max}/2$
5.21 1.19 HP
5.24 (a) 32,800 HP
    (b) −1.92 × 10⁸ Btu/hr
    4.47 × 10⁷ Btu/hr
    2.287 × 10⁸ Btu/hr
    (c) 4.82 ft
    (d) 19,200 gal/min
5.27 (a) 2160 lbm/hr
    (b) 346 F
    (c) 1.16 × 10⁶ Btu/hr
5.30 298 Btu
5.33 0.245 lbm
5.36 (a) 770 F
    (b) 620 F
    (c) 500 F
5.39 8700 Btu
5.42 95.3%
5.45 (a) 516 Btu/lbm,
        0.408 Btu/lbm-R
    (b) 471 Btu/lbm,
        0.383 Btu/lbm-R
5.48 5.65 HP, 1440 Btu/hr
5.51 (a) 108 HP
    (b) 850 Btu/hr
5.54 9270 HP, 5260 HP
5.57 52.5 lbf/in.²
5.60 (a) 195 lbf/in.²
    (b) 192 lbf/in.²
    (c) 189 lbf/in.²

6.6 53.6 HP
6.9 2.02 HP
6.12 1402 Cal

7.3 (b) 0.8535, 0.165
       (c) 165.2 Btu
7.6 19.4 Btu
7.9 216 ft/sec
7.12 1.09 HP
7.15 2030 lbm/min
7.18 -4.1 Btu/lbm
7.21 677 Btu, 462 F
7.24 52.7 Btu/lbm
7.27 101 HP
7.30 (a) -72.7 Btu/lbm;
            -0.130 Btu/lbm-R;
            -72.7 Btu/lbm
       (b) -88.0 Btu/lbm;
            -0.039 Btu/lbm-R;
            -26.3 Btu/lbm
       (c) -96.8 Btu/lbm; 0; 0
7.33 1.46 lbm; 591 R
7.36 (c) 785.2 ft³/lbm,
            1150.4 Btu/lbm,
            2.1265 Btu/lbm-R at 200 F
7.39 0.0116 Btu/lbm-R
7.42 (a) 1.435 ft³
       (b) -1334.5 Btu
       (c) -6728.5 Btu
       (d) -698 Btu
       (e) 1.78 Btu/R
7.45 2.02 Btu/R; 21.65 Btu/R;
       65.6 Btu/R
7.48 (a) 441 HP
       (b) 538 HP
7.51 83 lbf/in.²; 121.6 F; 15.7 Btu;
       0.017 Btu/R
7.54 (a) 39.5 lbf/in.²
       (b) 6.4 Btu
       (c) 8.9 Btu
       (d) 0.0108 Btu/R
7.57 678 R

8.3 -68.0 Btu/lbm; 11.8 Btu/lbm
8.6 14.25 Btu; 7.16 Btu
8.9 1922 Btu
8.12 57.1 Btu/lbm, 48.5 Btu/lbm,
       172 Btu
8.15 (a) 41.6 Btu/lbm
       (b) 122.1 Btu/lbm
       (c) 5.3 Btu/lbm
       (d) 5.1 Btu/lbm

8.18 1250 R; 239 Btu
8.21 22,600 Btu
8.24 169,677 Btu/mole

9.3 30.8%, 0.2495; 31.6%, 0.1893;
       34.9%, 0.0904;   38.7%, 0.0151
9.6 33.8%, 342.4 Btu/lbm
9.9 (b) 700,000 lbm/hr
       (c) 56.7 HP, 990 HP
       (d) 50,500 gal/min
       (e) 13.8 ft
9.12 (a) 36.7%
       (b) 39.8%
       (c) 41.2%
9.18 (a) 5.2 Btu/lbm
       (b) 1.183 tons
       (c) 2.23
9.21 2.55
9.24 54.7%, 175 lbf/in.²
9.27 62.1%
9.30 45.6 lbf/in.²
9.33 (a) 46,200 HP
       (b) 0.567
       (c) 190,000 ft³/min
9.36 (b) 42.2%
9.39 0.577

10.3 Yes
10.18 (a) 3800 ft/sec
       (b) -4790 ft-lbf
10.21 $-44,800$ Btu/min
10.24 (a) 461 R
       (b) 3020 Btu
10.27 34.6 lbm
10.30 -105.2 Btu/lbm;
       -149 Btu/lbm
10.33 (a) -84.8 Btu/lbm;
            -91.5 Btu/lbm
       (b) 0; 0.105 Btu/lbm-R
10.36 (a) 13.2 Btu/lbm
       (b) 13.6 Btu/lbm
       (c) 17.0 Btu/lbm
10.39 (a) 84.5%
       (b) 885 R
       (c) -238 Btu/lbm
10.42 590 lbf/in.², 615 R

11.3 4.9×10^{-4} lbf/in.²
11.6 266 lbf/in.²; 1282 R;
       -132 Btu/lbm
11.9 (a) 0.013
       (b) 64.5 F
       (c) 1.47 lbm

11.12 −1960 Btu/min
11.15 64 F; 0.00282 lbm
11.18 0.39
11.21 214 lbm/hr
11.24 (a) 0.272 lbm/hr
　　　 (b) 134 Btu/hr
　　　 (c) 0.022
11.27 2.86 ft³/mole; 4.59 ft³/mole
11.30 285 R; 112 ft/sec

12.3 (a) 126 F
　　　 (b) 1.33 moles
12.6 (a) 46.3 HP
　　　 (b) 9.46% CO_2, 2.36% CO,
　　　　　 4.87% O_2, 83.31% N_2;
　　　　　 120.6 F
12.9 326%
12.12 (a) 3.52 atm
　　　 (b) −95,117 Btu
12.15 (a) 141.5%
　　　 (b) 2.54 lbm/hr
　　　 (c) 234 ft³/min
12.18 (a) 314%
　　　 (b) 95.8 F
12.21 (a) 20,113 Btu/mole
　　　 (b) −545,500 Btu/mole
12.24 −3698 Btu/lbm
12.27 2893 R
12.30 (a) 907,094 Btu/mole
　　　 (b) 898,876 Btu/mole
12.33 (a) −884,400 Btu
　　　 (b) 1,055,200 Btu
12.36 (a) 522%
　　　 (b) 6042 Btu/R

12.39 (b) −4100 Btu/hr
　　　 (c) 18.32 Btu/R-hr

13.3 (a) 2217 lbf/in.², 89.7% CH_4
　　　 (b) 2290 lbf/in.², 88.7% CH_4
13.6 (a) 0.0068
　　　 (b) 0.0322
　　　 (c) 0.0256
13.12 30.2% CO_2, 13.0% CO,
　　　　 56.8% O_2
13.15 (a) 89.5% H_2, 10.5% H;
　　　　 49,080 Btu
13.18 (a) −37,830 Btu
　　　 (b) 40,620 Btu
13.21 43.4 Btu/R
13.24 28.5% CO_2, 4.1% CO, 67.4% O_2
13.27 (a) 1.442
　　　 (b) −101,924 Btu/mole
　　　 (c) 10.8% CO, 35.8% H_2O,
　　　　　 39.2% CO_2, 14.2% H_2
　　　 (d) 33,750 Btu/min
13.30 86,880 Btu
13.33 1.05% Ar, 48.35% Ar^+,
　　　　 0.7% Ar^{++}, 49.9% e^-

14.3 88 lbf/in.², 466 F
14.6 (b) 2.76 in.², 5.34 in.²
14.9 186.6 lbf/in.²
14.12 10.34 lbf/in.², 531 R, 0.463
14.15 9.52 lbf/in.², 531 R, 0.427
14.18 24.4 in.²
14.21 4.95 lbm/sec
14.24 80%

Index